GUIDE TO ARCHITECTURE SCHOOLS

Association of Collegiate Schools of Architecture

8th Edition

ACSA Press, Washington, DC

ISBN 978-0-935502-69-5

ISSN 1097-2552

Printed in the United States of America

Published by the ACSA Press and distributed by the

Association of Collegiate Schools of Architecture
1735 New York Ave, NW
Washington, DC 20006 USA

Tel: 202.785.2324
www.acsa-arch.org

CONTENTS

ABOUT THIS GUIDE

The ACSA Guide to Architecture Schools is published for the many people who are interested in pursuing an architectural education. Readers will find an introduction to the rich array of educational and career options in architecture, and a concise delineation of the various educational opportunities available. The 134 profiles of professional degree programs in the United States and Canada present sufficient statistical and narrative detail for prospective students to match their backtground and interests with appropriate programs and for others interested in architectural education to gloss the diversity of opportunities available to study architecture.

The material in this eighth edition covers the full range of programs, schools, degrees, and paths available in architecture and many of its related fields. ACSA has the benefit of claiming all professional architecture degree granting programs in the United States and Canada, as well as more than 60 affiliate member schools around the world.

All facts, figures, and descriptive material about the programs in this book were primarily supplied by the schools themselves, although in some cases statistical and tuition information

was gathered from public sources such as the *Chronicle of Higher Education* or the annual statistical data gathered by the National Architectural Accrediting Board (www.naab.org). Programs were asked to report information based on the 2007-2008 academic year. Such information, including specific degree programs offered by any one school, are subject to change. Prospective students should always contact the institutions in which they are interested directly to ensure they receive the most up-to-date information.

ONLINE EDITION
A new companion to this printed eighth edition is the publication of an online version of the ACSA Guide. Found at **www.archschools.org**, the online edition offers a searchable database of all the programs included in the printed edition, with the added benefit to users of customizing searches to find programs that best match their interests.

ABOUT THE PUBLISHER
The Association of Collegiate Schools of Architecture is a 501(c)(3) nonprofit membership association founded in 1912 to advance the quality of architectural education.

The school membership in ACSA has grown from 10 charter members to over 250 schools in several membership categories. These include full membership for all accredited programs in the United States and government-sanctioned schools in Canada, candidate membership for schools seeking accreditation, and affiliate membership for schools for two-year and international programs. Through these schools, over 5,000 architecture faculty are represented. In addition, over 500 supporting members composed of architecture firms, product associations and individuals add to the breadth of interest and support of ACSA goals.

ACSA, unique in its representative role for schools of architecture, provides a forum for ideas on the leading edge of architectural thought. Issues that will affect the architectural profession in the future are being examined today in ACSA members schools.

The association maintains a variety of activities that influence, communicate, and record important issues. Such endeavors include scholarly meetings, workshops, publications, awards and competition programs, support for architectural research, policy development, and liaison with allied organizations.

ABOUT ARCHITECTURE AS A CAREER

THE DISCIPLINE

Architecture involves the study and transformation of the constructed environment, from the scale of furniture to the scale of the city. The goal of an architectural education is to develop a synthetic thought process of critical thinking and creative problem solving. Creative thinkers must address all aspects of the built environment in its cultural, social, and ethical context.

THE PROFESSION

Architects meet the challenges of a rapidly changing world with a broad range of skills and professional design services. Architects work in many different ways, interacting with clients, users, colleagues, consultants, community groups, and contractors.

Aspiring architects should learn as much as possible about the field of architecture, by talking to architects and by visiting architectural offices. The profession is changing rapidly: some offices are diversifying their services to assist clients through interior design, project consultation, master-planning, construction management, and facility management. Other offices are specializing in certain building types or professional services, such as historic preservation or educational facilities.

Architectural offices have a broad range of sizes and "personalities" reflecting different business priorities and goals. Different firms appeal to different types of clients and recruit different types of staff members. Successful and respected architecture firms range from small offices with less than 10 employees to large corporate firms with hundreds of staff architects in branch offices around the world.

Architecture firms often partner with each other for different projects. In addition to professional skills, understanding the importance of teamwork and communication are keys to success in the business world.

POSSIBLE CAREER PATHS

An architectural education, with its emphasis on problem solving through analytical and creative thinking, is an excellent preparation for many different career paths within architecture, and in other fields, such as real estate development, construction, consulting, multimedia design, industrial design, product development, law, and computers.

DIVERSE RESPONSIBILITIES/TEAMS

Depending on personal strengths, skills, and interests, different architects within a firm may focus on marketing, client presentations, programming consultation, design, technical issues, construction details and specifications, construction administration, interiors, or project management within the office. Teamwork maximizes these diverse skills.

Architects may also make important contributions to the quality of the built environment by working in construction companies, by working with building product companies, by developing specialized expertise as a consultant to other architecture firms, or by working directly for clients such as developers, hotel chains, or for government.

COMPENSATION AND REWARDS

As a profession, architecture tends to follow trends in the economy. Both booms and recessions can seriously affect architecture practice. Client fees are highly competitive, and the salary structure of the profession can fluctuate. Beginning salaries for architecture interns also fluctuate widely, depending in part on geographical location, demand for building activity, availability of applicants, and, most important, the capability of the individual applicant. An intern architect typically earns $39,500–$50,500 per year (*Almanac of Architecture & Design*, 2006). Because a new graduate may work as an intern architect for approximately three years before taking the licensing exam and becoming a registered architect, the salaries are for interns, not registered architects. Remember, your entire educational experience requires approximately eight to nine years of combined formal schooling and internship. Essentially, your internship salary allows you to earn an income while completing the last two or three years of your education. Compensation varies by the areas in the firm in which you work. Principals in firms earn a range of $80,000–$155,000 annually, while partners earn $140,000–$220,000, although these ranges are composites of a range of firm sizes.

Nevertheless, architects have the gratification of seeing each different project evolve from an abstract idea into a permanent reality transforming the daily lives and well-being of the project's users. The work of an architect is unique, lasting, and meaningful.

STEPS TO LICENSURE

To protect the health, safety, and welfare of its citizens, each state has regulations for the licensing of architects. Before a person can claim the title architect, most states require three components for a license, often referred to as the "three E's":

- Education: a professional degree (B. Arch, M. Arch, D. Arch)
- Experience: the completion of the Intern Development Program.
- Exam: passing the nationwide Architect Registration Exam.

Many architects hold a license in more than one state. A system of national reciprocity has been established by the National Council of Architecture Registration Boards (NCARB). While these requirements describe most states, each state is different, and licensing laws can be revised.

INTERN DEVELOPMENT PROGRAM
The preparation to become an architect involves academic education as well as an internship period in the profession. Education and practice offer complementary learning experiences. While not required in every state, the Intern Development Program (IDP) is a national program that structures the learning goals for the internship period.

Typical IDP requirements include time spent in different aspects of professional work, such as design, project management, construction administration, and community service.

Even before one's first job, architecture students, in professional degree programs should enroll in the IDP program through NCARB. As a result, students will receive up-to-date information about requirements, which include a time limit on reporting experience. Furthermore, employment while in school will often count toward IDP credit.

ARCHITECT REGISTRATION EXAM
Even though different states have different licensure laws, the Architect Registration Exam (ARE) is a single national exam recognized by all states. It is developed and administered by NCARB. The specific exam content is modified over the years, but typically addresses building design/materials and methods, building planning, building technology, construction documents and services, general structures, lateral forces, mechanical and electrical systems, pre-design, and site planning.

The ARE is divided into different sections, which can be repeated. Many states will allow individuals to take some portions of the exam immediately after graduation. In general, however, completion of IDP provides important knowledge and skills for the licensing exam.

For the most up-to-date information regarding particular state requirements, contact NCARB. In Canada, similar standards for examination and internship are developed by the Canadian Architectural Certification Board (CACB).

INTERNATIONAL CONSIDERATIONS
In general, it is best to pursue professional architectural education in the country in which one intends to practice and be registered. However, in the past several years discussions regarding reciprocity between countries (such as essentially exists between the United States and Canada) have been promising and may lead to increased portability of credentials among countries in the future. Nevertheless, international educational and licensure credentials are governed by complex regulations.

ARCHITECTURAL EDUCATION

GOALS OF ARCHITECTURAL EDUCATION

As a professional discipline, architecture spans both the arts and the sciences. Students must have an understanding of the arts and humanities, as well as a basic technical understanding of structures and construction. Skills in communication, both visual and verbal, are essential. While knowledge and skills must be developed, design is ultimately a process of critical thinking, analysis, and creative activity. The best way to face the global challenges of the 21st century is with a well-rounded education that establishes a foundation for lifelong learning.

PROFESSIONAL DEGREES

With few exceptions, this path starts with earning a professional degree. At one extreme, a high school student may enter a professional program; at the other extreme, a person (with a college degree in any background) may make a mid-career decision to become an architect, and can enroll in a three-year professional graduate program.

Many students from other majors may transfer into architecture. In some ways, it is never too late to become an architect. However, it is important that students are aware of the differences among degree paths and are enrolled in a program that is appropriate for their interests and long-term career plans.

THREE MAIN PATHS TO A PROFESSIONAL DEGREE

In general, three types of programs lead to an accredited, professional degree. All professional degrees meet similar minimal standards, including professional requirements and general education courses.

Professional Master of Architecture programs may cause some confusion to readers, because individuals enter an M. Arch program with a variety of educational credentials, and hence with varied paths ahead to graduation. In many cases, schools in the guide list multiple paths to the M. Arch programs. In other cases, a school may list only one M. Arch degree, even though it admits students on multiple paths.

Following are three common paths for professional architectural education.

5 year programs (B. Arch or M. Arch)

These are five-year professional degree programs, typically for undergraduates, with approximately 30% of the curriculum devoted to the humanities and electives. Since 1995, some five-year B. Arch. programs have made a transition to a five-year M. Arch package. In most cases, high school graduates enter the program as a freshmen.

4 + 2 Programs

These programs grant a pre-professional degree (majoring in architecture or environmental design) after four years, followed by a two-year program of intense study leading to a Master of Architecture (M. Arch) professional degree.

The four-year pre-professional degree, where offered, is not an accredited professional degree. The pre-professional degree is useful for those wishing a foundation in the field of architecture, as preparation for either a professional degree program or employment options in architecturally related areas.

3-Year (or 3 ½ Year) Graduate Programs (M. Arch or D. Arch)

These graduate programs are not advanced study, but professional degree graduate programs for students holding a four-year undergraduate degree in any subject matter.

PROFESSIONAL ACCREDITATION
NAAB: National Architectural Accrediting Board
CACB: Canadian Architectural Certification Board

The professional degrees in architecture are accredited by the National Architecture Accreditation Board (NAAB) or by the Canadian Architectural Certification Board (CACB) in Canada. These organizations are composed of representatives from the profession, from schools of architecture, from student organizations, and from the public. They have established conditions and criteria for accreditation that apply to all professional degree programs. Programs are accredited on a regular cycle, and the current accreditation status of individual programs and different schools can be found on the NAAB or CACB websites.

It should be noted that schools of architecture are not accredited; only specific professional degree program paths are accredited.

POST-PROFESSIONAL DEGREES AND OTHER "NON-PROFESSIONAL" GRADUATE DEGREES

Many universities offer additional degree programs of advanced study for students with or without a professional degree. Post-professional degree programs may be one to five years in length, may address many areas of specialization such as urban design, sustainability, computer visualization, health care, historic preservation in architectural history, and may have many different degree names, such as M. Arch, D. Arch, D.Design, M.UD, etc. Such degree programs are not accredited by NAAB nor CACB. Some institutions offer both the professional M. Arch and a post-professional M. Arch.

A "non-professional graduate degree" does not necessarily require a professional degree background. For example, PhD programs provide in-depth exposure to a specific topic or area of exploration. These kinds of degrees may be related to architectural history, behavioral science, environmental studies, and other areas of research and scholarship.

NON-PROFESSIONAL UNDERGRADUATE DEGREES

Many accredited universities offer architecture "majors" or programs such as "architectural technology" that are not part of a professionally accredited degree.

The value of non-professional type programs and majors depends on individual career goals. These programs give a broad view of the discipline of architecture or the construction industry. These degrees may prepare graduates for a range of job opportunities, including entry level at an architecture firm. This may also be a good preparation for graduate study in architecture in a professional degree program.

In practicing architecture as a career, long-term success may be limited by not having a professional degree, which is required by most states for a license. Furthermore, NCARB standards for reciprocity across state borders require a professional degree.

MISSIONS AND CURRICULA OF PROFESSIONAL DEGREE PROGRAMS

The professional accrediting boards establish common standards for ar-

chitecture programs, yet try to avoid "standardization" by encouraging each program to articulate its own mission and by recognizing that the accreditation requirements can be met in many different ways.

While there are broad differences among schools, the typical architecture curriculum covers topics related to design, history and theory, visualization (including drawing and computing), building technology, structures, sustainability, and professional practice, as well as a requirement for electives and exposure to general education and courses outside of architecture.

At the heart of the academic environment is the design studio, which is both a course and a place. In the design studio, faculty challenge students to synthesize all aspects of learning. As a result of the rigorous design curriculum, students develop a process of design thinking that is simultaneously analytical and creative. This cross–functional thought process is applicable to the many challenges that graduates will face in the future, no matter what career path they ultimately pursue.

PROGRAM VARIATIONS

While the architecture schools in the United States and Canada must meet similar accreditation criteria, the programs are remarkably different, with unique missions and philosophies.

- Many schools support diverse international programs and travel courses, which may be open to students from other schools as well.
- Some schools have established a permanent educational facility in an international setting.
- Some schools have formal "ex-

change" agreements with international schools or have offices to assist in placing students in international programs.
- Each year, individual faculty may develop a variety of international summer programs.
- Many schools engage in community service projects and efforts.
- Most schools work with alumni and regional professionals in formulating career development and placement efforts.
- Some schools have "design-build" studio experiences.
- Some programs include a required co-op internship, typically at an architecture firm.
- Some programs are structured to allow students to work full-time while attaining a degree.
- Some programs have opportunities for students to be involved in working at the school, either in course work or in support services.
- Some programs have opportunies for students to work in faculty research efforts.
- Some programs require off-campus experiences.
- Some schools offer summer programs for high school students and others who are interested in a career in architecture: these may range from a few days to six weeks.

Within the diversity of American and Canadian architecture programs, dedicated faculty strive to create meaningful and diverse learning experiences for their students.

PREPARING FOR AND SELECTING AN ARCHITECTURE PROGRAM

Because architecture programs vary so significantly, students should look carefully at their options. Some factors to consider when selecting a school include:

- program type and length of study (described above)
- institutional context
- large university, small private college, religious affiliation, public, etc.
- program philosophy, emphasis, and curriculum
- tuition costs and fees
- financial issues
- work-study opportunities
- living costs
- teaching assistantships
- scholarships, loans, grants
- student–faculty ratios
- Expertise of faculty involved in the program
- internship opportunities or requirements
- off–campus and foreign study opportunities
- community service opportunities
- other special curriculum opportunities such as double majors or interdisciplinary connections
- facilities and resources, related to studio space, library, and digital support
- long term career options
- accreditation status of the program

Each student should match all of these considerations with personal circumstances and goals.

ADMISSION CONSIDERATIONS
Admission requirements are set by each institution. Typically, admission decisions involve a review of the student's past academic history and test scores. Some undergraduate programs may require a portfolio or interview. Some programs may have "open admission," with minimal entry requirements, but internal review processes for advancement in the program. Most graduate programs will require a portfolio, even if a college graduate's background is not in architecture.

PORTFOLIOS
Because architecture is a visual discipline, an individual's portfolio is often an important consideration in admission decisions and, later, in interviewing for jobs.

For admission as a beginning student in architecture, the portfolio should show potential as a visual thinker and personal initiative as a designer. Potential can be demonstrated in many ways, including drawings, fine art work, ceramics, sculpture, graphic design, photography or constructed projects such as stage sets or pieces of furniture. Probably the least significant component of such a portfolio would be CAD drawings from a high school course that tend to demonstrate technical drafting skills rather than potential.

Some programs have portfolio reviews periodically to determine advancement within the program, including the transition into the graduate component of a 4+2 program. Not only would these portfolios show potential, but they would document course work completed to date.

Almost all architecture firms review candidate portfolios in the interview process. In this case, they will be looking for accomplishments, potential, the ability to be part of a team, technical understanding, and communication skills, both verbal and visual. Free-hand drawing as well as digital expertise are typically valued.

While the portfolio has different purposes and audiences, it should be well organized. Labeling should indicate if work was for a course assignment or if it was completed independently; it is also useful to know when the work was completed and the approximate amount of time involved. Students should document and preserve their work. Submission of original items is not usually necessary, although different programs may have different requirements.

Visually, the portfolio itself is a type of design project, and will reflect the design personality and organizational capabilities of its author.

ADVICE TO INTERNATIONAL STUDENTS
International students are welcome at American and Canadian universities. However, visas, licensure requirements, and accreditation requirements are quite detailed, and international students should understand these requirements well. The diversity of professional degrees and university programs can be confusing. In particular, when universities offer more than one type of M. Arch, it is important to understand the difference between a professionally accredited M. Arch related to licensure, and a non-accredited M. Arch intended for students with another professional architecture degree.

ADVICE TO COLLEGE GRADUATES
Because of the diversity of degree paths in architecture, it is not uncommon for architecture students to have a variety of educational experiences. Some stu-

dents in 4+2 programs may change institutions after the bachelor's degree, but should not assume that all of their undergraduate course credit will meet the architecture requirements of the graduate institution.

While many architecture students select an architecture program as an undergraduate, it is possible for individuals to make a mid-career decision to enter architecture by entering a graduate program. Portfolios are typically required for graduate programs.

ADVICE TO TRANSFER STUDENTS
Policies for transferring vary at all institutions, and students should never "assume" that credit will easily transfer from one institution to another. Most universities accept credit of transfer students, but this does not necessarily mean that the transfer credit will meet professional course requirements. Often transfer credit will meet "elective" requirements, for courses outside of the architecture professional core requirements.

In a professional architecture program, transfer credit is usually handled on a case-by-case basis, and transfer students should be vigilant in maintaining accurate academic records, including a complete portfolio of course work and assignments.

Some community colleges may have an "articulation agreement" with a specific accredited architecture program to apply credits earned in an associate's degree program. Unless this is the case, transfer students from community colleges should not assume that their prior course work will easily meet professional degree course requirements.

Undergraduate students who are not in architecture and want to transfer in should compare the degree options, especially if considering transferring into a five-year program. It may be just as easy to finish an undergraduate degree and pursue a three-year graduate M. Arch degree rather than start a new five-year program as a junior or senior.

ADVICE TO HIGH SCHOOL STUDENTS
Successful architects are thoughtful, curious, self-disciplined, well-rounded, and intelligent, not just "talented." They may have been at the top of their high school class, or may have been underperforming high school students who blossomed in a design-based educational program.

Ideally, the beginning architecture student will have a high school experience with a strong proficiency in oral and written communication; a breadth of knowledge in the humanities; a solid background in the physical sciences, including mathematics; an ability to "conceptualize" at an above-average level; and the ability to draw and sketch with ease. Many universities have entry requirements related to high-school languages, although few architecture program curricula require college-level language courses

In general, high school students interested in architecture are encouraged to take challenging courses. Courses in the humanities provide a well-rounded educational foundation, ideal for a successful architect.

Students enrolled in Advanced Placement courses should take the AP Exam. While different universities have different standards for AP credit, receiving AP credit gives a college student much more flexibility to take other courses, to take a lighter load, or to graduate early.

Math and structures are important components in architecture programs, so advanced math courses in high school are recommended. Many architecture programs require calculus, which can often be met with AP calculus credit or by taking a placement exam. High school physics courses are strongly recommended as an excellent preparation for understanding basic principles in structures, electricity, heating/cooling, lighting, acoustics, and energy conservation.

In the same way that a student who wants to become a writer would not necessarily take typing courses, any student who wants to become an architect need not take drafting or CAD courses. Many drafting courses simply emphasize copying drawings neatly, and are not intellectually challenging. Understanding CAD software in high school may be helpful, but is not necessary.

Architecture involves visual thinking and composition that can best be developed in a good drawing or art course. Not all high schools offer these types of courses, and most architecture programs will include required drawing courses. Students who are in a high school that does not offer drawing could develop drawing skills independently by making a 15-minute freehand line sketch (from observation) each day in a sketchbook with high quality sketching pencils or pens. Local museums and evening schools often offer short

non-credit courses that could be very helpful.

While "design" is the primary emphasis of study in most programs, the faculty do not expect students to be good designers when entering—only when graduating. Faculty welcome students who are above average in intelligence, have diverse skills, and are self-motivated, thoughtful, and interested in learning.

SELF-MOTIVATION, WORK ETHIC, AND TIME MANAGEMENT
Design can be a time-consuming process, and the seemingly infinite possibilities of a design assignment are a new challenge to students familiar with traditional high school expectations. Architecture students traditionally work many long hours in the studio on architectural projects. The studio environment is not all work, however, and students develop close bonds with other students and faculty members.

Time management in professional programs is essential to maximize the college experience with its opportunities for new challenges, for extra curricular activities, and for new friends. Students should expect to work hard, in an efficient and effective way.

FINANCIAL ASSISTANCE AND WORKING
Most institutions have an office of financial aid to assist students with the complexities of loans, grants, payment programs, scholarships, and work-study options. Tuition rates are a major consideration and the difference between in-state, out-of-state, and private tuition rates can be significant.

Students who plan to work during their college years should plan this carefully. With proper time management, holding a job should be possible and can even be a very gratifying experience. Some programs are structured to allow students to work.

However, in the typical undergraduate environment, students who need to work more that 12 hours per week may consider taking a lighter course load to maximize the college experience. Adding an extra year or two to the planned curriculum may be worthwhile in reducing stress and in maximizing involvement in a range of meaningful activities. Each situation is different, and time management is important.

FREQUENTLY ASKED QUESTIONS

1. What is the difference between a B. Arch and an M. Arch?
The professional degrees accredited by NAAB or CACB have essentially the same professional content requirements for a B. Arch, M. Arch, or a D. Arch. General education courses are expected in all three degree types. The definition of graduate level study is made by the institution.

2. Can I expect a higher salary with an M. Arch?
In general, salaries in architecture firms are not calibrated by degree types, but by level of experience, personal skill-sets, and quality of work demonstrated by a review of the portfolio. Grade transcripts are rarely requested. Success in practice is a combination of many factors, and the professional degree type alone does not affect salary levels, like it might in other fields. However, lack of a professional degree can negatively impact long-term success in licensure issues.

3. Can I get a job with a pre-professional architecture degree (in a 4+2 type of program)?
Yes, but you likely will not be able to get a license to practice independently. Having completed the first part of a 4+2 program is often reasonable preparation for an entry-level job in a firm. However, long-term success in architectural practice may be limited by not having a professional degree (NAAB or CACB), which is required by most states for a license. Furthermore, NCARB standards for reciprocity across state borders require a NAAB degree.

4. Would it be a good idea to attend a community college for two years and finish up at an NAAB program?
Some community colleges have a for-mal "articulation agreement" with a specific NAAB program that provides a cost-effective path to a professional degree. However, it is not wise to simply assume that community college courses will meet professional course requirements and give you advance standing in any NAAB program. While many professional programs may accept individual technical courses from a community college, it is quite common to place the transfer student in the first year of a 4- or 5-year design sequence. If you do attend community college, maintain good records including all course materials and your assignments. (See Advice To Transfer Students)

6. How can I put together a portfolio if I have never had any architecture courses?
Some undergraduate programs and most graduate programs will require a portfolio. The purpose of this is to demonstrate your potential for what you will learn in an architecture program. Indications of visual thinking and design ability can be demonstrated in many ways: drawings, artwork, sculpture, things you've made or built, graphic design, and photography. Architecture projects are not typically expected in this kind of portfolio. In general, CAD drawings alone are discouraged in a portfolio. Unless executed as part of design course, CAD is generally considered a technical skill, not necessarily a demonstration of visual thinking or design. Programs that require a portfolio typically give more specific advice about what to include.

7. How do I know if a program is professionally accredited?
For the current list of accredited programs and their status, check the NAAB or CACB websites.
Most universities are "accredited" by different entities, but you want to look for a "professionally accredited" program in architecture.

8. I am enrolled in "architecture technology" at a large university that is accredited. I thought it was an architecture program, but I just discovered that it is not "professionally" accredited by NAAB. What should I do?
Depending on your career goals and depending on how many years you have been in school, you may consider transferring to a NAAB program, or you may consider graduating and applying to a NAAB 3-year graduate program. You may receive advance standing in the program. (See Advice to Transfer Students above)
The value of an architecture technology program (and similar affiliated types of majors) depends on your career goals. These programs give a broad view of the construction industry, and these degrees prepare graduates for a broad range of job opportunities, including entry level at an architecture firm. This may be a good preparation for graduate study in architecture.
If you want to practice architecture as a career, long-term success in architectural practice may be limited by not having a NAAB degree, which is required by most states for a license. Furthermore, NCARB standards for reciprocity across state borders require a NAAB degree.

9. If I am not sure about committing to an architecture career, what advice would you give?
Everyone is different, so you may consider different options. There is no single best path. Because there are many diverse paths to becoming an architect, it

is important to understand the differences and select the course of action that meets your particular circumstances.

Most 5-year programs, and some 4+2 programs, start immediately with design courses in the freshman year. In this environment you will receive an immediate exposure to design and architecture so that you can understand your commitment early.

Most 4+2 programs and some 5-year programs have a freshman year devoted to general studies, and introduce architecture courses in the 2nd year. This may be useful for students who want a more general university experience before committing to architecture.

You may consider a non-professional bachelor's degree in any major, or in a major related to architecture such as urban studies, engineering, fine arts, business, or architectural technology. After graduation, if you are still interested in architecture, you could enter a 3-year M. Arch program designed for graduate students with minimal background in architecture. This may also be a good path for collegiate scholar-athletes who may not have the time for both sports and professional undergraduate degree requirements.

Finally, someone considering architecture as a career should talk to and visit as many architects as possible.

10. What else can an architecture degree prepare me for?

Not all students who start in an architecture program will finish the program, and not all graduates of architecture programs go on to get a license and practice architecture.

Most of these people who do not use their architectural education in traditional architectural practice still appreciate the "problem solving" abilities they gained from their architectural education. Through the challenges in the design studio, students learn to analyze problems and to creatively develop alternative solutions leading to a final design.

The problem-solving ability of design thinking is applicable to many fields, not just architecture. Individuals education in architecture will be well prepared for many careers.

QUESTIONS YOU SHOULD ASK SCHOOLS

The following are basic questions and do not fully address the quality of the education offered at any institution. Try to visit the schools you are interested in, including a visit to the architectural studios and facilities. After reviewing all the available materials you should formulate your own questions based on your personal aspirations and requirements.

1. Accreditation
- Is the program professionally accredited by the National Architectural Accrediting Board (NAAB) or the Canadian Architectural Certification Board (CACB)?
- If not, what is the school's accreditation status (e.g., candidate status, not seeking accreditation)? Can I be reasonably assured that the school will be accredited during the time I am in school?

2. Degree Options
- Is the first degree that I receive an accredited professional degree that will fulfill the educational requirement to become a registered architect?
- If I receive a degree as an architecture major, will it allow me to apply to the professional architectural degree program at this school or other schools?
- Is the pre-professional degree one that will allow me to proceed to professional or graduate design programs in other disciplines such as landscape architecture, urban design, or historic preservation?
- How many years will this pre-professional or post professional degree normally require?
- If I decide not to go on with the professional program or the graduate professional degree program, what are my career alternatives with a pre-professional degree?

3. Curriculum Options
- How is the first year handled? What kind of studio facilities can I expect?
- Are there special offerings at this school that allow me to focus on a particular interest, such as design, computers, energy, sustainability, preservation?
- Are there special offerings at this school that allow me to take advantage of its geographic location?
- Are there enrichment opportunities such as foreign or off-campus study?
- Are there special lab facilities or an outstanding library that would help with my special interests?

4. General
- Are scholarships available? Are they academic or need-based?
- What are the specific interests and notable accomplishments of the faculty?
- What is the average number of students in the design studios and lecture classes?
- Who will teach my classes? Full-time faculty? Part-time? Graduate students?
- What are the advantages of this school's teaching system?
- What are recent graduates of the program doing?

QUESTIONS YOU SHOULD ASK YOURSELF

After all of this discussion on how to narrow the choices to a few schools that are best for you, you are probably still asking, "Yes, but which are the best schools?" There really is no way to say which are the best schools. Best for what? For what you can afford? For the location you desire? For the size of institution you wish to attend? For the special interest on which you wish to focus? In general, "best" should mean best for you.

Most schools are excellent in their chosen areas of emphasis, but no school is excellent in all aspects of what you ought to learn. Because of the diverse nature of architecture programs and the varied interests, aptitudes, and objectives of students, it is impossible to rank architecture schools. While some program aspects can be measured for example, number of library books, student–faculty ratio, studio space per students—there is no method of assessing accurately the quality of instruction from one program to another or quantifying different points of view.

Probably the most important factor in any educational endeavor is the student's motivation. Most architectural employers are far more interested in what you have accomplished and can do as a person than in your degree.

While you should seek as much information and as many opinions as possible, with a conscientious effort you will probably be in as good a position as anyone to make decisions regarding your own education and career. Besides, having faith in one's own ability to make non-quantifiable judgments is an ideal starting point for your future education.

A (BRIEF) HISTORY OF ARCHITECTURAL EDUCATION

In 1814 Thomas Jefferson (the United States' only architect-president) proposed that a professional curriculum in architecture be established in the School of Mathematics of the University of Virginia. Unfortunately, the search for an appropriate architect/mathematician was fruitless, and the University of Virginia delayed its entrance into the architectural field for many years. Instead, formal architectural education in the United States began in 1865 at the Massachusetts Institute of Technology, five years after the institution's founding. MIT's action was followed in 1867 by the University of Illinois at Urbana and in 1871 by Cornell University. The universities of Toronto and Montréal started the first schools of architecture in Canada in 1876.

The Morrill Act, passed by the U.S. Congress in 1862, had great and lasting repercussions for higher education, including architecture. In exchange for land granted by Congress, colleges were expected to provide "practical" education for America's youth. This contrasted strongly with European traditions that more clearly separated education and training: at the university one was "educated," and, once in the office, one was "trained." Of course, not all institutions of higher education founded since then have been "land-grant" colleges, but the tradition the system developed was a pervasive one, particularly in the South, Midwest, and West.

The European tradition, however, is a second important historical thread in North American architectural education. Many people considered the system described above rather uncouth. Looking to Europe for a standard, as Americans often did in the nineteenth century, eyes settled on the prestigious École des Beaux Arts in Paris as the ultimate in architectural training. The École's philosophy was imported to the United States, and most architecture schools in the early part of this century had at least one Paris-trained professor. If you were the "unfortunate" graduate of a school devoid of such influence, you could always go to an academy in New York and learn the mysteries through a graduate course taught by an exclusively Beaux Arts staff. Or you could go to the École des Beaux Arts for a year, as over 500 Americans did between 1850 and 1968, when it closed. The grand prize of almost all superior fellowships and competitions of the time was specifically for travel to Europe to study examples of the "masters" and their successors.

Canada was also importing a number of Beaux Arts-trained teachers at this time, especially in the French-speaking provinces. Because Canada had stronger ties with England and Scotland than did the United States, however, many of Canada's first professors came directly from the British Isles.

The cornerstone of the Beaux Arts system was the "design problem" assigned to the student early in the term and carefully developed under close tutelage. It began as an esquisse, or sketch problem, and ended en charrette. Charrette, French for "cart," refers to the carts in which the finished drawings were placed at the deadline hour for transport to the "master" for critique. The Beaux Arts teaching systems relied heavily on brilliant teachers and learning-by-doing. Competition was intense and the end results were beautifully drawn projects in traditional styles which were often defensible only on grounds of "good taste" and intuition. The style was mostly neoclassical and the favorite building type was the monument. Projects were judged by a jury of professors and guest architects, usually without the students present. The jurors used the same criteria by which the students designed: "good taste." (Most schools still use some type of "jury" or review system today.)

In the early part of the twentieth century, both the United States and Canada were developing cultures of their own and outgrowing their European dependence. The power of individualism affected architecture no less than it did all other aspects of American culture. With the advent of "modern" architecture in Europe, the growing fame of the Chicago skyscraper idiom, and Frank Lloyd Wright's "Prairie School" architecture, intense pressures for change began to build in architectural education.

Like all emerging disciplines, architectural education grew up under very different roofs on different campuses, usually depending on the nature of other colleges already established at the time the decision was made to offer architecture programs. There are separate and autonomous schools or colleges of architecture; departments and programs within graduate schools; schools of art or design; schools oriented toward engineering, technology, or sociology; and, more recently, schools of urban planning and design. Columbia University made a dramatic shift in 1934 away from the French methods toward those of the modern German movement exemplified by the Bauhaus school. The Bauhaus, formed in 1919, moved to its famous Dessau, Germany, location in 1925, but was closed down by the Nazis in 1933. The influence of that school was felt throughout the world. Its director, Walter Gropius, said that design was neither an intellectual nor a material affair but simply an integral part of modern concepts of mass production and modern technology, which the Beaux Arts had refused to accept. Instruction at the Bauhaus was of a practical nature, providing actual work with materials in the shops and on buildings under construction.

In 1936, Walter Gropius came to the United States and from 1938 to 1952 was head of the architecture department at Harvard University. Also in 1936, Harvard integrated architecture, landscape architecture, and urban planning into a single school—the triangular model of many schools of environmental design today. Gropius' distinguished colleague from the Bauhaus, Ludwig Mies van der Rohe, also came to the United States and became the head of the architecture school at the Illinois Institute of Technology in 1938.

As the architectural curriculum expanded beyond the art of rendering to include utilitarian subjects such as mechanical equipment and structural analysis, the standard four-year program began to bulge at the seams. There was also a growing tendency to include work in crafts and fine arts. The first school to adopt a five-year professional program of study in architecture was Cornell University, which did so in 1922. By 1940 almost all architecture schools had a standard course of five years leading to a Bachelor of Architecture degree.

The last thirty years have demonstrated that there is a great deal more to the building disciplines than ever realized in the previous 2,000 years. In the 1940s, Harvard's Joseph Hudnut made a list of all the subjects that he deemed essential for a sound and complete architectural education. When the list was complete he calculated the length of time it would take to learn everything on it—22 years. While this is ridiculously long, the pressures for the modern architect to know more and assume greater responsibility have had their effect, even when tempered with the realization that not all need be learned in school.

The "four-plus-two" program became a model for expanding the professional curriculum in the 1960s. This program usually took the form of a four-year course of study in environmental design followed by two years with a strong concentration in architecture. A report by the American Institute of Architects' Special Committee on Education published in 1962 has been generally recognized as the impetus behind this development. The first such programs in the United States were developed at the University of California, Berkeley, and Washington University in St. Louis. Many schools stayed with the five-year Bachelor of Architecture program, however, confident that within its time constraints they could provide both a liberal and a professional education.

Another pattern that emerged in the 1960s recognized the possibilities of studying architecture solely at the graduate level. Many schools offer graduate professional education for students whose undergraduate degrees are in fields as diverse as philosophy, languages, and physics. The idea of professional programs offered exclusively at the graduate level recognizes the option of having a solid university education before embarking on a professional education.

Another interesting trend that emerged in the 1960s was the notion of the free clinic for urban problems and architectural design. The movement really began with "CDCs," or community design centers. As architecture, along with other professions, woke up to social responsibility, the nonprofit CDCs began to provide architectural and planning services for the disadvantaged, usually in urban areas. Some CDCs were born of negativism—for example, to stop a thoughtlessly planned freeway—while others grew out of positive motives such as creating playgrounds or low-cost housing. At any rate, by the late 1960s it became clear that the market for nonprofit design services was larger than originally thought and extended beyond minorities to many segments of society. This gave rise to the "clinic" notion, a logical extension of the original CDC. The clinic may be in a school of architecture or exist as a separate but related institution. Normally it is staffed by members of a school's faculty and provides students an opportunity to work on "real" proj-

ects with "real" clients, often with local architects. Successful CDCs are now operating at several schools. Although many are located in large urban areas, rural problems deserve equal attention, and the challenge has been taken up wherever resources permit.

Architecture currently continues to increase in complexity. Projects in general are larger, often involving greater areas of land. The nature of the client is also changing. Formerly, even very large projects were identified with single clients—individuals whose intentions and needs could easily be made clear. Today's client is more likely to be a board of directors or trustees, a special committee, or representatives of a government agency. There are also many new technological developments, such as automatic control systems for air conditioning, complicated structural systems for long spans, and elaborate factory prefabrication. The concerns for efficient use of energy and ecologically responsible design have also become permanent considerations.

Perhaps the most complex issues in recent architecture are not new at all but rather matters that were obvious to any sharp observer all along. These are the impacts of social, psychological, political, and economic issues on the built environment. It is obvious that architecture and planning broadcast messages, often loudly and clearly. A work of architecture, like any other human artifact, embodies values and cultural priorities. Archaeologists have for years been trying to reconstruct the values of ancient cultures from their artifacts. Only recently have we begun to examine this process in the present, before it becomes ancient history.

Today, 125 schools in the United States and Canada offer professional degrees in architecture, and more than 100 offer nonprofessional one- or two-year programs in architectural studies or technology. The vast demands of society and the profession, and the corresponding range of programs dealing with these issues, provide the entering student with an excellent opportunity for finding the program best suited to his/her talents and interests.

REFERENCE AND RESOURCES

WEBSITES

All of these web sites have information specifically for prospective students in architecture.

ArchCareers.org

A mini-portal for information on becoming an architect. Sponsored by AIA and AIAS.

The American Institute of Architects (AIA)

www.aia.org
1735 New York Avenue, NW
Washington DC 20006

The major professional organization for architects, with information for practitioners, students, and the public.

American Institute of Architecture Students (AIAS)

www.aias.org
1735 New York Avenue, NW
Washington DC 20006

The major independent organization for students in architecture schools, with information on student-focused events, activities, and resources.

Association of Collegiate Schools of Architecture (ACSA)

www.acsa-arch.org
www.archschools.org
1735 New York Avenue, NW
Washington DC 20006

The membership organization for architectural schools in the United States and Canada, publishers of this book and its online edition, found at www.archschools.org. The ACSA website includes resources on education, student design competitions, and other information on architectural education.

National Architectural Accreditation Board (NAAB)

www.naab.org
1735 New York Avenue, NW
Washington DC 20006

The accrediting body for U.S. professional architecture degree programs, with information on the accreditation process and information on the accreditation history of schools.

Canadian Architectural Certification Board (CACB)

www.cacb-ccca.ca

The accrediting body for Canadian professional architecture degree programs.

National Council of Architectural Registration Boards (NCARB)

www.ncarb.org

The federation of licensing boards in the United States that oversees the national Architect Registration Exam, the Internship Development Program, and architectural licensing procedures.

REFERENCE BOOKS FOR ARCHITECTURE CAREERS

- James P. Cramer and Jennifer Evans Yankopolus (Eds.), *Almanac of Architecture & Design 2009*, Greenway Communications, LLC.
- Roger K. Lewis, *Architect? A Candid Guide to the Profession*, 1998 MIT Press.
- Thomas Fisher, *Architectural Design and Ethics: Tools for Survival*, 2008 Elsevier Ltd.
- Andy Pressman, *Architecture 101, A Guide to the Design Studio*, 1993 John Wiley & Sons Inc.
- Lee W. Waldrep, PhD, *Becoming an Architect: A Guide to Careers in Design*, 2006 John Wiley & Sons Inc.
- Grace Kim, *Survival Guide to Architectural Internship and Career Development*, 2006 John Wiley & Sons Inc.

ACSA FULL AND CANDIDATE MEMBER SCHOOLS

The 134 United States and Canadian schools with professional degree programs in architecture are the primary members of ACSA. Accredited schools are full members; schools in the process of gaining accreditation are candidate members.

8th Annual ACSA/AISC Steel Design Student Competition, 2007–08
Second Place Winner — Open Category
Student: Courtney Anne Brown, Oklahoma State University
Faculty Sponsors: Jeffrey K. Williams & Paolo Sanza, Oklahoma State University
Project Title: MEDIA[space]

ACADEMY *of* **ART UNIVERSITY**

FOUNDED IN SAN FRANCISCO 1929

ADDRESS

Main
Academy of Art University
School of Architecture
79 New Montgomery Street
San Francisco, CA 94105
Tel.: 415.618.3564
Fax: 415.618.3566
www.academyart.edu

STUDENT AND FACULTY DEMOGRAPHICS

% of Female Students	60
% of International Students	61
% of Minority Students	55
% of Out-of-State U.S. Students	16
No. Full-Time Faculty	1
No. Part-Time Faculty	20
No. Full-Time Students	65
No. Part-Time Students	10

FINANCIAL INFORMATION

Main Source of University Funding	Private
Annual Tuition & Fees (graduate)	$13,860 ($770/unit)
Annual Tuition & Fees (undergraduate)	
% Students Receiving Federal Financial Aid	
% Students Receiving University Financial Aid	
% Students Receiving Departmental Financial Aid	
% Students Receiving Scholarships (assistantships or fellowships)	
Average Annual Scholarship for Department	

ACADEMIC SESSIONS

Fall Semester: September to December; Application Deadline: Rolling
Summer Session I: June to August; Application Deadline: Rolling

Spring Semester: January to May; Application Deadline: Rolling

ARCHITECTURE AND RELATED DEGREE PROGRAMS							
Degree	Min. Yrs. to Complete	Professional Accreditation	# of FT Students	# of PT Students	# of First-Year Students	# of Degrees Conferred	Admissions Requirements
Architecture							
M. Arch	2.5/3.5	NAAB	65	10	27	18	Undergraduate Architecture degree or undergraduate degree, Transcripts, Portfolio, Rec.Letters
Interior Design/Interior Architecture							
M.F.A. Interior Design		NASAD					

SPECIALIZATIONS

Architectural Design
Art and Design
Building Information Modeling

Community Design
Computer-Aided Design
Environment/Sustainability

Housing Urban Planning and Design
Interior Design/Architecture
Landscape Design

Sustainability
Urban Planning and Design

ARCHITECTURE PROGRAM SUMMARY

The Academy of Art University graduate candidate engages in a unique interdisciplinary approach to master's degree preparation. Comprising studio work and academic investigation, the programs extend for a period of 2½ years. Attainment of the various master's degrees requires the graduate candidate to successfully complete studio courses, directed study, academic study, and electives.

UNIVERSITY SETTING

The city of San Francisco is one of the great cultural centers of the world, a melting pot of diversity, ethnicity, and creativity that has spawned major museums and galleries, world-class architecture, technological innovation and numerous other cultural opportunities. The city offers myriad locations for field trips and studio visits. World-renowned artists display their creations in the Academy's large Bush Street gallery. The Academy of Art University is an urban institution that both draws upon and contributes to the cultural wealth of the community in which it resides.

SCHOOL PHILOSOPHY

Through the process of design, discovery of meaning and experience of making, the 63 and 87 unit Master of Architecture (M. ARCH) program at AAU provide the graduate student the confidence needed to incorporate aesthetical and physical possibilities for new buildings into our existing built environment. At the Graduate School, Architecture and Urban Design are considered inseparable and mutually inclusive components of a cohesive academic process.

PROGRAM DESCRIPTION

During their tenure at the school, students' work will represent the result of a process focusing on the following program goals:

- To stimulate and support the exploration of new and old architectural ideas.
- To encourage the student to be an active contributor to studios organized as laboratories of design.
- To investigate the possible, understand the past and question the present.
- To engage the San Francisco urban environment as a field of research.
- To explore and understand the urban consequences of architectural design.

FACILITIES

Computer Lab

Workstations: 18 Dell Precision 690 (Dual Intel Xeon 3.0 CPU's)

Scanners and Printers: 1 Epson 15000+ Scanner SP, 1 RICOH 3600 large format print/copy/scan 1 HP 4000ps DesignJet Plotter with state of the art media/color calibration software 1 HP 9500 Color Laser Jet

Shop

Architecture students have access to a 4000 sq ft model shop, which is equipped with drill presses, band saw, scroll saw, table saw, belt sander, laser cutter, and miscellaneous hand tools.

SCHOLARSHIPS AND FINANCIAL AID

The Academy offers need-based financial aid packages consisting of grants, loans, and work-study to eligible students. Low-interest loans are available to all eligible students. As financial aid programs, procedures, and eligibility requirements change frequently, applicants should contact the Financial Aid office for current requirements at 79 New Montgomery Street, 3rd Floor, San Francisco, California 94105, or by telephone at the University's toll free phone number 1.800.544.2787.

ADMINISTRATION

Alberto Bertoli, AIA: Director

AMERICAN UNIVERSITY OF SHARJAH

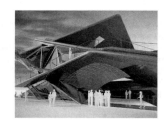

ADDRESS

Main
American University of Sharjah
School of Architecture & Design
P.O. Box 26666
Sharjah, United Arab Emirates
Tel.: (971)-6-515-2868
Fax: (971)-6-515-5800
Deanarcdes@aus.edu
www.aus.edu

ACADEMIC SESSIONS

Fall Semester: August to December
Spring Semester: January to May

STUDENT AND FACULTY DEMOGRAPHICS

% of Female Students	75
% of International Students	85
% of Minority Students	
% of Out-of-State U.S. Students	22
No. Full-Time Faculty	37
No. Part-Time Faculty	5
No. Full-Time Students	532
No. Part-Time Students	

FINANCIAL INFORMATION

Main Source of University Funding	Private
Annual Tuition & Fees (graduate, resident)	
Annual Tuition & Fees (graduate, nonresident)	
Annual Tuition & Fees (undergraduate, resident)	$16,712
Annual Tuition & Fees (undergraduate, nonresident)	$16,712
% Students Receiving Federal Financial Aid	
% Students Receiving University Financial Aid	28
% Students Receiving Departmental Financial Aid	
% Students Receiving Scholarships (assistantships or fellowships)	36
Average Annual Scholarship for Department	

Summer Session I: June to July
Summer Session II: July

ARCHITECTURE AND RELATED DEGREE PROGRAMS

Degree	Min. Yrs. to Complete	Professional Accreditation	# of FT Students	# of PT Students	# of First-Year Students	# of Degrees Conferred	Admissions Requirements
Architecture							
B. Arch	5	NAAB Candidate	264		98	165	Secondary education certificate, SAT scores, TOEFL, Number of qualified applicants, Number of available seats

SPECIALIZATIONS

Architectural Design	Energy	Landscape Design	Theory/Criticism
Building Technology/Env. Systems	History	Professional Practice	Urban Planning and Design
Computer-Aided Design	International/Regional Architecture	Sustainability	

ARCHITECTURE PROGRAM SUMMARY

The Department of Architecture is a regionally accredited progressive academic unit in the School of Architecture and Design of the American University of Sharjah that takes advantage of the unique professional and educational opportunities in the Gulf region. The five-year professional program is equivalent in scope and curricular structure to North American professional degree programs and has received candidacy status for full accreditation from NAAB. The curriculum consists of a total of 172 hours of which 127 are in required design studios, and core and elective courses in architecture. Students can also pursue minors Urban Design and Interior Design as well as take courses in the Visual Communication and Multi Media Design programs in the sister department in the School. General education requirements consist of 42 credits and take advantage of the interdisciplinary nature of the AUS campus.

Architecture students are required to complete two 6-week summer internships in local and international architecture firms active in the area and engage in state of the art global practice.

Our graduates have significantly contributed to architectural practice in the region and beyond and have been recognized for their professional skills and for their unique contribution to the synthesis of East and West. Many alumni arepursuing or some have completed graduate studies in prestigious universities in North America and Western Europe after their undergraduate studies in our B.Arch. program.

UNIVERSITY SETTING

American University of Sharjah (AUS), founded in 1997, is a not-for-profit coeducational institution formed on the American model. AUS integrates liberal studies and professional education to give its graduates both breadth and specialization. Since its inception, it has gained a reputation as the leading provider of American-style education in the Gulf. AUS is accredited in the United States of American (USA) by the Commission on Higher Education of the Middle States Association of Colleges and Schools(3624 Market Street, Philadelphia,

PA 19104, 215 6625626). AUS is licensed in the USA by the Department of Education of the State of Delaware. AUS admits students solely on the basis of their academic qualifications regardless of race, color, gender, religion, disabilities, age or national origin. AUS offers 21 bachelor's degrees, 41 minors and 13 master's degrees through the College of Arts and Sciences, College of Engineering, School of Architecture and Design, and School of Business and Management.

Comprising 37 full-time faculty, over 500 students, and 15 professional staff, the School of Architecture and Design (SA+D) offers five undergraduate degrees in the following fields of study: Architecture and Interior Design in its Architecture Department, and Visual Communication, Multimedia Design, and Design Management in its Department of Design. SA+D also offers a graduate degree in Urban Planning. All the undergraduate and graduate curricula in SA+D, as in all American University of Sharjah programs, are based on the North American model that integrates liberal studies with professional education. The School is housed in over eleven thousand square meters of well-equipped and state-of-art facilities, including high-tech digital design studios, photography and printmaking laboratories, wood and metal ateliers, and a fledgling digital fabrication laboratory, which are on par with similar architecture and design institutions of higher learning in North America and Europe.

Since its founding in 1997, the School today continues to attract a diverse group of top students from leading high schools in the Gulf region and beyond. Every Fall semester, the 144 incoming freshmen, who earn admission into the School through a very highly competitive application and evaluation process, begin their first year of studies in the School's highly effective Foundations Program run by the Architecture and Design faculty. In the upper years, design studios in the student's major form the core of the undergraduate programs in all except the Design Management program, which is the only non-studio based course of study at undergraduate level. In its first decade, The School of Architecture and Design has successfully prepared its over 550 graduates to enter the architecture and design professions in the UAE and the Gulf region as well as in many foreign countries. Many of its graduates have also been accepted into numerous leading graduate programs in the United States, Canada and Europe and have successfully completed further studies.

After establishing a regional reputation in higher learning and a record of success by its alumni, the school seeks to further its mission of "providing a comprehensive education that will enable its graduates to make significant contributions to the Gulf region and the broader global community through conscientious participation in practice." In progressing from its foundation to its maturity phase, the School is seeking to secure professional accreditation of the undergraduate degrees it offers. To achieve this goal, efforts are underway to obtain candidacy status for accreditation for the Bachelor of Architecture curriculum from the National Architectural Accrediting Board in the United States.

The School is dedicated to hands-on technical skills and competence in digital and other advanced media in the pursuit of design investigations. It fosters a regional and cultural awareness and the responsibility for creating humane environments. As it embarks on a new era of development and maturity in its second decade following its founding years, new initiatives are underway at the School of Architecture and Design to provide an extensive spectrum of coursework in both architecture and design. New courses in allied fields of studies of Landscape Architecture and Industrial Design will be offered with the vision of developing these into concentrations, minors, and eventually degree programs in the near future.

The existing degree programs and development of new programs depend upon an energetic faculty rigorously active in scholarship and professional practice and community service and academic administrators who emphasize fairness, transparency, and consistency in decision-making. Our academic community's biggest asset is the enthusiasm to shape the future of our programs while nurturing the current offerings in the school.

SCHOOL PHILOSOPHY

Architecture arises from the same wellspring of civilization as other universal manifestations of material culture: arts, histories, letters, religion and commerce. Still, the artifacts we designate as architecture possess a scale, permanence and a pervasive influence unique among human endeavors. These qualities endow the discipline with a cultural prominence few other professions enjoy.

In its contemporary university setting, the study of architecture is naturally concerned with complex, interdisciplinary issues. Some matters are primarily individual and practical: the basic human need for shelter and the desire to contrive efficient, adequate forms for the patterns of daily life. Architecture, in this sense, may concern aspirations and meanings, but its primary intent is to attain a practical advantage for us, here and now.

Architecture also has a transcendent motive, arising from an imperative to articulate, physically and spatially, the social, ceremonial and environmental choices a given culture makes within a given setting. Architecture expresses our living values. It gives abiding form, order and proportion to our activities. Architecture is a message to the world about our certainties and doubts, our values and beliefs, our preoccupations and our neglects. It both expresses and reveals.

The practice of architecture today, as in the past, requires coordinated contributions from multiple of fields. The craft of the architect runs a gamut of expertise and awareness: technical, environmental, aesthetic, cultural, historical and commercial. Consequently, the study of architecture investigates principles and applications of technology, art, humanities, engineering, physical and social sciences, business and management. Architectural design, finally, is the synthetic practice that links and gives significant form to these interdisciplinary contributions.

PROGRAM DESCRIPTION

The Bachelor of Architecture (BArch) degree (five-year professional program) is intended for the student seeking a professional career in architecture. The program entails a minimum of five years of university studies plus professional training. A minimum of 172 credits comprises the degree program, including a minimum of 109 credits of required course work in architecture and closely associated fields.

Each student is required to extend the core curriculum with 18 credits of approved architecture electives. The intent is to balance the concern for in-depth professional competence with another for the individual's interest and aptitude. These courses should be selected in consultation with the student's advisor.

The specialized professional curriculum is supported by a minimum of 42 credits of general education requirements. Designed to ensure a broad educational foundation, this base is held in common among all graduates of the American University of Sharjah.

Completion of two 6-week long summer internships in local and international architecture firms active in the area and elsewhere in the world during the summers between third and fourth and between fourth and fifth years of study is a graduation requirement and is intended to engage students in state of the art global practice.

University studies present a unique opportunity to explore other fields of interest. Based solely on individual interests, each architecture student must select nine credits of free electives from general university offerings. Some major required courses count toward general education requirements. In such cases, both requirements are considered as being met but the credits only count once toward total degree hours.

The curriculum is designed to meet the requirements for licensure in the region and to prepare the graduate for professional practice throughout the region. Some students may aspire either to advanced study in the field or to practice in a broader global setting. Accordingly, the curriculum follows established international norms for a first professional degree in architecture.

AREAS OF FOCUS AND RESEARCH
- Urban Design
- Digital Fabrication
- Sacred places
- Cultural influences on architecture
- Sustainability

SPECIAL ACTIVITIES AND PROGRAMS
- Public lectures, exhibitions, and scholarly and professional gatherings
- Student collaborations with visiting groups from universities abroad
- Local field trips to architecture and design firms, construction sites, historic areas, urban developments
- Global Day (showcasing cultures of student groups)
- American Institute of Architecture Students Chapter activities
- Study abroad

FACILITIES

The School is housed in over eleven thousand square meters of well-equipped and state-of-art facilities, including high-tech digital design studios that are fully networked via wireless and, photography and printmaking laboratories, Technical Equipment Center and Documentation facilities, wood and metal ateliers, and a fledgling digital fabrication laboratory. School's facilities are on par with similar architecture and design institutions of higher learning in North America and Europe.

SCHOLARSHIPS AND FINANCIAL AID
Please see above

ADMINISTRATION
Dr. Fatih Rifki: Dean, School of Architecture and Design
Alcibiades Tsolakis: Head, Architecture Department

ANDREWS UNIVERSITY

ADDRESS

Main
Andrews University
School of Architecture
Berrien Springs, MI 49104-0450
Tel.: 269.471.6003
Fax: 269.471.6261
architecture@andrews.edu
www.arch.andrews.edu

STUDENT AND FACULTY DEMOGRAPHICS

% of Female Students	35
% of International Students	20
% of Minority Students	55
% of Out-of-State U.S. Students	50
No. Full-Time Faculty	9
No. Part-Time Faculty	2
No. Full-Time Students	158
No. Part-Time Students	9

FINANCIAL INFORMATION

Main Source of University Funding	Private
Annual Tuition & Fees (graduate)	$26,656
Annual Tuition & Fees (undergraduate)	$21,774
% Students Receiving Federal Financial Aid	64
% Students Receiving University Financial Aid	81
% Students Receiving Departmental Financial Aid	5
% Students Receiving Scholarships (assistantships or fellowships)	0
Average Annual Scholarship for Department	$450

ACADEMIC SESSIONS

Fall Semester: August to December
Spring Semester: January to May

ARCHITECTURE AND RELATED DEGREE PROGRAMS

Degree	Min. Yrs. to Complete	Professional Accreditation	# of FT Students	# of PT Students	# of First-Year Students	# of Degrees Conferred	Admissions Requirements
Architecture							
BS Arch. Studies	4		9	0	43	4	
M. Arch —1 year + undergrad degree	5.5	NAAB	148	2		27	

SPECIALIZATIONS

Architectural Design   Community Design   Sustainability   Urban Planning and Design

UNIVERSITY SETTING

Andrews University is sponsored by the Seventh-day Adventist Church, established to provide high-quality Christian education in the context of the Adventist faith and to prepare students for leadership, stewardship, and service. Andrews welcomes men and women from all nations and faiths who meet the qualifications established by the institution and who subscribe to the ideals of the university. The university is set in a small town on a wellgroomed and spacious campus. Located between Grand Rapids and Chicago in the southwest Michigan village of Berrien Springs, Andrews is a residential university with a population of approximately 3,000 students from more than 80 countries. The School of Architecture's faculty/student ratio of 1:15 allows students to receive considerable individual attention in classes and design studios, and is consistent with the university's commitment to holistic and integrative education. Architecture faculty members have wide-ranging professional experience and advanced degrees from various academic institutions. The School of Architecture offers a concentrated first-year studio during the summer for transfer students who wish to enter pre-architecture year two and who have the appropriate general education requirements completed. Transfer students from other architecture programs may apply for advanced standing (third or fourth year) four year pre-professional (BSA) program, and will be considered on a case by case basis. The School of Architecture does not accept applications to the fifth year of study (M. Arch).

SCHOOL PHILOSOPHY

The School of Architecture at Andrews University aspires to teach its students sound thinking, practical skills, and rigorous scholarship in the discipline of architecture. It promotes students who:

Craft buildings that are dignified, durable, and purposeful;

Design communities that foster civility;

Serve mankind in accord with their professional and Christian vocation;

Seek the virtues of joy, beauty, wholeness and moderation in their lifelong pursuit of learning.

All this, for God's honor and His glory until the risen Christ comes again.

PROGRAM DESCRIPTION

The Bachelor of Science degree with a major in architectural studies can lead to advanced degrees or employment in the construction industry, the arts,

business, and other fields. The Bachelor of Science is not a professional program, and does NOT qualify the recipient to take state or national examinations in architecture.

The professional degree program consists of a pre-professional Bachelor of Science in Architecture degree, followed by a Master of Architecture degree. When earned sequentially, this degree track results in an accredited professional education. The Master of Architecture 3 1/2 year degree track is designed for students who have previously earned an undergraduate degree in an unrelated area of study. The undergraduate program is organized around two primary areas: the craft of construction and making buildings supportive of community. The focus of the first two years of the curriculum is more directed to the first area, with studio courses on graphics, formal composition, place-making, and the craft of construction supported by lecture courses on construction materials and methods, structures, environmental technologies, and architectural history. Beginning in the third year, students are introduced to the history and typology of urban form, and take studios in sustainable design, urban background buildings, and urban foreground buildings, all emphasizing both environmental and community sustainability. In the Integrative Design studio in the fourth year students are expected to bring together their studies in both craft and community in the design of a building in greater detail than in previous studios. In the fifth year they take the Urban Design Studio, which typically involves an off-campus community design charrette in a small town or city neighborhood and the subsequent production of a master plan, code, and ordinance. In addition to these required areas of the curriculum students have various elective options in the third, fourth, and fifth years, and take a studio from a Visiting Critic in the fifth year.

AREAS OF FOCUS AND RESEARCH

The School of Architecture encourages its faculty to participate in professional practice as an important component of research within the context of its professional degree program. In addition to involvement in the profession, and in keeping with the school's understanding of both its mission and the larger mission of Andrews University, there are three primary areas of current and future research within the program. First, the area of community building and urban design is explored and advanced annually in the fifth year Urban Design studio and its accompanying on-site charrettes. Second, person and environment theory is explored from a phenomenological and humanistic point of view cognizant of the scientific literature in the field but intentionally distanced from positivist approaches to the subject. Finally, professional practice is conscientiously examined and taught from within a commitment to a social and environmental

ethic of Christian stewardship. We anticipate that additional areas of research will emerge as the program grows.

SPECIAL ACTIVITIES AND PROGRAMS

School of Architecture students have access to a wide variety of special activities and programs. Because of its proximity and historic architectural significance, Chicago is a particularly rich resource for design studios and class field trips; and these have become integral to the architecture curriculum. Studio projects in recent years have been located in (and included trips to) locations as diverse as Chicago, Milwaukee, Mississippi, New Orleans, and Alaska and the Bahamas. The architecture lecture series brings renowned architects and scholars from throughout the United States and abroad. Summer study opportunities include study tours in the Piedmonts of Italy, Austria and Germany, a European Art and Architecture tour (offered in odd numbered years), a Jordan archaeological dig (offered in even numbered years), and an ongoing design/construction project in Lajas, Bolivia. Professional Intern Development Program (IDP) seminars are held annually to assist upper-level students with their transition into the architectural profession. Andrews has active chapters of the American Institute of Architecture Students (AIAS) and Tau Sigma Delta (the national architecture honor society); and Students for the New Urbanism.

FACILITIES

Classrooms, design studios, and office space are located in the main architecture building, which also houses the architecture library. The library holdings include more than 26,000 volumes, 90 periodical titles, and a growing video collection, and is distinguished in part by its special relationship with the Environmental Design Research Association. The Architecture Resource Center houses the world's most comprehensive collection of books and materials in the area of environmental psychology and design. The architecture facilities also include a well-equipped and staffed woodworking shop (2,500 sq. ft.); a computer laboratory for word processing, CAD, and other drawing programs, a print shop with direct access to large sheet Xerox duplicating; and a growing slide collection of approximately 28,000 slides.

SCHOLARSHIPS AND FINANCIAL AID

Financial Aid and Scholarship applications are available through the University Financial Aid Office. Limited scholarships are available through the School of Architecture.

ADMINISTRATION

Carey Carscallen: Dean
Paula Dronen: Assistant Dean

ARIZONA STATE UNIVERSITY

ADDRESS

Main
Arizona State University
School of Architecture+Landscape
Architecture
P.O. Box 871905
North Architecture Building, Rm 162
Tempe, AZ 85287-1605
Tel.: 480.965.3536
Fax: 480.965.0968
design.asu.edu/sala/index.shtml

ACADEMIC SESSIONS

Fall Semester: August to December
Spring Semester: January to May
Summer Session I: June to July

Summer Session II: July to August
Summer Session III: June to August

STUDENT AND FACULTY DEMOGRAPHICS

% of Female Students	36
% of International Students	6.5
% of Minority Students	27
% of Out-of-State U.S. Students	40
No. Full-Time Faculty	28
No. Part-Time Faculty	20
No. Full-Time Students	810
No. Part-Time Students	182

FINANCIAL INFORMATION

Main Source of University Funding	Public
Annual Tuition & Fees (graduate, resident)	$5,147
Annual Tuition & Fees (graduate, nonresident)	$11,429
Annual Tuition & Fees (undergraduate, resident)	$2,832
Annual Tuition & Fees (undergraduate, nonresident)	$8,976
% Students Receiving Federal Financial Aid	
% Students Receiving University Financial Aid	
% Students Receiving Departmental Financial Aid	0
% Students Receiving Scholarships (assistantships or fellowships)	50
Average Annual Scholarship for Department	$2,750

ARCHITECTURE AND RELATED DEGREE PROGRAMS

Degree	Min. Yrs. to Complete	Professional Accreditation	# of FT Students	# of PT Students	# of First-Year Students	# of Degrees Conferred	Admissions Requirements
Architecture							
BSD	4		362	162			SAT, ACT
M. Arch 2 years	2	NAAB	18	1		18	Undergraduate Architecture degree
M. Arch 3+ years	3+	NAAB	40	0		8	
Landscape Architecture							
BSLA	4	LAAB	37	20			SAT, ACT, Portfolio
MLA	2	LAAB	1	3	4	0	Prof. Landscape Architecture degree, GRE, TOEFL, Portfolio, Rec. Letters
Environmental Design							
Master of Science in the Built Environment	2		16	0	8	8	TOEFL, Portfolio, Rec. Letters
Urban Design							
MUD	2						GRE, TOEFL, Portfolio, Rec. Letters
Other							
PhD	3		13	13	8	6	

SPECIALIZATIONS

Architectural Design
Building Information Modeling
Building Technology/Env. Systems
Community Design

Computer-Aided Design
Energy
History
Housing

International/Regional Architecture
Landscape Design
Professional Practice
Sustainability

Theory/Criticism
Urban Planning and Design

ARCHITECTURE PROGRAM SUMMARY

Located within one of the nation's largest and fastest growing universities, set in the context of one of the country's most rapidly urbanizing metropolises, the School of Architecture and Landscape Architecture (SALA) is engaging in a new paradigm for teaching and research in the 21st century. In this dynamic context, SALA is redefining the mission of environmental design as not only a holistic pedagogical approach to architecture and landscape architecture, but also a form of inquiry that crosses disciplinary boundaries, synthesizes the qualitative with the quantitative, and promotes an inventive approach to systems thinking. The extreme climate and dynamic cultural conditions make Phoenix a perfect laboratory for demonstrating innovation within and among the fields of architecture, landscape architecture, and urbanism. To this end, SALA dedicates itself to creating an educational setting for learning, teaching, research, and discovery that helps create a particularly responsible vision for the future of our built environment.

UNIVERSITY SETTING

Arizona State University is located in the city of Tempe, an urban center within the Phoenix metropolitan area. The Phoenix metropolitan area is a region of 3 million people settled within the beauty of the Sonoran Desert and is one of the fastest growing cities in the country. Out of this growth is developing a sophisticated city of creative talent, thinkers, professionals and a new generation of institutions of contemporary culture.

SCHOOL PHILOSOPHY

RISE (Responsible Innovation Serving the Environment)
INNOVATIONTHROUGHINTEGRATION
The School of Architecture and Landscape Architecture (SALA) brings together the expertise of architecture, landscape architecture, urban design and environmental science to pool knowledge among these fields of study in an attempt to synthesize, discover, and define relationships among culture, technology, and design as they relate to the built environment. SALA's collaborative structure fosters innovation through the integration of expertise among academic units, university-based research, and practitioners. As part of the College of Design and the larger ASU community, SALA provides education, research, and design expertise relative to all scales of the built environment: local, regional, national, and international.

The School educates students for the profession of architecture and landscape architecture, emphasizing knowledge of the discipline and contemporary culture. The undergraduate program teaches to the disciplines of architecture and landscape architecture. The program provides students with a general history and theory of architecture and landscape architecture. The graduate program teaches to the profession of architecture and landscape architecture with emphasis on transdisciplinary education and collaboration. The faculty has depth in areas of architectural knowledge including design theory, urban design, sustainability, and the tectonics of practice. Architectural history emphasizes the humanities, arts, sciences, technology and religion as forms of knowledge and imagination that help to elucidate the idea of architecture and landscape architecture. Computing represents an area of knowledge that communicates with traditional knowledge bases in architecture, stimulating new possibilities for design and technology.

PROGRAM DESCRIPTION
Undergraduate Program

The undergraduate curriculum leads to the Bachelor of Science in Design degree with a major in Architectural Studies or a Bachelor of Landscape Architecture degree. The program offers an integrated curriculum of professional courses and liberal arts education with a focus on the design laboratory. Through scholarship, teaching, creative activity and community service the school seeks to develop a deep awareness of the discipline and skills in communication, theory, technology, and design as preparation for completing studies leading to the professional degree, Master of Architecture. The undergraduate program consists of one introductory year and three upper-division years. In the first lower-division year the students take a university general studies core consisting of courses in English, math, physical sciences, social sciences, humanities, and fine arts, as well as introductory architectural history and theory courses, two courses in design fundamentals, and one in computer modeling. At the end of the one-year period, there is a screening process based on grade point average and a portfolio of creative work from which approximately 50 applicants are admitted into the final three upper-division years of architecture and 30 into the Bachelor of Landscape Architecture accredited program. The upper-division focus is on design studios and an advanced understanding of history, theory, construction, building systems and social/cultural responsibility.

Graduate Program

The accredited Master of Architecture program and Master of Landscape Architecture program is intended to promote development of those broad areas of knowledge, professional skill and social awareness essential to the discipline and the profession of architecture and landscape architecture. The design studio sequence concludes with five final project options from student-initiated projects to collaborative studios. Other required courses include advanced courses in history, theory, building technology and professional practice. Students are expected to use electives to develop a program of study reflecting the opportunities of graduate education and the development of a particular theory of architecture. The School offers a post-professional degree, the Master of Science in the Built Environment, with concentrations in Design Knowledge and Computing, Energy and Climate Responsive Design and Facilities, Development and Management. Certificate programs are offered for M.Arch students, reflecting knowledge bases of the MS program. The College and School offer an interdisciplinary Master of Urban Design degree as well as an interdisciplinary PhD in Planning and Environmental Design. The graduate school promotes a concurrent degree program that allows students to broaden their education through a combined curriculum that adds one year to their graduate studies. The objectives of the dual degree programs are to gain knowledge and skill in complimentary disciplines, increasing professional opportunities, and working toward a more sustainable design future.

AREAS OF FOCUS AND RESEARCH
Focus
- Urbanism
- Architectural History
- Architectural Theory
- Design Theory
- Energy and Climate Responsive Design
- Tectonics of Practice
- Computing and Design Knowledge

Research

Faculty are involved in a wide range of research and scholarship in areas of urbanism, sustainability, computing and design knowledge, building technology, history and theory. A majority of the faculty are actively involved in professional practice.

SPECIAL ACTIVITIES AND PROGRAMS
- Urban Design Program
- Integral Studios
- Concurrent Degree Master Programs, MLA, MArch, MSBE, MUD.
- Summer Intern Program
- International Abroad Program in Buenos Aires
- International Graduate Studios
- Summer Session Foreign Travel Program
- Career Discovery for High School Students
- Visiting Faculty and Critics
- Lecture Series and Exhibitions
- Annual Design Excellence Awards Program
- Student chapter of AIAS

FACILITIES

The programs of the college are housed in a 150,000 square foot building complex that includes an award-winning addition designed by the Hillier Group. The complex includes the Howe Library, Digital Visual Collections, an excellent wood/metal/plastics shop, Digital fabrication shop, media center, computer laboratories and wireless design studios, All graduate student desks are equipped with 20 Inched digital displays, the Herberger Center for Design Excellence, the Phoenix Urban Research Lab, Solar Lab:experimental energy and building science research areas, and the Gallery of Design.

SCHOLARSHIPS AND FINANCIAL AID

Financial aid, work-study employment, and loans are available to students in all programs of the college. Students may compete on the basis of scholastic standing and/or financial need for numerous scholarships, awards, and prizes. The School typically awards 25-30 graduate assistantships in teaching and/or research. The award is approximately $2,054 a semester for 10 hrs.wk. Both Arizona residents and non-resident students receive tuition waivers.

ADMINISTRATION

Mark Searle: Interim Dean
Darren Petrucci: Director

AUBURN UNIVERSITY

ADDRESS

Main
Auburn University
College of Architecture,
Design and Construction
School of Architecture
104 Dudley Hall
Auburn, AL 36849-5316
Tel.: 334.844.4516
Fax: 334.844.5419
cadc.auburn.edu/soa

STUDENT AND FACULTY DEMOGRAPHICS

% of Female Students	43
% of International Students	3
% of Minority Students	17
% of Out-of-State U.S. Students	40
No. Full-Time Faculty	29
No. Part-Time Faculty	5
No. Full-Time Students	578
No. Part-Time Students	0

FINANCIAL INFORMATION

Main Source of University Funding	Public
Annual Tuition & Fees (graduate, resident)	$2,625
Annual Tuition & Fees (graduate, nonresident)	$7,875
Annual Tuition & Fees (undergraduate, resident)	$2,625
Annual Tuition & Fees (undergraduate, nonresident)	$7,875
% Students Receiving Federal Financial Aid	62
% Students Receiving University Financial Aid	
% Students Receiving Departmental Financial Aid	
% Students Receiving Scholarships (assistantships or fellowships)	60
Average Annual Scholarship for Department	$1,795

ACADEMIC SESSIONS

Fall Semester: September to December; Application Deadline: April 1
Spring Semester: January to May; Application Deadline: November 15

Summer Session I: May to June

ARCHITECTURE AND RELATED DEGREE PROGRAMS

Degree	Min. Yrs. to Complete	Professional Accreditation	# of FT Students	# of PT Students	# of First-Year Students	# of Degrees Conferred	Admissions Requirements
Architecture							
B. Arch	5	NAAB	320	30	110	60	SAT, ACT
Landscape Architecture							
Master of Landscape Architecture	3	LAAB	50	2	12	18	Undergraduate degree, GRE, Portfolio, Rec. Letters, Essay
Master of Landscape Architecture	2	LAAB					Undergraduate Architecture degree, GRE, TOEFL, Portfolio, Rec. Letters, Essay
Interior Design/Interior Architecture							
B Int Arch	5.5		39	0	15	12	
Planning							
Master of Community Planning	2	PAB	41	5	18	20	Undergraduate degree, GRE, TOEFL, Rec. Letters, Essay
Construction Management/Technology							
Bachelor of Science in Building Construction	4	ACCE	569		124	120	Undergraduate degree, SAT, ACT
Master of Building Construction	1		7			6	Undergraduate degree, GRE, TOEFL, Rec. Letters
Industrial Design							
Bachelor of Industrial Design	4	NASAD	204		25	36	Undergraduate degree, SAT, ACT
Graphic Design							
Bachelor of Graphic Design	4	NASAD	109		31	25	Undergraduate degree
Other							
Master of Design-Build	1						Undergraduate degree, Prof. Architecture degree, GRE, TOEFL, Portfolio, Rec. Letters, Essay

SPECIALIZATIONS

Architectural Design	Computer-Aided Design	History	Professional Practice
Art and Design	Energy	Housing	Sustainability
Building Information Modeling	Environment/Sustainability	Interior Design/Architecture	Tectonics
Building Technology/Env. Systems	Graphic Design	Landscape Design	Urban Planning and Design
Community Design			

ARCHITECTURE PROGRAM SUMMARY

The Bachelor of Architecture degree program (B.Arch) is a five-year, NAAB-accredited professional degree. The Architecture program at Auburn is the oldest architecture program in its region, and has a strong tradition of excellence in architectural education. The program is committed to providing both a focused and comprehensive professional education in architectural design, and to providing a broad exposure to the career possibilities available within a rapidly changing practice context. The School of Architecture also includes degree programs in landscape architecture, community planning, interior architecture, and a rich culture of interdisciplinary education between these disciplines enriches all four programs.

UNIVERSITY SETTING

Auburn University is located in east central Alabama (100 miles southeast of Birmingham, 110 miles southwest of Atlanta, GA), in the city of Auburn. The School of Architecture is in the College of Architecture, Design and Construction, together with the Department of Industrial Design, and the McWhorter School of Building Science. Established in 1907, the School of Architecture at Auburn is one of the oldest programs in architecture in the country and the oldest in the South.

SCHOOL PHILOSOPHY

The School of Architecture has a unique and valued set of educational intentions and opportunities made possible by the relationship of architecture, landscape architecture, interior architecture, and community planning within one school. This coalition exemplifies interdisciplinary collaboration as a model of professional activity; insures that students have an overview of the various components in the design and building process; and promotes the connection between landscape architecture, interior architecture and architecture as a single artifact. This forum for exchange of ideas is exciting and challenging and forms the basis for our framework of primary educational priorities, the most fundamental of which is our focus on the simple and basic issues of building. The design studio forms the integrating venue of this framework, creating an environment for intense collaboration between students and faculty working to foster understanding and mastery of the issues and abilities necessary for shaping the built environment. The School of Architecture is also committed to cultivating an ethic of civic engagement and service in all graduates of our professional programs. This commitment is made manifest via a broad spectrum of community outreach and service learning opportunities in all programs.

PROGRAM DESCRIPTION

The Bachelor of Architecture degree program (B.Arch) is a five-year, NAAB-accredited professional degree aimed at preparing students for entry into the practice of architecture. The curriculum of the B.Arch program is organized around a core of design studios, supported by lecture courses and seminars in history, theory, and technical subjects specific to the discipline. Design studios, which begin in the first year of the program (or in the first summer) act as the organizing/integrating venue of this framework, creating an environment for intense collaboration between faculty and students working to foster understanding and mastery of the issues and abilities necessary for shaping the built environment. The Architecture program at Auburn has a strong tradition of excellence in architectural education, and is committed to providing both a focused and comprehensive professional education in architectural design, and to providing a broad exposure to the career possibilities available within a rapidly changing practice context. Central to this goal is our commitment to providing our students with a learning experience rich in exposure to digital technology. Students have access to several computer labs equipped with high-end equipment, as well as digital media integrated into the studio environment.

AREAS OF FOCUS AND RESEARCH

- Rural Studio
- Birmingham Center for Architecture and Urban Studies
- Digital Media
- Interior Architecture
- Landscape Architecture
- Community Design & Planning

Faculty of the School have a broad spectrum of research interests including sustainable methods of design and construction, environmentally responsible development and planning, leadership, community engagement, community design, emerging practice models, and affordable housing.

SPECIAL ACTIVITIES AND PROGRAMS

The School maintains two remote studios: The Center for Architecture and Urban Studies (The Urban Studio) in Birmingham, AL, and The Rural Studio in Newbern, AL. that engage students in a wide variety of community-focused service-learning activities. Each offer unique learning environments that, together with community-focused studios offered from the Auburn Campus, serve to both educate our students in the "traditional" skills and knowledge associated with an architectural education, and to cultivate an ethic of civic engagement among our students and faculty. The School offers several national and international travel/study programs, including an optional semester of study and travel in Western Europe. The student chapter of the American Institute of Architecture Students is actively involved in school governance, outreach and social activities, and social events. The School offers a lecture series featuring distinguished practitioners and academics from around the world, as well as a wide variety of vertical and interdisciplinary design studios addressing architecture, landscape architecture, interior architecture and planning issues.

FACILITIES

- Architecture Library - 31,000 volumes
- Digital Media — 3 high-end computer labs/classrooms
- 2D/3D CAD equipped computers in studios
- Woodworking Shop
- Photographic Darkroom and print room
- Materials Resource Center
- Laser cutter
- CNC router

SCHOLARSHIPS AND FINANCIAL AID

Auburn University awards over $1,500,000 in scholarships and over $5,000,000 in grants each year. Students in the School of Architecture are eligible for and receive many of these awards. The School also awards over $110,000 each year in scholarships to students based on performance in the program.

ADMINISTRATION

Daniel Bennett, FAIA: Dean
Rebecca O'Neal Dagg: Associate Dean
Karen Rogers, PhD: Associate Dean
David Hinson, FAIA: Head

BALL STATE UNIVERSITY

ADDRESS

Main
Ball State University
College of Architecture & Planning
AB 402
Muncie, IN 47306
Tel.: 765.285.1900
Fax: 765.285.1765
www.bsu.edu/architecture

STUDENT AND FACULTY DEMOGRAPHICS

% of Female Students	37
% of International Students	5
% of Minority Students	13
% of Out-of-State U.S. Students	22
No. Full-Time Faculty	23
No. Part-Time Faculty	8
No. Full-Time Students	341
No. Part-Time Students	0

FINANCIAL INFORMATION

Main Source of University Funding	Public
Annual Tuition & Fees (graduate, resident)	$5,536
Annual Tuition & Fees (graduate, nonresident)	$17,340
Annual Tuition & Fees (undergraduate, resident)	$5,536
Annual Tuition & Fees (undergraduate, nonresident)	$17,340
% Students Receiving Federal Financial Aid	73
% Students Receiving University Financial Aid	62
% Students Receiving Departmental Financial Aid	0
% Students Receiving Scholarships (assistantships or fellowships)	73
Average Annual Scholarship for Department	$4,034

ACADEMIC SESSIONS

Fall Semester: August to December
Spring Semester: January to May; Application Deadline: January 16

Summer Session I: May to June
Summer Session II: June to July

ARCHITECTURE AND RELATED DEGREE PROGRAMS

Degree	Min. Yrs. to Complete	Professional Accreditation	# of FT Students	# of PT Students	# of First-Year Students	# of Degrees Conferred	Admissions Requirements
Architecture							
B.S. or B.A., with a major in Architecture	4		0	0	140	185	SAT, ACT
M. Arch I Professional	2	NAAB	59	0	29	22	Undergraduate Architecture degree, GRE, Portfolio, Rec. Letters, Essay
M. Arch II Post-Professional	1.5		12	0	0	3	TOEFL
Landscape Architecture							
BLA	5		99	0	191	29	
MLA			25	0	0	4	
Environmental Design							
B.S. or B.A. w/major in Environmental Design	4		0	0	140	185	SAT, ACT

SPECIALIZATIONS

Architectural Design
Art and Design
Building Information Modeling
Building Technology/Env. Systems
Community Design
Computer-Aided Design

Energy
Engineering
Environment/Sustainability
Graphic Design
History
Housing

Interior Design/Architecture
International Development
International/Regional Architecture
Landscape Design
Photography
Preservation

Professional Practice
Sacred Spaces
Sustainability
Tectonics
Theory/Criticism
Urban Planning and Design

UNIVERSITY SETTING

Ball State University houses Indiana's only state-supported architecture school. With an enrollment of approximately 15,500 undergraduate and 2,000 graduate students, BSU is a nationally recognized comprehensive university. Its tree-filled 900-acre residential campus is located in Muncie, a city of 70,000 inhabitants, an hour from Indianapolis (home of the BSU/CAP Indianapolis Center) and is close to other major Midwestern cities. The College of Architecture and Planning, founded in 1965, has over 700 students in Architecture, Landscape Architecture, Urban Planning and Historic Preservation. Approximately 30% of CAP students are out-of-state or foreign students. Transfer students are accepted.

SCHOOL PHILOSOPHY

Active in practice, research, design, design-build, creative and scholarly activities, department faculty represents diverse views about the profession and its future in regional, national and international settings. It is strongly committed to the worldwide effort to achieve sustainability and to explore appropriate ways to apply computer technology in learning and practice. The Department offers undergraduate and graduate programs, and encourages interdisciplinary studies through numerous minors and other collaborative opportunities. Department of Architecture faculty hold degrees from a wide range of institutions. Nine faculty hold Ph.Ds. Several research centers in the College add to the rich intellectual environment for students, faculty and alumni.

PROGRAM DESCRIPTION
Undegraduate

The department offers Bachelor of Science, Bachelor of Arts and Architecture as well as Bachelor of Environmental Design degrees. All undergraduate students entering the College take a common first-year program after which students select a degree major in either Architecture, Landscape Architecture or Urban Planning. A Major in Environmental Design is offered as a non-professional terminal degree intended to prepare students for a broad spectrum of career options.

Graduate

The Masters of Architecture (M.Arch) first professional degree is offered for students committed to collaboratively developing the attitudes, skills and methods needed to work as architects to create a sustainable built environment of the highest quality. Students must complete between 45 and 70 graduate credit hours depending on the chosen track. A distinct part of our program is the required INTERNSHIP. Students work in architecture firms all over the country and the world. Our program makes it possible to complete the internship requirement in a variety of ways. Detailed case studies of projects are undertaken by students on internships, supported by a mentor in the firm, but guided by a faculty member within the Department of Architecture.

Another distinct component of our program is the CONCENTRATIONS, which presently includes digital fabrication, historic preservation, landscape architecture, sustainability or urban planning. Students may also define independent areas of focus with the approval of the M.Arch Program Director.

The post-professional Master's degree (MArchII) provides a flexible, thesis-based platform to pursue independent research and take advantage of the rich resources in the form of institutes, centers and labs that offer cutting edge technologies and approaches to design.

The Master of Science in Historic Preservation (MSHP) program offers unique opportunity to explore technologies, philosophies and design approches to working with historic environments. The Center for Historic Preservation offers opportunities to be engaged in an array of real projects.

AREAS OF FOCUS AND RESEARCH
Research

The Department and College encourage and support research, scholarship, service, professional practice and creative work. Collaboration with other departments and universities is encouraged. Faculty are active in academic scholarship that appears in national and international peer-reviewed publications. Others are engaged in funded and non-funded studies that combine empirical investigations meeting academic criteria with findings that have impact outside the university. Some of this work is conducted under the aegis of college and university-level research units such as Building Futures Institute (BFI), Center for Energy Research (CERES), Institute for Digital Fabrication (IDF), Center for Media Design (CMD), and others. The scholarship of design pedagogy is also a high priority in the department. Efforts to incorporate findings from practice, service and research into teaching activities are highly valued. Design-build activities, installations and community-building are common activities in the department. The university has identified Emerging Media as a thrust area across all academic disciplines.

SPECIAL ACTIVITIES AND PROGRAMS

The Department and College offer a rich spectrum of special activities and programs:

- Field Studies, workshops and exchanges in England, Italy, Germany, Netherlands, Nepal, India, China, Japan, Korea, Thailand, New Zealand, Latin America and major American and Canadian cities
- Full semester study programs in London, Australia, Miami Beach (TROPICALIA) and Prescott, Arizona (ECOSA)
- Guest lectures, exhibits and special symposia on a wide range of topics
- Scholarship and research awards programs

- Architecture student journal entitled *glue*
- Active student chapters of the American Institute of Architecture Students (AIAS), Construction Specifications Institute (CSI), Emerging Green Builders (EGB), Freedom By Design (FBD) and National Organization of Minority Architecture Students (NOMAS)
- Required internship for Master of Architecture students
- Approximately 25 approved Minors in the university
- Visiting faculty, critics, advisors and guest scholars from around the world and from local professions
- Writing in the Design Curriculum program
- Design / Build opportunities

FACILITIES

The Architecture Building contains:

- A branch of the University library; a slide/digital image library;
- The Indiana Historical Archive;
- Several electronic design labs;
- Studios with accommodations for individual work stations;
- A wood and metals shop;
- A fabrication lab with advanced digital tools;
- A SIM LAB for digital simulation research;
- A lab for materials testing associated with the Historic Preservation program;
- And offices and research labs for Building Futures Institute, Center for Energy Research, Institute for Digital Fabrication, and Community Based Projects.

SCHOLARSHIPS AND FINANCIAL AID

Scholarships, grants, loans and employment are offered based primarily on financial need. Some scholarships, awarded to freshmen admitted with honors, are not need based. Scholarships exist at all year levels in the undergraduate and graduate programs. A large number of graduate assistantships are available annually to qualified students in the M.Arch program. These assistantships include stipends and tuition waivers. Graduate assistants support research, teaching, and other departmental and college programs. Other financial aid is available through the University Office of Scholarships and Financial Aid. Out-of-state and international students admitted to the university with distinction qualify for a waiver of the out-of-state portion of their tuition. Research awards are available through an adjudicated RFP process whereby students work with faculty on research projects funded by outside sources.

ADMINISTRATION

Guillermo de Velasco: Dean
Michel Mounayar, RA: Associate Dean
Mahesh Senagala, LEED AP: Department Chair

BOSTON ARCHITECTURAL COLLEGE

ADDRESS

Main
Boston Architectural College
320 Newbury Street
Boston, MA 02115
Tel.: 617.585.0200
Fax: 617.585.0111
www.the-bac.edu

STUDENT AND FACULTY DEMOGRAPHICS

% of Female Students	41
% of International Students	3
% of Minority Students	17
% of Out-of-State U.S. Students	13
No. Full-Time Faculty	27
No. Part-Time Faculty	320
No. Full-Time Students	1,171
No. Part-Time Students	350

FINANCIAL INFORMATION

Main Source of University Funding	Private
Annual Tuition & Fees (graduate)	$15,840
Annual Tuition & Fees (undergraduate)	$10,600
% Students Receiving Federal Financial Aid	75
% Students Receiving University Financial Aid	13
% Students Receiving Departmental Financial Aid	
% Students Receiving Scholarships (assistantships or fellowships)	7
Average Annual Scholarship for Department	$1,500

ACADEMIC SESSIONS

Fall Semester: September to December; Application Deadline: Rolling
Spring Semester: January to May; Application Deadline: Rolling

Summer Session I: June to July; Application Deadline: Rolling

ARCHITECTURE AND RELATED DEGREE PROGRAMS

Degree	Min. Yrs. to Complete	Professional Accreditation	# of FT Students	# of PT Students	# of First-Year Students	# of Degrees Conferred	Admissions Requirements
Architecture							
B. Arch	7	NAAB	423	0	155	40	
M. Arch	5	NAAB	350	0	110	28	Undergraduate Degree, TOEFL
Landscape Architecture							
Bachelor of Landscape Architecture	7		27	0	18	0	TOEFL
Interior Design/Interior Architecture							
Bachelor of Interior Design	7	CIDA/FIDER	84	0	30	8	
Master of Interior Design	5	CIDA/FIDER	101	0	29	12	Undergraduate degree, TOEFL
Other							
Bachelor of Design Studies	5	RIBA	37	0	12	4	TOEFL

SPECIALIZATIONS

Architectural Design
Building Information Modeling
Building Technology/Env. Systems

Computer-Aided Design
Environment/Sustainability
Interior Design/Architecture

Landscape Design
Preservation
Professional Practice

Sustainability
Theory/Criticism

ARCHITECTURE PROGRAM SUMMARY

The 120-year-old Boston Architectural College is a dynamic institution on the leading edge of design education. Located in the heart of Boston's historic Back Bay, the BAC's teaching and learning are based in professional practice, providing students and practitioners with an interdisciplinary learning laboratory that functions day and night.

UNIVERSITY SETTING

The Boston Architectural College is an Independent Design school located in the heart of Boston's historic Back Bay neighborhood. The school inhabits a series of significant architectural landmarks, including its most recent acquisition, a Richardson Romanesque building that served as Boston's Institute of Contemporary Art for much of the 20th century. Boston serves as the school's learning laboratory, both day and night, its students engaged in practice positions in more than 300 design firms throughout the city.

SCHOOL PHILOSOPHY

Education at the BAC results from concurrent academic and practice-based learning that takes place in both the classroom and in the design workplace. Students learn their profession by being mentored by, and working for practicing architects. The BAC views architecture as the art of making places for sustainable human habitation.

Concurrent degree students work in the design profession during the day and attend classes that begin in late afternoon. This interplay of education and practice provides graduates with solid preparation for careers in design, with a strong professional network, and the opportunity to complete the internship requirements for NCARB licensing before graduation.

To prepare them to take full advantage of the BAC's concurrent curriculum, a special Academic Only Program (AOP) is offered to first-year students who elect to participate in it that focuses on developing design and thinking and communication skills.

PROGRAM DESCRIPTION
Undergraduate Program

The BAC's B.Arch program comprises two structured curricular components: Academic and Practice. To graduate, a B.Arch student must earn 120 academic credits and 54 practice credits. To fulfill the practice component of the degree requirement, students are employed during the day in paid professional positions. BAC students enlist their supervisors as mentors and together they endorse statements of professional goals and objectives each semester. The 54 practice credits may be completed in approximately three years of full-time work. After completion of the practice curriculum degree requirements, additional earned practice credits may be applied to NCARB's internship requirement, allowing students to complete this prior to graduation.

During the evening, students engage the academic curriculum: design studios, courses in history and theory, visual studies, technology and management, liberal studies. The academic curriculum has three segments. In Segment I, or Foundation, the focus is on basic design principles. Segment II emphasizes building design and also covers a wide range of topics including urban design and the theoretical issues of form-making and design study. In Segment III students enter Degree Project Studio, a two-semester comprehensive project that unites the skills, education and experience gained through both academic and practice learning.

Graduate Program

The BAC's graduate program structure mirrors that of the undergraduate program, comprising concurrent academic and practice curricula. To graduate, an M. Arch student must earn 105 academic credits and 54 practice credits.

To fulfill the practice component of the degree requirement, students are employed during the day in paid professional positions. Unique to the M.Arch program, students may earn practice curriculum credits and NCARB internship credits simultaneously. After satisfying a minimum residency requirement, students are permitted to enroll in NCARB's internship program, and may then complete IDP prior to graduation and sit for licensing examinations immediately after graduation. All M.Arch students are assigned a practice curriculum mentor who monitors a student's educational and career progress.

Because the M.Arch program is a first professional degree, its academic curriculum covers the same breadth of material as does the B.Arch. In addition, students participate in a series of master's-level seminars that address issues of design theory, architectural history and the interplay of values and design at an advanced level. In the third segment of the curriculum, M.Arch students participate in the master's thesis program, which involves primary research and addresses the role of architecture and its impact on society.

For selected students across the US who hold pre-professional degrees in architecture and who are actively engaged in professional practice the BAC's M. Arch program is able to be delivered in a hybrid Distance M.Arch format, involving both online learning and intensive in-residence experiences.

AREAS OF FOCUS AND RESEARCH
Focus

The practice component of the curriculum is the experiential element of the BAC's concurrent education model. Participation in the practice component is expressed through a structured sequence of office-based skill levels/steps under a program of contract learning developed by the American Council on Education. A student's professional development is closely linked to the sequence of practice learning on the basis of setting, supervision and task. This sequence is tied to the academic component of the BAC degree programs' three segments. The Practice Curriculum Faculty, a 50-member body of practicing design professionals, is responsible for certifying credit in the practice component.

Research

A multi-year grant has been awarded the BAC by the American Institute of Architects to enable funded, cross-disciplinary research into Building Information Modeling and Integrated Practice Delivery. The BAC is engaged in this research with students, faculty and practitioners.

The BAC's Community Design Center enables interested students to volunteer their skills on projects for, generally, non-profit clients who require feasibility studies. A recipient of a Graham Foundation grant, the CDC has accepted over 300 projects in its 30 year history, averaging 12 per calendar year.

BAC students and faculty continue to undertake design projects and applied research onsite in America's hurricane-damaged Gulf Coast.

A Green Roof Green Alley Initiative has connected students and faculty researchers to practicing engineers and designers to posit retrofits for BAC campus buildings and environs. This ongoing research is resulting in implementable projects.

SPECIAL ACTIVITIES AND PROGRAMS

The Pro-Arts Consortium is an association of six Boston colleges—including BAC—dedicated to the visual and performing Arts. BAC students may cross-register for courses, attend events and lectures, and access campus resources at any of the Pro-Arts schools.

The BAC Summer Academy is a program of design career exploration for high school students. It provides an introduction to careers in architecture, landscape architecture, interior design, planning and urban design. BAC Study Abroad programs include destinations in England, France, Italy, Cuba, Mexico, the Netherlands, Turkey and Korea.

The Sasaki Distinguished Visiting Critic program brings renowned young architects to the BAC each year to offer a design studio and public lectures.

The BAC has been selected as one of 20 schools to participate in the US Department of Energy's Solar Decathlon for 2009.

The College has developed an expanded offering of certificate programs, both online and in residence. Most notable are the BAC's Sustainable Design Certificate (offered internationally), the Certificate in Design Education and programs in Historic Preservation and the decorative arts.

FACILITIES

The BAC Library houses a collection of 26,000 books and 120 periodicals. Resources focus on architecture, interior design, landscape architecture, urban planning, green building and sustainability and architectural history. In addition the BAC maintains an image library that contains approximately 40,000 architecture, landscape and interior design slides that survey historical and contemporary design. The McCormick and Stankowicz galleries host significant design exhibitions throughout the year.

Fully-equipped computer facilities support an array of BIM and design-related applications for both two- and three-dimensional work; modeling and rendering applications; desktop publishing; multimedia production and web development software. Additional equipment includes large format plotters, scanners, color and black and white laser printers, laser cutters and wood shop.

SCHOLARSHIPS AND FINANCIAL AID

The BAC provides both institutional and federal or state-funded assistance to qualified students who demonstrate financial need. Sources of aid include federally funded subsidized loans and federal, state, and institutional grants and scholarships. Tuition, fees, food, housing, books, supplies, transportation and personal costs are taken into account to determine need. Additional institutional aid is available to qualified students who have completed one semester. Numerous design scholarships and awards are also available.

ADMINISTRATION

Theodore C. Landsmark, PhD, M.Ev.D, Assoc. AIA: President
Curt Lamb: Executive Director for Institutional Initiatives
Jeffrey Stein, AIA: Head of the School of Architecture
    and Dean
Tiffany Andersen: Associate Provost

CALIFORNIA COLLEGE OF THE ARTS

ADDRESS

Main
California College of the Arts
School of Architecture
1111 Eighth Street
San Francisco, CA 94107
Tel.: 415.703.9562
Fax: 415.703.9524
www.cca.edu

STUDENT AND FACULTY DEMOGRAPHICS

% of Female Students	42
% of International Students	12
% of Minority Students	32
% of Out-of-State U.S. Students	52
No. Full-Time Faculty	4
No. Part-Time Faculty	63
No. Full-Time Students	250
No. Part-Time Students	13

FINANCIAL INFORMATION

Main Source of University Funding	Private
Annual Tuition & Fees (graduate)	$30,510
Annual Tuition & Fees (undergraduate)	$29,280
% Students Receiving Federal Financial Aid	79
% Students Receiving University Financial Aid	76
% Students Receiving Departmental Financial Aid	0
% Students Receiving Scholarships (assistantships or fellowships)	5
Average Annual Scholarship for Department	$6,481

ACADEMIC SESSIONS

Fall Semester: September to December
Spring Semester: January to May

ARCHITECTURE AND RELATED DEGREE PROGRAMS

Degree	Min. Yrs. to Complete	Professional Accreditation	# of FT Students	# of PT Students	# of First-Year Students	# of Degrees Conferred	Admissions Requirements
Architecture							
B. Arch	5	NAAB	187	10	38	24	TOEFL, Portfolio, Rec. Letters, Essay
M. Arch	2	NAAB	84	3	27	20	Undergraduate degree, Portfolio, Rec. Letters, Essay. Advanced standing (2 year completion) to undergradudate architecture degree holders.

SPECIALIZATIONS

Architectural Design	Computer-Aided Design	Housing	Sustainability
Art and Design	Energy	Interior Design/Architecture	Tectonics
Building Information Modeling	Environment/Sustainability	International/Regional Architecture	Theory/Criticism
Building Technology/Env. Systems	Graphic Design	Photography	Urban Planning and Design
Community Design	History	Professional Practice	

ARCHITECTURE PROGRAM SUMMARY

CCA's architecture programs prepare students for positions of leadership in the design professions. Academic programs and professional preparation are offered within a context of rigorous scholarship and creative endeavor, bringing innovative developments in culture, media, and technology to bear on the process of architectural production, and allowing students to capitalize on new opportunities in a rapidly changing profession. CCA's architecture programs currently enroll 260+ students, and its faculty is composed of leading researchers and design professionals.

UNIVERSITY SETTING

Founded in 1907, the California College of the Arts prepares students to shape culture and contribute to their communities through their work as architects, artists, and designers. As the role of creativity throughout our society and economy is recognized, CCA's mission has never been more relevant. Artists, architects and designers have become leaders in a culture that relies on a combined expansion of technological innovation and creative content. CCA offers undergraduate programs in animation, architecture, ceramics, fashion design, film and media arts, furniture design, glass, graphic design, illustration, industrial design, interior design, jewelry/metal arts, painting, photography, printmaking, sculpture, and textiles. Graduate programs include architecture, design, design strategy, fine arts, visual criticism, and writing. With campuses in San Francisco and Oakland, the College has a student population of 1700+ made up of undergraduate and graduate students in the many different programs.

SCHOOL PHILOSOPHY

CCA's architecture programs integrate critical, artistic, and material approaches to the study and practice of architecture. Using both advanced digital investigation and conventional artistic modes of expression, students learn to meld abstract ideas with material reality. The College's location also informs the educational experience. The San Francisco Bay Area is a polycentric urban laboratory, inspiring new ways to configure architectural form and space. Throughout their studies, CCA students are encouraged to collaborate within and across disciplines; this integrated approach provides a fertile ground for their emerging design sensibilities. CCA architecture students develop into leaders in the field by addressing contemporary design challenges through their creative investigations.

PROGRAM DESCRIPTION

Undergraduate and Graduate Professional Degree Programs: The architecture program offers an undergraduate five-year course of study leading to a first professional degree of Bachelor of Architecture, and a graduate three-year course of study leading to the professional degree of Master of Architecture. Students with undergraduate degrees in architectural studies (Bachelor of Architectural Science or equivalent) are eligible to apply for advanced standing upon enrollment into the MArch program. Both the BArch and MArch degree programs are NAAB accredited.

At CCA, students study architecture in a rigorous, creative, and supportive environment. The faculty includes highly accomplished designers, historians, and theorists who bring a diversity of thought and approaches to teaching. In the undergraduate program, architecture students begin their studies with students from other disciplines in a common first-year core experience. This program of interdisciplinary courses is designed to introduce students to formal and conceptual issues applicable to a wide range of practices in art and design. A comprehensive course of study in the humanities and sciences is also required. Central to the architecture curriculum is the design studio. Studio projects begin as controlled, focused exercises that grow in complexity and freedom of interpretation as the student progresses. A select number of students also complete a thesis project for their final studio. Classes in history, theory, technology, urbanism and visual and digital media are designed to reinforce the studio experience and enhance the students' intellectual, professional, and ethical development. Students also participate in an internship program that connects them directly to the profession and to the needs of the community. Expanded opportunities for travel and advanced research supplement the core professional program.

AREAS OF FOCUS AND RESEARCH

In addition to providing an education that gives students a firm foundation in the discipline and the profession, the architecture program at CCA offers special areas of focus. Because of the unique artistic environment and the abundant resources for art making and design offered by the College, architecture students at CCA are encouraged to seek out other disciplines that intersect with, or engage architecture, such as industrial design, furniture design, and graphic design, or media intensive disciplines such as glass, metal arts and film. With the architecture program's location in San Francisco's technology and new media corridor and its proximity to Silicon Valley, digital tools and technologies are an important component of the program with specialized research opportunities offered in the CCA MEDIAlab.

The architecture program also focuses on the environment and culture of the San Francisco Bay Area and its larger global network, conducting local, regional and international city and environmental research in the CCA URBANlab and ECOlabs. Faculty in the architecture program conduct research on a variety of topics that engage contemporary architectural culture and that provide expanded educational opportunities for students. Many architecture professors also participate as faculty of the graduate program in visual criticism in scholarly work that emphasizes interdisciplinary and cross-cultural study of contemporary society.

SPECIAL ACTIVITIES AND PROGRAMS

CCA has a wide range of special activities and programs to enhance the learning experience. Throughout the year, CCA's Wattis Institute presents an array of public programs including exhibitions, installations, symposia, film series, and lectures. Visiting artists and designers such as Asymptote Architecture, Guillermo Gomez-Peña, Werner Herzog, Jim Hodges, Sylvia Kolbowski, John Maeda, Karim Rashid, and Kara Walker have participated in residencies and lectures. The weekly architecture lecture series has featured Isaac Broid, Rosalyn Deutsche, Julie Eisenberg, Walter Hood, Fumihiko Maki, Rubén Martínez, Thom Mayne, Pierre de Meuron, Sam Mockbee, Rafael Viñoly, Rodolfo Machado, LOT-EK, ARO, William Massie and many more. CCA's Center for Art and Public Life provides many opportunities for students to engage with the community through activities such as designing posters for nonprofit organizations, painting a neighborhood mural, or designing an urban playground. CCA publishes Design Book Review, a renowned journal on architecture, design, and urban-ism. Students may participate in a mobility program at one of the thirty independent art schools in the United States, or they may choose from a number of opportunities to study abroad.

Recent international studios and travel abroad opportunities have included Brasil and Argentina, China and Taiwan, and many locations in Europe. Student groups include: American Institute of Architecture Students, Alpha Rho Chi, and the National Organization of Minority Architects as well as the Architecture Student Government. CCA students have joined with students from Santa Clara University to form a team that will compete in the 2009 Solar Decathlon in Washington, DC.

FACILITIES

CCA's San Francisco campus is situated in a newly renovated masterpiece of postwar industrial architecture. It is located in the South of Market district, in an urban neighborhood populated by entrepreneurial design practices and new technology start-ups. The 160,000-square-foot building includes graduate and undergraduate studio space, classrooms, six image labs, the Timken Lecture Hall, academic office space, the Simpson Library, the Logan Galleries, the Bruce Undergraduate Student Galleries, the Pollack/Long Graduate Student Galleries, extensive shop facilities including the Wornick Wood and Furniture Studios and Digital Fabrication center, and the A2 Café. The San Francisco campus also includes a new Graduate Center that houses graduate fine arts studios and two large installation/exhibition areas. The Oakland campus, which houses most of the fine arts programs, features specialized facilities including a foundry, metal shop, glass studio, ceramics studios, photography labs, and textiles facilities.

SCHOLARSHIPS AND FINANCIAL AID

CCA is strongly committed to making education accessible and affordable to all students. More than 73 percent of CCA students receive financial aid; scholarships range from $1,000 to $32,000. In all, more than $12 million in aid is awarded each year through various programs that include merit, need-based as well as diversity scholarships. The Financial Aid Office is active in working with students to create financial aid packages to meet their individual needs.

ACADEMIC ADMINISTRATION

Ila Berman, DDES, MRAIC: Director, Architecture
Chris Falliers: MArch Program Coordinator
and Graduate Advisor
Jordan Geiger: BArch Program Coordinator

ADMINISTRATIVE STAFF

Judy Krasnick: Assistant Director, Architecture
Sheri McKenzie: VP Enrollment, Incoming Students
Noel Dahl: Director of Graduate Admissions

CALIFORNIA POLYTECHNIC STATE UNIVERSITY, SAN LUIS OBISPO

ADDRESS

Main
California Polytechnic State University
College Of Architecture &
Environmental Design
Architecture Department
One Grand Avenue
San Luis Obispo, CA 93407
Tel.: 805.756.1316
Fax: 805.756.1500
www.arch.calpoly.edu

STUDENT AND FACULTY DEMOGRAPHICS

% of Female Students	47
% of International Students	3
% of Minority Students	37
% of Out-of-State U.S. Students	5
No. Full-Time Faculty	34
No. Part-Time Faculty	13
No. Full-Time Students	800
No. Part-Time Students	0

FINANCIAL INFORMATION

Main Source of University Funding	Public
Annual Tuition & Fees (graduate, resident)	$5,751
Annual Tuition & Fees (graduate, nonresident)	
Annual Tuition & Fees (undergraduate, resident)	$4,689
Annual Tuition & Fees (undergraduate, nonresident)	$14,859
% Students Receiving Federal Financial Aid	40
% Students Receiving University Financial Aid	20
% Students Receiving Departmental Financial Aid	
% Students Receiving Scholarships (assistantships or fellowships)	
Average Annual Scholarship for Department	

ACADEMIC SESSIONS

Fall Quarter/Trimester: September to November
Winter Quarter/Trimester: January to March

Spring Quarter/Trimester: April to June
Summer Session I: June to August

ARCHITECTURE AND RELATED DEGREE PROGRAMS

Degree	Min. Yrs. to Complete	Professional Accreditation	# of FT Students	# of PT Students	# of First-Year Students	# of Degrees Conferred	Admissions Requirements
Architecture							
B. Arch	5	NAAB	742	0	147	104	
MS Arch	1		16	0	7	10	

SPECIALIZATIONS

Architectural Design
Building Technology/Env. Systems

Community Design

Environment/Sustainability

Urban Planning and Design

UNIVERSITY SETTING

Cal Poly's Architecture Department, one of five departments in the College of Architecture and Environmental Design (CAED), is among the largest and in the country. Accepted freshman and transfer students have the highest entrance scores in a university renowned for the quality of its graduates. Fifteen thousand Cal Poly students, as diverse as the general population of California, enjoy a pastoral setting ten minutes from the Pacific Ocean, in the pleasant community of San Luis Obispo.

SCHOOL PHILOSOPHY

Architecture epitomizes the "learn by doing" philosophy of Cal Poly. The five year program is rigorous, combining a sequential-based design and technical curriculum, the melding of traditional skills with digital technology, and elective opportunities. The common denominators of intelligence and motivation, characterize both incoming freshmen and transfer students. A discipline that is the marriage of art and engineering offers great challenges for students drawn by problem solving, aesthetics and technology. An outstanding reputation within the profession assures graduates of employment in the practice of architecture and other professions that recognize the holistic education of our students.

PROGRAM DESCRIPTION

The five-year B.Arch program offers many opportunities for both prescribed and self-directed studies. The size of the program assures that students will get a diverse perspective on design, steeped in a tradition of integrating practice, structures and environmental design with the studio/lab format. The quarter system provides for three different design professors in each of the first four years. This diversity of teaching styles and formats, all subscribing to common pedagogical goals, eliminates a singular design approach and helps students to start formulating their own individuality.

Cal Poly is primarily a teaching institution, with virtually all classes taught by professors. The exit year focuses on a self-selected thesis dealing with various issues and topics that become a seminal point in the educational process, a gateway to graduate studies or multiple career options. The overwhelming number of graduates seek employment in the profession. As part of the CAED, architecture students can participate in inter-disciplinary studies and projects, and learn to appreciate early on the work and ethics of their peers in related disciplines. Located on the Central Coast of California, the bucolic atmosphere stimulates many field trips for urban experiences and projects.

AREAS OF FOCUS AND RESEARCH

Focus

The incorporation of courses in environmental control systems and architectural practice into all levels of the design program, coupled with courses in structures, highlight the polytechnic focus of the program. Students select a topic of research and focus for their year-long fifth-year thesis project. Topics offered each year vary, but currently include: interior construct, housing and sustainable environments, professional development and mentorship, the symbiotic relationship between architecture and the landscape, comprehensive architectural design, hospitality, leisure, entertainment, and educational facilities. The Built Environments Educational Program takes Cal Poly students to local elementary schools to introduce architecture to K–6 students.

Research

Cal Poly is primarily a teaching university, but many architecture faculty are engaged in research projects. There is a strong emphasis in the program on Sustainable Design, and research pertinent to this area of study is broad. The Harold and Evelyn Hay Grant focuses on energy-conscious solar design, including the design and construction of solar roof pond systems. The Renewable Energy Institute has developed far-reaching concepts that combine the research and skills of many campus departments and colleges. Other faculty are engaged in the research of lighting, digital design, Native American architecture, Asian architecture, and computer aided design.

SPECIAL ACTIVITIES AND PROGRAMS

Architecture students begin taking major courses their first quarter at Cal Poly. Entering freshmen have the opportunity to select a first-year design/graphics sequence that incorporates computer applications, enabling them to begin using 3-dimensional design concepts and computer-aided design software in their first quarter of instruction. The fourth year program includes several off-campus opportunities that augment and uniquely qualify the educational process. Included are year-long study/travel in Australia, Denmark, France, Germany, Italy and Washington, DC. There are currently one-quarter study opportunities in India, Thailand, and San Francisco, plus summer programs abroad. Several minors are offered within the CAED, including Construction Management, Real Property Development, and Sustainable Design. Students may apply to one of our "joint degree programs" and thus earn a Master of City Planning or a Master of Business Administration with one additional year of study.

FACILITIES

The university is a mélange of architectural styles, all nestling comfortably at the foot of the Central Coast gentle mountains. The CAED buildings house all the "major" courses, and all but first-year studios are dedicated spaces for the 24/7 use of our students. In addition to the main university library, within the architecture building, the CAED has its own Media Resource Center, computer lab and photographic presentation lab. A full wood and metal support shop is also available for CAED student use. There are two galleries, but the climate facilitates use of many outdoor areas for display and review.

SCHOLARSHIPS AND FINANCIAL AID

The fees at Cal Poly are among the lowest in the country. Although there are no scholarships available for entering freshman, there are many available for continuing. A high percentage of students are on some form of financial assistance, via government or university programs, and work study programs, and scholarships within the CAED. Scholarships are not available to students until they have completed one quarter in residence at Cal Poly. Please refer to www.fees.calpoly.edu for complete information of fees, including on-campus housing, meal costs, and parking fees.

ADMINISTRATION

R. Thomas Jones, AIA: Dean
K.Richard Zweifel, FASLA: Associate Dean
Henri de Hahn, EPFL, SIA: Department Head

CALIFORNIA STATE POLYTECHNIC UNIVERSITY, POMONA

ADDRESS

Main
California State Polytechnic University, Pomona
Department Of Architecture
College of Environmental Design
3801 West Temple Avenue
Pomona, CA 91768
Tel.: 909.869.2683
Fax: 909.869.4331
www.csupomona.edu

STUDENT AND FACULTY DEMOGRAPHICS

% of Female Students	42
% of International Students	1
% of Minority Students	66
% of Out-of-State U.S. Students	1
No. Full-Time Faculty	16
No. Part-Time Faculty	16
No. Full-Time Students	498

FINANCIAL INFORMATION

Main Source of University Funding	Public
Annual Tuition & Fees (graduate, resident)	$3,414
Annual Tuition & Fees (graduate, nonresident)	$10,170
Annual Tuition & Fees (undergraduate, resident)	$2,772
% Students Receiving Federal Financial Aid	41
% Students Receiving University Financial Aid	75
% Students Receiving Departmental Financial Aid	0
% Students Receiving Scholarships (assistantships or fellowships)	0
Average Annual Scholarship for Department	0

ACADEMIC SESSIONS

Fall Quarter/Trimester: September to December;
   Application Deadline: January 15
Winter Quarter/Trimester: January to March

Spring Quarter/Trimester: April to June
Summer Session I: June to August

ARCHITECTURE AND RELATED DEGREE PROGRAMS

Degree	Min. Yrs. to Complete	Professional Accreditation	# of FT Students	# of PT Students	# of First-Year Students	# of Degrees Conferred	Admissions Requirements
Architecture							
B. Arch	5	NAAB	418	51	89	68	See website
M. Arch	3.3	NAAB	70	0	18	16	Undergraduate degree, GRE, TOEFL, Portfolio, Rec. Letters, Essay
Landscape Architecture							
BSL Arch	4	LAAB	169	48	58	29	See website
MLA		LAAB	46	3	11	17	See website
Planning							
BSURP	4	PAAB	148	32	61	34	See website
MURP	2	PAAB	30	50	27	19	Undergraduate degree, GRE, TOEFL, Rec. Letters, Essay

SPECIALIZATIONS

Architectural Design
Building Information Modeling
Building Technology/Env. Systems
Community Design

Computer-Aided Design
Energy
Environment/Sustainability
Graphic Design

History
Housing
Landscape Design
Preservation

Professional Practice
Sustainability
Urban Planning and Design

UNIVERSITY SETTING

The Department of Architecture is one of four departments within the College of Environmental Design. The College has approximately 1,800 students, with 500 of them in Architecture. Along with the three other departments, Art, Landscape Architecture, and Urban and Regional Planning, the College also includes the John T. Lyle Center for Regenerative Studies, which has multidisciplinary programs taught by faculty from the entire University.

SCHOOL PHILOSOPHY

The College is dedicated to the pursuit of the design professions as a human imperative. Its programs are distinguished by a strong interdisciplinary course of instruction combined with a hands-on approach to the educational process. Excellence in design, enhanced by social and environmental concerns, is the basis of the curriculum as well as the measure of the faculty and programs. The College remains committed to the "learn by doing" polytechnic approach to education, which links theory to practice. Consequently, our graduates are recognized by business and industry for their superior preparation to enter the workforce.

PROGRAM DESCRIPTION

The Bachelor of Architecture degree is a five-year program that is focused on the integration of knowledge-based areas of the curriculum into the design studios. Courses in Architecture Theory and History, Human Behavior, Programming, Sustainability, Building Technology, Structures, Codes and Digital Media are closely coordinated with Design studio classes, and students are expected to demonstrate their knowledge of these areas in their design projects. The program is directed toward the realities of architectural practice and decision-making processes as they relate to the profession

of architecture. The three-and-a-quarter year Master's of Architecture degree is very similar in focus to the Bachelor's program, but also offers students an opportunity to concentrate in Sustainability or Historic Preservation, areas in which our faculty has special expertise. It is the intention of the Department, which has a very diverse student body and faculty, to prepare individuals who will be able to make knowledgeable, thoughtful and socially responsible contributions to professional practice. The Bachelor's program is highly impacted; because of the large demand for the program, it is limited to California residents. The Master's is open to out-of-state residents including international students. In addition to the accredited degrees, the Department is offering a new post-professional Master's degree in which students can pursue advanced studies in Sustainability or Historic Preservation.

SPECIAL ACTIVITIES AND PROGRAMS

The College offers a number of opportunities for International study, including summer programs in Europe and China, fall quarter programs in Taiwan and Italy, and year long programs in Italy, Denmark and Japan. The Department also has a program developed with the Extended University, originally designed for members of the architecture profession who needed additional credits in order to complete a professional degree. The program has expanded to include students who need to work full-time while completing their degree and students who want to explore architecture before applying as transfer students or to the graduate program.

FACILITIES

The College of Environmental Design houses the ENV Archives-Special Collections, which includes drawings, photos and papers of a number of well-known southern California practitioners who have been associated

with the school. Works of architects Richard Neutra, Craig Ellwood, Raphael Soriano and Don Wexler as well as those of landscape architect Francis Dean are some of the holdings used by scholars and available for our students to study. Related to these collections is the Richard and Dion Neutra VDL Research House II, which was left to the University by Dione Neutra and is operated by the College. It is open to the public and used as a laboratory for faculty and students. The College maintains its own Resource Center with over 15,000 books, technical reports and periodicals, which supplements the main University library collection. The College also has a Visual Resources collection containing an extensive slide collection, much of which has been converted to digital files, along with significant video resources.

SCHOLARSHIPS AND FINANCIAL AID

Information about Financial Aid provided through the university can be found on the website. The Department has a number of scholarships for which students can apply, several of which are specifically designed to support travel. The College also awards several scholarships, based, in part, on financial need. Several local and state organizations provide competitive scholarships that our students have been awarded, including the AIA chapters, the Association of Women in Construction, the Asian American Architects and Engineers Association, and the California Architecture Foundation.

ADMINISTRATION

Kyle D. Brown, PhD, ASLA: Interim Dean
Noel Vernon: Associate Dean
Judith Sheine, RA: Chair

ADDRESS

Main
Carleton University
Azrieli School of Architecture
and Urbanism
1125 Colonel By Drive
Ottawa, ON K1S 5B6
Canada
Tel.: 613.520.2855
Fax: 613.520.2849
architecture@carleton.ca
www.arch.carleton.ca

STUDENT AND FACULTY DEMOGRAPHICS

% of Female Students	44
% of International Students	4
% of Minority Students	
No. Full-Time Faculty	13
No. Part-Time Faculty	1
No. Full-Time Students	336
No. Part-Time Students	

FINANCIAL INFORMATION

Main Source of University Funding	Public
Annual Tuition & Fees (graduate, resident)	C$4,953
Annual Tuition & Fees (graduate, nonresident)	C$10,777
Annual Tuition & Fees (undergraduate, resident)	C$6,598
Annual Tuition & Fees (undergraduate, nonresident)	C$16,696
% Students Receiving Federal Financial Aid	
% Students Receiving University Financial Aid	
% Students Receiving Departmental Financial Aid	
% Students Receiving Scholarships (assistantships or fellowships)	
Average Annual Scholarship for Department	

ACADEMIC SESSIONS

Fall Semester: September to December; Application Deadline: 01 February
Spring Semester: January to April

ARCHITECTURE AND RELATED DEGREE PROGRAMS							
Degree	Min. Yrs. to Complete	Professional Accreditation	# of FT Students	# of PT Students	# of First-Year Students	# of Degrees Conferred	Admissions Requirements
Architecture							
Bachelor of Architectural Studies	4		275	0	74	63	TOEFL, Portfolio
M. Arch--2 years	2	CACB	61	0	28	21	Undergraduate Architecture degree

SPECIALIZATIONS

Architectural Design	History	Sustainability	Theory/Criticism
Computer-Aided Design	Housing	Tectonics	Urban Planning and Design
Environment/Sustainability	Professional Practice		

UNIVERSITY SETTING

Carleton University's Azrieli School of Architecture and Urbanism is fortunate to be located in Ottawa, Canada's capital city. Because of this unique location, the School enjoys access to the research facilities and expertise of Canada's national libraries, museums, galleries, and government agencies. The Azrieli School of Architecture and Urbanism has also established a close relationship with the city's computer and information technology sector.

SCHOOL PHILOSOPHY

The practice of architecture demands a breadth of knowledge and range of skills unparalleled in other professions. The responsibility for teaching these lessons is shared between academia and the profession. In addition to the demands of practice, however, it is the responsibility of the Azrieli School of Architecture and Urbanism to test the limits of architectural convention and discourse. This questioning, undertaken primarily in the design studio, is of particular relevance in the context of Canada's policy of cultural diversity.

PROGRAM DESCRIPTION

The Bachelor of Architectural Studies (BAS) is a four-year program that investigates architecture as a professional discipline, cultural phenomenon, and historical legacy. Students have the option to study in one of four concentrations—Design, Urbanism, Conservation & Sustainability, and Philosophy & Criticism. The Design Studio sequence undertakes architectural projects of increasing complexity from the carefully crafted and poetic investigations of form and material in the first year to a comprehensive design of a complex building in the fourth year. The concentration in Urbanism explores architecture as a component of the larger built environment. The curriculum is designed to raise awareness and promote stewardship of the built environment.

Students enrolled in the Conservation & Sustainability concentration will partake in specialized courses in the conservation of historial architecture as well as courses and workshops in the principles of sustainable design of architecture and the urban fabric. The concentration in Philosophy & Criticism will consist of humanistic courses in the intellectual contexts of historical architecture, with particular emphasis on artistic and scientific theory in architectural theory since the Enlightment. Courses are supplemented by electives and workshops offered by other departments in the University. In the Design concentration, the School offers a Directed Studies Abroad option in the second term of third year that allows students to study outside of Ottawa under the supervision of a faculty member. The School also offers a well-established Co-Op option.

AREAS OF FOCUS AND RESEARCH

The Azrieli School of Architecture and Urbanism is recognized internationally as a research leader in the history and theory of architecture, architectural pedagogy, conservation of heritage architecture, hybrid forms of representation, and materials and methods of construction. While faculty-specific projects are diverse, four intersecting paths of inquiry structure the areas of research at the School: Genetic Representation, Materiality, Alterity, and Deformation. Research Groups and Facilities: **The Carleton Immersive Media Studio (CIMS)** The mandate of CIMS is to advance the study and use of innovative forms of representation that can both reveal the invisible measures of architecture and animate the visible world of construction. **Carleton Solids and Light Tectonics Laboratory for studies in Materiality (CSALT):** The CSALT laboratory is committed to the study of materiality in architecture. The objective is to research traditional building technologies and those material properties that have been displaced or forgotten in current practice. For details, visit www.arch.carleton.ca

FACILITIES

The program operates out of three on-campus buildings: the Architecture Building, the David J. Azrieli Pavilion, and the Visualization and Simulation Building. Designed specifically for the School by Carmine Corneil and built in 1972, the Architecture Building has proven to be an exceptional environment for the study of architecture. Studios and classrooms in the Architecture Building are augmented by a metal and woodworking shop, video editing facility, dark room, computer labs, and the Carleton Solids and Light Tectonics Laboratory (CSALT). The David J. Azrieli Pavilion is home to the David J. Azrieli Institute for Graduate Studies in Architecture, graduate studios, and computing facilities. The newly constructed Visualization and Simulation Building is home to the Carleton Immersive Media Studio (CIMS).

SCHOLARSHIPS AND FINANCIAL AID

The Azrieli School of Architecture and Urbanism, with the Faculty of Graduate Studies, offers scholarships and teaching assistantships to applicants that demonstrate exceptional ability. Qualified students may apply for Ontario Student Loans and Ontario Graduate Scholarships.

ADMINISTRATION

Marco Frascari, PhD, MRAIC: Director
Yvan Cazabon, MRAIC: Associate Director/Undergraduate
Stephen Fai: Associate Director/Graduate

CARNEGIE MELLON UNIVERSITY

ADDRESS

Main
Carnegie Mellon University
School of Architecture
College of Fine Arts 201
Pittsburgh, PA 15213
Tel.: 412.268.2355
Fax: 412.268.7819
stevelee@cmu.edu
www.arc.cmu.edu

STUDENT AND FACULTY DEMOGRAPHICS

% of Female Students	45
% of International Students	18
% of Minority Students	10
% of Out-of-State U.S. Students	77
No. Full-Time Faculty	17
No. Part-Time Faculty	44
No. Full-Time Students	329
No. Part-Time Students	5

FINANCIAL INFORMATION

Main Source of University Funding	Private
Annual Tuition & Fees (graduate)	$31,750
Annual Tuition & Fees (undergraduate)	$39,150
% Students Receiving Federal Financial Aid	60
% Students Receiving University Financial Aid	68
% Students Receiving Departmental Financial Aid	
% Students Receiving Scholarships (assistantships or fellowships)	
Average Annual Scholarship for Department	

ACADEMIC SESSIONS

Fall Semester: August to December; Application Deadline: November 1
Spring Semester: January to May

ARCHITECTURE AND RELATED DEGREE PROGRAMS

Degree	Min. Yrs. to Complete	Professional Accreditation	# of FT Students	# of PT Students	# of First-Year Students	# of Degrees Conferred	Admissions Requirements
Architecture							
B. Arch	5	NAAB	262	2	65	55	SAT, TOEFL, Essay
MS in Architecture	1		1	1	1	1	Undergraduate degree, GRE, TOEFL, Rec. Letters, Essay
MS in Computational Design	1.5		1	0	1	1	GRE, TOEFL, Rec. Letters, Essay
Master of Sustainable Design	1		5	0	5	5	GRE, TOEFL, Rec. Letters, Essay
Master of Tangible Interaction Design	1		0	0	0	0	GRE, TOEFL, Rec. Letters, Essay
MS in Building Performance and Diagnostics	2		0	0	0	0	GRE, TOEFL, Rec. Letters, Essay
PhD Building Performance and Diagnostics	3.5		15	0	2	2	GRE, TOEFL, Rec. Letters, Essay
PhD Computational Design	3.5		14	0	0	2	GRE, TOEFL, Rec. Letters, Essay
Urban Design							
Master of Urban Design	1		3	0	2	1	GRE, TOEFL, Portfolio, Rec. Letters, Essay
Construction Management/Technology							
Arch Engineering Construction Management	1		6	2	6	3	GRE, TOEFL, Rec. Letters, Essay
PhD Arch Engineering Construction Management	3.5		0	0	0	0	GRE, TOEFL, Rec. Letters, Essay

SPECIALIZATIONS

Architectural Design	Building Technology/Env. Systems	Computer-Aided Design	Sustainability
Building Information Modeling	Community Design	Environment/Sustainability	Urban Planning and Design

ARCHITECTURE PROGRAM SUMMARY

The School of Architecture, with 65 faculty, 14 staff, 275 undergraduate students, 30 master students, and 30 PhD students, offers 11 degree programs: a professional Bachelor of Architecture degree, 7 master degrees and 3 PhD concentrations. Complimentary to these programs are five centers, labs and institutes: The Center for Building Performance and Diagnostics, The CoDe Lab, The Digital Fabrication Lab, The Remaking Cities Institute, and the Sustainable Design Academy.

The School of Architecture advances a shared vision to be recognized as a global leader of **integrated design** education, practice, research, scholarship and service. As one of the first PhD in Architecture programs in the country, the School enjoys a prominent record of research, and has populated the globe with graduates of significant stature. Through long-term strategic academic, government, industry, and practice partnerships we have defined innovative and collaborative approaches to research and scholarship within the School, while continuing to educate students for leadership roles in professional practice and a wealth of other environments.

UNIVERSITY SETTING

A top-ranked institution in the world, Carnegie Mellon manifests itself as a research university of a unique character, "where art and technology meet to create innovation with impact." Founded in 1900, the university has a distinguished history and a determined future for educating leaders across domains of teaching, practice, research, scholarship and service. Carnegie Mellon is a leader among educational institutions by building on its traditions of innovation, problem solving and interdisciplinary collaboration to meet the changing needs of society.

Having celebrated its 100th anniversary in 2006, the College of Fine Arts enjoys a century of impact and recognition related to its notable legacy as a "School of Fine and Applied Arts." The College is comprised of several interdisciplinary programs, research centers, and five schools including two performing art conservatories—the School of Music and he School of Drama—as well as Architecture, Art, and Design. The College mission is to provide a challenging, encouraging environment where students and faculty maximize their artistic and intellectual potential through open critical inquiry and creative production.

SCHOOL PHILOSOPHY

Our mission is to educate outstanding professionals with design creativity, social responsibility, historical perspective, technical excellence and global environmental leadership. We use the studio setting as an educational laboratory for analytical reasoning, creative exploration, exchange of ideas, integration, and critical thought. In recognition of continuously changing professional requirements, social conditions, and environmental challenges, we promote a highly investigative and research-oriented professional attitude

emphasizing the preparation needed for practice and lifelong learning. We respond to continuously changing technology through acquisition and development of advanced educational and professional media and instrumentation.

PROGRAM DESCRIPTION

The Bachelor of Architecture Program is a five-year, first professional degree program in preparation for entry into practice. It is fully accredited by the National Architectural Accreditation Board. The curriculum consists of six sequences in Integrated Design, Drawing and Digital Media, Building and Environmental Technology, History, Practice and Departmental/University Electives. The centerpiece of the curriculum is an in-depth studio-based design education with rigorous, generative knowledge-based foci in: composition, materials, site, environment, structures, occupancy, systems integration, and urban design. Studios are sequenced to build expertise, and are supported by parallel lectures aimed at concept-generation, performance, and the feasibility of design. Pre- and co-requisite core lecture courses are also sequenced to build the student's disciplinary strength in generative/design knowledge bases such as: Fundamental Design Strategies, Structures and Building, Environment and Ecology, Architecture Management, History, Communications & Media, Social Responsibility and Human Factors, and Urban and Regional Sustainability. These sequences enable students to develop minors, pursue dual degrees, or complete requirements for advanced standing in our Master's Programs following the completion of their Bachelor of Architecture degree.

AREAS OF FOCUS AND RESEARCH

Focus

- The design sequence curriculum features collaboration, digital media, community-based learning, interdisciplinary projects, technical skills, and a diverse faculty of professionals and researchers.
- The School of Architecture is a recognized leader in sustainable design and computational design.
- The Urban Laboratory immerses students in Pittsburgh's neighborhoods and assists in revitalizing depressed areas.
- Through our flexible curriculum, students engage in majors and minors throughout the university
- Students teach in the Architecture for Children program (grades 3–12) with full enrollment every fall.
- The School has strong alliances with the professional community and related practice organizations such as the AIA.

Research

Carnegie Mellon is a major research university. The School of Architecture is part of this effort with projects in computational design and building diagnostics. Research frequently crosses disciplines, and our faculty and students work with others in design, art, music, drama, civil and computer engineering. The Intelligent

Workplace is a learning laboratory in building technologies available to graduates and undergraduates to test state-of-the-art work environments and new building materials.

SPECIAL ACTIVITIES AND PROGRAMS

- Carnegie Mellon offers a summer program for high school students between their junior and senior years. This program introduces students to architecture and simulates our first-year curriculum.
- Faculty offers Summer Study Abroad programs each summer. Past programs include: China, Turkey, Egypt, France, Italy, Spain, and England. Students also study abroad in their fourth year for a year or semester in Switzerland, Denmark, Singapore, Australia, and Mexico.
- Faculty, staff and students form the Professional Development Committee, an intensive placement program for summer and permanent employment.
- We have an outstanding AIAS chapter, which has won numerous honor awards for research and overall excellence. AIAS organizes lectures, discussions, workshops, field trips and social events.
- In the Mentorship Program, fifth-year students pair with first-year students acting as resources throughout the year helping them to make the transition from high school into the study of architecture.

FACILITIES

CMU is the nation's "most wired campus." The School of Architecture maintains its own integrated computer studios with high-end graphic machines. The School recently opened a million-dollar digital fabrication lab. A multimedia lab with video and sound manipulation equipment is available for all Fine Arts students, as well as advanced darkrooms. We have a woodshop where students are trained in woodworking skills beginning in their first year. An architecture library and slide and video collection is also a prominent resource. The studio spaces have recently been renovated and all students are assigned a personal space according to their year in studio.

SCHOLARSHIPS AND FINANCIAL AID

At Carnegie Mellon, a student's admission is not dependent on their ability to pay tuition. The Financial Aid Office determines undergraduate aid; they attempt to meet financial needs with a combination of scholarships and loans. The School of Architecture offers several traveling scholarships for students in their fourth year of undergraduate education. These scholarships, based on academic success, are used for travel the summer between the fourth and fifth year. Graduate financial aid is decided by the School of Architecture and is based on research funds combined with other sources.

ADMINISTRATION

Hilary Robinson, PhD: Dean
Stephen R. Lee, AIA: Interim Head

THE CATHOLIC UNIVERSITY OF AMERICA

CUArch

ADDRESS

Main
The Catholic University of America
School of Architecture and Planning
Crough Center for Architectural
Studies
620 Michigan Avenue, NE
Washington, DC 20064
Tel.: 202.319.5188
Fax: 202.319.5728
architecture.cua.edu
cua-arch@cua.edu

STUDENT AND FACULTY DEMOGRAPHICS

% of Female Students	37
% of International Students	4
% of Minority Students	16
% of Out-of-State U.S. Students	85
No. Full-Time Faculty	25
No. Part-Time Faculty	
No. Full-Time Students	403
No. Part-Time Students	44

FINANCIAL INFORMATION

Main Source of University Funding	Private
Annual Tuition & Fees (graduate)	$31,220
Annual Tuition & Fees (undergraduate)	$31,370
% Students Receiving Federal Financial Aid	51
% Students Receiving University Financial Aid	37
% Students Receiving Departmental Financial Aid	
% Students Receiving Scholarships (assistantships or fellowships)	60
Average Annual Scholarship for Department	$15,818

ACADEMIC SESSIONS

Fall Semester: August to December; Application Deadline: January 15
Spring Semester: January to May; Application Deadline: October 15
Summer Session I: May to August

ARCHITECTURE AND RELATED DEGREE PROGRAMS							
Degree	**Min. Yrs. to Complete**	**Professional Accreditation**	**# of FT Students**	**# of PT Students**	**# of First-Year Students**	**# of Degrees Conferred**	**Admissions Requirements**
Architecture							
BS Arch	4		319	10	97	75	SAT, Rec. Letters, Essay
M. Arch 2	2	NAAB	54	20	35	32	Undergraduate Architecture degree, GRE, TOEFL, Portfolio, Rec. Letters, Essay
M. Arch 3	3	NAAB	30	8	14	9	Undergraduate degree, GRE, TOEFL, Rec. Letters, Essay
M. Arch Studies	1		2	1	1	1	GRE, TOEFL, Portfolio, Rec. Letters, Essay
Planning							
Master of City and Regional Planning	2		5	1	6		Undergraduate degree, GRE, Portfolio, Rec. Letters, Essay, TOEFL
Other							
Master of Science in Sustainable Design	1		8	3	11		Undergraduate Architecture degree, GRE, TOEFL, Portfolio, Rec. Letters, Essay

SPECIALIZATIONS

Architectural Design
Community Design

Computer-Aided Design
Environment/Sustainability

International/Regional Architecture
Sacred Spaces

Sustainability
Urban Planning and Design

UNIVERSITY SETTING

The Catholic University of America, located in Washington, DC, was established as a graduate and research center for the study of "all branches of literature and science, both sacred and profane." A founding member of the Association of American Universities, Catholic University is proud of its achievements—producing outstanding graduates from the School of Architecture and Planning, the Columbus School of Law, the Rome School of Music, and the School of Religious Studies.

SCHOOL PHILOSOPHY

Our school's mission, *Building Stewardship*, focuses on preparing architects and designers to assume a personal responsibility for the welfare of the world. We stress the interdependence of the words 'building' and 'stewardship.' We focus on how stewardship itself must be designed and constructed, as process and result—how humanity must actively *envision and build* a collective ethos of stewardship. Experienced in the integrative, creative and holistic process of design, architects and planners are uniquely positioned to help forge a compelling contemporary attitude toward stewardship for society at large. In addition, our school focuses on how we must be capable *stewards* when we indeed do physically build. We must care deeply for the impact our projects will have upon past and future human efforts and upon the fragile natural wonder of our globe.

To embrace this holistic approach, CUArch emphasizes:

- **Design Excellence**
- **Interdisciplinary Study**
- **Washington, DC, as a Design Laboratory**

Our belief is that we are all stewards of this earth. Architects and planners have the skills to help forge a true difference in humanity's future.

PROGRAM DESCRIPTION

Bachelor of Science

The undergraduate program is offered to those seeking a foundation in the field of architecture, as preparation for continued education in a professional degree program, or for employment options in fields related to architecture. The undergraduate curriculum introduces the student to the world of architecture in increasingly intensive stages. The first two years of study include introductory courses in design, history, theory, graphics and computer applications, as well grounding in the liberal arts. The third and fourth years consist mainly of design, technology, and history offerings. In addition, students may elect to enter the dual-degree curriculum in Architecture and Civil Engineering, giving the option of entering either one or both of these fields after graduation.

Master of Architecture

CUA offers two options for earning the Master of Architecture professional degree. The first is a two-year program for students from other institutions with a four-year undergraduate preprofessional degree in architecture. The second option is a three-year program for students who have an undergraduate degree in a field other than architecture. The graduate architecture program at CUA synthesizes design, creative, and professional rigor. Students may elect to enroll in one of five graduate concentrations: Cultural Studies/Sacred Space, Design Technologies, Digital Media, Real Estate Development and Urban Design. These concentrations have been developed to allow students the opportunity for more focused specialization during their graduate education.

AREAS OF FOCUS AND RESEARCH

Focus

In addition to the graduate specializations in the areas mentioned above, Catholic University's position in Washington, DC allows close cooperation with national and international institutions as well as with the local community. In 2005, the School of Architecture and Planning founded the Catholic University of America Design Collaborative (CUAdc). The mission of CUAdc is to train effective architects with a strong social commitment by guiding architecture students through actual design projects. CUAdc provides opportunities for students to learn outside of the classroom, thereby fostering a lifelong commitment to continuing education, and allows them to gain hands-on experience through work on actual projects with community clients. CUAdc provides architectural services to those nonprofit and community groups in the District of Columbia who could not otherwise afford architectural design services with the ultimate goal of repairing and improving the city, its neighborhoods and its buildings.

Research

Research in many areas of the architectural profession, history and theory are possible owing to Catholic University's location in the nation's capital. The Library of Congress for example, which is only three Metro stops away from the campus, provides students access to one of the world's largest libraries. Additionally, Catholic University has established agreements with the National Building Museum, the Smithsonian, the national AIA headquarters and other institutions to effectively transform Washington, DC into one of Catholic University's "classrooms." The creation of two new graduate degrees in sustainability and planning has increased the school's capacity to conduct research in these specialized areas as well.

SPECIAL ACTIVITIES AND PROGRAMS

The school offers a variety of foreign study options at both the undergraduate and graduate level. In the third year of the undergraduate curriculum, students may participate in semester-long programs in Rome and Barcelona. Graduate students and select undergraduate students can participate in a semester-long program in Paris. Our longest running program, The Cardinal O'Boyle Summer Foreign Studies Program is an offering for graduate and fourth-year undergraduate students. The program focuses on studio work in Rome and Italy, with additional travel to two other venues in and around Europe.

In addition to these programs, CUA offers many other opportunities for domestic and foreign travel. The Spirit of Place/Spirit of Design program is a design-build program. Projects have been completed in a variety of locations, including Ireland, Nepal and Peru. Opportunities also exist for students to participate in landscape and urban design studies in Asia and France,

environmental workshops at Casa Malaparte in Italy, and other auxiliary programs in Europe and North and Central America.

Each summer, the School of Architecture and Planning conducts the Summer Institute for Architecture, during which numerous courses at both the undergraduate and graduate levels are offered. Most of the design studios are offered, as are most of the required technology courses, including computer-aided design. In addition, numerous courses in history of architecture, graphics, furniture design, landscape architecture, and other related areas are offered. The faculty consists of selected members of the School of Architecture and Planning and invited faculty from other institutions.

The School also conducts the Experiences in Architecture program, a three-week session for high school or college students who are interested in investigating the field of architecture as a possible career. The students are introduced to all aspects of the study and practice of architecture, from design and history to office practice. The students live on campus and work in the design studios alongside architecture students attending the Summer Institute.

The Summer Institute accepts students from other academic units at The Catholic University of America, and from other institutions. Students interested in either program should contact the Office of the School of Architecture and Planning for further information and applications.

FACILITIES

Our award-winning facilities are housed in the original CUA gymnasium and provide a classic example of adaptive re-use at its best. Designed by a faculty member, it is conceived as a small city with "streets" filled with students and their work, a "piazza" for special exhibits, and a "town hall" for lectures and meetings. Additionally, students' needs are served by our library, CAD lab and output room, visual resource center and fabrication lab, which includes wood and metalworking shops, Co2 laser cutter and engraving system and three axis CNC milling machines.

SCHOLARSHIPS AND FINANCIAL AID

Catholic University offers scholarships, grants, loans, and work appointments to students at the undergraduate and graduate levels. Federal funds are, by statute, awarded solely on the basis of financial need as determined by a federally approved-needs analysis system. Awards of teaching assistantships and some scholarships based on academic achievement are also available. Undergraduate and graduate students may qualify for summer travel/study programs for academic achievement and awards granted in juried competitions.

ADMINISTRATION

Randall Ott, AIA: Dean
Ann Cederna, RA: Associate Dean for Graduate Studies
Barry Yatt, FAIA: Associate Dean for Graduate Studies
Michelle A. Rinehart: Assistant Dean for Administration
Luis Eduardo Boza: Director, Summer Institute
  for Architecture
David Shove-Brown, AIA: Director, Foreign Programs

CITY COLLEGE OF NEW YORK

ADDRESS

Main
City College of New York
School of Urban Design and
Landscape Architecture
Shepard Hall, 103
138th and Convent Avenue
New York, NY 10031
Fax: 212.650.6566
www1.ccny.cuny.edu/prospective/
architecture

STUDENT AND FACULTY DEMOGRAPHICS

% of Female Students	42
% of International Students	21
% of Minority Students	47
% of Out-of-State U.S. Students	18
No. Full-Time Faculty	25
No. Part-Time Faculty	30
No. Full-Time Students	360
No. Part-Time Students	30

FINANCIAL INFORMATION

Main Source of University Funding	Public
Annual Tuition & Fees (graduate, resident)	$7,500
Annual Tuition & Fees (graduate, nonresident)	$19,980
Annual Tuition & Fees (undergraduate, resident)	$4,000
Annual Tuition & Fees (undergraduate, nonresident)	$12,960
% Students Receiving Federal Financial Aid	60
% Students Receiving University Financial Aid	
% Students Receiving Departmental Financial Aid	15
% Students Receiving Scholarships (assistantships or fellowships)	8
Average Annual Scholarship for Department	

ACADEMIC SESSIONS

Fall Semester: August to December
Spring Semester: January to May

Summer Session I: June to July

ARCHITECTURE AND RELATED DEGREE PROGRAMS

Degree	Min. Yrs. to Complete	Professional Accreditation	# of FT Students	# of PT Students	# of First-Year Students	# of Degrees Conferred	Admissions Requirements
Architecture							
B. Arch	5	NAAB	264	29	60	42	SAT
BS Arch	4					5	
M. Arch I	3	NAAB	40	0	13	12	Undergraduate Degree
Landscape Architecture							
Master of Landscape Architecture I	3	LAAB	45	2	13	10	Undergraduate Degree

SPECIALIZATIONS

Architectural Design
Building Information Modeling

Building Technology/Env. Systems
Environment/Sustainability

Landscape Design
Sustainability

Urban Planning and Design

ARCHITECTURE PROGRAM SUMMARY

The City College School of Architecture, Urban Design, and Landscape Architecture offers undergraduate and graduate professional programs in architecture, landscape architecture and urban design including a five-year Bachelor of Architecture degree, a three-year Master of Architecture degree, and a one-year second Masters degree. There are also graduate programs in Landscape Architecture and Urban Design leading to masters degrees. Located in New York City, the school is housed in a new dedicated building on an attractive urban campus within a major multi-campus university and with easy access to a wide variety of institutions, architecture and urban spaces. A distinguished faculty comprised of scholars and practitioners offers a rich variety of courses to a diverse and dedicated student body.

UNIVERSITY SETTING

The School is located in a brand-new 130,000 square foot facility on the City College campus located in upper Manhattan, accessible to major museums and world-prominent architecture and urban spaces with afford-able student housing including a new college dormitory within a short walk. As the oldest publicly supported urban college in America (founded 1847), and the flagship college in the City University of New York, City College provides a broad traditional academic program of humanities and science as well as the university professional schools of engineering, and medicine, and architecture—all in physical proximity on a tight campus of both historic and modern buildings. Within a few hundred feet of the School premises students can pursue required and elective courses in the many college departments within the City University system which is comprised of 21 senior and community colleges and an extensive graduate center.

SCHOOL PHILOSOPHY

The City College School of Architecture, Urban Design and Landscape Architecture is deeply committed to providing the finest education in the art, theory and technology of architecture, urban design and landscape architecture to a broad and diverse student population. It is concerned with the quality of life of the larger community in our complex urban environment, and is thus committed to partnerships with institutions and agencies in the University, the City of New York and beyond. Our goal is to educate students who will create sustainable, equitable, and beautiful solutions for the global community of the 21st century, working in the spirit of CCNY's Ephebic Oath: "To transmit the city, not only not less, but greater, better and more beautiful than it was transmitted to us."

All programs, undergraduate and graduate, are focused on the design studio as a learning experience which draws together and synthesizes the diverse aspects and subjects of professional education. To ensure that each student gains maximum benefit, the faculty encourages a code of behavior in the studio through a "studio culture" policy which enumerates what is expected of students, faculty and administration.

PROGRAM DESCRIPTION

Undergraduate Program

Bachelor of Architecture (five-year) professional degree

In the first two-year phase, the student is offered a general education in liberal arts and sciences, as well as a series of lecture and design workshop courses that serve as an introduction to the processes of change and design in the physical environment of the past and present. In the second phase (third and fourth years), course work is devoted almost exclusively to professional education wherein each student is required to take parallel courses in three areas: design workshops, history and theory, and construction technology. In the third phase (fifth year), work is focused on advanced studies in architecture. The development of independent professional judgment applied to comprehensive design is emphasized.

Bachelor of Science in Architecture (four-year) degree

After successful completion of the first four years of the five-year professional program, a student may elect to exit and receive a Bachelor of Science degree. Students who elect this option may not receive a B.Arch (five-year) degree at City College.

Graduate Program

Master of Architecture I

Students are admitted to the Master of Architecture I program after completing an undergraduate degree in another discipline. The curriculum is dedicated to investigating the union of architectural form and thought. It understands architecture as the meeting ground between public and private expression and sees the city as its preeminent site. The program seeks to impart mastery of the fundamental skills and ideas necessary for the practice of architecture in the 21st Century. The principal medium for this is the design studio. Supported by courses in technology, environment, history, and theory, students will undertake problems of growing complexity over the three years of the program. Comprehensive design and the exercise of independent judgment is the primary focus of work in the third year. The required Master's curriculum covers the full range

of topics—from basic design to structures and environmental systems, to history and philosophy. The program is designed to be completed in three full-time, sequential years.

Master of Architecture II

The Master of Architecture II program is directed at students who hold a first professional degree in architecture who wish to deepen their design abilities and expand their knowledge of contemporary theory, technology, and environmental systems. The three studios in the sequence provide in-depth studies of architectural problems that seek to integrate the forms, ideas, and technologies that anticipate construction. Projects may also explore the far boundaries of the discipline of architecture. Students are encouraged to pursue an individualized program of study utilizing the many resources available throughout the school, the college, university and the city.

Other Programs

Master of Landscape Architecture I – Six-semester program for students who hold degrees in disciplines other than landscape architecture.

Master of Landscape Architecture II – Two-semester program for students with a first professional degree in landscape architecture.

Urban Design - One-year program for applicants who hold a professional degree in either architecture or landscape architecture.

AREAS OF FOCUS AND RESEARCH

The school, since it is located in a major urban region, seeks to use the city as a laboratory and a resource. Many projects are located in the city, student research often draws on the resources of neighboring institutions, and faculty are actively engaged in the vast professional and scholarly community of the New York region.

The school's faculty fully recognizes the complex responsibility the design professions have toward a healthy and sustainable environment. The school focuses on sustainable architecture, urban design and landscape architecture as major considerations in environmental planning and management that seek to improve overall living conditions while preventing inequity and exclusion.

The school is dedicated to providing the resources and infrastructure required to support computation, digital media, rapid prototyping and other technologies as an integral part of the curriculum.

The Faculty of the School of Architecture, Urban Design and Landscape Architecture believe the principle of a 'studio culture' is an important pedagogical method for building an intellectual and professional atmosphere within which to learn, examine and practice the application of knowledge, ideas and skills associated with a design education.

SPECIAL ACTIVITIES AND PROGRAMS

- Summer study programs in Germany and Spain.
- Participation in Fontainebleau School of Fine Arts.
- Cooperative work-study programs.
- Community service work in the City College Architectural Center.
- Chapter of the AIAS and ASLAS

Associated Programs

Master of Landscape Architecture I - The Master of Landscape Architecture first professional degree option is intended for students who hold degrees in disciplines other than landscape architecture. This six-semester program leads to a first professional degree (M.L.A.). The program objective is to prepare degree candidates to practice the profession of Landscape Architecture

with the knowledge and skill required to manage and design the process of change associated with the creation of places in urban, suburban, and natural landscapes. The principal medium of instruction is the design studio. Students will undertake design and planning problems of growing complexity over the three-year sequence, supported by classes and seminars in natural science, technology, history, and theory.

Master of Landscape Architecture II - This option, leading to a graduate or second degree (M.L.A.), is a two-semester program for students with a first professional undergraduate degree in Landscape Architecture (B.A. or B.S. in Landscape Architecture). The program is of particular interest to those seeking a more extensive understanding of the theory of landscape architecture and for those interested in the opportunity to teach in a university setting.

Urban Design - Applicants should hold a professional degree in either architecture or landscape architecture. Applicants from other backgrounds are considered in exceptional circumstances. This program is focused on the design of new forms for the city and urban life. Committed to experiment, it seeks to investigate the effects on and prospects for the city arising from contemporary transformations in technology, culture, lifestyles, environment, economic organization, governance, and architecture. The program aims to stimulate analytical rigor and formal creativity in a variety of media. The studio travels annually to observe a city under unusual stress. To date these have included Nicosia, Havana, Johannesburg, and Beijing.

Joint Degree in Sustainability - The School of Architecture, Landscape Architecture and Urban Design is a joint effort with the Grove School of Engineering and the Science Division to offer a Master of Sci. Degree in Sustainability.

FACILITIES

- Fully-equipped model shop
- Slide library: slide-duplicating equipment, copy-stand equipment
- Architectural library
- Computer studios for computer-aided design work: 50 work stations, networked
- City College Architectural Center: community service work; research

SCHOLARSHIPS AND FINANCIAL AID

The City College School of Architecture, Urban Design and Landscape Architecture has both merit and need-based financial assistance. Approximately 60 percent of students are receiving financial aid, including a full spectrum of New York State and federal grants and loans. In addition, there are supplemental opportunity grants, the City College Honors Program for undergraduates, the Seek Program, and College Work/Study Programs. Graduate students are eligible for teaching fellowships for faculty-supervised support of undergraduate courses. Professional organizations offer scholarships through the school, and the New York State Regents offer professional scholarships as well. Gifts from alumni and others are continually expanding scholarship and other financial assistance to students in the school. City College maintains a financial aid office. Scholarship and financial aid information and opportunities are posted in the school.

ADMINISTRATION

George Ranalli, AIA: Dean
Peter Gisolfi, AIA: Chair
Gordon A. Gebert, RA: Deputy Chair

CLEMSON UNIVERSITY

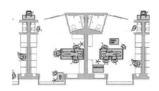  

ADDRESS

Main
Clemson University
School of Architecture
Box 340503, 145 Lee Hall
Clemson, SC 29634-0503
Tel.: 864.656.3896
Fax: 864.656.1810
mauric@clemson.edu
www.clemson.edu/caah/architecture/
mauric@clemson.edu

STUDENT AND FACULTY DEMOGRAPHICS

% of Female Students	32
% of International Students	2
% of Minority Students	5
% of Out-of-State U.S. Students	36
No. Full-Time Faculty	28
No. Part-Time Faculty	15
No. Full-Time Students	300
No. Part-Time Students	200

FINANCIAL INFORMATION

Main Source of University Funding	Public
Annual Tuition & Fees (graduate, resident)	$3,641
Annual Tuition & Fees (graduate, nonresident)	$7,285
Annual Tuition & Fees (undergraduate, resident)	$10,370
Annual Tuition & Fees (undergraduate, nonresident)	$22,300
% Students Receiving Federal Financial Aid	39
% Students Receiving University Financial Aid	20
% Students Receiving Departmental Financial Aid	
% Students Receiving Scholarships (assistantships or fellowships)	
Average Annual Scholarship for Department	$3,144

ACADEMIC SESSIONS

Fall Semester: September to December; Application Deadline: Rolling
Spring Semester: January to May; Application Deadline: Rolling

Summer Session I: June to August; Application Deadline: Rolling

ARCHITECTURE AND RELATED DEGREE PROGRAMS

Degree	Min. Yrs. to Complete	Professional Acceditation	# of FT Students	# of PT Students	# of First-Year Students	# of Degrees Conferred	Admissions Requirements
Architecture							
BA. Arch	4		286	10	73	82	
M. Arch—2 years	2	NAAB	15	8	33	19	Undergraduate Architecture degree
M. Arch— 3.5 years	3	NAAB	16	0	16	0	Undergraduate degree, GRE, TOEFL, Portfolio, Rec. Letters, Essay
MS Arch	1		2	0	0	35	
PhD	3		15		6	0	GRE, TOEFL
Landscape Architecture							
BLA	5	LAAB	112	0	27	21	
MLA							
Historic Preservation							
MS Historic Preservation							
Planning							
MCRP							
Construction Management/Technology							
BS Construction Science and Management							
MS Construction Science and Management							
PhD Environmental Design & Planning							

UNIVERSITY SETTING

Clemson University is a selective, public, land-grant university in a college-town setting along a dynamic south-eastern corridor. The University is situated on a 1,400-acre main campus. Clemson's student body has a combined total of 17,500 undergraduate and graduate students. The School of Architecture is a cornerstone member of the College of Architecture, Arts and Humanities. The College was formed to promote interdisciplinary and collaborative efforts amongst its member schools and departments. Architecture students are encouraged to take classes within the College and throughout the University.

SCHOOL PHILOSOPHY

As the sole architecture program in South Carolina and being part of a land-grant University, the primary goal of the School is to prepare our students to take on productive, responsible and critical roles within the practicing profession and related disciplines. Within this role, we also have the responsibility to expand the body of knowledge of both the practice and discipline of architecture through research and public service. Consequently, the School has built a program of study with an attentive view to its regional context while seeking a perspective of national and global dimension.

PROGRAM DESCRIPTION

The School has adopted the 4+2 curricular structure. Our four year undergraduate program leads to a well-rounded Bachelor of Arts in Architecture degree. We have recently revised the curriculum to incorporate an interdisciplinary approach to the design studio. The first two years of study are a collaborative effort with Clemson's award-winning Communications department focusing on oral communication skills. The last two years of study are a writing-intensive design experience.

Undergraduate and graduate students have the opportunity to enrich their education and develop a global perspective by studying at any of the three off-campus programs in Charleston, SC; Barcelona, Spain; or Genoa, Italy. Entering students are expected to be academically well qualified as well as imaginative and intellectually curious. A mix of students with varied backgrounds, both from within and outside the state, is encouraged. Each year's freshman class is normally limited to one hundred in order to assure academic excellence and preserve a close working relationship between student and professor. Students graduating with a Bachelor of Arts in Architecture are well-poised to enter our own Graduate program as well as continue their education at other institutions of higher learning.

AREAS OF FOCUS AND RESEARCH
Focus

The School places primary emphasis on the design studio as a learning tool. Within that, each faculty member determines the focus and agenda of the semester, relative to their research interest. Of particular note is the Graduate Program in Architecture + Health where students study how architectural settings impact health, and how to create architectural settings that support human health and well-being. These relationships are examined at a wide range of scales from details to communities. The program is focused around the design studio. The studio is supported by seminars examining issues such as the socialpolitical-cultural context of healthcare and healthcare design, the history and theory of healthcare architecture, therapeutic design, functional planning, and accommodating change.

Research

Research forms one side of the land-grant university triad which also includes service and teaching. Students in the graduate program have the opportunity to pursue advanced research through the Master of Science in Architecture program. Students in the Master of Architecture program are also expected to achieve a high level of scholarly research in their thesis work. Faculty research interests include: design communication, industrial design, architecture + health, urban planning, regional studies and tectonics. Clemson University supports an environment of collaborative work among all faculty and departments.

SPECIAL ACTIVITIES AND PROGRAMS

Undergraduate and graduate students have the opportunity to study in one of our off-campus programs in Genoa, Italy at the Charles E. Daniel Center for Building Research and Urban Studies or the Charleston Architecture Center in Charleston, South Carolina. In addition, undergraduate students may study in our Barcelona, Spain program. All off-campus programs are taught collaboratively with School of Architecture faculty and local invited faculty. These programs allow students to focus on the architectural settings of particular urban environments with classes in design, history and technology. The School also sponsors exchange programs in St. Petersburg, Russia, Prague, and Czech Republic. In addition, at each level of undergraduate study students have the opportunity to participate in class field trips. Recent trips include New York City, Chicago, Washington, DC, and Philadelphia. Additional activities: summer design workshops for high school students; lecture series; film series; visiting distinguished critics; and interviews with practitioners.

FACILITIES

Lee Hall houses the School of Architecture and associated design programs. The School provides traditional studio spaces outfitted with wireless transponders. Lee Hall also offers seminar rooms, and auditoriums; the Rudolph E. Lee Gallery, which displays traveling art exhibits and student projects; a wood shop; digital solid modeling; both PC- and Mac-based computer facilities; and the Emery A. Gunnin Architectural Library, which carries over 30,000 volumes covering architecture and related disciplines. The Gunnin Library also holds more than 145,000 slides and 6,000 planning documents.

SCHOLARSHIPS AND FINANCIAL AID

The University Office of Financial Aid administers and coordinates various types of undergraduate financial aid including scholarships, loans and part-time employment. A number of graduate teaching assistantships are available each year. In addition to paying a modest salary, the assistantship entitles the student to a reduction of academic fees. Alumni fellowships of up to $10,000, awarded to outstanding graduates, require no services of the recipients.

ADMINISTRATION

Clifton S.M. "Chip" Egan: Interim Dean
Ted Cavanagh, PhD, MRAIC: Chair

COLUMBIA UNIVERSITY

ADDRESS

Main
Columbia University
Graduate School of Architecture
Planning and Preservation
400 Avery Hall/1172 Amsterdam Ave.
New York, NY 10027
Tel.: 212.854.3414
Fax: 212.864.0410
www.arch.columbia.edu

STUDENT AND FACULTY DEMOGRAPHICS

% of Female Students	47
% of International Students	34
% of Minority Students	
% of Out-of-State U.S. Students	
No. Full-Time Faculty	25
No. Part-Time Faculty	170
No. Full-Time Students	629
No. Part-Time Students	14

FINANCIAL INFORMATION

Main Source of University Funding	Private
Annual Tuition & Fees (graduate)	$18,000
Annual Tuition (NY/P, resident)	$13,500
Annual Tuition (NY/P nonresident)	$13,500
% Students Receiving Federal Financial Aid	
% Students Receiving University Financial Aid	
% Students Receiving Departmental Financial Aid	
% Students Receiving Scholarships (assistantships or fellowships)	
Average Annual Scholarship for Department	

ACADEMIC SESSIONS

The MArch program is in session during the academic year; fall and spring terms.

ARCHITECTURE AND RELATED DEGREE PROGRAMS

Degree	Min. Yrs. to Complete	Professional Accreditation	# of FT Students	# of PT Students	# of First-Year Students	# of Degrees Conferred	Admissions Requirements
Architecture							
M. Arch — 3 years	3	NAAB	235	0	89	72	
MS Advanced Architectural Design							
MS Critical, Curatiorial, and Conceptual Practices							
PhD							
Historic Preservation							
MS Historic Preservation							
Planning							
MS Urban Planning							
PhD Urban Planning							
Urban Design							
MS Architecture and Urban Design							
Other							
MS Real Estate Development							

ARCHITECTURE PROGRAM SUMMARY

The Master of Architecture Program is a three-year first professional degree program that examines the importance of architectural design concepts in relation to historic and contemporary issues in an evolving culture.

Being part of a great university located in a major metropolis has determined much of what is unique about the Architecture Program. The School is not only able to attract excellent faculty members, but it is also able to draw upon the large and diverse community of architects, theorists, practitioners, and scholars in New York. Thus the program is able to expose student architects to architecture as a complex and pluralistic cultural endeavor.

At the same time that it explores the richness of architecture culture, the program seeks to provide an orderly system for integrating the various aspects of architectural study. Therefore, the curriculum is broadly divided into the study of history and theory, technology, methods, visual studies, and design. Learning about architecture involves, on the one hand, examining those historical, social, cultural, technical, and economic forces that shape buildings; on the other hand, it means mastering these forces with means traditionally available to the architect. The design studio is the main focus of the curriculum in that it offers the opportunity to integrate and synthesize what is being studied.

In general, the program seeks to impart basic principles and knowledge, to develop visual and analytical skills, and to relate creativity to given cultural situations. It is hoped that architects, thus trained, will be able to use their knowledge and insight by responding to and improving the built environment.

UNIVERSITY SETTING

Columbia University is one of the world's most important centers of research and at the same time a distinctive and distinguished learning environment for undergraduates and graduate students in many scholarly and professional elds. The University recognizes the importance of its location in New York City and seeks to link its research and teaching to the vast resources of a great metropolis. It seeks to attract a diverse and international faculty and student body, to support research and teaching on global issues, and to create academic relationships with many countries and regions. It expects all areas of the university to advance knowledge and learning at the highest level and to convey the products of its efforts to the world.

SPECIAL ACTIVITIES AND PROGRAMS

The School offers a wide range of events in the form of evening lectures, lunchtime lectures, debates, conferences, symposia, colloquia, and informal discussions that reflect the diversity and interests of its programs. Intended to further enrich the GSAPP experience, school events are generally open to the public—inviting all who attend to engage in the ideas explored and contribute to discussions. There are more than 250 guest speakers at the school in a typical semester. The Wednesday evening lecture series brings internationally-prominent practitioners, historians, and theorists to the school to speak on issues of architecture, planning, development, and urbanism. Monday nights typically feature public debates on major questions facing the disciplines or discussions of recent exhibitions, books, and films. The School and its programs sponsor special symposia and large-scale conferences—often in collaboration with other universities, museums, and cultural institutions—drawing prominent guests, faculty, and students together to discuss issues of timely and historical importance. There are also impromptu lunchtime lectures scheduled throughout the semester featuring the recent work of important visitors to New York City or young practitioners and scholars. The School also presents an array of exhibitions each semester, many of which tie in with the events described above. GSAPP publications retain as their goal the expansion of the range and engagement of architectural discourse. Beyond just the presentation of work completed in the design studios, the publications of the School endeavor to capture the overlapping experimental practices at the GSAPP at Columbia, producing the image of the School as an environment of learning, debate and exchange.

A new set of research laboratories has been established at the School to focus resources, creativity, and precision on key issues facing the next generations of experts devoted to the built environment. While new forms of expertise are constantly being developed within the individual programs at the School, these new labs gather some of these emergent trajectories together and focus them on a series of applied research experiments. Each lab constitutes a mini-think tank that takes on a limited set of collaborative partnerships with other units of the University and with colleagues outside the University to carry out projects that could not be done independently of such partnerships. Some of the labs will themselves collaborate when their particular joint expertise is needed. The work of the labs is integrated into the teaching programs within the School.

AREAS OF FOCUS AND RESEARCH

At GSAPP, the line between teaching and research is systematically blurred. Students and teachers stand together on the edge between the known and the unknown, determined to invent the best step forward for their fields.

The School is committed to a wide-ranging multidisciplinary approach that establishes the highest level of professional, technical, and creative expertise in each of its fields of study while actively analyzing and rethinking the very basis of those fields. The whole school operates as a research laboratory. The heart of this experimental mentality is the studio culture in which each design project is treated as an independent experiment on an intriguing question, an attitude that permeates the rest of the school in classes, individual research projects, laboratories, centers, lectures, symposia, and publications.

At any one time, certain questions galvanize a number of experiments within this diverse array of overlapping probes and the school starts to develop a collective expertise around these interdisciplinary initiatives.

FACILITIES

The school is located in its own building, Avery Hall; in the adjacent building, Fayerweather Hall; in the Avery extension, which connects the two; and in Buell Hall, directly south of Avery Hall. This complex houses design studios, classrooms, lounges, exhibition galleries, a carpentry workshop, audiovisual facilities, a slide library, a photography darkroom, a 300-seat auditorium, and a 70-seat lecture hall. The resources of the world's leading architecture library, the Avery Architectural and Fine Arts Library, are located in Avery Hall and the Avery extension; they are available to the students of the school. It is ranked by scholars as the outstanding international research center on the history of architecture. Its holdings consist of over 300,000 books and periodicals on architecture, urban planning, art history, historic preservation, archaeology, the decorative arts, and a broad variety of related background material. In addition, the library has over 300,000 original architectural drawings, collections of prints, and rare photographic material and archives.

SCHOLARSHIPS AND FINANCIAL AID

The goal of the School's program of financial assistance is to provide financial aid to those who have demonstrated need consistent with university guidelines and the analysis of the Graduate and Professional School Financial Aid Service. Financial need is met through a combination of grants and/or loans. Students should apply under the separate state-guaranteed loan programs. An entering student who receives a scholarship grant should be able to meet, through a combination of the grant, loan funds, parental contributions, summer earnings, and other resources, all expenses through the academic year.

ADMINISTRATION

Mark Wigley: Dean

THE COOPER UNION

ADDRESS

Main
The Cooper Union
Irwin S. Chanin School of Architecture
Cooper Square
7 East 7th Street
New York, NY 10003
Tel.: 212.353.4220
Fax: 212.353.4009
www.cooper.edu

STUDENT AND FACULTY DEMOGRAPHICS

% of Female Students	46
% of International Students	9
% of Minority Students	26
% of Out-of-State U.S. Students	44
No. Full-Time Faculty	4
No. Part-Time Faculty	40
No. Full-Time Students	140
No. Part-Time Students	0

FINANCIAL INFORMATION

Main Source of University Funding	Private
Annual Tuition & Fees (graduate)	$31,500
Annual Tuition & Fees (undergraduate)	$31,500
% Students Receiving Federal Financial Aid	22
% Students Receiving University Financial Aid	100
% Students Receiving Departmental Financial Aid	
% Students Receiving Scholarships (assistantships or fellowships)	26
Average Annual Scholarship for Department	$35,966

ACADEMIC SESSIONS

Fall Semester: September to December;
  Application Deadline: January 1
Spring Semester: January to May; Application Deadline: not applicable

ARCHITECTURE AND RELATED DEGREE PROGRAMS							
Degree	Min. Yrs. to Complete	Professional Accreditation	# of FT Students	# of PT Students	# of First-Year Students	# of Degrees Conferred	Admissions Requirements
Architecture							
B. Arch	5	NAAB	140	0	30	21	
M. Arch.II							B.Arch./M.Arch.I, GRE, Portfolio, Recommendation Letters, Essay

ARCHITECTURE PROGRAM SUMMARY

The Cooper Union for the Advancement of Science and Art, through outstanding academic programs in architecture, art and engineering prepares students admitted on merit to make enlightened contributions to society. The Cooper Union provides all students with full tuition scholarships, close contact with a distinguished faculty, and a rigorous, humanistic learning environment in which to develop intellectually, creatively and professionally. Admission to the B.Arch. program is based on academic records, SAT scores and completion of the School of Architecture Home Test. Please consult our website for more detailed application information and deadlines.

UNIVERSITY SETTING

The Cooper Union's location in New York City in the heart of downtown Manhattan provides a stimulating professional, social and cultural context for the education of an architect as well as an urban laboratory for the study of design in society. The many cultural, educational and civic institutions of the city provide an inexhaustible resource for research and experience outside the studio and classroom. Within The Cooper Union, the School of Architecture draws on the resources of the School of Art, the School of Engineering, and the Faculty of Humanities and Social Sciences, as well as the extensive library holdings of a consortium which includes The Cooper Union, New York University and the New School/Parsons.

SCHOOL PHILOSOPHY

At a time when the nature, role and scope of the architect is rapidly assuming new directions and dimensions in both social and technological domains, the school emphasizes the principles of design and their underlying human values. The architecture curriculum is designed to prepare students for a rich array of opportunities in the profession, while offering a broad cultural and intellectual foundation in the liberal arts as they relate to the design of the environment at all scales. The discipline of architecture interpreted in the widest possible sense is seen as a basis for a fully-rounded education at the undergraduate level. Students are encouraged to develop their design skills within a comprehensive framework of studios and courses that stimulate debate and research into all aspects of architecture in society—historical, aesthetic, technological, and political. There is a strong emphasis on the ethical responsibilities of the design professions toward society, and the role of the architect as interpreter and framer of the spatial needs of the community, specifically in the domain of environmental and conservation issues. Participation in student government is an opportunity for further professional and civic development.

PROGRAM DESCRIPTION

The School of Architecture offers a five-year program leading to the Bachelor of Architecture, a first professional degree. The five-year Design sequence is carefully structured to introduce the student to the principles of architectonics, the investigation of program, site, structures and environmental and building technolo-

gies, in a comprehensive and integrated curriculum. The design sequence moves from an introduction to the basic elements of form, space, and structure, to complex institutional design problems in their urban context, culminating in a year-long thesis that demonstrates the student's ability to synthesize a comprehensive understanding of a significant architecture in society. The traditional and essential skills of drawing, modeling, and design development are complemented by a full investigation of the analytical and critical uses of digital technology. The study of world architecture and urbanism is deepened by the understanding of individual cultures, environmental, and technological issues at every scale. The theory of the discipline, past and present, is investigated through the close analysis of critical texts, and is related to the theory and practice of other arts, such as public art, film, and video. The new one-year M.Arch.II program is a design-research post-professional degree program intended for professionals who wish to continue in practice with higher research and design skills as well as those who wish to prepare for teaching and/or study toward a Ph.D. at another institution.

AREAS OF FOCUS AND RESEARCH

The curriculum of the undergraduate program is directed toward the education of the architect in the broadest sense of the word, with a special and deep understanding of design as it relates to the fundamental needs of society, culture and the environment. Beyond the required courses, the program offers multiple electives and advanced seminars in allied fields. Faculty conduct their own research, often with the participation of students. The educational program stresses research into all aspects of architecture from design to the history and theory of architecture and urbanism, urban design, environmental design, structures, and the relation of architecture to the other arts. Together with the Schools of Art and Engineering and the Faculty of Humanities and Social Sciences, the School of Architecture offers a unique opportunity for interaction and interdisciplinary research and experience. The new M.Arch.II degree offers concentrations in one or a combination of three areas of study: Urban Studies; History, Theory and Criticism of Architecture; Technologies.

SPECIAL ACTIVITIES AND PROGRAMS

The school hosts lectures, seminars, public symposia, and exhibitions each year including a Student Lecture Series, organized by a committee of students who invite a varied roster of design professionals, artists, historians, and intellectuals; and lectures, panel discussions and symposia co-sponsored with The Architectural League of New York, the New Museum of Contemporary Art, the Whitney Museum of Art Independent Study Program and other cultural institutions in the city. An annual exhibition of student work as well as other exhibitions curated by the school are seen as integral to the educational program. Independently arranged opportunities for study abroad or in the United States may be available; however, there are currently no formal exchange or study abroad programs. In addition, the Saturday Program for high school students affords opportunities

for community service and teaching. The Cooper Union's Continuing Education program sponsors free lectures by distinguished leaders in politics, the arts and social sciences, and its courses may be open to matriculated students with permission.

FACILITIES

The facilities of the School of Architecture are housed on the third and seventh floors of the Foundation Building, initially completed in 1859 and now a National Historic Landmark. In 1974, The Cooper Union completed a full renovation of the interior of the Foundation Building designed by John Hejduk, the first dean of the School of Architecture. All students in the School of Architecture are provided individual workspace within a shared studio. With the first through fourth years sharing a single large studio and the fifth-year thesis class in more intimate individual spaces, a unique environment fostering cross-fertilization between classes and individual students is maintained. In addition to their individual studio work space, students have access to other shops and laboratories in the Foundation Building. The school has developed a computing facility specifically intended to support a design curriculum that recognizes the growing use of computing as an instrument of practice and which urges students to explore its formal and cultural implications. The facility now has cross-platform work stations as well as scanning, printing and plotting capabilities. In addition, computing facilities in the Schools of Art and Engineering are open for use by students of the School of Architecture. An outstanding all-college sculpture shop is located on the fourth floor. Integral to both the program and pedagogy of the School of Architecture, the shop is equipped for projects in wood, metal, plastics, plaster and clay, and includes a bronze casting foundry. The School of Architecture Archive is responsible for the ongoing collection, documentation and storage of student work, and now has a record of student work produced at the school since 1983, an invaluable record of the pedagogy of the school used for exhibitions, publications and student research.

SCHOLARSHIPS AND FINANCIAL AID

The Cooper Union offers full tuition scholarships to all admitted students. In addition, students may also be eligible to receive financial aid. The Cooper Union offers "packages" (more than one type of aid is provided) financial aid awards suited to each student's need. In recognition of the pressing financial burden of the ever-increasing cost of living in New York City, many alumni and non-alumni have supported Cooper's students by establishing named scholarships, to offer vital financial aid to deserving students. For the most current information about financial aid at The Cooper Union, please visit www.cooper.edu/admin/financial/index.html

ADMINISTRATION

Anthony Vidler: Dean
Elizabeth O'Donnell, RA: Associate Dean

CORNELL UNIVERSITY

ADDRESS

Main
Cornell University
College of Architecture, Art & Planning
Department of Architecture
143 E. Sibley Hall
Ithaca, NY 14853-6701
Tel.: 607.255.5236
Fax: 607.255.0291
cuarch@cornell.edu
www.architecture.cornell.edu

STUDENT AND FACULTY DEMOGRAPHICS

% of Female Students	47
% of International Students	27
% of Minority Students	15
% of Out-of-State U.S. Students	77
No. Full-Time Faculty	39
No. Part-Time Faculty	8
No. Full-Time Students	281
No. Part-Time Students	5

FINANCIAL INFORMATION

Main Source of University Funding	Private
Annual Tuition & Fees (graduate)	$36,300
Annual Tuition & Fees (undergraduate)	$34,781
% Students Receiving Federal Financial Aid	
% Students Receiving University Financial Aid	
% Students Receiving Departmental Financial Aid	
% Students Receiving Scholarships (assistantships or fellowships)	
Average Annual Scholarship for Department	

ACADEMIC SESSIONS

Fall Semester: August to December
Spring Semester: January to May

Summer Session I: June to August

ARCHITECTURE AND RELATED DEGREE PROGRAMS

Degree	Min. Yrs. to Complete	Professional Accreditation	# of FT Students	# of PT Students	# of First-Year Students	# of Degrees Conferred	Admissions Requirements
Architecture							
B. Arch	5	NAAB	300	0	60	45	
M. Arch: Post-professional	2		20	0	10	10	Prof. Architecture degree
M. Arch—Professional	3.5	NAAB Candidate	70	0	20	0	Undergraduate degree
Planning							
MA Historic Preservation Planning							
PhD City & Regional Planning							
Other							
MA History of Architecture and Urban Development							
PhD History of Architecture and Urban Development							
MS Computer Graphics							

SPECIALIZATIONS

Architectural Design
Building Technology/Env. Systems
Computer-Aided Design

Environment/Sustainability
History

Professional Practice
Sustainability

Theory/Criticism
Urban Planning and Design

ARCHITECTURE PROGRAM SUMMARY

With a tradition of more than 130 years of dedication to the teaching of architecture, The Department of Architecture at Cornell University appreciates and respects the challenge of working closely with the exceptionally talented students who are the backbone of our program. We strive to offer the best architectural education available, respecting our tradition while continuing to evolve to meet current and future challenges.

UNIVERSITY SETTING

Cornell is a privately endowed university with a number of statutory units that are also part of the State University of New York system. The College of Architecture, Art, and Planning is part of the endowed portion. As an Ivy League university and also the land grant institution of New York State, Cornell is a unique combination of public and private divisions. Cornell's vast array of opportunities for study makes possible the pursuit of nearly any field of knowledge. The university attracts an outstanding faculty and brings to the campus each year a host of distinguished scholars, artists, and practitioners to present lectures and concerts. These along with other cultural and sporting events form a continuous part of university life.

The small-town setting of the university in central New York—its main campus framed by two dramatic gorges and situated on a hillside overlooking Cayuga, the longest of the Finger Lakes—puts Cornell students in closer touch with the natural environment than would occur on many campuses. For architecture students, these natural and rural surroundings are balanced by participation in field trips, the Rome Program, the New York City Program and frequent summer travel programs, all of which offer invaluable opportunities for study in a larger urban context.

PROGRAM DESCRIPTION

Architectural education at Cornell is about balance: between philosophy and pragmatism, between virtual and physical creative realms, between refined tradition and transcendent vision.

Cornell's architecture program is one of the oldest, most respected, and best endowed, but it also thrives in the midst of the university that *Newsweek* recently dubbed the "Hottest Ivy." Cornell earned that designation in part for its emphasis on solving real-world problems as well as theoretical ones and for working to incorporate environmental sustainability into every aspect of campus life. Cornell is unmatched for enabling access to collaboration across disciplines and colleges.

Located in a landscape of stunning natural beauty in upstate New York, Cornell's architecture program also encourages off-campus study initiatives in Asia, Africa, and South America as well as at our own facilities in central Rome and New York City. Research domains in the Department of Architecture include ecology, urbanism, building technology, advanced computation, and architectural history. Studio culture values criticism, ethics, and intellectual diversity.

Undergraduate Program

For undergraduates in our five-year professional Bachelor of Architecture degree program, design is the focal point of every semester. Basic conceptual skills are emphasized early on, along with introducing the elements of architecture. This highly focused and intensive curriculum also emphasizes theory, history, and building technology. Simultaneously, it is a constituent within a world-class research university and students are encouraged to take advantage of its wider resources. Faculty-led study-abroad opportunities are further highlights of the design program. Undergraduates complete their studies with supervised thesis projects in their final year.

B.S. History of Architecture

The program is designed for transfer students, so you must first complete two years of college in order to be eligible. The curriculum introduces students to the built domain from earliest times to the present. Students learn methods of scholarly research, analysis and interpretation; study historic monuments in their full cultural, social and urban contexts; and examine building traditions within specific periods and regions. Students will be learning architectural history within a professional school of architecture—a context that enriches the scholarly understanding of buildings by emphasizing the immediacy of architectural problems and their solutions in the present.

Master of Architecture (Professional)

The new professional Master of Architecture program, presently in NAAB candidacy status, is committed to the view that the question of appropriate practice must be continually investigated and reassessed in today's globally expansive and technologically dynamic context. Placing this question at the center of the learning process, the program offers bachelor's degree holders from any field a rich curriculum dedicated to building broad-based expertise and complemented by six semesters of design studios. The intensive course of study encourages the development of individual research trajectories and culminates in a design thesis.

Three-Semester Post-Professional M.Arch.2 Program

Cornell's post-professional Master of Architecture is a three-semester advanced design research program. Open to individuals holding a B. Arch or first-professional M. Arch. degree, the program offers a critical framework for investigating pertinent 21st-century design concerns, practices, and technologies in architecture and urbanism. Through core and elective studios and courses, students pursue specialization within one of five interrelated areas: urbanism, ecology, technology, discourse, and media. The final semester takes place at the college's New York City Center and draws on an unmatched range of practitioners and critics within the metropolis.

M.A. / Ph.D. HAUD

The history program provides opportunities for the dialogue between various programs and constituencies within the college as well as the greater university. The program is committed to the study of the built environment and cultural landscape from the point of view of cultural history. As is evidenced in lectures and seminars, faculty research and student projects, there is a sustained interest in analyzing the cultural context of the built domain—whether at the scale of the building, cities or landscapes, both monumental and mundane.

M.S. in Computer Graphics

Graduate students currently have two principal options for study under a major advisor associated with the Program of Computer Graphics. The first option is to enter the Master of Science program with a major in Computer Graphics. Students on this degree path normally then minor in Computer Science, with the bulk of their coursework in that department. For those students wishing to study the relationship of computer graphics to an application field (e.g., architecture or engineering) the minor is usually in the most closely related subject area. The second path is to major in computer graphics while obtaining a Ph.D. degree in Computer Science. The basic academic requirements are the satisfactory completion of six graduate computer science courses in preparation for the Ph.D. qualifying exam. Following successful completion of that exam, it is expected that all research will be conducted at the facilities of the Program of Computer Graphics.

SPECIAL ACTIVITIES AND PROGRAMS

Rome Program

The program offers students a semester in Rome and access to academic facilities in the Palazzo Lazzaroni. It is a special opportunity to observe, analyze, and speculate about the city in a direct, empirical way. The city, its architecture, painting, and sculpture, and the connections between those forms, as well as the personal and cultural conditions of their creation, are the subjects of the program.

New York City

The College of Architecture, Art, and Planning's newest off-campus facility in New York City offers an immersive, urban experience for undergraduate and graduate students providing a unique opportunity to live and study in one of the most culturally vital urban centers in the world as well as gaining valuable professional experience at design firms and innovative public, private, and nonprofit organizations throughout the city. AAP NYC offers a full roster of courses enriched by Manhattan's unique artistic, historical, and cultural resources, and AAP's extensive alumni network of noted metropolitan professionals, who frequently teach and serve as guest critics and mentors.

Summer Term in Architectural Design

On-Campus

The eight-week summer term in architectural design offers undergraduate students a concentrated period of design work. Undergraduate design-sequence courses are offered at the second through fifth-year levels on the Ithaca campus.

Off-Campus

The Department of Architecture also provides a variety of opportunities for study abroad through the summer design studio offered at the third-, fourth-, and fifth-year levels. Faculty members have conducted programs in Japan, Chile, Northern Europe, and the Aegean area. Students from other schools of architecture are welcome to apply to any summer program in architecture.

Introduction to Architecture Summer Program

People contemplating a career in architecture, or even those who would simply like to indulge their passion for it, should consider the Exploration in Architecture program. This rigorous six-week exploration requires no specialized knowledge or background, just a serious interest in design.

FACILITIES

The college is housed in four closely related buildings providing classrooms, drafting rooms, studio spaces, and faculty and administrative offices. Milstein Hall, a new building for the Department of Architecture, is scheduled to be completed in 2011. The Fine Arts Library is housed in Sibley Hall as a division of the University Library system and its collection is capable of supporting undergraduate, graduate, and research programs. In addition, the George and Adelaide Knight Visual Resource Facility in East Sibley Hall contains the F.M. Wells Memorial Slide Collection which consists of a large and growing collection of slides of architecture, architectural history, and art. In close proximity to the college is the Herbert F. Johnson Museum of Art, which has a strong and varied collection and a continuous series of high-quality exhibitions, fulfilling its mission as a center for the visual arts at Cornell. To assist students in preparation of models, a fabrication shop is located in Rand Hall, including a laser cutter. Also located in Rand Hall are the computer-aided design labs, continually provided with state-of-the-art modeling and rendering software.

SCHOLARSHIPS AND FINANCIAL AID

Undergraduate financial aid awards are made according to need. Various merit-based fellowships and assistantships are available at the graduate level. To apply for financial assistance, undergraduate applicants must complete the form included in the Cornell application packet and the Financial Aid Form of the College Scholarship Service. Awards include a combination of scholarship/loan funds and work-study employment.

ADMINISTRATION

Kent Kleinman: Dean
Mark Cruvellier: Chair

DALHOUSIE UNIVERSITY

ADDRESS

Main
Dalhousie University
School of Architecture
P.O. Box 1000
5410 Spring Garden Road
Halifax, NS B3J 2X4
Canada
Tel.: 902.494.3971
Fax: 902.423.6672
arch.office@dal.ca
archplan.dal.ca

STUDENT AND FACULTY DEMOGRAPHICS

% of Female Students	40
% of International Students	10
% of Minority Students	
No. Full-Time Faculty	13
No. Part-Time Faculty	25
No. Full-Time Students	203
No. Part-Time Students	2

FINANCIAL INFORMATION

Main Source of University Funding	Public
Annual Tuition & Fees (graduate)	C$7,260
Annual Tuition & Fees (undergraduate)	C$6,720
% Students Receiving Federal Financial Aid	
% Students Receiving University Financial Aid	
% Students Receiving Departmental Financial Aid	
% Students Receiving Scholarships (assistantships or fellowships)	12
Average Annual Scholarship for Department	$4,100

ACADEMIC SESSIONS

Fall Semester: September to December; Application Deadline: March 1
Spring Semester: January to April; Application Deadline: October 1

Summer Session I: May to July; Application Deadline: February 1

ARCHITECTURE AND RELATED DEGREE PROGRAMS

Degree	Min. Yrs. to Complete	Professional Accreditation	# of FT Students	# of PT Students	# of First-Year Students	# of Degrees Conferred	Admissions Requirements
Architecture							
Bachelor of Environmental Design Studies	2		115	0	60	52	TOEFL, Portfolio, Rec. Letters, Essay
Master of Architecture	2	CACB	93	0	42	37	Undergraduate Architecture degree, TOEFL, Portfolio, Rec. Letters, Essay

SPECIALIZATIONS

Architectural Design
Building Technology/Env. Systems
Community Design

Environment/Sustainability
Housing
International Development

International/Regional Architecture
Professional Practice

Sustainability
Theory/Criticism

ARCHITECTURE PROGRAM SUMMARY

Dalhousie University is one of Canada's top research and teaching universities. It is located in downtown Halifax, a vibrant port city with a population of 350,000 and an unsurpassed natural setting on the Atlantic coast. Halifax was founded in 1749 and is the academic, cultural, and economic centre of Atlantic Canada. With over 15,000 students, Dalhousie is the largest of the six universities in Halifax.

UNIVERSITY SETTING

The School of Architecture is located in a grand old building in the South End of Halifax, in a prime commercial area three blocks from the Halifax Citadel and five blocks from the harbour. Its urban campus is surrounded by housing, parks, shops, and distractions of all kinds.

SCHOOL PHILOSOPHY

The primary aim of the School of Architecture is to educate students who plan to become professional architects. The craft of architectural education requires critical and imaginative reflection. The School of Architecture not only teaches design principles that explore form and composition through the design of possible buildings, it teaches students to ask the right questions, to challenge their assumptions, and to position themselves intellectually in various physical and cultural world contexts. At Dalhousie both the studio and local environs act as ongoing laboratories for testing architectural design, often with the interest and support of local communities. The school emphasizes design as a means of studying and practicing architecture. Studios investigate principles of built form through design exercises and historical studies. Technology and humanities courses provide an understanding of material means and human intentions in architecture. Integrated co-op work terms introduce students to responsible professional practice and anticipate career directions. The School of Architecture enjoys an international reputation, with graduates working in many countries around the world.

PROGRAM DESCRIPTION

Dalhousie's professional architecture program is compact: three years and eight months at the School of Architecture. It recognizes a student's previous undergraduate studies and leads to a fully accredited master's degree. Its co-op work terms enable students to live and work in Canada and abroad. The tuition fees are competitive in Canada and substantially lower than at comparable universities in the United States. American students can study architecture at Dalhousie and return to the United States with a recognized professional degree. Applications from transfer students are welcome. The professional architecture program includes two degrees:

- Years 1–2: general studies in university subjects other than architecture
- Years 3–4: Bachelor of Environmental Design Studies (BEDS)
- Years 5–6: Master of Architecture (MArch)

The BEDS program develops a basic knowledge of architecture in five subject areas: design (building design, site design, program design); humanities (history, theory, research, criticism); technology (construction, structure, environmental systems); representation (drawing, modeling, computer applications); and professional practice (professional responsibility, office management, co-op work term). The MArch program continues the subject streams and aligns students with areas of faculty research, culminating in the final year with an individual design thesis supervised by a faculty member.

AREAS OF FOCUS AND RESEARCH

Areas of research for faculty and graduate students include sustainable building, urban housing, urban infrastructure, adaptive reuse, architectural history, architectural representation, lightweight structures, vernacular building, and community development in Canadian and international locations. The school is strongly committed to materiality and craft through hands-on learning and on-site design-build projects.

Faculty research and community development projects are often integrated into design studios, involving community interaction and the realization of small building and landscape projects.

SPECIAL ACTIVITIES AND PROGRAMS

- The School of Architecture and its setting on the Atlantic coast attract students from all across Canada, especially the Pacific coast. The school is unique for its intensive trimester system and its integrated cooperative work terms: four months during the undergraduate program and eight months during the graduate program. The co-op work terms are managed by a full-time co-op coordinator and enable students to be employed in architectural offices in Canada and all over the world, as far away as Australia and India.
- The School of Architecture's summer semester features design-build "free labs" in which Dalhousie faculty and guest instructors explore hands-on building with various communities in Nova Scotia. The School's free labs have become well known in architectural circles in Canada and the United States and were documented recently in *Free Lab*, a book edited by Professor Christine Macy and published by Tuns Press, which chronicles free labs from the past fifteen years.
- In the MArch program, semester-long exchange programs enable students to study and travel with partner universities in Germany (Düsseldorf),

Mexico (Mexico City and Monterrey), and the United States (Austin, Texas and Muncie, Indiana). Federally funded research and teaching projects in Botswana and The Gambia have expanded the School's international network and opportunities for graduates. Although the School's location and focus are regional, its outlook and networks are national and international.
- Dalhousie students have been recent winners of national competitions, including the Student Award of Excellence from Canadian Architect, the Royal College of Art's Ernest Annau Traveling Scholarship, and the LEAP national housing competition organized by the Université de Montréal. Dalhousie graduates also have won the Canada Council's Prix de Rome three times. Industrial design work by a firm of recent Dalhousie graduates is also part of the permanent collection at the Museum of Modern Art in New York.
- Closer to home, students and faculty have designed and built award-winning floats for the annual Halifax Business Association's Parade of Lights. The Architecture Students Association runs the School's annual lecture series, is represented on all academic committees, and produces *StudioEast*, an annual publication of student work.

FACILITIES

One-third of the Faculty of Architecture and Planning building is devoted to studios that are open to students at all times. Each student is provided with an individual studio space. The building has several computer labs, large-format print facilities, a woodworking shop, a construction lab, a CNC lab, a photographic studio, and a large exhibition hall. The Faculty's resource centre houses reference materials and an image collection, and is managed by a full-time visual media librarian. Dalhousie's School of Planning is also located in the Architecture and Planning building. The university's architecture library is nearby.

SCHOLARSHIPS AND FINANCIAL AID

Applicants with an excellent academic record (3.70 GPA or higher) may be eligible for a partial tuition scholarship. Most students should expect to finance their architectural education through personal funds and/or student loans.

ADMINISTRATION

Christine Macy: Dean
Terrance Galvin: Director

DREXEL UNIVERSITY

ADDRESS

Main
Drexel University
Antoinette Westphal College of Media
Arts & Design
Department of Architecture & Interiors
3201 Arch Street, Suite 110
Philadelphia, PA 19104
Fax: 215.895.4921
architecture@drexel.edu
www.drexel.edu/westphal/
academics/undergraduate/architecture

STUDENT AND FACULTY DEMOGRAPHICS

% of Female Students	35
% of International Students	1
% of Minority Students	18
% of Out-of-State U.S. Students	50
No. Full-Time Faculty	5
No. Part-Time Faculty	60
No. Full-Time Students	50
No. Part-Time Students	330

FINANCIAL INFORMATION

Main Source of University Funding	Private
Annual Tuition & Fees (graduate)	
Annual Tuition & Fees (undergraduate)	$35,100
% Students Receiving Federal Financial Aid	70
% Students Receiving University Financial Aid	95
Students Receiving Departmental Financial Aid	
% Students Receiving Scholarships (assistantships or fellowships)	95
Average Annual Scholarship for Department	$21,000

ACADEMIC SESSIONS

Fall Quarter/Trimester: September to December
Winter Quarter/Trimester: January to March

Spring Quarter/Trimester: April to June
Summer Session I: June to August

ARCHITECTURE AND RELATED DEGREE PROGRAMS							
Degree	Min. Yrs. to Complete	Professional Accreditation	# of FT Students	# of PT Students	# of First-Year Students	# of Degrees Conferred	Admissions Requirements
Architecture							
B. Arch — 2 + 4 Option	6	NAAB	50	0	30	20	SAT, Rec. Letters, Essay
B. Arch — Evening Program	7	NAAB	0	330	36	35	

SPECIALIZATIONS

Architectural Design
Computer-Aided Design

Energy
Environment/Sustainability

Interior Design/Architecture
Sustainability

Urban Planning and Design

ARCHITECTURE PROGRAM SUMMARY

Drexel University has been committed to work/study programs since its founding in 1891. Evening study creates an opportunity for concurrent full-time employment in architectural firms and opens the study of architecture to a great diversity of students. Transfer students are accepted from professional and pre-professional programs. The Architecture Program also offers the Two + Four Option for students who are just graduating from high school. This option combines two years of full-time study with four additional years in the part-time evening program. In the third year these students start full-time employment with placement assistance from the Architecture Program, providing a head start to their professional careers.

The Drexel program offers the ability to work and to advance in the profession while pursuing a professional degree. This advantage is supported by a rich variety of outstanding offices in the Philadelphia region. Drexel students often develop positions of responsibility in their firms, and full-time work experience before graduation receives credit toward state licensing requirements. It is not unusual for Drexel students to pass their registration exams immediately following graduation. The part-time evening format enables the Architecture Program to draw on the expertise and experience of the professional community in the Philadelphia area and to maintain a strong practitioner faculty.

UNIVERSITY SETTING

The Drexel campus is located on the edge of central Philadelphia in University City, a neighborhood that includes several centers of education and research. Students have ample opportunities for outside cultural, educational, and architectural experiences. Libraries, museums, theaters, and concert halls are within easy reach. Philadelphia offers an unparalleled collection of landmark buildings and examples of urban planning that span 325 years. This rich tradition makes the city an ideal laboratory for the study of architecture.

SCHOOL PHILOSOPHY

Graduates should master the basic knowledge and skills of professional practice, as well as developing an awareness of the values and aspirations of contemporary society. Drexel's work/study opportunity offers a continuous dialogue between school and work; between theory and practice. Placing students in this dual position reinforces the notion that the practice of architecture is a continuous learning process and that self-education continues after graduation. The goals of this program are appropriately transmitted by a carefully formed faculty of practitioners who are committed to Drexel's educational mission and are enthusiastic about Architecture's challenges.

PROGRAM DESCRIPTION

There are two paths to the Bachelor of Architecture degree at Drexel.

The Part-Time Evening Program: This course of study usually takes 7 years to complete, but transfer students with advanced studio placement will pursue shorter programs. The curriculum includes: (1) the studio design sequence (87 quarter credits); (2) required and elective architectural coursework (65 quarter credits); (3) general education requirements (69 quarter credits). Although the program permits considerable flexibility and choice in the selection and scheduling of coursework, the studio sequence regulates the student's progress. Studios offer problems of increasing formal, social, and technical complexity culminating in Studio 5 which emphasizes the integration of building systems into the design process. This studio is surrounded by two specialized years which significantly broaden the scope of architectural concern. Studio 4 stresses issues of environmental planning and sustainable design while Studio 6 focuses on issues of urban design and planning in an urban context. Year-long independent thesis projects complete the studio sequence. All evening classes meet once a week in 3-hour sessions. Most students take two or three courses per quarter. Students are expected to supplement their academic work through full-time employment in architectural offices.

The Two + Four Option: This is an accelerated route for a small class of recent high school graduates into the part-time, evening B Arch program. Two years of full-time study address the basic principles of architectural design, fundamental university core requirements in the arts and sciences, as well as professional skills and knowledge needed for entry level professional positions. Full-time students are provided with dedicated studio facilities. In the third year, students begin full-time employment, with placement assistance from the Department, and continue their studies in the part-time evening program. This unique option provides Drexel students a head start to their professional careers.

SPECIAL ACTIVITIES AND PROGRAMS

Study tours visit Rome and Paris every summer. These travel programs are supported by a variety of travel grants. The Arfaa Lecture Series in Architecture brings distinguished practitioners and theorists to campus. Annual exhibits of student and alumni work are presented in the Leonard Pearlstein Gallery. AIAS Drexel is an active student chapter which sponsors a mentoring program and an annual career day plus a variety of social activities. It publishes a quarterly newsletter. The Michael Pearson Prize awards recognize outstanding Thesis projects with travel stipends. Every summer the program sponsors Discovering Architecture, a two week career discovery program for high school students.

FACILITIES

Dedicated studio facilities are provided for both program options, each tailored to their particular needs. A fully equipped studio with 24 hour access is located in the Department's facility at 3201 Arch Street for students in the full-time Two + Four Option. A generous space, located in the University's historic Main Building, is dedicated to the part-time evening program. Originally the University's gymnasium, this large space is sub-divided into teaching alcoves fully equipped to support the evening program's teaching methods. In Nesbitt Hall the Leonard Pearlstein Gallery is available to the Architecture Program for annual exhibitions of student and faculty work, as well as traveling exhibitions.

SCHOLARSHIPS AND FINANCIAL AID

For full-time students, scholarships, grants, loans and work-study opportunities are available based on financial need, and the A.J. Drexel Program awards scholarships on the basis of academic merit. Eighty percent of Drexel full-time undergraduates receive some form of financial aid. Drexel's work-study opportunity plays an important role in helping students finance their education. Part-time students obtain full-time employment with area architectural firms and are generally able to cover tuition and fees from current earnings. Moreover, certain architectural employers in the Philadelphia area offer tuition remission to their employees. Students in the Two + Four Option share these advantages in their final four years of study.

ADMINISTRATION

Paul M. Hirshorn, AIA: Head, Dept. of
    Architecture & Interiors
Ulrike Altenmüller, Dr.-Ing. Architectin:
    Associate Program Director

DRURY UNIVERSITY

ADDRESS

Main
Drury University
Hammons School of Architecture
900 North Benton Avenue
Springfield, MO 65802
Tel.: 417.873.7288
Fax: 417.873.7446
arch@drury.edu
www.drury.edu

STUDENT AND FACULTY DEMOGRAPHICS

% of Female Students	32
% of International Students	3
% of Minority Students	9
% of Out-of-State U.S. Students	12
No. Full-Time Faculty	13
No. Part-Time Faculty	4
No. Full-Time Students	202
No. Part-Time Students	

FINANCIAL INFORMATION

Main Source of University Funding	Private
Annual Tuition & Fees (graduate)	
Annual Tuition & Fees (undergraduate)	$18,285
% Students Receiving Federal Financial Aid	82.5
% Students Receiving University Financial Aid	84
% Students Receiving Departmental Financial Aid	3
% Students Receiving Scholarships (assistantships or fellowships)	0
Average Annual Scholarship for Department	$4,850

ACADEMIC SESSIONS

Fall Semester: August to November; Application Deadline: early August
Spring Semester: January to May; Application Deadline: early January
Summer Session I: June to June; Application Deadline: early June

Summer Session II: July to August; Application Deadline: early July
Summer Session III: June to August; Application Deadline: early June

ARCHITECTURE AND RELATED DEGREE PROGRAMS

Degree	Min. Yrs. to Complete	Professional Accreditation	# of FT Students	# of PT Students	# of First-Year Students	# of Degrees Conferred	Admissions Requirements
Architecture							
B. Arch	5	NAAB	225	0	80	25	

SPECIALIZATIONS

Architectural Design
Art and Design

Building Information Modeling
Community Design

Environment/Sustainability

Theory/Criticism

ARCHITECTURE PROGRAM SUMMARY

The Hammons School of Architecture offers a five-year professional bachelor of architecture degree. The required architecture courses are integrated with the Drury University Global Perspectives 21 liberal arts curriculum. The objective of this integrated curriculum approach is preparation for professional architectural practice within the broadest possible educational context.

UNIVERSITY SETTING

Drury University, a small private institution centrally located in the Ozarks region of Missouri, has an enrollment of 1,500 day students and 2,900 evening students. Founded in 1873 as an undergraduate liberal arts college, Drury has remained true to that mission, while developing several high-quality graduate and professional programs which are distinctive because of their liberal arts orientation (MBA, MA, M. Ed and B. Arch).

SCHOOL PHILOSOPHY

Drury is an independent university, grounded in the liberal arts tradition and committed to personalized education in a community of scholars who value the arts of teaching and (life-long) learning. Education at Drury seeks to cultivate spiritual sensibilities and imaginative faculties, as well as ethical insight and critical thought; to foster the integration of theoretical and practical knowledge; and, to liberate persons to participate responsibly in and contribute to life in a global community. The small liberal arts college context provides a positive framework for the development of a professional architecture program which seeks to prepare graduates who can fully participate as citizens and as professionals in the global community of the future.

PROGRAM DESCRIPTION

Undergraduate Program

The Bachelor of Architecture degree is a 2+3 program of study. The first two years constitute the pre-professional portion of the program and focus on the ideational aspects of architecture. Admission to the pre-professional portion of the program is open to all Drury University students. The last three years of the curriculum are considered the professional portion of the program and focus specifically on the quantitative aspects of architecture. Students apply for admission to the professional program at the end of the fall semester of their sophomore year. This application requires a written goal statement, transcript, and portfolio of work. The five-year program requires 169 credit hours of instruction, a foreign study course, and a 12-week summer work experience. Included are 59–61 credit hours of general education courses, which is required of all Drury students, and 15–18 credit hours of free electives which may be used to develop a minor in any of the 26 programs of study at Drury University. The school is committed to the concept of personalized instruction. Toward this end, the school works to maintain a low 14:1 student/teacher ratio, individual academic advisors, personalized assessment of professional development, and alternate career guidance.

AREAS OF FOCUS AND RESEARCH

Focus

Each student in his/her fourth year must participate in a community studio. The community-based projects are sponsored and funded by local governmental and nonprofit agencies across the region. Drury University has a coordinated honors program, and architecture students admitted participate in community service, advanced learning/research efforts and individually motivated projects tied to the architectural curriculum.

Research

Research, scholarship, and creative activity efforts are explored in the support of teaching. Faculty pursue research in areas of history and theory, technology, and sustainable design.

SPECIAL ACTIVITIES AND PROGRAMS

- Architecture Awareness day, held each year in October, provides regional high school students an opportunity to spend the day on campus and to socialize and attend class with Drury architecture students.
- Transfer students who desire to study architecture may enroll in a summer start program potentially reducing their course study by two semesters.
- Drury has an active lecture/exhibit program in art and architecture. Distinguished national and international speakers make presentations to the campus.
- Each student, after completion of their third year, must participate in a foreign study program.

Students may choose between a semester-long program in Volos, Greece or five-week programs, conducted during the summer. The five-week programs have in recent years, been centered around Florence, Italy; Paris, France; Barcelona, Spain; Tokyo, Japan; and Beijing, China.
- Drury offers the joint B.Arch/MBA degree program. With the completion of a required core of undergraduate courses taken during the five year B.Arch program, the MBA can be completed in an additional year and summer.
- When the opportunity presents itself, architecture students participate in design - build activities. Projects completed over the past four years have been a farmers' market pavilion and a Habitat for Humanity House that received a LEED Platinum certification.

FACILITIES

The 42,000 sq. ft. facility, which opened in the fall of 1990, provides quality space for 200 students and fourteen faculty. In addition to the open, well-lighted studio areas, the building includes three seminar/critique rooms, a large exhibition/multipurpose room, a student lounge, a woodworking shop, a model building shop, a photography lab, a technology lab, and a computer lab with a networked system throughout the building. The architecture slide collection numbers over 55,000 slides.

SCHOLARSHIPS AND FINANCIAL AID

Eighty percent of Drury students receive scholarship and/or financial aid from a broad range of sources. The university participates in all of the available federal and state programs designed to assist students to attend college. Scholarships based on merit are available at Drury ranging from $500 for the academic year to full tuition. Students should apply early in the senior year of high school for full consideration for financial aid.

ADMINISTRATION

Michael J. Buono, AIA: Director, School of Architecture
Bruce E. Moore, AIA: Associate Director, School of Architecture
Jay Garrott, AIA: Director, Center for Community Studies
Jacqueline Tygart: Librarian

FLORIDA AGRICULTURAL AND MECHANICAL UNIVERSITY

ADDRESS

Main
Florida Agricultural and Mechanical
University
School of Architecture
1938 S. Martin Luther King Jr. Blvd.
Tallahassee, FL 32307-4200
Tel: 850.599.3244
Fax: 850.599.3436
arch@famu.edu
www.famusoa.net

STUDENT AND FACULTY DEMOGRAPHICS

% of Female Students	28
% of International Students	3
% of Minority Students	64
% of Out-of-State U.S. Students	
No. Full-Time Faculty	25
No. Part-Time Faculty	5
No. Full-Time Students	239
No. Part-Time Students	60

FINANCIAL INFORMATION

Main Source of University Funding	Public
Annual Tuition & Fees (graduate, resident)	$6,390
Annual Tuition & Fees (graduate, nonresident)	$25,020
Annual Tuition & Fees (undergraduate, resident)	$3,150
Annual Tuition & Fees (undergraduate, nonresident)	$15,090
% Students Receiving Federal Financial Aid	
% Students Receiving University Financial Aid	
% Students Receiving Departmental Financial Aid	
% Students Receiving Scholarships (assistantships or fellowships)	
Average Annual Scholarship for Department	

ACADEMIC SESSIONS

Fall Semester: August to December; Application Deadline: May
Spring Semester: January to April; Application Deadline: November
Summer Session I: May to June

Summer Session II: July to August
Summer Session III: May to August

ARCHITECTURE AND RELATED DEGREE PROGRAMS

Degree	Min. Yrs. to Complete	Professional Accreditation	# of FT Students	# of PT Students	# of First-Year Students	# of Degrees Conferred	Admissions Requirements
Architecture							
B. Arch	5	NAAB	14	13	14	18	Undergraduate Architecture degree, Portfolio, Rec. Letters, Essay
Bachelor of Science in Architecture Studies	4		189	46	60	40	SAT, ACT
M. Arch	2	NAAB	36	1	17	5	Undergraduate degree, Undergraduate Architecture degree, GRE, Portfolio, Rec. Letters, Essay
Master of Science in Architecture	1			0	0	0	Undergraduate Architecture degree, GRE, Rec. Letters, Essay
Landscape Architecture							
Master of Landscape Architecture	2	LAAB	8	2	4	2	Undergraduate degree, GRE, Portfolio, Rec. Letters, Essay

UNIVERSITY SETTING

Founded in 1887, Florida A&M University (FAMU) is a comprehensive, co-educational, residential, multi-level, land-grant university offering a broad range of instruction, research, and service programs at the undergraduate, professional, and graduate levels. Twelve accredited colleges and schools offer students wide choices in nearly every academic endeavor, as well as extracurricular life through sports, music, theater, and student organizations. FAMU, Florida's only publicly funded Historically Black College & University (HBCU), is located in Tallahassee, the capital city of Florida, and is only 20 miles north of the Gulf of Mexico. Tallahassee provides a variety of resources unique to state government. Florida State University and Tallahassee Community College provide additional opportunities in the form of elective courses, library materials, and extracurricular activities.

SCHOOL PHILOSOPHY

From its inception in 1975, the School of Architecture (SOA) has maintained a strong commitment to provide a thorough, high-quality, professional architectural education suitable as preparation for the practice of architecture in all its forms and learning opportunities appropriate to the interests of a culturally diverse student body with a wide range of career objectives. Upon graduation, students are expected to have well developed professional skills, as well as a philosophy regarding architecture and architectural design that forms the basis for life-long growth as an architect. The graduate programs emphasize preparation for expanding the field of action for architecture while setting the graduate's sights on eventual leadership opportunities.

PROGRAM DESCRIPTION

The School offers professional and non-professional programs at the undergraduate and graduate levels. The four-year undergraduate program is a non-professional Bachelor of Science in Architectural Studies. It is a limited-access program that consists of two years in the pre-architecture program and two years in the upper division. Applicants to the School of Architecture are evaluated individually for admission and placement in the program. Only those applicants who have received an Associate of Arts degree from an approved "prearchitecture" program will be considered for direct admission into the junior year at FAMU. Other community college transfer students are required to complete pre-professional courses. This non-professional undergraduate curriculum provides course sequences in architectural design, history, structures, environmental technology, construction, theory and professional practice.

Students with a four-year architecture degree may consider our professional Bachelor of Architecture (B. Arch), Master of Architecture (M.Arch), or Master of Landscape Architecture (M.L.A.) degree programs. The B.Arch degree may be completed in one year as a full time student in residence, or in two years as a part time student in the evening/ weekend program. The M.Arch degree requires 2 or 3.5 years of study, depending on a student's previous degree. The M.Arch Thesis/ Research Project is a vehicle for students to develop their own personal area of interest (i.e. technology, preservation, education, theory, urban design, etc). The M.L.A. degree requires 2 or 3 years of study, depending on a student's previous degree. A research thesis is required for completion of the degree.

AREAS OF FOCUS AND RESEARCH

The Institute for Building Sciences (IBS) coordinates all research, service, and continuing education activities conducted at the School. IBS endeavors to foster excellence in faculty and student work that increases knowledge; enhances the building environment; and serves the profession, the local community, the state of Florida, and the nation. IBS projects are not only of academic interest, but also have many valuable practical applications. Projects have included laboratory-based experimentation; technology-transfer and field-verification studies; analysis and development of building codes; compliance surveys related to the Americans with Disabilities Act; and promotion of sustainable development and the design and delivery of high-performance buildings.

SPECIAL ACTIVITIES AND PROGRAMS

The School's Lecture Series exposes students to a broad range of views on current architectural thought and practice. The Exhibition Gallery sponsors traveling national and international exhibits as well as student and faculty work. Travel experiences are regular events. First- and second-year students take local and regional field trips; upper-level students have the opportunity to travel nationally and abroad. The State's study centers in Florence and London provide structured educational experiences in settings unparalleled in architectural and cultural significance. Recently, the SOA has been coordinating its own study trips to Barcelona. To expose students to a wide variety of perspectives, the School invites a number of guest critics and visiting faculty to work in studio and offer special electives. Local practitioners are invited on a regular basis to serve in reviews and juries.

FACILITIES

The School has undergone a $12 million expansion and renovation to the facility. Studios provide students with his/her own workspace with 24-hour access, computer connectivity, and a support area for model construction. A fully-equipped construction lab provides separate areas for wood, metal, plastic, painting, and welding. The computer labs offer contemporary computer resources and the entire facility is wireless networked to provide intra-communication and on-line resources. Additional lab support areas are available for the structures, materials and methods, and environmental technology courses.

SCHOLARSHIPS AND FINANCIAL AID

The university offers aid to students in the form of scholarships, grants, loans, and part-time employment. Information on national, state, and local scholarships that are available to architecture students is kept on reserve in the Architecture Library. Assistance in applying is available through the Office of the Dean. Graduate students may receive assistance from the School through research assistantships and also through the University's Graduate Studies Office. In-State Tuition Waivers are available to some applicants through two sources (1) SREB Academic Common Market and (2) the Latin American/Caribbean Student Award Program.

ADMINISTRATION

Rodner B. Wright, AIA: Dean
Andrew D. Chin: Assistant Dean
Thomas D. Pugh: Director, Institute for Building Sciences
Richard C. Rome, ASLA: Director, MLA Program

FLORIDA ATLANTIC UNIVERSITY

ADDRESS

Main
Florida Atlantic University
School of Architecture
111 East Las Olas Boulevard
Fort Lauderdale, FL 33301
Tel.: 954.762.5654
Fax: 954.762.5367
www.fau.edu/arch

STUDENT AND FACULTY DEMOGRAPHICS

% of Female Students	32
% of International Students	4
% of Minority Students	50
% of Out-of-State U.S. Students	9
No. Full-Time Faculty	10
No. Part-Time Faculty	21
No. Full-Time Students	232
No. Part-Time Students	174

FINANCIAL INFORMATION

Main Source of University Funding	Public
Annual Tuition & Fees (graduate, resident)	$8,140
Annual Tuition & Fees (graduate, nonresident)	$29,087
Annual Tuition & Fees (undergraduate, resident)	$3,689
Annual Tuition & Fees (undergraduate, nonresident)	$17,417
% Students Receiving Federal Financial Aid	33
% Students Receiving University Financial Aid	18
% Students Receiving Departmental Financial Aid	5
% Students Receiving Scholarships (assistantships or fellowships)	39
Average Annual Scholarship for Department	$3,875

ACADEMIC SESSIONS

Fall Semester: August to December
Spring Semester: January to May
Summer Session I: May to June
Summer Session II: June to August
Summer Session III: May to August

Application Deadlines: check www.fau.edu/arch/admissions

ARCHITECTURE AND RELATED DEGREE PROGRAMS

Degree	Min. Yrs. to Complete	Professional Accreditation	# of FT Students	# of PT Students	# of First-Year Students	# of Degrees Conferred	Admissions Requirements
Architecture							
B. Arch	5	NAAB	232	174	32	75	
MS Arch	1.5						GRE, Portfolio, Rec. Letters, Essay

SPECIALIZATIONS

Architectural Design
Community Design

Environment/Sustainability

International/Regional Architecture

Urban Planning and Design

ARCHITECTURE PROGRAM SUMMARY

Situated in an urban, downtown campus in Fort Lauderdale, the Florida Atlantic University School of Architecture is immersed in the diverse international community of South Florida. The School resides in the College of Architecture, Urban and Public Affairs and is complemented by faculties in urban and regional planning, public administration, social work, and criminal justice. In this context human culture, social responsibility, ecological sustainability, and the subtropical built environment inform the study of architectural design. The School has more than doubled in size since its inception in 1996 yet remains small enough for each member of the faculty and student body to engage significantly in the program and contribute to the continuing evolution of a meaningful design culture.

UNIVERSITY SETTING

Florida Atlantic University is a large and diverse institution with more than 26,000 students on six different campuses along Florida's eastern coast. The School of Architecture is based in downtown Fort Lauderdale, the geographic center of one of the largest metropolitan areas in the United States, including Miami-Dade, Broward, and Palm Beach counties with over six million inhabitants. The city and region span a complex range of modern urban, suburban and natural environments from the Everglades conservation area to the west and the Atlantic Ocean to the east.

SCHOOL PHILOSOPHY

The School of Architecture is an environment where designers and thinkers from a broad range of backgrounds and perspectives converge to share their interest and knowledge about the human, natural, and built environment and the continuing evolution of the discipline of architecture. Design thinking is a powerful means toward innovation and change. The School of Architecture is fortunate to include a diverse faculty representing a wide range of interests and perspectives as well as a highly diverse student body, and considers the unique makeup of its human capital to be a valuable resource. The curriculum of the School provides a broad range of courses that include theory, history, materials, construction methods, professional practice, structural design, environmental systems and the important skills of design research and graphic presentation we rely on to initiate, develop and effectively communicate design solutions. The curriculum is focused on preparing students for developing design solutions that are informed by the past, active in the present, and aimed for the future.

Each year new design opportunities and problems initiated by the communities of South Florida become subjects for the school's studio and research projects. These activities involve learning by doing, together with faculty and the community. Student work is presented at community meetings and workshops, exhibited in community centers, and juried in public. These experiences provide students with the opportunity to develop a variety of skills, including how to formulate a question, how to listen thoughtfully, and how to synthesize information from a range of issues including complex community desires, varying municipal codes and policies, and the dynamic economy that continues to sculpt an evolving metropolis to arrive at an inspired or innovative design.

PROGRAM DESCRIPTION

The School offers a professional Bachelor of Architecture and a post-professional Master of Science in Architecture. The Bachelor of Architecture is a five-year professional degree for students pursuing professional licensure and practice. The three-semester Master of Science degree is intended for students who have already completed a professional degree and seek advanced study toward a research/practice concentration.

Lower Division — The first two years toward the B.Arch. degree may be completed on the University's main campus in Boca Raton, dual enrolled at the University and a regional community college, or in a lower-division program at another institution. The School's lower division program in Boca Raton is limited to thirty students in each of the first two years. The upper division (the third, fourth, and fifth years) accommodates additional students transferring from other institutions. The number of students in the upper division transferring from other schools contributes to the diversity in background and experience of the student body in the professional sequence.

Undergraduate Admissions — Students may apply for admission to the School either as freshmen or as transfer students in the upper division. Detailed information about the admission requirements is available on the University and School websites.

B.Arch. — The core of the degree program is the architectural design studio. The Bachelor of Architecture sequence requires students to engage progressively complex building typologies and programs through eight semesters followed by the fifth "thesis" year, which includes an urban design studio and a comprehensive final building design project in the last semester. Issues of order and composition, technology and environment, materials and structure, spatial expression and functionality, culture and context, anthropometrics and scale, analysis and synthesis inform the design inquiry throughout this sequence.

M.S. Arch. — The Master of Science program is a three-semester sequence permitting advanced students to pursue a design research specialization. This program begins with an overview of design theories and courses in advanced design research methods. After the first semester students develop a research plan that serves as a framework for studio-based design exploration in the following two semesters. Studio work must be architectural in nature, but does permit the study of building systems or theories as well as the development of more traditional building designs. The program encourages graduate students to find a crossover focus area from the within the College.

AREAS OF FOCUS AND RESEARCH

The faculty of the School conducts research in the areas of architectural history, design theory, design methods, graphic communication and delineation, urban design, environmental systems and building technology. Ongoing projects include studies of color theory and its relationship to architecture, both historically and in contemporary design practice; the relationship between ethics and conscious design action; analysis and optimization methods for sustainable design and building; digital design tools as methods for 4d visualization, biomimicry and fabrication; community design and design advocacy for underserved communities; design pedagogy; and sustainable design for sub-tropical cities and buildings.

The metropolitan Fort Lauderdale, South Florida, and Florida-Caribbean regions are subtropical, dynamic environments in which to study design. The culturally diverse local and regional context provides a complex history and setting for the study and practice of design. Design for the subtropics demands very particular considerations with regard to weather and climate conditions, a limited palette of regionally derived building materials, and fragile freshwater and saltwater ecosystems. The work of the School has proven to be of interest to colleagues and scholars throughout the subtropics of both hemispheres.

The College of Architecture, Urban and Public Affairs houses several centers that provide additional opportunity for study, research and community service activities including the *Broward Community Design Collaborative* (BCDC) and the *Center for the Conservation of Architectural and Cultural Heritage* (CCACH).

SPECIAL ACTIVITIES AND PROGRAMS

Travel Opportunities — Each year faculty conduct study tours and studios in several different locations. In the past these have included travel study to the Bahamas, England, Germany, Puerto Rico, Mexico, Spain, as well as Chicago and New York City.

Study in Germany — The Architecture School maintains an exciting student-exchange relationship with Anhalt University of Applied Science in Dessau, Germany—a neighbor and affiliate of the Bauhaus—providing an opportunity for FAU School of Architecture students and graduates to live and study in Germany. Undergraduate students may participate in the summer studio program and graduates can pursue a Master of Architecture degree through the Master class of the Dessau Institute of Architecture (DIA). Both programs are taught in English although students are encouraged to study German while enrolled.

Combined B.Arch./M.U.R.P. — Students in the Bachelor of Architecture program may elect, in their fourth year to pursue a combined Bachelor of Architecture and Master of Urban and Regional Planning degree. Through this program selected students may earn both degrees in six years. The allied field of planning is a valuable complement to a design education providing students with a strong background in city planning issues and policies.

FACILITIES

The School of Architecture is based in the Higher Education Complex and Askew Tower of FAU's downtown Fort Lauderdale campus. These facilities include design studios, offices, a university gallery, two large exhibit spaces, a well-equipped woodshop, and shared printing/plotting resources. The School recently acquired digital fabrication tools for student use: a CNC router table is now available to complement model building and design work. All of the studios have both wired and wireless access to networked printers and plotters. While most students use their own computers there are also several School computers available in each studio area. Both the Macintosh and Windows operating systems are supported on campus. Students may use either platform for coursework.

This is an urban commuter campus and does not include housing. Students in the first two years of the program are based on the University's main campus in Boca Raton, where several dormitories are available for students. After their sophomore year, in the upper division, students are based in Fort Lauderdale. Students who do not already have living arrangements typically find apartments for rent in the many surrounding residential neighborhoods.

SCHOLARSHIPS AND FINANCIAL AID

Both merit-based and need-based financial assistance is available.

ADMINISTRATION

Rosalyn Carter: Dean
Aron Temkin: Director

FLORIDA INTERNATIONAL UNIVERSITY

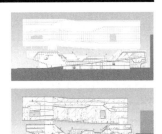

ADDRESS

Main
Florida International University
School of Architecture
PCA 272
Miami, FL 33199
Tel.: 305.348.3181
Fax: 305.348.2650
Arch@fiu.edu
www.fiu.edu/~soa

STUDENT AND FACULTY DEMOGRAPHICS

% of Female Students	53
% of International Students	15
% of Minority Students	64
% of Out-of-State U.S. Students	10
No. Full-Time Faculty	14
No. Part-Time Faculty	22
No. Full-Time Students	280
No. Part-Time Students	114

FINANCIAL INFORMATION

Main Source of University Funding	Public
Annual Tuition & Fees (graduate, resident)	$8,160
Annual Tuition & Fees (graduate, nonresident)	$23,100
Annual Tuition & Fees (undergraduate, resident)	$2,900
Annual Tuition & Fees (undergraduate, nonresident)	$16,085
% Students Receiving Federal Financial Aid	
% Students Receiving University Financial Aid	
% Students Receiving Departmental Financial Aid	
% Students Receiving Scholarships (assistantships or fellowships)	
Average Annual Scholarship for Department	

ACADEMIC SESSIONS

Fall Semester: August to December; Application Deadline: February 1
Spring Semester: January to April; Application Deadline: NA

Summer Session I: May to August; Application Deadline: NA

ARCHITECTURE AND RELATED DEGREE PROGRAMS

Degree	Min. Yrs. to Complete	Professional Accreditation	# of FT Students	# of PT Students	# of First-Year Students	# of Degrees Conferred	Admissions Requirements
Architecture							
BA in Architecture	4	NAAB	205	105	60	60	SAT, ACT, TOEFL, Portfolio
M. Arch—2 year track	2	NAAB	74	9	45	30	Undergraduate Architecture degree, GRE, TOEFL, Portfolio
M.Arch—3 year track	3	NAAB	45	6	15	10	Undergraduate degree, GRE, Portfolio
MA in Architecture	1						Prof. Architecture degree, GRE, TOEFL
Landscape Architecture							
Bachelor of Landscape Architecture	4	LAAB	30	0	15		SAT, ACT, TOEFL, Portfolio
Master of Landscape Architecture	2	LAAB	9	11	4	0	
Interior Design/Interior Architecture							
Bachelor of Interior Design	4	CIDA/FIDER	60		15	20	SAT, ACT, TOEFL, Portfolio
Master of Interior Design	2	CIDA/FIDER					Undergraduate degree, GRE, TOEFL, Portfolio

SPECIALIZATIONS

Architectural Design	Environment/Sustainability	Landscape Design	Tectonics
Art and Design	Interior Design/Architecture	Professional Practice	Theory/Criticism
Computer-Aided Design	International/Regional Architecture	Sustainability	

ARCHITECTURE PROGRAM SUMMARY

Architecture involves the study and transformation of the built environment, from the scale of furniture to the scale of the city. The goal of the educational experience is to educate knowledgeable and creative designers who will be informed citizens and innovative professionals. The program is committed to nurturing and promoting critical thinking and the creative design process by encouraging students to form independent, imaginative and creative decisions grounded in the broader contexts of intellectual knowledge and inquiry. The course of study provides students with the intellectual knowledge and technical skills that will enable them to respond creatively, effectively and responsibly to the challenges confronting urban society. The program maintains a commitment to excellence in teaching, creative activity, research and scholarship and seeks to attract a diverse student body with a variety of academic backgrounds, experiences and interests. Our student body and our faculty reflect the diverse areas of knowledge which play a critical role in the making of the built environment and in the establishment of successful design practices.

Trans-disciplinarity: The extensive range of coordinated disciplines within the School of Architecture (architecture, interior design and landscape architecture) provides an opportunity for the student to work with colleagues and faculty in a wide array of educational, scholarly, and professional initiatives. Students at the School of Architecture benefit from the cross-fertilization via multidisciplinary studio classes, open electives, lectures, as well as the sharing of faculty and resources between the disciplines. Sub-specialties and certificate programs include; design, technology, history/theory, digital technologies and urban design, and provide opportunities for the student to work with colleagues and faculty in a wide array of educational, scholarly, and professional initiatives that cut across boundaries.

UNIVERSITY SETTING
FIU boasts a faculty of over 1,100 who are renowned for outstanding teaching and research, and over 38,000 students from the U.S. and 130 foreign countries. Miami itself is an outdoor laboratory of modern architecture. Rapidly changing, well-known for innovative architectural design, Miami is also a resource for exploring issues of community design, urban design, and historic preservation.

SCHOOL PHILOSOPHY
As part of FIU, a "top public research university," the Architecture Department is dedicated to educating future generations of ethical professionals, creative designers and informed citizens. We believe architecture to be a conceptually based intellectual endeavor and a form of critical inquiry that addresses the physical environment from the scale of the city to the scale of furniture. The Architecture Department is committed to producing conceptual thinkers and skilled makers who are versed in the techniques, history and theory of the discipline and who are grounded in the broad intellectual and societal values that engender the production and reception of architecture. To realize these objectives, design is taught as a critical and creative endeavor that embraces both the humanities and the sciences. Our mission embraces:

Diversity
To serve a diverse student body with a variety of academic backgrounds, experiences and interests by creating an open atmosphere of inquiry and exchange that engages the varied cultural and academic experiences of faculty and students.

Design as Critical Thinking
To present architecture as a reflective and conceptually based problem-solving discipline. We encourage students to form thoughtful and imaginative solutions to the challenges confronting urban society here and abroad and to cultivate intellectual curiosity and life-long learning.

Knowledge & Skill-Based Learning
To explore the diverse areas of knowledge and the technical skills that play a critical role in thoughtful formation of the constructed environment and which are essential for successful design practices.

A Commitment to Innovation
To celebrate the power of innovation and experimentation and our discipline's commitment to imagine and construct beautiful, healthful and responsible environments.

An Appreciation for Constructed and Natural Environments
To foster sensitivity and appreciation for the constructed and natural environments of South Florida. The Architecture Department values the unique opportunities and challenges for creative exploration and problem solving afforded by South Florida's rich sub-tropical ecologies, urban contexts, multicultural and multilingual populace.

A Culture of Connectivity
To promote connections between the Architecture Department and members of the design community in local, national and international, academic, professional and lay contexts. In particular, we seek to engage our colleagues in the College and the School, local practitioners in design education and to develop cooperative links with schools of design in North America, Latin America and Europe.

An Ethos of Trans-Disciplinarity
To engage adjacent disciplines within the School of Architecture to create an atmosphere of trans-disciplinary cooperation that can collaboratively address the complex spatial, social and environmental challenges of contemporary practice.

PROGRAM DESCRIPTION
The **undergraduate program** is committed to providing an exceptional design education to qualified students wishing to pursue an undergraduate course of study in architecture. The four-year **Bachelor of Arts in Architecture** is a pre-professional undergraduate degree program offering a gradually intensifying focus on the study of architecture combined with an expansive, humanistic, liberal arts education. The program encourages the generation and communication of design ideas which are supported by historical, theoretical, technological and practical knowledge. The undergraduate program prepares students for continued education in a professional graduate degree program; and for careers in the design disciplines.

The **graduate program** offers both the accredited professional **Master of Architecture** degree and the post-professional **Master of Arts in Architecture** degree. The program is characterized by intensive and focused study in architecture which is supported by a broad interdisciplinary framework that includes landscape architecture and interior design.

The **Master of Architecture** degree is accredited by the National Architecture Accrediting Board (NAAB). With a dedication to excellence in design and studio-based work as the foundation to the program, the intensive course of study is organized into five thematic areas: design, history/theory, building technology, digital technology, and professional practice. The course of study is comprehensive and rigorous, preparing graduates to be creative leaders, and skilled innovators in all aspects of the profession. The Master of Architecture degree has two tracks.

3-Year Track: Is a professional degree program for students with no background in architecture and who possess a four-year undergraduate Bachelor's degree in any area. The track consists of 106 credit hours and is usually completed in three and one half years. The course of study consists of six semesters of design studio course work followed by a semester-long master's project. Supporting courses in history/ theory, building technology, digital technology, professional practice as well as cross-disciplinary electives complete the course of study. Students are eligible to spend their sixth semester studying in Genoa, Italy.

2-Year Track: Is a professional degree program for students who possess a four-year undergraduate degree in architecture. Students will continue their architectural education by following a course of 60 credit hours that is usually completed in two years. The course of study consists of four semesters of design studio course work followed by a semester-long master's project. Supporting courses in history/theory, building technology, digital technology, professional practice as well as cross-disciplinary electives complete the course of study. Students are eligible to spend their sixth semester studying in Genoa, Italy.

SPECIAL ACTIVITIES AND PROGRAMS
Miami—An Urban Laboratory for Design Education:
The School of Architecture at FIU is located in a unique place and time in the culture of America. The city of Miami is a rich and diverse laboratory for the study of architecture, interior design and the landscape. The great diversity of the greater Miami area provides limitless possibilities for exploring historic architecture, unique and cutting edge new work created by many of the world's leading designers. At the same time, the challenges of rapid growth and development in Miami and the region have created an ideal crucible for research and study within the School. In addition, Miami continues to be one of America's principal academic and business gateways to Latin America and to Europe. As such, the School of Architecture enjoys relationships to institutions, faculty, design firms and designers in the Caribbean basin, Latin America and Europe.

Study Abroad: The Architecture Program is committed to study abroad opportunities. Architecture students may opt to spend a semester at the School of Architecture's facility in Genoa, Italy. The Genoa program consists of a full semester taught by FIU faculty in conjunction with Italian visiting faculty from the University of Genoa school of Architecture. The Genoa center is located in the newly renovated Convento S. Maria di Castello which dates from the renaissance and is conveniently located within the historic center of this remarkable city. The program maintains a strong affiliation with the Facolta di Architettura at the University of Genova.

Advising: The architecture program maintains an individualized advising program. Throughout your time at FIU, faculty advisors and our advising staff will help you select courses, evaluate graduate programs, and contemplate future career paths. You will find faculty advisors accessible, sensitive to your individual needs, and knowledgeable about options. School of Architecture undergraduates go on to pursue graduate work and professional degrees at the best universities in the country. Many also choose to remain at the School of Architecture and continue in our graduate degree programs.

FACILITIES
The new, $15.5 million, 93,850 square-foot Paul L. Cejas Architecture Building, designed by Bernard Tschumi provides a range of specialized facilities, including a large lecture/film hall, outdoor lecture hall, an architecture gallery, computer facilities, digital lab, wood/model building shop, digital fabrication lab, CNC milling and 3D printing lab, architecture reading room, student function room, studios with designated workspace for each student, jury rooms, classrooms, demonstration lab, and faculty/administrative offices. Formal and informal gathering spaces have been designed to create a lively studio culture that entices the university and professional communities to interact with colleagues in the design disciplines. The SOA Genoa Italy Center is located in the newly renovated Convento S. Maria di Castello which dates from the renaissance and is conveniently located within the historic center of this remarkable city. The program maintains a strong affiliation with the Facolta di Architettura at the University of Genova.

SCHOLARSHIPS AND FINANCIAL AID
FIU boasts among the lowest tuition rates in the United States. Notwithstanding, the School offers financial assistance, including: Graduate teaching assistantships and outright scholarships; research assistantships for graduate students; an internship program for undergraduate and graduate students, with pay, at significant local architecture firms; undergraduate and graduate work/study positions; and the Latin American and Caribbean Scholarship Program, enabling qualified foreign students to pay in-state tuition fees. These students are also eligible for assistantships and stipends.

ADMINISTRATION
Juan A. Bueno: Dean
Nathaniel Quincy Belcher, AIA: Director
Adam Drisin, AIA: Chair

FRANK LLOYD WRIGHT SCHOOL OF ARCHITECTURE

ADDRESS

Main
Frank Lloyd Wright
School of Architecture
P.O. Box 4430
Scottsdale, AZ 85261
Tel.: 480.860.2700
Fax: 480.391.4014
info@taliesin.edu
www.taliesin.edu

STUDENT AND FACULTY DEMOGRAPHICS

% of Female Students	50
% of International Students	25
% of Out-of-State U.S. Students	75
No. Full-Time Faculty	5
No. Part-Time Faculty	15
No. Full-Time Students	30
No. Part-Time Students	0

FINANCIAL INFORMATION

Main Source of University Funding	Private
Annual Tuition & Fees (graduate)	$30,000
Annual Tuition & Fees (undergraduate)	$30,000
% Students Receiving Federal Financial Aid	0
% Students Receiving University Financial Aid	34
% Students Receiving Departmental Financial Aid	0
% Students Receiving Scholarships (assistantships or fellowships)	35
Average Annual Scholarship for Department	$4,000

ACADEMIC SESSIONS

Fall Term: October to December; Application Deadline: July 1
Spring Term: January to May; Application Deadline: November 1

Summer Term: May to September

ARCHITECTURE AND RELATED DEGREE PROGRAMS

Degree	Min. Yrs. to Complete	Professional Accreditation	# of FT Students	# of PT Students	# of First-Year Students	# of Degrees Conferred	Admissions Requirements
Architecture							
Bachelor of Architectural Studies	2 - 4		15	0	6	4	Portfolio, Rec. Letters, Essay
M. Arch	2 - 3	NAAB	15	0	6	7	Undergraduate degree, Portfolio, Rec. Letters, Essay

SPECIALIZATIONS

Architectural Design	Energy	Landscape Design	Sustainability
Art and Design	Environment/Sustainability	Preservation	Theory/Criticism
Community Design	History	Professional Practice	Urban Planning and Design
Computer-Aided Design	Interior Design/Architecture		

ARCHITECTURE PROGRAM SUMMARY

Taliesin, the Frank Lloyd Wright School of Architecture, offers two fully accredited degrees in architecture: the professional Master of Architecture (M.Arch) degree, and the pre-professional Bachelor of Architectural Studies (BAS) degree. The Taliesin educational experience is closely linked to its two architecturally stunning campuses, the main Arizona campus (Taliesin West) and the summer Wisconsin campus (Taliesin). Project-based learning and portfolio assessment are central to the curriculum.

UNIVERSITY SETTING

The School of Architecture is a stand-alone school, founded by Frank Lloyd Wright in 1932 as an alternative to traditional architectural education. The School remains small in scale, enabling students to explore the discipline through one-on-one interaction with faculty and through work in the design studio, through architectural practice, and on design-build projects. All students are provided with on-campus housing at both locations and are encouraged to participate in the life of the academic community.

SCHOOL PHILOSOPHY

The program is rigorous but noncompetitive; traditional grading is replaced by assessment of the student's learning by faculty, mentors, and practicing architects on the basis of evidence in semi-annual portfolio documentation. Students develop technical and theoretical skills in architecture in a wide range of formats. The academic community that supports the School facilitates both the development of the individual student's architectural voice, and encourages leadership within the society in which the architectural discipline is practiced.

With more than 90 percent of its graduates actively practicing architecture, the Frank Lloyd Wright School of Architecture builds upon the foundation of the educational ideas of Frank Lloyd Wright and interprets them within the context of our rapidly changing world.

PROGRAM DESCRIPTION

Master of Architecture (M.Arch)

The M.Arch degree is a professional graduate degree leading to qualifications for architectural licensing. An undergraduate degree in a related or an unrelated field and post-secondary prerequisites are required for admission. Graduates of the program are prepared to enter leadership roles within the architectural profession and become licensed architects upon completion of internship experience and passing the architectural exam.

Bachelor of Architectural Studies (BAS)

The BAS degree is an undergraduate pre-professional degree. High school graduation and post-secondary prerequisites are required for admission. Graduates of the program are prepared to enter professional-level graduate schools in architecture and related fields.

Both degree programs are designed for students who thrive in a multifaceted environment focusing on rigorous design, critical thinking, and hands-on learning. The small scale of the School facilitates an individualized educational experience and fosters a close relationship between students, faculty, and staff.

Students are active participants in the design of their curriculum, and draw on a variety of resources throughout their education. Students explore architecture through the resources of design, technical and professional practices, liberal studies, and the Arts throughout the learning process. Project-based learning is central to the educational experience.

The Taliesin educational experience is closely linked to its two architecturally stunning campuses and is fueled by the intense year-round educational community that is marked by residency at the main Arizona campus (Taliesin West) and the summer Wisconsin campus (Taliesin).

AREAS OF FOCUS AND RESEARCH

The School's curriculum supports applied project-based design and research. Innovation in architecture is explored through experimentation of materials and processes related to a project, through the lens of the social and cultural context of that project. An example of this aspect of the curriculum is the Shelter Construction Program, which challenges students to design and build small structures as case studies of how materials come together, how they withstand severe environmental conditions, and how the project realization can happen with resourcefulness and invention. The shelters form a core component of the housing stock for enrolled students.

Many of the studio-based projects center around architectural work for non-profit and entrepreneurial organizations with specific focus on projects that are socially responsible, environmentally sustainable, and culturally relevant.

During the final year in the M.Arch program, students are encouraged to pursue a thesis project, which enables them to explore a project in both depth and breadth in an area related to their research and design interests.

SPECIAL ACTIVITIES AND PROGRAMS

The Study Abroad component of the curriculum is optional but provides students with the opportunity to engage in specific interest areas outside of the main campus. Generally the study abroad experience is one to four months in duration. Students can either study at another university, intern in an architectural office, or work with a specific client on a project. These experiences often occur in other countries, or alternately in other cultural contexts within the United States. The student works with the faculty to determine and pursue the study abroad opportunity.

FACILITIES

The School's main campus, Taliesin West, is located in Scottsdale, Arizona. The School's summer campus, Taliesin, is located in Spring Green, Wisconsin. Each campus is listed on the National Register of Historic Places and both are National Landmark Properties. Each campus is located in architecturally expressive buildings set within stunning natural landscapes. The buildings and the landscapes are learning laboratories of architectural experimentation and environmental stewardship. As well, the campuses continuously attract architects, scholars, artists, and public visitors from all parts of the world. The construction of Taliesin West began in 1937. It was designed by Frank Lloyd Wright and built over many years by architecture students as part of Wright's experimental architectural curriculum. The campus is nestled into 500 acres of pristine Sonoran Desert adjacent to a large mountain nature preserve. The buildings at Taliesin West include drafting studios that provide well-equipped workspace for students and faculty, classrooms, study rooms, a library, and exhibition spaces, and two theaters. Workshops and equipment are available for woodwork, metal work, painting, photography, sculpture, pottery, and model making. Taliesin West is a complex of buildings and garden courts linked together by walks and terraces, and surrounded by the natural desert.

Students at Taliesin West have the opportunity live in the celebrated "desert shelters," experimental dwellings built over the years by students, for students. Students otherwise have the option of modest dormitory rooms, based on availability. Locker room facilities and a study/reading room are provided for all students. A limited number of apartments for married students are available, generally for additional fees.

Each summer, students and faculty move to Taliesin, in Wisconsin. The campus consists of over 600 acres of rolling hills and fertile valleys adjacent to the scenic Wisconsin River. The buildings at Taliesin include two drafting and design studios, classrooms, meeting spaces, a theater, workshops, and library. At Taliesin, students are assigned to rooms in the various building complexes on campus; rooms have shared or in-room baths.

SCHOLARSHIPS AND FINANCIAL AID

School-sponsored financial aid in the form of scholarships and/or work/learn opportunities is available to students who demonstrate financial need and/or merit. Limited external employment through internships is also available pending approval.

The School does not participate in Title IV federal financial aid programs such as the Stafford Loan, Pell Grant, and PLUS programs. However, several major lending institutions and state agencies offer comparable private loans to qualified applicants. Students in need of financial assistance should contact the Director of Admissions for more information. VA funding is also available.

ADMINISTRATION

Victor Sidy, AIA: Dean
Pamela Stefansson: Director of Admissions
Madalena Maestri: Education Coordinator

GEORGIA INSTITUTE OF TECHNOLOGY

ADDRESS

Main
Georgia Institute of Technology
College of Architecture
247 4th Street, NW
Atlanta, GA 30332-0155
Tel.: 404.894.4885
Fax: 404.894.0572
program.office@arch.gatech.edu
www.arch.gatech.edu

STUDENT AND FACULTY DEMOGRAPHICS

% of Female Students	50
% of International Students	10
% of Minority Students	20
% of Out-of-State U.S. Students	35
No. Full-Time Faculty	25
No. Part-Time Faculty	35
No. Full-Time Students	550
No. Part-Time Students	30

FINANCIAL INFORMATION

Main Source of University Funding	Public
Annual Tuition & Fees (graduate, resident)	$2,835
Annual Tuition & Fees (graduate, nonresident)	$11,871
Annual Tuition & Fees (undergraduate, resident)	$2,428
Annual Tuition & Fees (undergraduate, nonresident)	$11,999
% Students Receiving Federal Financial Aid	42
% Students Receiving University Financial Aid	15
% Students Receiving Departmental Financial Aid	10
% Students Receiving Scholarships (assistantships or fellowships)	0
Average Annual Scholarship for Department	$1,000

ACADEMIC SESSIONS

Fall Semester: August to December; Application Deadline: January 15
Spring Semester: January to May; Application Deadline: January 15

Summer Session I: May to August; Application Deadline: January 15

ARCHITECTURE AND RELATED DEGREE PROGRAMS

Degree	Min. Yrs. to Complete	Professional Accreditation	# of FT Students	# of PT Students	# of First-Year Students	# of Degrees Conferred	Admissions Requirements
Architecture							
BS Arch.	4		317	31	0	69	SAT, TOEFL, Rec. Letters, Essay
M. Arch: Full Advanced Standing	2	NAAB	60	2	0	40	Undergraduate Architecture degree, GRE, TOEFL, Portfolio, Rec. Letters, Essay
M. Arch: No Advanced Standing	3.5	NAAB	64	0	22	22	Undergraduate degree, GRE, TOEFL, Portfolio, Rec. Letters, Essay
M.S. Arch	1		30	0	15	10	Undergraduate Architecture degree, GRE, TOEFL, Rec. Letters, Essay
PhD Arch	3		60	1	0	2	Undergraduate degree, GRE, Rec. Letters, Essay

SPECIALIZATIONS

Building Technology/Env. Systems
Building Information Modeling
Computer-Aided Design
Energy

Environment/Sustainability
History
Housing
International Development

International/Regional Architecture
Photography
Sustainability

Tectonics
Theory/Criticism
Urban Planning and Design

ARCHITECTURE PROGRAM SUMMARY

Architecture has a long and distinguished tradition at Georgia Tech dating back to 1908. Today, besides its nationally-ranked professional program in architecture leading to the Master of Architecture degree, the Architecture Program offers an innovative undergraduate major in the discipline as well as both post-professional and research-oriented degree options at the graduate level. The Faculty prides itself on the quality of the design education it provides and is internationally active in areas of both practice and research.

UNIVERSITY SETTING

Georgia Tech was established by an act of the Geor-

gia legislature in 1885, and first admitted students in 1888. The School's creation signaled the beginning of the transformation of the agrarian South to an industrial economy. Today, Georgia Tech is one of 34 public institutions comprising the University System of Georgia and one of four major research universities in the state. Georgia Tech has established a tradition of excellence in technological research and education, is well known for its high academic standards, and stands among the top ranks of U.S. research universities. *U.S. News & World Report* consistently lists Georgia Tech among the 50 best universities in the nation with many of our individual programs ranking within the top 10.

Located on a lush campus in midtown Atlanta, Geor-

gia Tech is an urban university known for its focus on cutting-edge technologies and integration of academic and practical training. The Institute enrolls approximately 17,400 students in six colleges: Architecture; Computing; Engineering; Science; Management; and the Ivan Allen (Liberal Arts) College. The College of Architecture offers programs to approximately 1,100 students.

SCHOOL PHILOSOPHY

The most profound purpose of a university is the fostering of conversations where ideas and knowledge are exchanged, debated, and advanced. The ultimate purpose of an architecture school is the improvement of the built environment. Fertile conversations are ample throughout the Architecture Program at Georgia Tech. The collegial interaction between faculty and students with diverse expertise is one of the school's particular and distinguishing strengths. Committed to preparing the next generation of architects with the generalist education they need to synthesize multiple concerns into responsive designs, the Program also recognizes the growing need for specialized theoretical, technological, and performance-related knowledge of various kinds. Eschewing the division of designers into stylistic camps, the school is more interested in the overlaps and propelling learning through the synthesis of depth, breadth, and engagement. With a particular pedagogical focus on design in relation to the contemporary city, the Program encourages reciprocity between historical understanding, analysis, outreach, critical thought, tectonic elaboration, and the exploration of representational means—both traditional and electronic. Committed to research, scholarship, and public service, the Program engages faculty and students in creative design research and community outreach.

PROGRAM DESCRIPTION

The **Undergraduate Program** in the College of Architecture at Georgia Tech offers three undergraduate degrees in architecture, building construction, and industrial design. Students are introduced to all three through the Common Freshman Year's fundamental design studios and lectures. The four-year, pre-professional Architecture Program leads to the Bachelor of Science in Architecture degree and prepares students for entry to the two-year Master of Architecture degree or work or study in related fields. The Undergraduate Program provides (1) a general university education in the liberal arts, fine arts, technology, science and mathematics (2) a broad foundation in architectural studies with the design studio as a major focus of the curriculum and additional courses in architectural history, building structures and construction, visual communications, and electives in architectural theory, city planning, environment, computation, fine arts, etc. (3) substantial opportunities for students to explore other disciplines; and (4) opportunity to participate in the nine-month study abroad program in Paris, France during the senior year.

Graduate Studies in Architecture at Georgia Tech are comprised of two distinct degree-granting programs: the Master of Architecture (M.Arch.) and the Master of Science (M.S.). The M.Arch. Program is the professional program in architecture leading to the NAAB-accredited Master of Architecture Degree. This program accommodates both a 2-year-long curriculum for those students with a 4-year, pre-professional degree in architecture and a 3-1/2 year-long curriculum for those students without a pre-professional degree in architecture.

AREAS OF FOCUS AND RESEARCH

With attention to the growing importance of the global context and of interdisciplinary activities to architecture's effectiveness at improving the built environment, the school's four strategic directions are: (1) Design and The Arts: The liberal and fine arts have long shaped the discipline of architecture in ways that distinguish it from engineering and science. The Program's commitment to this design tradition is evident throughout this book in the framing of unanswerable but profound theoretical questions and the production of installations, artworks, and musical compositions that investigate spatial, material, and cultural conditions.

(2) Sustainability and Ecological Literacy: From the integration of basic ecological principles into beginning design studios to the design and construction of a fully-functioning off-the-grid house for the Solar Decathlon Competition, discussions of green construction, sustainable urbanism, energy efficiency, and environmental stewardship permeate the school and the faculty's work at a variety of scales. Colleagues in engineering, biology, earth and atmospheric sciences, and the Southface Energy Institute further enrich the conversation and research in this area. (3) Urban Design and Policy: Our location in Atlanta—a city that leads the nation, both in suburban sprawl and intown redevelopment—has long positioned us to both analyze and shape the emerging contemporary city. Working with colleagues in City and Regional Planning, the Center for Quality Growth and Regional Development, and in studios operated in conjunction with City Council and the City of Atlanta, architecture students and faculty are empowered to reconfigure and transform underutilized urban areas—such as the Beltline and Atlantic Station, projects that emerged from thesis work in the College of Architecture. (4) Digital Manufacturing and Technology Integration: Under the broad labels of digital manufacturing and AEC integration, the processes of the design and construction of buildings are undergoing dramatic change. The College's unrivaled CNC equipment at the Advanced Wood Products Laboratory, the Thomas W. Ventulett III Distinguished Chair in Architectural Design, the IMAGINE Lab, and the PhD Program's pioneering leadership in Building Information Modeling are but a few of the resources contributing to our leading position in this area.

Current faculty research topics include: ecological design, smart skins, and emerging materials; digital design and visualization, CNC fabrication and manufacturing; electronic media; urban sprawl and retrofitting suburbs; professional practice; minimalism; structural use of composite materials; public architecture and healthy buildings; shape grammars and space syntax.

SPECIAL ACTIVITIES AND PROGRAMS

The Architecture Program provides considerable, additional opportunities for various forms of learning. The lectures and exhibitions series brings the work of noted individuals and firms to the school. Annual sponsored studio competitions bring nationally recognized architects in as jurors. Joint degree programs with Building Construction, City and Regional Planning, Management, and Civil Engineering further broaden students' horizons. In addition to the nine-month foreign study program in Paris, France, there are regular summer travel programs offered in Rome and Barcelona, Berlin, Amsterdam and Paris, as well as a variety of single, short-term programs, with visits to Kuala Lumpur, Equador, and Tokyo. Graduate students have the opportunity to learn and pay off their tuition while working in professional offices during the school year through the Co-Op program. Urban Design Workshops offer students course credit or paid research involvement in contemporary planning and urban development projects. A pre-architecture program is offered to high school and mid-career students.

In addition, and unique among American universities, Georgia Tech's International Plan (IP) offers an intensive degree-long program designed to prepare undergraduates, professionally and personally, for successful lives within the 21st century's global community. The IP program allows participants to take a global

perspective on their education "within their discipline." IP is a challenging and coherent academic program intended to develop global competence within the context of the participating student's major. The program integrates internationally related studies as well as experience abroad into the current programs of study for those GT majors that participate.

FACILITIES

The College of Architecture is located in the heart of the Georgia Tech campus. The College has a total floor area of 154,835 gross square feet with 5,119 square feet of jury space, multiple computer labs and workstations, five large design studios, an additional large studio space in the Hinman Building, and a materials testing lab. The two primary inter-connected architecture buildings house the Architecture, City Planning, Industrial Design, and Doctoral Programs, the IMAGINE Lab, as well as the Dean's Office. The Preston Stevens Architecture Library with 45,000 volumes, is located on the first floor of Architecture West, off the building atrium. The Architecture Library is critical to the academic life of the Architecture Program. The recent addition of 15 computer workstations purchased with student technology fees has significantly expanded the web-based research capabilities of that facility. The Coffee Cart Café is also located in the atrium. The wood and metal shops, totaling 3,313 square feet on the first floor of Architecture East, serving primarily architecture and industrial design students. The Photo Lab is housed on the first floor of Architecture East and has 1,300 square feet of space. It serves as an area for teaching photography and darkroom skills for both architecture and industrial design students. The Heffernan Design Archives include the creation of a guest facility for visitors; storage and maintenance of Heffernan's papers, drawings, and slides; archiving of design work of students and alumni. The Heffernan House is located approximately one block east of the College of Architecture. Since 1993, the Paris Study Abroad Program has been affiliated with the Ecole Nationale Superieure d'Architecture Paris-La Villette (ENSAPLV). The Paris Program uses classroom, studio, library, office, and other space within the host school. Students are housed in a combination of rental housing within the Peripherique and dormitory space at the Fondation des États-Unis of the Cité Universitaire.

SCHOLARSHIPS AND FINANCIAL AID

The Architecture Program offers merit-based financial assistance through (1) scholarships and fellowships, ranging from $1,000 to as much as $15,000 per academic year including tuition and (2) graduate research and teaching assistantships with stipends of approximately $7,200 per academic year plus a tuition waiver. In addition, a graduate cooperative program provides graduate research assistantships in conjunction with one-third time internships in architectural firms. Loans, grants, and work-study programs based on financial need are administered by the Institute's Office of Financial Aid.

ADMINISTRATION

Alan Balfour: Dean
Sabir Khan, RA: Associate Dean
Ellen Dunham-Jones, AIA: Director
Christopher Jarrett, RA: Associate Director
George B. Johnston, PhD, RA: Associate Professor

HAMPTON UNIVERSITY

  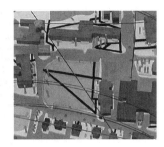

ADDRESS

Main
Hampton University
School of Engineering & Technology
Department of Architecture
Bemis Laboratory
Hampton, VA 23668
Tel.: 757.727.5440
Fax: 757.728.6680
robert.easter@hampton.edu
www.hamptonu.edu/academics/
schools/engineering/architecture

ACADEMIC SESSIONS

Fall Semester: September to December
Spring Semester: January to May

STUDENT AND FACULTY DEMOGRAPHICS

% of Female Students	42
% of International Students	6
% of Minority Students	88
% of Out-of-State U.S. Students	70
No. Full-Time Faculty	7
No. Part-Time Faculty	4
No. Full-Time Students	173
No. Part-Time Students	7

FINANCIAL INFORMATION

Main Source of University Funding	Private
Annual Tuition & Fees (graduate)	$14,728
Annual Tuition & Fees (undergraduate)	$18,298
% Students Receiving Federal Financial Aid	
% Students Receiving University Financial Aid	5
% Students Receiving Departmental Financial Aid	1
% Students Receiving Scholarships (assistantships or fellowships)	
Average Annual Scholarship for Department	$500

Summer Semester: June to July

ARCHITECTURE AND RELATED DEGREE PROGRAMS

Degree	Min. Yrs. to Complete	Professional Accreditation	# of FT Students	# of PT Students	# of First-Year Students	# of Degrees Conferred	Admissions Requirements
Architecture							
M. Arch	5.5	NAAB	174	12	64	14	SAT, ACT

SPECIALIZATIONS

Architectural Design   Computer-Aided Design   Environment/Sustainability   Sustainability

ARCHITECTURE PROGRAM SUMMARY

The Department of Architecture offers a professional degree program that supports the education and the preparation of students for professional positions of environmental design practice, leadership, and service. The Department of Architecture is committed to the development of critical inquiry and the pursuit of life-long learning necessary for participation in a changing society and profession. Education in the Department of Architecture, as a connection with engineering, the fine arts, the humanities, and social sciences, strives to provide an important synthesis of pragmatic, technical, and theoretical learning. The Department of Architecture sets the framework to explore the roles of African American identity in design and other cultural, technical, and social factors in architectural education. The Department is dedicated to promoting a global environmental sensitivity and to developing an ability and desire in students to help bring about important social and environmental change, especially in transitional urban areas and "communities of color." The Department regularly takes advantage of its urban location at the midpoint of a major metropolitan center with a rich history of early American architecture, diverse urban communities, and water's edge development.

UNIVERSITY SETTING

Hampton University's main campus is located on 270 acres of the Virginia Peninsula at the mouth of the Chesapeake Bay. It is the oldest private, nonsectarian, coeducational, postsecondary institution in the southeast Commonwealth of Virginia. Hampton University is a historically black, privately endowed institution founded in 1868 for the education of African Americans and committed to multiculturalism. Located on the banks of the Hampton River were the James and York rivers join, the region is closely associated with early American history. Located 40 miles from Jamestown, Yorktown and Williamsburg, it provides a setting rich in historic value. The City of Hampton is the oldest continuous English speaking settlement in America. The Hampton Roads area is presently the hub of Norfolk-Newport News-Portsmouth military defense activity, with a thriving economic base that centers on tourism, water sports, public beaches, campgrounds, natural harbors and historic attractions.

SCHOOL PHILOSOPHY

The Department of Architecture offers an accredited, professional degree program that supports the education and preparation of students for positions of professional environmental design practice, leadership and service. The Department is committed to the development of critical inquiry and the pursuit of lifelong learning necessary for responsible participation in a changing society and profession. Architecture education at Hampton strives toward synthesis in its educational mission; integration of individual imagination with communal responsibility, theoretical insight with pragmatic speculations, conceptual or expressive gestures with tectonic resolutions; and historical and cultural fabric with contemporary interpretations of architecture. The Department sets a framework for the students to explore the roles of African American identity in design and other cultural, technical, and social factors in architecture education. The Department is dedicated to promoting a global environmental sensitivity and to develop the student's ability to bring about important environmental and social change, especially in transitional urban areas and "communities of color."

PROGRAM DESCRIPTION
Graduate Program

The five-and-one-half year (5-½) curriculum leads to the first professional accredited Master of Architecture degree. The architecture curriculum is formally structured to provide for both general and professional educations. The first two years consist of core pre-professional and general education coursework. The second two years comprise the professional component, and the final year provides the graduate research component. The curriculum is designed to escalate in complexity, culminating with a thesis in the final year.

AREAS OF FOCUS AND RESEARCH
Focus

The mission of the Department of Architecture and the Urban Institute is to fuse progressive environmental design education and faculty/student development with community service and social environmental design action. We utilize our surrounding urban area as an active learning laboratory for students and community members. As the sole institution offering a professional degree in Architecture in Southeastern Virginia, we have a tremendous role in offering outreach programs to members of our vast urban region.

Research

Research in the Department of Architecture at Hampton University focuses on community and urban design, through the Department's Urban Institute. The Urban Institute coordinates service learning projects, activity and workshops that contribute to the exploration and enhancement of local urban neighborhoods. Working to make connections with the local communities, the Urban Institute becomes the vehicle for citizens, community groups and governmental municipalities in collaboration with Hampton University professors and students to explore pressing social and environmental design issues.

SPECIAL ACTIVITES AND PROGRAMS

The Department of Architecture has full accreditation by the National Architecture Accreditation Board (NAAB), the Southern Association of Colleges and Schools (SACS), and the Department of Education of the Commonwealth of Virginia. The Department facilitates a required foreign Study Travel Program, which has taken students to such countries as Panama, Italy, Tanzania, Thailand, Turkey, Brazil, Greece and Spain, to explore the architecture, urban design and culture of these important global centers. The program incorporates an array of digital media, including CADD and BIM, into the curriculum and requires a laptop computer with appropriate software by the second-year level. The curriculum incorporates urban design studios where students work directly, through their coursework, with local community groups and municipalities in addressing pressing community design issues while also making available professional Co-ops and internships during the upper- level years.

FACILITIES

The physical facilities for most of the Department of Architecture instructional functions are housed in the Bemis Laboratory Building, a three-story industrial arts structure constructed in the 1930s. It contains a model shop with state-of-the-art laser cutting equipment, a computer/CADD lab, an Architectural Library. Additional resources include a more comprehensive computer lab in the Olin Engineering Building, and the Architecture resources of the main campus's Harvey Library.

SCHOLARSHIPS AND FINANCIAL AID

The majority of scholarship and fellowship opportunities available to students in the Department of Architecture are reserved for upper division students (3rd, 4th, and 5th year). The University does award Presidential Scholarships and Army and Navy scholarships to top qualified beginning students. The Department supervises competitive scholarships/fellowships and sponsorship programs from local architecture firms, foundations and endowments. Other financial assistance information is available through the University Financial Aid Office (Pell Grant, work-study, Federal Direct Loan Programs, etc.).

ADMINISTRATION

Eric Sheppard: Dean
Robert Easter: Chair

HARVARD UNIVERSITY

ADDRESS

Main
Harvard University
Graduate School of Design
48 Quincy Street
Cambridge, MA 02138
Tel.: 617.495.2591
Fax: 617.495.8916
www.gsd.harvard.edu

STUDENT AND FACULTY DEMOGRAPHICS

% of Female Students	48
% of International Students	30
% of Minority Students	20
% of Out-of-State U.S. Students	
No. Full-Time Faculty	23
No. Part-Time Faculty	42
No. Full-Time Students	592
No. Part-Time Students	0

FINANCIAL INFORMATION

Main Source of University Funding	Private
Annual Tuition & Fees (graduate)	$33,430
Annual Tuition & Fees (undergraduate)	
% Students Receiving Federal Financial Aid	75
% Students Receiving University Financial Aid	80
% Students Receiving Departmental Financial Aid	0
% Students Receiving Scholarships (assistantships or fellowships)	0
Average Annual Scholarship for Department	$0

ACADEMIC SESSIONS

Fall Semester: September to January;
    Application Deadline: December 14, 2008

Spring Semester: February to May

ARCHITECTURE AND RELATED DEGREE PROGRAMS							
Degree	Min. Yrs. to Complete	Professional Accreditation	# of FT Students	# of PT Students	# of First-Year Students	# of Degrees Conferred	Admissions Requirements
Architecture							
M. Arch I	3.5	NAAB	217	0	48	60	Undergraduate degree, GRE, TOEFL, Portfolio, Rec. Letters, Essay
M, Arch I AP	2.5	NAAB	49	0	16	11	Undergraduate Architecture degree, GRE, TOEFL, Portfolio, Rec. Letters, Essay
M. Arch II	1.5		62	0	29	29	GRE, TOEFL, Portfolio, Rec. Letters, Essay
Landscape Architecture							
MLA I	3	LAAB	55	0	24	22	Undergraduate degree, GRE, TOEFL, Portfolio, Rec. Letters, Essay
MLA I AP	2	LAAB	14	0	7	11	GRE, TOEFL, Portfolio, Rec. Letters, Essay
MLA II	1.5		14	0	7	4	GRE, TOEFL, Portfolio, Rec. Letters, Essay
Planning							
MUP	2	PAB	52	0	19	24	Undergraduate degree, GRE, TOEFL, Rec. Letters, Essay
Urban Design							
MAUD	2		38	0	18	24	GRE, TOEFL, Portfolio, Rec. Letters, Essay
Other							
DDes	2		31	0	7	9	GRE, TOEFL, Portfolio, Rec. Letters, Essay
MDesS	1.5		59	0	32	11	GRE, TOEFL, Portfolio, Rec. Letters, Essay
PhD							GRE, TOEFL, Rec. Letters, Essay

UNIVERSITY SETTING

The Harvard Design School is located on a distinctive urban campus, one of the oldest in the country. It provides students with access to the unparalleled resources of Harvard University, including its museums, libraries, cultural events and courses in the humanities, social and natural sciences, government, business and law. The Cambridge/Boston area serves as a living design laboratory, with important architectural, landscape, and urban landmarks from the colonial period to the present day.

SCHOOL PHILOSOPHY

Central to the school's philosophy is the commitment to design excellence that demands not only the skillful manipulation of form, but also inspiration from a broad body of knowledge. Instruction and research encompass design theory, as well as visual studies, history, technology and professional practice. The Design School's information infrastructure provides a foundation for design exploration and communication, offering students new ways to access design references, model buildings and present ideas.

AREAS OF FOCUS AND RESEARCH

Focus

The GSD is distinguished by its faculty of scholars and practitioners, who bring to the classroom firsthand knowledge of real-life issues related to design. Noted visiting professionals, as well as emerging talent in design thinking and practice, expose students to the widest range of design approaches and ideologies. Our renowned faculty from around the world are innovators and leaders in design. Through hands-on, intensive teaching, we strive to integrate different design approaches, techniques, and traditions. We stress a commitment to design excellence that demands not only the skillful ma-

nipulation of form and technology, but also inspiration from a broad range of social and cultural issues.

Research

Sponsored studios, technical assistance, and individual and collaborative research at the GSD are interdisciplinary and have addressed a broad range of issues and problems. Faculty research complements the core curriculum and instruction at the School. Specializations include: Design Technology, Environmental and Regional Studies, History, Theory, and Representation, Housing, Infrastructure, and Urbanization and the City. The following special units within the GSD are especially mandated to organize and support sponsored research projects: Center for Design Informatics; Instructional Technology Group; The Center for Urban Development Studies; and the Joint Center for Housing Studies (a joint venture of the GSD and the Kennedy School of Government).

SPECIAL ACTIVITIES AND PROGRAMS

The GSD is a center for exploring a broad range of social, political, economic and aesthetic interests and issues. Students benefit from interaction with a rich network of professionals who spend time teaching and participating in studios, critiques, conferences and lectures. Students are directly connected with design and planning issues in communities throughout the U.S. and the world; recent studios have included site visits for projects in Bilbao, Cuba, Singapore, Berlin, Hong Kong, and Mexico City. Lectures, conferences and exhibitions enrich the stimulating intellectual environment of the school. An extensive publications program includes Harvard Design magazine, Studio Works, conference proceedings, exhibition catalogs, monographs, books on history, theory, and the city, and studio options reports. The GSD offers education programs to support lifelong learning, from the Career Discovery program to

professional development courses for design practitioners and executive education programs for business and government leaders. Career Services provides job listings, career advice and networking opportunities.

FACILITIES

Studios are housed in the multidisciplinary environment of Gund Hall, enabling students to focus their studies in one discipline while gaining a broader perspective from related fields. Extending through five levels of the building under a clear-span roof that admits natural light to all levels, the studio "trays" are conducive to creative thinking, discussion, collaboration and spontaneity. The CAD/CAM Center provides access to computer controlled laser cutting, rapid prototyping and modeling software. The Digital Imaging and Media Center includes access to video cameras, image processing and presentation tools. The Frances Loeb Library contains design volumes, magazines, Visual Resources, rare books, and archival collections such as the Le Corbusier Research Collection. Other facilities include a woodshop, photo labs and darkroom, cafe, and student-run exhibition space.

SCHOLARSHIPS AND FINANCIAL AID

Financial Assistance is offered to admitted students and is based on demonstrated need. Applying for Financial Aid has no bearing on an application for admission. Students must apply each year to be reviewed for Financial Assistance. Most students receive a consistent award package from year to year, provided their financial situation does not change.

ADMINISTRATION

Mohsen Mostafavi: Dean
Preston Scott Cohen: Chair

HOWARD UNIVERSITY

ADDRESS

Main
Howard University
School of Architecture & Design
2366 6th Street NW, Rm 100
Washington, DC 20059
Fax: 202.462.1810
bcgrant@howard.edu
www.howard.edu/ceacs

STUDENT AND FACULTY DEMOGRAPHICS

% of Female Students	35
% of International Students	23
% of Minority Students	99
% of Out-of-State U.S. Students	68
No. Full-Time Faculty	13
No. Part-Time Faculty	7
No. Full-Time Students	135
No. Part-Time Students	25

FINANCIAL INFORMATION

Main Source of University Funding	Private
Annual Tuition & Fees (graduate)	$16,171
Annual Tuition & Fees (undergraduate)	$14,020
% Students Receiving Federal Financial Aid	74
% Students Receiving University Financial Aid	60
% Students Receiving Departmental Financial Aid	40
% Students Receiving Scholarships (assistantships or fellowships)	45
Average Annual Scholarship for Department	$6,500

ARCHITECTURE AND RELATED DEGREE PROGRAMS

Degree	Min. Yrs. to Complete	Professional Accreditation	# of FT Students	# of PT Students	# of First-Year Students	# of Degrees Conferred	Admissions Requirements
Architecture							
B. Arch	5	NAAB	115	25	40	26	

SPECIALIZATIONS

Community Design

Preservation

Urban Planning and Design

ARCHITECTURE PROGRAM SUMMARY

The Department of Architecture offers a program of study leading to the five-year Bachelor of Architecture (B.Arch) professional degree accredited by the National Architectural Accreditation Board (NAAB). The program places emphasis on student competence in the following pragmatic areas: design, inquiry/research, architectural history and theory, human behavior and environment, technical systems, computer usage and professional practice. These are complemented by elective courses in general/liberal education, natural sciences, humanities and social sciences that supplement the major courses. Study in these areas provides the student with fundamental design and communication skills through critical thinking, conflict resolution, visual literacy, knowledge of forces that shape and influence societal and human affairs and the impact of new technologies in an ever-changing world.

The Design Studio serves as the core synthesizing forum of the program for design and social and human behavior concerns, response to the physical environment, the ethical responsibility for ecologically sustainable design, and the cultural context in which architecture is developed. These and other issues are addressed as an interrelated whole, both horizontally and vertically in the curriculum. The department believes that architecture and design are rigorous acts of creativity, research and scholarship and encourages a pluralistic intellectual environment in which diverse ideas can be investigated and tested.

UNIVERSITY SETTING

The School of Architecture and Design is within one of twelve academic units of Howard University. Located in one of the most stimulating international cities in the world, Washington, DC, has a multi-cultural and diversified population, and provides a rich cultural context for the study and promotion of architectural and design ideas and values. The city serves as a laboratory for design studio projects. Students and faculty enjoy a close proximity to theaters, museums, libraries and a diversity of monuments and open spaces of national significance.

SCHOOL PHILOSOPHY

The School of Architecture and Design advances the philosophy that the built environment must critically reflect and reinforce the positive values of human cultural experience. All activities at the school, including instruction, research, and public service, are directed toward the development of individuals who are capable of providing leadership in all sectors and at all levels of the profession and society. The school advances the position that the making of architecture is essentially a rigorous act of creativity, research, and scholarship and encourages a pluralistic intellectual environment in which a diversity of ideas are investigated and tested.

PROGRAM DESCRIPTION
Undergraduate Program

The program emphasizes the philosophy that design is a method of inquiry and resolution. The design studio serves as the synthesizing element of the curriculum. Students take a total of 171 credits in a five-year curriculum.

AREAS OF FOCUS AND RESEARCH
Focus

The framework of the School's program is to educate future activist practitioners. The coursework includes good grounding in general education with sound community-centered design studio project experiences. Students are able to express their social intervention responsibility for different cultures/societies globally. Discussions on design theories, principles and process in the curriculum offer students a forum where diversity of ideas are investigated and tested. Independent/Directed Study courses and the Community-Centered Outreach Partnership Programs offer students additional options for exploration within the professional programs.

Areas of Research

The School's Research includes:

- Urban/Rural development, community planning and design issues in developed and developing countries.
- Alternative practice—focuses on underserved regions in the United States and abroad.
- Local and National issues and problems associated with Historic Preservation, adaptive reuse, historic places threatened by neglect, insufficient funds, inappropriate development or insensitive public policy.

The research activities within the program are consistent with the University's Strategic Framework for Action II with emphasis on:

- Enhancing national and community service
- Strengthening academic programs and services
- Promoting excellence in teaching and research
- Increasing private support for the institution

SPECIAL ACTIVITIES AND PROGRAMS

- The Domestic and International Travel/Study and Exchange Programs offer students opportunities for a wide range of design/charrette and research experiences in Africa, the Caribbean, Europe, and South America.
- The pre-college program, ArchAdventure/CityPlace, is a summer program for junior and senior high school students to explore the discipline of Architecture and civic/urban design.
- Distinguished Guest Lecture Series/Exhibitions.
- The African American Architect Initiative plans conferences, lectures, exhibitions, research projects, award programs, and archives-documenting work, philosophies and achievements of African American architects.
- Highly successful design/technical assistance community-based projects program (work–study and internships).
- Student organizations: School of Architecture and Design Student Assembly (SADSA); American Institute of Architects Students (AIAS); National Organization of Minority Architects Student Chapter (NOMAS); Black Women in Architecture Student Chapter (BWAS); Tau Sigma Delta National Honor Society (Alpha Beta Chapter).

FACILITIES

Classes are taught in a 68,000 square-foot facility that is open 24-hours per day during the academic year. In addition to the design studios, classrooms, and faculty offices, the facility houses the 60,000-volume Architecture and Design Library with an extensive slide collection. Other support facilities include two computer-aided laboratories, a photographic laboratory, a model shop, a building materials and systems resource center, an exhibition gallery, a 200-seat auditorium, and several conference/seminar (smart rooms) equipped for multimedia presentations.

SCHOLARSHIPS AND FINANCIAL AID

The school makes available a range of scholarships, grants, and loans to students in the School of Architecture and Design. Students who apply for Early Admission Decision are given priority consideration for the Howard University Freshman Scholarships. Scholarships are also available to students at all year levels. For financial aid information, applicants should contact the Office of Financial Aid, 2400 Sixth Street, NW, Howard University, Washington, DC 20059 or call (202) 806-2820.

ADMINISTRATION

Bradford C. Grant, AIA, NOMA:
    Associate Dean, Director
Victor C.W. Dzidzienyo, AIA: Associate Dean

ILLINOIS INSTITUTE OF TECHNOLOGY

ADDRESS

Main
Illinois Institute of Technology
College of Architecture
3360 South State Street
S. R. Crown Hall
Chicago, IL 60616
Tel.: 312.567.3230
Fax: 312.567.5820
arch@iit.edu
www.arch.iit.edu

STUDENT AND FACULTY DEMOGRAPHICS

% of Female Students	37
% of International Students	35
% of Minority Students	15
% of Out-of-State U.S. Students	34
No. Full-Time Faculty	42
No. Part-Time Faculty	71
No. Full-Time Students	795
No. Part-Time Students	33

FINANCIAL INFORMATION

Main Source of University Funding	Private
Annual Tuition & Fees (graduate)	$23,340
Annual Tuition & Fees (undergraduate)	$24,962
% Students Receiving Federal Financial Aid	66
% Students Receiving University Financial Aid	96
% Students Receiving Departmental Financial Aid	4
% Students Receiving Scholarships (assistantships or fellowships)	
Average Annual Scholarship for Department	$7,550

ACADEMIC SESSIONS

(Early Action 1) Nov 5 or (Early Action II) Jan 7 (undergraduate)
Jan 15 (graduate)

Spring Semester: January to May;
Application Deadline: Fall admission only Summer Session I: June to July

ARCHITECTURE AND RELATED DEGREE PROGRAMS

Degree	Min. Yrs. to Complete	Professional Accreditation	# of FT Students	# of PT Students	# of First-Year Students	# of Degrees Conferred	Admissions Requirements
Architecture							
B. Arch	5	NAAB	585	0	108	65	SAT, ACT, GRE, TOEFL, Portfolio, Rec. Letters, Essay
M. Arch—2 years	2	NAAB	59	18	37	45	
M. Arch—3 years	3	NAAB	66	2	25	20	GRE, Portfolio, Rec. Letters, Essay
M. Arch—1 year (Post-Professional Degree)	1		1	4	1	1	GRE, Portfolio, Rec. Letters, Essay
PhD	5		10	4	5	2	
Landscape Architecture							
Master of Landscape Architecture	2		12	3	8	0	Undergraduate degree, GRE, Portfolio, Rec. Letters, Essay

SPECIALIZATIONS

Architectural Design	Environment/Sustainability	Sustainability	Urban Planning and Design
Computer-Aided Design	History	Theory/Criticism	

ARCHITECTURE PROGRAM SUMMARY

With a history of design excellence and technical expertise, a comprehensive studio curriculum, and inspiring urban surroundings, IIT's College of Architecture is committed to educating a diverse student population prepared for complex global practice and design imperatives. Technical expertise, sustainable design ideals, and inventive use of advanced materials define our students as among the most respected by architectural firms around the world. The College offers the following degrees: the Doctor of Philosophy (Ph.D.) in Architecture; the M.S. of Architecture degree, defined in the College as Program 1 (Post-Professional Degree), the Master of Architecture (M.Arch.) degree termed Program 2 Master of Architecture (NAAB-accredited Professional Degree with Advanced Standing), and Program 3 Master of Architecture (NAAB-accredited Professional Degree). The Master of Landscape Architecture (M.L.A.) integrates Chicago's urban planning legacy, contemporary

sustainable/green planning initiatives, and the city's landscape professionals.

UNIVERSITY SETTING

Founded in 1890, IIT is a Ph.D.-granting university with more than 7,600 students in engineering, sciences, architecture, psychology, design, humanities, business and law. IIT's interprofessional, technology-focused curriculum is designed to advance knowledge through research and scholarship, to cultivate invention improving the human condition, and to prepare students from throughout the world for a life of professional achievement, service to society, and individual fulfillment. Situated on approximately 120 acres, three miles south of Chicago's downtown, IIT's Main Campus was designed by modernist architect Ludwig Mies van der Rohe. Landscape architect Alfred Caldwell integrated native plantings to complement the Miesian urban grid. Main Campus was placed on the National Register of

Historic Places in 2005 in recognition of Mies' contributions to 20th century architecture. Mies' most significant building on campus, S. R. Crown Hall, was designated as a National Historic Landmark in 2001. IIT's College of Architecture is housed in Crown Hall, one of three buildings occupied by the College's 912 students. Two widely-praised new buildings opened on Main Campus to initiate the university's growth in the 21st century. An international competition resulted in 2003 with the campus center designed by Pritzker Prize-winning architect Rem Koolhaas. Next, State Street Village, a new residence hall, was designed by Chicago architect Helmut Jahn. IIT's prominence is linked to the architectural and cultural legacy of Chicago, recognized internationally for an award-winning heritage of leadership in the architectural profession.

SCHOOL PHILOSOPHY

The College of Architecture's programs of study emphasize investigations in architectural and landscape architectural design and technology, while expanding the significance of these investigations through a rigorous application of critical thought and intellectual inquiry. The College draws strength from its unique traditions and circumstances, such as its Miesian legacy as a preeminent school of modernism, its location in Chicago with its profuse architectural heritage and devotion to enhanced landscapes, and the city's present-day connections to progressively minded global practitioners. The students, faculty, and alumni foster an academic environment that is intellectually stimulating, professionally challenging, committed to innovation, and international in scope. Architectural and landscape architectural education at IIT combines top-tier educators and enhanced educational resources with a setting in an unparalleled urban laboratory with the top practices in the world. Our commitment encompasses the needs of our south Chicago neighborhood, our city, and its inhabitants. An immersive program of studies intertwines analytical skills, design, technology, and practical knowledge. Our perspective invites collaborations with the programs' allied disciplines and is committed to the highest standards of professional preparation. Our mission incorporates the values of design excellence, technical expertise, and the advancement of professional practice and educational significance. Our goal is to graduate professionals who are ethical, thoughtful, and informed creators of buildings, landscapes and related visual and physical environments. In addition to our historic strength in architecture and planning, our curriculum emphasizes landscape architecture, digital applications (including building information management), advanced technologies, history and theory, development and design/build, and sustainable design and planning. IIT's College of Architecture seeks to become a force for designing environments through the incorporation of planning, technology, materials, space, and formal generation. We believe the responsible integration of these attributes arm the student with historical, social, moral, and environmental tools for creating a better world.

PROGRAM DESCRIPTION
Undergraduate Program
The professional architecture program at IIT is defined by a comprehensive five-year, NAAB-accredited Bachelor of Architecture (B.Arch.) degree. With careful attention to sustainable design and advanced materials, students are prepared to respond to an increasingly complex global condition, working collaboratively with established architects and allied professionals to produce efficient, functional buildings of enduring quality. Tenured faculty and practicing architects combine contemporary practice with hands-on teaching at the design tables and in the materials shops.

Engaging artistic ability with technical expertise, the integrated curriculum is grounded in a sequence of design studios, from materials- and systems-based fundamental studios in the first three years to advanced, comprehensive building design studios in the last two years. Foundation studios are team taught to provide a fundamental body of knowledge about materials, modern technology, building systems, and related universal design principles. Advanced studios in the 4th and 5th years are taught by a single studio professor, a practitioner working with a small group to develop and design a complex building at a specific site, nearby or elsewhere in the world. This disciplined and proven curriculum is enriched by travel, independent study, and the opportunity to specialize or diversify studies among several specializations.
Graduate Program
The College attracts highly qualified applicants

holding undergraduate four-year accredited bachelor degrees in architecture who seek to complete the NAAB-accredited M.Arch. degree at IIT. In addition, students with undergraduate degrees with advanced standing in other liberal arts and science degrees join the three-year M.Arch. degree program. The Master of Landscape Architecture is a new, not yet accredited program dedicated to the integration of advanced architectural design and carefully designed landscape settings.

While technical proficiency will always be fundamental to IIT's graduate and undergraduate programs, the College recognizes that architecture schools must educate students to work as part of interdisciplinary teams, to communicate well, and to understand the economic, social, cultural, and international context of their profession. A longstanding emphasis on active and collaborative learning, when combined with a new global vision and advanced computer and communication technologies, positions both IIT and the College of Architecture at the leading edge of higher education.

AREAS OF FOCUS AND RESEARCH
- Advanced building technologies
- Digital application in design
- Sustainability
- Design/build/development
- Community partnerships

SPECIAL ACTIVITIES AND PROGRAMS
The College of Architecture offers numerous programs to enhance the architectural and professional education of its students, including study abroad programs, career development opportunities, and community service. The Paris Program is offered each semester, permitting a small group of students to enroll in a Paris-based studio and architecture elective courses. In addition, advanced studios have been situated for one month in many different countries. Frequently, students in advanced studios travel to distant sites in the United States to develop their projects. On campus, each semester offers an active program of lectures in Crown Hall and occasional special seminars in conjunction with Chicago institutions. Working with IIT's International Center and the College faculty, students are permitted to arrange for pre-approved architectural study in renowned universities around the world. To further their career plans, students are encouraged to join national student organizations including the American Institute of Architecture Students (AIAS), Arquitectos, and the National Organization for Minority Architects (NOMA). IIT Architecture students have recently founded Architecture That Matters, an organization dedicated to global community service. In the spring semester, a career fair brings representatives from architectural offices and the construction industry to Crown Hall as they recruit students for internships and other positions. Throughout the academic year, monthly profession days operate on a smaller scale to provide architectural offices an opportunity to present their firm to the College and meet with students. The Career Management Center offers architecture students workshops in job-search strategies, resumes, and interview skills. An active program of lectures and symposia introduces students to the latest work and significant advances in the field.

FACILITIES
The College of Architecture is located primarily in S. R. Crown Hall, designated a National Historic Landmark in 2001. Designed by Ludwig Mies van der Rohe, Crown Hall represents his most significant thinking about clarity of structure and enclosure, refinement of proportion, and universal space. With growth in both graduate and undergraduate programs, and the addition of the landscape architecture program, the College of Architecture

occupies two nearby buildings for faculty offices, materials and computer labs, thesis studios, advanced studios, and the design-build program. The Mies-designed Minerals and Metals Building has housed the third-year undergraduate studio and faculty, as well as the design-build studio and facilities. Future plans will centralize all production equipment and model building machinery in this building, allowing for full-scale construction of building details and 3-D digital modeling projects. Teaching facilities include two well-equipped model shops for wood and multi-material models; multimedia computer labs equipped with up-to-date CAD technology and laser cutters; a photography darkroom, freehand drawing studios, and the newly renovated and expanded Graham Resource Center (GRC). The GRC is equipped with computers and quiet study areas where groups and individuals may investigate their design projects. The GRC holds a large and broad collection of books and journals dedicated to supporting the College's educational mission and the research goals of its faculty.

SCHOLARSHIPS AND FINANCIAL AID
The university provides several types of financial assistance in the form of IIT, state, and federal tuition scholarships and grants, work study, and loans for new and transfer students. In addition to athletic and Heald scholarships, students may apply for a wide range of need-based and merit-based scholarships. The Collens Scholars Program offers full financial support for qualifying families with eligible students inside the Chicago Public School system. For entering first-year students, the College of Architecture offers highly competitive, merit-based Camras Scholarships, the Crown Scholarship, and the Thomas A. Roszak Scholarship. The Crown Scholarship awards full tuition for five years to an outstanding freshman student with exceptional drawing ability and demonstrated leadership. Camras Scholarships are awarded to several new students with exceptional academic achievement and leadership potential. The Thomas A. Roszak Scholarship is awarded to a single first-year student. The College's annual Spring Awards provide faculty-nominated undergraduate and graduate students with tuition scholarships and travel fellowships. Chicago's ties to professional organizations and the construction industry provide annual tuition scholarships to honor outstanding design ability.

The College of Architecture provides a select number of graduate tuition awards and scholarships upon entry to the architecture program. The Morgenstern Scholar Program is a highly competitive opportunity for new graduate students who are rewarded with significant tuition support and an internship in an important Chicago architectural office. TA fellowships are awarded to graduate students in good standing to assist with teaching and a wide range of College initiatives.

ADMINISTRATION
Donna V. Robertson, FAIA: Dean
Peter Beltemacchi: Associate Dean
Timothy Brown: Director or International Affairs, Director of Graduate Admissions
Kimberly Campbell: Manager, Communications and Stewardship
Susan Conger-Austin: Thesis Director
Matthew Cook: Director of Research Resources
Blake Davis: Director of Community Affairs
Mahjoub Elnimeiri, PE: Director of Ph.D. in Arch. Program
Faith Kancauski: Director of Administration and Financial Affairs
Robert Krawczyk: Director of B.Arch. Program
Harry Francis Mallgrave: Director, International Center for Sustainable New Cities

IOWA STATE UNIVERSITY

ADDRESS

Main
Iowa State University
Department of Architecture
158 College of Design
Ames, IA 50011-3093
Tel.: 515.294.2557
Fax: 515.294.1440
jholt@iastate.edu
www.arch.iastate.edu

STUDENT AND FACULTY DEMOGRAPHICS

% of Female Students	34
% of International Students	4
% of Minority Students	12
% of Out-of-State U.S. Students	36
No. Full-Time Faculty	27
No. Part-Time Faculty	8
No. Full-Time Students	653
No. Part-Time Students	8

FINANCIAL INFORMATION

Main Source of University Funding	Public
Annual Tuition & Fees (graduate, resident)	$7,236
Annual Tuition & Fees (graduate, nonresident)	$18,120
Annual Tuition & Fees (undergraduate, resident)	$6,360
Annual Tuition & Fees (undergraduate, nonresident)	$17,350
% Students Receiving Federal Financial Aid	
% Students Receiving University Financial Aid	
% Students Receiving Departmental Financial Aid	10
% Students Receiving Scholarships (assistantships or fellowships)	63
Average Annual Scholarship for Department	$1,000

ACADEMIC SESSIONS

Fall Semester: August to December
Spring Semester: January to May

Summer Session: June to July
Deadline for Graduate Admission: January 1 for Fall Admission

ARCHITECTURE AND RELATED DEGREE PROGRAMS							
Degree	Min. Yrs. to Complete	Professional Accreditation	# of FT Students	# of PT Students	# of First-Year Students	# of Degrees Conferred	Admissions Requirements
Architecture							
B. Arch	5	NAAB	613	4	357	64	
M. Arch	1		0	2	2	1	
M. Arch	2	NAAB	6	1	2	3	
M. Arch	3	NAAB	34	0	7	16	
MS Arch			0	1	0	0	

SPECIALIZATIONS

Architectural Design   Environment/Sustainability   Urban Planning and Design

ARCHITECTURE PROGRAM SUMMARY

From our gracious home in the heartland, the Department of Architecture at Iowa State University attracts close to half of its students from across the country and around the globe. We reciprocate that broad interest by preparing all of our students for amazing architectural opportunities across those same varied venues, including our own great home state of Iowa with its rich architectural heritage. One validation of the high-quality preparation our students receive comes from the prestigious professional publication, *DesignIntelligence*. Their survey of "*America's Best Architecture and Design Schools*," is conducted by soliciting responses directly from architectural practices. Firms are asked to evaluate which school produced architecture graduates over the last five years that are best prepared for the profession. Our undergraduate program has been ranked among their top fifteen national programs for the last five years in a row, one of only ten schools to receive that consistent national recognition. Our specific annual rankings have ranged from 7th to 14th. This year our graduate program earned national recognition in these rankings as well. Knowledgeable firms within our competitive 12-state Midwest region are also asked to rank the top national schools, and this year they ranked our graduate program first and our undergraduate program second among our peer programs in all U.S. architecture schools. There are 115 programs in the United States that offer accredited graduate and undergraduate degrees in architecture; the consistently high national ranking of our Department of Architecture clearly places us among the elite schools in the nation.

The acknowledged success of our students is the direct result of our talented and committed faculty. The faculty recognition bestowed by the Association of Collegiate Schools of Architecture (ACSA) is a testament to the high standards exhibited by our faculty team. In the last five years, they have received three ACSA Creative Achievement Awards, the only program in the country to do so, as well as three ACSA/AIA New Faculty Teaching Awards, one of only two programs in the country to do so. We are the only program in the nation to receive at least one ACSA award in each of the last seven years. The most recent recognition occurring in 2008 was a coveted ACSA Distinguished Professor Award. We were also selected as one of only twenty international architecture programs allowed to compete in the Fall 09 Solar Decathlon; a prestigious bi-annual event to construct an energy efficient residential prototype on the mall in Washington, DC.

The high achievements of our faculty represent a broad range of individual and collective academic pursuits. We do not require allegiance to a particular doctrine; we encourage exploration and value exposure to a balance of diverse aspirations and perspectives. We reside in the middle of our state in the middle of our country. We build upon that stable grounding by aggressively expanding our students' awareness through projects and fieldtrips to distant venues that range from Montreal to Miami and New York to New Mexico. In addition to our popular semester-long program in Rome, we also have optional summer programs in various venues around the globe.

We are committed to the design studio as a workshop in which conceptual and theoretical thinking is integrated with the everyday, the material, the technological, and the humane. In the Department of Architecture we offer an accredited professional 5-year undergraduate B.Arch. program and an accredited professional 3.5-year M.Arch. program that links research and experimentation with the professional requisites. Post-professional programs (M.Arch. 30 cr. and MSAS) interrelate theory and practice in specialized explorations of architecture in collaboration with our faculty.

Our program is housed in an award-winning building that shares an active interdisciplinary environment with our partners in the College of Design, including highly ranked departments and programs in Landscape Architecture, Community & Regional Planning, Interior Design, Graphic Design, and Integrated Studio Arts, as well as multiple minors including Environmental Design, Digital Media, and more. We are currently constructing a building addition that will provide valuable contiguous facilities and a positive example of our commitment to sustainability; we expect that critical message to be embedded in all of our programs. Our campus received an ASLA Centennial Medallion as a landmark of landscape design by legendary Frederick Olmsted. Here with us you will find affordable living, beautiful rolling hills, four glorious seasons, a big blue sky, and a quality life-style full of opportunity.

UNIVERSITY SETTING
Iowa State University is a public, land-grant Research I University, with about 25,000 students that is located in Ames, Iowa where it engages its situation in the mid-American Landscape. Ames is adjacent to the central Iowa urban center and state capital of Des Moines, which shares a vibrant urban setting and rich architectural heritage. The Department of Architecture is a comprehensive center for teaching, research, and public service in architecture.

SCHOOL PHILOSOPHY
The department is committed to the study of architecture as a cultural discipline in which issues of practice, of the multiplicity of social formations in which buildings exist, and of environmental effect are enfolded with the subject matter of building design—construction, space, material, form, and use. The complexity of architectural production is mirrored in an intentional pluralistic student body and faculty. The professional programs are grounded in the requisites of a professional education. The five-year undergraduate program positions architectural design as an armature within a broad-based field of general studies. The graduate program is research-based and allows the student to explore special areas of interest in addition to the core curriculum in architecture.

PROGRAM DESCRIPTION
Undergraduate Program
The bachelor of architecture program is both an intense professional course of study and a broadly conceived experience in general education. The design studio is the armature of the program and students explore the possibilities of design as a synthesizing practice. The work of the studio is an assemblage of the elements of experience and intention, of the subject matter of building design and of the engendering effects of a pluralistic cultural field. In this engagement, the curriculum mirrors contemporary practice as it simultaneously constructs the broad historical range of architecture both as discipline and practice. The undergraduate curriculum is composed of a preprofessional program (29.5 credits—two semesters) followed by a 140-credit professional program that is typically four years in length. At the end of the first year, applicants are reviewed for admission to the professional program, which is currently limited to 80 students. The professional curriculum is structured by a progressive and sequential involvement in the elements of the field of architecture: design, communications, technology, history, theory, human behavior, and practice. Each year level is composed of a set of interconnected courses that enhance the student's learning experience. From the beginning, the student is involved in the construction, representation, and simulation of architecture. All students are expected to be computer literate by the completion of their course of study. The curriculum includes a semester-long individual project in the 5th year as well as a broad selection of interdisciplinary option studios shared across the college.

AREAS OF FOCUS AND RESEARCH
Focus
The social dimensions of architecture, both in its purposes and in its practices, permeate student work in both undergraduate senior projects and in graduate theses. As students work closely with selected faculty

members, they draw inspiration and direction from the research topics above as they pursue their individual projects. The student workspaces incorporate traditional drawing and physical modeling as well as digital media design tools. The studio environment, as a precursor to practice, is one of collaboration as students support each other in learning and faculty members serve as facilitators and resources.
Research
Both undergraduate and graduate students have the opportunity to assist faculty with a wide variety of research activities in the theoretical and practical dimensions of architecture. Research in the department is typically individually conducted, but some projects involve multiple disciplines in collaboration. Recent topics of investigation include sustainability and the Solar Decathlon, architecture and human frailty, passive solar architecture, design media practices, digital modeling of urban areas, design education, contemporary western and non-western urbanism, materials for construction from agricultural fibers, social memory and technological change, building sciences and arts, popular culture, mobile architectures, universal accessibility, ethics, 'other' histories of architecture, evolution of the profession, cultural diffusion, and late 20th Century modernism, serial responsibility and design activities.

SPECIAL ACTIVITIES AND PROGRAMS
The department integrates a significant mid-American or North American urban setting into each studio. Studio trips are taken to Minneapolis, Chicago, the Prairie School of Wisconsin, Montreal, New York City, Boston, Seattle, and Los Angeles. In the fourth year of the undergraduate program and between the first and second years of the graduate program, students may elect to study for a semester in the College of Design facility in Rome. The department organizes an extensive lecture series of nationally recognized speakers. It also conducts a recognitions and awards ceremony with the AIAS, and the college's Career Services Office holds an enthusiastic Career Day.

FACILITIES
The studios are supplemented with specialized digital laboratories, modeling workshops, rapid prototyping equipment, and public review spaces constructed by the department's design/build studio. There is also a college supply store, exhibit gallery, cyber café, a new lecture hall, a branch reading room of the main university library, and a new addition currently under construction.

SCHOLARSHIPS AND FINANCIAL AID
Numerous scholarships and awards are provided by national practitioners and university sources each year. The university maintains a Student Financial Aid office to help students deal with financial matters. Most graduate students have teaching and research assistantship awards that include tuition scholarships and salaries.

ADMINISTRATION
Mark C. Engelbrecht, FAIA: Dean
Katherine L. Schwennsen, FAIA: Associate Dean
Calvin F. Lewis, FAIA: Department Chair

JUDSON UNIVERSITY

ADDRESS

Main
Judson University
School of Art, Design & Architecture
Department of Architecture
1151 North State Street
Elgin, IL 60123-1498
Tel.: 847.628.1010
Fax: 847.628.1008
www.judsonu.edu/academics/
undergraduate/art-design-and-architecture

STUDENT AND FACULTY DEMOGRAPHICS

% of Female Students	27
% of International Students	1
% of Minority Students	10
% of Out-of-State U.S. Students	53
No. Full-Time Faculty	8
No. Part-Time Faculty	12
No. Full-Time Students	168
No. Part-Time Students	30

FINANCIAL INFORMATION

Main Source of University Funding	Private
Annual Tuition & Fees (graduate, resident)	$25,300
Annual Tuition & Fees (graduate, nonresident)	$25,300
Annual Tuition & Fees (undergraduate, resident)	$21,850
Annual Tuition & Fees (undergraduate, nonresident)	$21,850
% Students Receiving Federal Financial Aid	90
% Students Receiving University Financial Aid	95
% Students Receiving Departmental Financial Aid	
% Students Receiving Scholarships (assistantships or fellowships)	
Average Annual Scholarship for Department	

ACADEMIC SESSIONS

Fall Semester: August to December; Application Deadline: April 1
Spring Semester: January to May; Application Deadline: See Website

Summer Session I: June to July; Application Deadline: See Website

ARCHITECTURE AND RELATED DEGREE PROGRAMS

Degree	Min. Yrs. to Complete	Professional Accreditation	# of FT Students	# of PT Students	# of First-Year Students	# of Degrees Conferred	Admissions Requirements
Architecture							
B.A.A.S.	4		156	7	65	28	ACT or SAT, TOEFL
M. Arch	2	NAAB	12	23		9	Undergraduate degree, GRE, TOEFL, Portfolio, Rec. Letters
Interior Design							
B.A. Interior Design	4		8	0	5	0	ACT or SAT, TOEFL
Art							
B.A. Visual Communications	4		41	2	10	13	ACT or SAT, TOEFL, Portfolio
Fine Arts Studio	4		3	0	0	1	ACT or SAT, TOEFL, Portfolio
General Art	4		11	1	3	2	ACT or SAT, TOEFL, Portfolio

SPECIALIZATIONS

Architectural Design
Community Design

Environment/Sustainable Design
History

Professional Practice

Sacred Spaces

ARCHITECTURE PROGRAM SUMMARY

Welcome to one of the finest institutions of higher education in the United States and the School that is doing extraordinary work in the disciplines of Art, Design and Architecture within a context of Christian community. We hope that you will find this information useful in describing the mission of this special place, a Christ-centered community of architects, artists and designers, who appreciate diversity, embrace critical and creative excellence, develop the visual and spatial imagination, and model stewardship and hope in service to local and global communities.

Please visit our School website at: www.judsonu.edu/academics/undergraduate/art-design-and-architecture/

UNIVERSITY SETTING

Judson University is a small (821 traditional students) private evangelical Christian institution in the Northwest Chicago suburb of Elgin, IL. A majority of the students live in campus residence halls and apartments. The small size allows close personal associations that extend beyond the classroom and studio. The physical campus provides a beautiful setting on the Fox River that includes ample athletic and recreational facilities. Opportunities in Christian ministries including theatrical, musical and artistic endeavors abound.

SCHOOL PHILOSOPHY

The Judson architecture program represents the Church at work in higher education and aspires to be a global leader in architectural education and Christian service.

PROGRAM DESCRIPTION

Founded in 1997, and accredited by NAAB in 2004, the program is widely acknowledged for its innovative approach to architectural education including a one year-preceptorship (internship) and its context of an evangelical Christian institution. Environmental stewardship is a design philosophy, which guides the program and its approach to architecture education. The program consists of a 137-credit-hour Bachelor of Arts in Architectural Studies and a 42-credit-hour professional Master of Architecture degree.

AREAS OF FOCUS AND RESEARCH

Students in architecture may elect to concentrate in Sustainable Design or Traditional Architecture and Urbanism. The program features numerous minors available including Visual Communications, Business, and Worship Arts.

SPECIAL ACTIVITIES AND PROGRAMS

The Architecture Study Tour provides faculty-guided learning opportunities, typically in Europe, including Italy, France and England. This tour explores both the traditional roots of Western architecture and the contemporary expressions of modern Europe. An annual lecture and gallery series provides monthly presentations during the academic year from the leading architects and artists of the Chicago area and from professionals from across the United States and around the world. Christian ministry groups seek out the students to provide architectural ministry services in the United States and around the world. The required graduate-level Community Outreach course is designed to assist local non-profits and ministries with programming and design services that otherwise could not be afforded. The professional internship program offers opportunities to work in significant architectural offices both in the United States and the world and is a one-year requirement of the M.Arch. program.

FACILITIES

The Department of Architecture is housed within the School of Art, Design and Architecture (SOADA) and occupies a LEED Gold facility, the Harm A. Weber Academic Center, designed by British architect C. Alan Short.

SCHOLARSHIPS AND FINANCIAL AID

The following academic awards are added to any grant aid awarded to a student. Each scholarship is automatically renewed every year of continuous attendance at Judson University, contingent upon the student maintaining the minimum GPA requirement. Students receive Academic Merit Awards whether or not they apply for financial aid.

Academic Merit Awards for Incoming Freshman (AY 07-08):

- ACT score of 30 (1340 SAT) or higher with a 3.6 GPA or higher will receive $10,000
- ACT score of 25-29 (1140-1300 SAT) with a 3.6 GPA or higher will receive $8,000
- ACT score of 25 (1140 SAT) or higher with a 3.59 GPA or lower will receive $6,000
- ACT score of 19-24 (910-1110 SAT) with a 3.33 GPA or higher will receive $6,000

Academic Merit Awards for Incoming Transfers (AY 07-08):

- 3.6 or higher GPA will receive $6,000
- 3.30-3.59 GPA will receive $5,000
- 3.00-3.29 GPA will receive $4,000

In addition, the Department offers a number of graduate-level scholarships, teaching assistantships, and research assistant opportunities based on academic excellence and need.

ADMINISTRATION

Curtis Sartor, PhD, Min. Assoc. NOMA, AIA: Dean
Stacie L. Burtelson: Interim Chair
Royce Earnest, AIA: Graduate Coordinator
G.E. Colpitts: Art and Design Chair

KANSAS STATE UNIVERSITY

ADDRESS

Main
Department of Architecture
College of Architecture, Planning &
Design
Kansas State University
211 Seaton Hall
Manhattan, KS 66506-2902
Tel.: 785.532.5953
Fax: 785.532.6722
architecture@ksu.edu
capd.ksu.edu/arch

STUDENT AND FACULTY DEMOGRAPHICS

% of Female Students	48
% of International Students	1
% of Minority Students	8
% of Out-of-State U.S. Students	52
No. Full-Time Faculty	25
No. Part-Time Faculty	4
No. Full-Time Students	388
No. Part-Time Students	0

FINANCIAL INFORMATION

Main Source of University Funding	Public
Annual Tuition & Fees (graduate, resident)	$4,732
Annual Tuition & Fees (graduate, nonresident)	$10,692
Annual Tuition & Fees (undergraduate, resident)	$6,422
Annual Tuition & Fees (undergraduate, nonresident)	$16,481
% Students Receiving Federal Financial Aid	61
% Students Receiving University Financial Aid	40
% Students Receiving Departmental Financial Aid	15
% Students Receiving Scholarships (assistantships or fellowships)	45
Average Annual Scholarship for Department	$1,673

ACADEMIC SESSIONS

Fall Semester: August to December; Application Deadline: Feb. 1
Spring Semester: January to May

ARCHITECTURE AND RELATED DEGREE PROGRAMS

Degree	Min. Yrs. to Complete	Professional Accreditation	# of FT Students	# of PT Students	# of First-Year Students	# of Degrees Conferred	Admissions Requirements
Architecture							
Non-baccalaureate M. Arch	5	NAAB	378	0	90	60	SAT, ACT, TOEFL
M.S. Architecture	1.5		10	0	6	3	TOEFL, Portfolio, Rec. Letters, Essay
Landscape Architecture							
Non-baccalaureate MLA	5	LAAB	138	0	30	11	SAT, ACT, TOEFL
Post-baccalaureate MLA	3	LAAB	26	0	10	2	Undergraduate degree, TOEFL, Portfolio, Rec. Letters, Essay
Interior Design/Interior Architecture							
Non-baccalaureate Master of Interior Architecture & Product Design	5	CIDA/FIDER	166	0	45	25	SAT, ACT, TOEFL
Environmental Design							
PhD in Environmental Design and Planning	3		1	1	2	0	GRE, Portfolio, Rec. Letters, Essay
Planning							
M.S. Community Development	2		10		8	0	Undergraduate degree, TOEFL, Rec. Letters, Essay
MRCP	2	PAB	14	0	4	2	Undergraduate degree, TOEFL, Rec. Letters, Essay
Non-baccalaureate M.R.C.P	5	PAB	24		15	0	SAT, ACT, TOEFL

SPECIALIZATIONS

Theory/Criticism   Sustainability

ARCHITECTURE PROGRAM SUMMARY

The College of Architecture, Planning and Design at KSU now offers 5-year accredited non-baccalaureate first professional master's degrees instead of bachelor's degrees. Students begin their education by taking undergraduate courses. After admission to the graduate school during third year, students take graduate coursework in addition to undergraduate to complete the M. Arch. The Department of Architecture also has a research-oriented post-professional M.S. Arch. program for those with degrees in architecture or related fields.

UNIVERSITY SETTING

Students from across America and abroad enjoy extraordinary opportunities for exploration and growth in this interdisciplinary college nationally recognized for design excellence. Our lively academic community includes students in architecture, interior architecture, landscape architecture, and regional and community planning. Beginning students share a year of interdisciplinary design study before selecting their field. Transfer and international exchange students broaden our academic dialogues. An array of courses, events, student organizations, and cultural resources is available at Kansas State.

SCHOOL PHILOSOPHY

The Department of Architecture prepares students to become leaders of the profession of architecture that is characterized by enduring principles and by ongoing change in response to social and technological developments. Design, complemented by liberal studies, is at the center of professional and critical discourse. A body of theoretical, artistic, social, and technical knowledge, understanding and skill that all architects share is offered as the basis for the identification and advancement of the individual student's interests and aptitudes through close interactions with the faculty.

PROGRAM DESCRIPTION

The accredited M. Arch. curriculum consists of a core of required professional courses supplemented by electives. These courses include an eight-semester architectural design studio sequence, a four-semester structural systems sequence, a three-semester environmental systems sequence, and a two-semester building science/construction systems sequence, among others.

170 credit hours are required for graduation. Of these, 31 hours are included in the Environmental Design Studies Program curriculum, completed before admission to the department. 140 credit hours are in the undergraduate component of the M. Arch degree (including the 31 in ENVD). Thirty hours are in the graduate program of study, taken primarily during the 5th year.

The post-professional M. S. in Architecture program requires 30 hours of graduate credit, with either a thesis or non-thesis option.

The areas of emphasis in the Master of Science in Architecture program reflect the research interests of many of the faculty: Ecological and Sustainable Design, Design Theory, and Environment-Behavior and Place Studies.

AREAS OF FOCUS AND RESEARCH

Faculty characteristically incorporate their research in design studios as well as other courses, and post-professional graduate students often undertake research paralleling that of their faculty advisors. Collaboration with colleagues in our college and university, as well as with peers in academia and the design professions, is widespread. Included among the subjects being pursued are: sustainable design, urban design, housing, healing environments, special populations/aging, environmental health, architectural history, architecture and landscape, Japanese architecture and urbanism, and Middle Eastern architecture and urbanism. A number of faculty are actively engaged in practice and other creative pursuits.

SPECIAL ACTIVITIES AND PROGRAMS

Most fourth-year students study for a semester in college programs in Orvieto or Castiglion Fiorentino, Italy, the Bauhaus in Dessau, Germany, or on other study abroad programs, or become Architectural Interns sponsored by professional firms worldwide. Selected fifth-year students may join an interdisciplinary Kansas City Academic Program. Second and third-year students visit major American cities each year on study tours. Edited and managed by students, OZ is widely recognized for the quality of its articles and graphic design. Lectures and exhibitions feature speakers and environments from across the nation and globe. The summer Design Discovery Program serving secondary school students, AIAS Chapter, and the Architecture Student

Advisory Board are among the many activities that contribute to the life of the department. Active dialogues with practitioners and excellent support from the Career and Employment Services office provides assistance in arranging internships and other employment. In the last year 96% of graduates were employed or furthering their education within months after graduation.

FACILITIES

Architecture students have used the Seaton Hall complex for more than a century. A multi-million dollar renovation completed in 2000 created state-of-the-art studios, seminar rooms, and faculty offices within the historic stone building envelope. Design/build studios transformed the lower level of the building into first-year studios and a multi-purpose college gathering space. Every architecture student is provided a computer networked studio workstation available 24/7. Third-year students are expected to have a computer suitable for use in design studio and other courses. The Weigel Library, Krider Visual Resource and Learning Center, and Chang Gallery as well as computing, daylighting and sun study facilities, support teaching and learning in the department.

SCHOLARSHIPS AND FINANCIAL AID

Almost seventy percent of the students in the department receive some form of assistance. In addition to university-administered scholarships, grants, loans and work-study programs, many merit and need based scholarships are available within the department and college. Several architectural foundations have generous scholarship programs for which our students qualify. Most undergraduate students who are permanent residents of Missouri receive waivers of out-of-state tuition. Many M.S. Arch. students receive assistantships carrying a stipend and tuition waiver, and some M.Arch. students are employed as teaching assistants during their 5th year on an hourly basis.

ADMINISTRATION

Dennis Law, FASLA: Dean
Dr. Peter Magyar: Head, Architecture
Dan Donelin: Head, Landscape Architecture
Lorraine Cuttler: Head, Int. & Prod Des.

KENT STATE UNIVERSITY

ADDRESS

Main
Kent State University
College of Architecture &
Environmental Design
304 Taylor Hall
Kent, OH 44242
Tel. : 330.672.2789
Fax: 330.672.3809
dmdavis@kent.edu
www.caed.kent.edu

STUDENT AND FACULTY DEMOGRAPHICS

% of Female Students	40
% of International Students	2
% of Minority Students	4
% of Out-of-State U.S. Students	11
No. Full-Time Faculty	22
No. Part-Time Faculty	42
No. Full-Time Students	552
No. Part-Time Students	46

FINANCIAL INFORMATION

Main Source of University Funding	Public
Annual Tuition & Fees (graduate, resident)	$8,968
Annual Tuition & Fees (graduate, nonresident)	$15,980
Annual Tuition & Fees (undergraduate, resident)	$8,430
Annual Tuition & Fees (undergraduate, nonresident)	$15,862
% Students Receiving Federal Financial Aid	
% Students Receiving University Financial Aid	
% Students Receiving Departmental Financial Aid	
% Students Receiving Scholarships (assistantships or fellowships)	15
Average Annual Scholarship for Department	$3,500

ACADEMIC SESSIONS

Fall Semester: August to December; Application Deadline: January 31st
Spring Semester: January to May

ARCHITECTURE AND RELATED DEGREE PROGRAMS							
Degree	Min. Yrs. to Complete	Professional Accreditation	# of FT Students	# of PT Students	# of First-Year Students	# of Degrees Conferred	Admissions Requirements
Architecture							
B Arts	4		20		20		Associate's Degree, ACT
BS Arch	4		350	22	100	75	SAT, ACT
M. Arch (Professional Degree)	1.5	NAAB	45	2	45	28	Undergraduate Architecture degree, GRE, TOEFL, Portfolio, Rec. Letters, Essay
M. Arch + M.B.A	2	NAAB	6	1	5	6	Undergraduate Architecture degree, GRE, TOEFL, Portfolio, Rec. Letters, Essay
M. Arch + M.U.D.	2.5	NAAB	12	0	12	3	Undergraduate Architecture degree, GRE, TOEFL, Portfolio, Rec. Letters, Essay
M.U.D.	1		2	2	2	1	Undergraduate degree, Undergraduate Architecture degree, GRE, TOEFL, Portfolio, Rec. Letters, Essay
Interior Design/Interior Architecture							
B.Arts - ID	4	CIDA	160	15	80	32	

SPECIALIZATIONS

Architectural Design	Environment/Sustainability	Preservation	Theory/Criticism
Building Technology/Env. Systems	History	Professional Practice	Urban Planning and Design

ARCHITECTURE PROGRAM SUMMARY

The architecture program at Kent State University enables students to acquire and apply knowledge that contributes to the betterment of our physical environments. Within a balanced curriculum of technology, visualization, history, theory and design studio coursework, the program offers a platform for scholarship, constructive discourse and debate. Northeast Ohio's rich history and dynamic urban landscape serve as a setting for academic learning and the study of "real world" conditions. By placing equal emphasis on the poetics and pragmatics of construction and design, the curriculum inspires experimentation, collaboration, discovery, critical thinking and innovation. The program fosters academic excellence and prepares students to be responsible and accomplished architectural professionals.

UNIVERSITY SETTING

Kent State University is centrally located in northeastern Ohio. The area has a metropolitan population of over 4,500,000 within a one-hour drive from campus and includes the cities of Cleveland, Akron, Canton, Youngstown, and Warren. The main campus has a student population of 23,000 with an additional 10,000 students on seven regional campuses. There are over 100 university buildings on the scenic 866-acre main Kent Campus. The university's land holdings include thousands of acres of a nearby wildlife refuge, as well as marsh and bog areas preserved by the university as learning laboratories and resources for the future.

SCHOOL PHILOSOPHY

Kent State University's College of Architecture and Environmental Design is dedicated to educating future professionals with an emphasis on improving quality of life, enhancing physical environments, and protecting public welfare. The college fosters inquiry and discovery through the promotion of research in the various environmental design professions, and assists communities in improving physical environments through outreach programs.

PROGRAM DESCRIPTION

Undergraduate Program—The Architecture Program offers a four-year pre-professional Bachelor of Science degree. The first two years are general in nature with emphasis placed on liberal arts education as well as introductory design and technology coursework. Third and fourth years provide students with a body of professional knowledge, a comprehensive design-technology studio experience, and an opportunity for a full semester of study in Florence, Italy.

The college also offers a four-year non-professional Bachelor of Arts Degree. This undergraduate program provides a broad-based educational experience coupled with a general introduction to the design disciplines. It is intended for students who are interested in fields aligned with architecture, and offers an alternative to the full studio and technically-based professional program.

Graduate Program—The Bachelor of Science plus the 1 1/2-year Master of Architecture program jointly comprise the first professional NAAB accredited degree in the Architecture Program. The Master of Architecture program prepares graduates to enter the profession of architecture by stimulating the growth of technical knowledge and design creativity. It enhances design skills acquired in undergraduate programs and offers a broad exposure to professional issues and knowledge.

AREAS OF FOCUS AND RESEARCH

Areas of research within the college include environmental design sciences, historic preservation, digital technologies, and urban design theories. The architecture program offers a certificate in Preservation Architecture as well as dual graduate degrees in Architecture and Business Administration, and Architecture and Urban Design.

SPECIAL ACTIVITIES AND PROGRAMS

Study Abroad—Each year the College of Architecture and Environmental Design (CAED) offers students in architecture (undergraduate & graduate), interior design, and urban design an option for a full semester of study in KSU's facility in Florence Italy, Palazzo dei Cerchi. These programs present students with the opportunity to study and experience first hand the historical evolution of European art, architecture, and urbanism, while familiarizing students with the contemporary "design scene" and the on-going modernization of European cities.

The Cleveland Urban Design Collaborative—The CUDC combines the public service outreach of the Urban Design Center of Northeast Ohio (UDC) and the graduate program in Urban Design. The CUDC serves as a resource for the public and private interests by gathering, analyzing, and disseminating information related to the design of the urban environment.

FACILITIES

The College of Architecture and Environmental Design at Kent State University is primarily located in Taylor Hall in the central part of campus. Studios for first- and second-year students in the Bachelor of Science program are located on the 4th floor, and the third, fourth, and graduate students are situated in two recently renovated adjacent buildings. Students participating in the full semester study abroad program are located in the 13th Century Palazzo dei Cerchi in the heart of Florence, Italy, while graduate students in Urban Design are located off campus in the Cleveland Urban Design Collaborative Point Building in downtown Cleveland.

SCHOLARSHIPS AND FINANCIAL AID

Kent State University has developed a financial aid program to assist students who lack the necessary funds for a college education. This program, consisting of scholarships, loans, grants, and part-time employment, is administered by the Office of Student Financial Aid. The Honors College also offers a number of scholarships to distinguished high school scholars and creative artists. Honors students are eligible to apply for scholarships up to four years ranging from $600 to full tuition per academic year.

ADMINISTRATION

James E. Dalton, FAIA: Dean
Diane M. Davis-Sikora, RA: Associate Dean
Dr. Pamela Evans: Associate Dean

LAWRENCE TECHNOLOGICAL UNIVERSITY

ADDRESS

Main
Lawrence Technological University
College of Architecture & Design
21000 West Ten Mile Road
Southfield, MI 48075-1058
Tel.: 248.204.2805
Fax: 248.204.2900
archdean@ltu.edu
 www.ltu.edu/architecture_and_design

STUDENT AND FACULTY DEMOGRAPHICS

% of Female Students	38.6
% of International Students	5.2
% of Minority Students	12.1
% of Out-of-State U.S. Students	2
No. Full-Time Faculty	22
No. Part-Time Faculty	64
No. Full-Time Students	567
No. Part-Time Students	276

FINANCIAL INFORMATION

Main Source of University Funding	Private
Annual Tuition & Fees (graduate)	$14,000
Annual Tuition & Fees (undergraduate)	$23,000
% Students Receiving Federal Financial Aid	63
% Students Receiving University Financial Aid	54
% Students Receiving Departmental Financial Aid	2
% Students Receiving Scholarships (assistantships or fellowships)	
Average Annual Scholarship for Department	$1,400

ACADEMIC SESSIONS

Fall Semester: August to December; Application Deadline: August 15
Spring Semester: January to May; Application Deadline: December 15

Summer Session I: May to July; Application Deadline: May 1

ARCHITECTURE AND RELATED DEGREE PROGRAMS

Degree	Min. Yrs. to Complete	Professional Accreditation	# of FT Students	# of PT Students	# of First-Year Students	# of Degrees Conferred	Admissions Requirements
Architecture							
BS Arch	4		548	163	170	121	ACT, TOEFL
M. Arch—2 years	1.3	NAAB	19	113	25	34	Undergraduate degree, Undergraduate Architecture degree, TOEFL, Portfolio, Rec. Letters, Essay
Interior Design/Interior Architecture							
B Int Arch	4	CIDA/FIDER	57	23	18	10	ACT, TOEFL
M Interior Design	1.3		6	19	3	0	Undergraduate degree, Portfolio, Rec. Letters, Essay
Graphic Design							
BFA Imaging	4	NASAD	42	10	9	6	ACT, TOEFL
Other							
B S Transportation Design	4	NASAD	6		6	0	ACT, TOEFL, Portfolio

SPECIALIZATIONS

Architectural Design
Art and Design
Community Design

Interior Design/Architecture
Preservation

Professional Practice
Sustainability

Theory/Criticism
Urban Planning and Design

UNIVERSITY SETTING

Lawrence Technological University is located in southeastern Michigan, approximately 10 miles north of the city of Detroit. A private university with approximately 4,000 students, Lawrence Tech has a rich diversity in its students. All classes are taught by professors and practitioners with class size limited in both lecture and studio courses. Dedicated studios are available to students in sophomore year through graduate studies. Tuition is identical for Michigan residents and non-residents. Transfer students are accepted.

SCHOOL PHILOSOPHY

The College of Architecture and Design motto is "Creativity, Integration, Leadership." All College curricula develops from the focus on Integrated Design Studios. A progressive Strategic Plan for the College guides program enrichment and all developments. The University motto is "Theory and Practice." All courses are offered both in day and evening schedules to assist students working in professional offices.

PROGRAM DESCRIPTION
Undergraduate Program

The Bachelor of Science in Architecture degree program focuses design education in the Integrated Design Studios that occur in the sophomore and junior years. There is a broad range of elective studies and courses offered in the senior year. Collaborative Urban Design, Sustainability, Landscape Architecture, Theory and Competitions, Preservation, and the Paris Summer Studio are examples. Other undergraduate degrees are in Interior Architecture, Transportation Design and a BFA in Imaging.

Graduate Program

There are two graduate programs, a NAAB accredited Master's in Architecture that is 36 credit hours. Students can select from four concentrations—Sustainable Design, Criticial Studies in Architecture, Architecture Design and Practice, and Urban Design. A year-long studio or research-based thesis is required in each concentration. The Master's in Interior Design is a post-professional degree and is available as a 37-credit program or a 3+ program for people who do not have an undergraduate degree in interior design.

AREAS OF FOCUS AND RESEARCH
Focus

Integrated design studio education is the focus of undergraduate study. Landscape architecture, interiors, lighting, urban planning and building technology as each relates to design are taught by professionals in a team setting. The graduate program offers four concentrations—Sustainable Architecture, Critical Studies in Architecture, Architecture Design and Practice, and Urban Design. At all levels, there are meaningful and ongoing partnerships with the design professions through full-time and adjunct faculty, guest lecturers and jury participation. The Detroit Studio, located in the New Center Area in Detroit, allows students to study urban design as they work with residents and firms within the city of Detroit.

Research

The University and College focus on the application of knowledge to professional education and links to professional practice, while strongly supporting faculty research, travel and writing. This includes funding for paper presentations, attendance at conferences and seminars, and other opportunities such as sabbaticals. Research by individual faculty includes community and urban design, sustainability, professional ethics, and ecology. Faculty members are also conducting research on teaching and learning.

SPECIAL ACTIVITIES AND PROGRAMS

The College annually sponsors a lecture series by recognized practicing professionals, open to the university and the public. Additional lecture series and field trips focus on curricular areas. Each year, an Outstanding Alumni Award is given to a recipient by voting alumni. The university owns the Frank Lloyd Wright designed Affleck House. The Summer Paris Studio and foreign travel offer rich study opportunities. The College has active chapters of AIAS and Tau Sigma Delta. Advantage is taken of close proximity to Cranbrook and the rapidly changing areas of Detroit and Pontiac. Students may choose to pursue dual degrees in any undergraduate program the University and College offer. Combinations may include architecture with Interior Architecture, Imaging or Civil Engineering. School publications include a newsletter, *Trace*. The graduate-level Master Class studio brings practitioners with emerging critical practices to the campus each summer to work with students.

FACILITIES

Facilities in the architecture building and Technology and Learning Center include dedicated studios for sophomore through graduate students, exhibition gallery, crit and seminar rooms, auditorium and advanced technology lecture hall, computing center, virtual reality laboratory, photography lab, wood shop, sculpture studio, and architectural resource center. The main campus library is in an adjacent building and includes the private library of Albert Kahn. All entering undergraduate students receive a laptop computer with software used in the college. The campus is wireless.

SCHOLARSHIPS AND FINANCIAL AID

Two-thirds of the students at Lawrence Technological University defray part of their educational costs through some form of financial assistance. Both need-based and academic-based scholarships and financial aid are offered annually to first-time students who are high school graduates with a minimum 3.00 GPA and transfer students. Financial need is not a requirement. Applications, available from the Financial Aid Office, must be received by March 1 for the following fall semester. Graduate students can apply for work–study scholarships, teaching, or graduate research scholarships.

ADMINISTRATION

Glen LeRoy, FAIA, FAICP: Dean
Joseph C. Veryser, AIA: Associate Dean
Virginia North: Assistant Dean-Graduate Studies
Daniel Faoro, AIA: Interim Chair

LOUISIANA STATE UNIVERSITY

 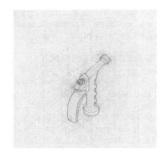 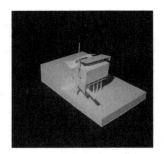

ADDRESS

Main
Louisiana State University
School of Architecture
136 Atkinson Hall
Baton Rouge, LA 70803
Tel.: 225.578.6885
Fax: 225.388-2168
sarch@lsu.edu
www.design.lsu.edu

STUDENT AND FACULTY DEMOGRAPHICS

% of Female Students	49
% of International Students	19
% of Minority Students	20
% of Out-of-State U.S. Students	12
No. Full-Time Faculty	14
No. Part-Time Faculty	8
No. Full-Time Students	289
No. Part-Time Students	16

FINANCIAL INFORMATION

Main Source of University Funding	Public
Annual Tuition & Fees (graduate, resident)	$5,000
Annual Tuition & Fees (graduate, nonresident)	$13,600
Annual Tuition & Fees (undergraduate, resident)	$5,000
Annual Tuition & Fees (undergraduate, nonresident)	$14,000
% Students Receiving Federal Financial Aid	34
% Students Receiving University Financial Aid	52
% Students Receiving Departmental Financial Aid	78
% Students Receiving Scholarships (assistantships or fellowships)	
Average Annual Scholarship for Department	$3,270

ACADEMIC SESSIONS

Fall Semester: August to December; Application Deadline: February 1st
Spring Semester: January to May

Summer Session I: June to July
Summer Session II: June to July

ARCHITECTURE AND RELATED DEGREE PROGRAMS							
Degree	Min. Yrs. to Complete	Professional Accreditation	# of FT Students	# of PT Students	# of First-Year Students	# of Degrees Conferred	Admissions Requirements
Architecture							
B. Arch	5	NAAB	235	16	80	24	
M. Arch—2 years	3	NAAB	24	0	12	12	
M. Arch—post-profes-sional							
Landscape Architecture							
BLA	5	LAAB	107	0	20	30	
MLA	3.5		56	0	12	15	
Interior Design/Interior Architecture							
Bachelor of Interior Design	4	CIDA/FIDER	200		30	35	

SPECIALIZATIONS

Community Design	Environment/Sustainability	Preservation	Urban Planning and Design
Computer-Aided Design	History		

UNIVERSITY SETTING

Louisiana State University is a Research I institution and Louisiana's only comprehensive university. The University enrolls 31,000 students from 48 states and over 120 foreign countries. The distinctive campus is designed in an Italian Renaissance domestic-style, its buildings surrounding quadrangles and linked by arcades. The School of Architecture is in the College of Art and Design, which offers degree programs in architecture, landscape architecture, interior design, graphic design, and the fine arts.

SCHOOL PHILOSOPHY

The rich cultural heritage and physical setting of Louisiana and the Lower Mississippi Delta region provides an invaluable resource for the study of architecture. An investigation of this shifting and fluid context results in the construction of useful frameworks for grasping architectural issues that can have both local and global import. Accordingly, the School's most valuable resource is our context. By making this resource central to our endeavors, graduates are set on a course toward professional leadership in the Gulf South, nationally, and globally.

PROGRAM DESCRIPTION

Undergraduate Program

The undergraduate program is a five-year, 162-credit baccalaureate degree program divided into three distinct phases of study, each contributing to the construction of frameworks to both view through and analyze with. The first phase concentrates on introducing the beginning student to the variety of opportunities in the design professions, as well as developing their design and form-making abilities. These investigations are conducted in design studios where students are asked to make inquiries into physical phenomena and distinctive sites. As a consequence, students develop a framework through which to appreciate the difference between conceptual "seeing" and perception. In the middle portion of the undergraduate curriculum, students integrate the technical and poetic through investigations of architectural projects and settlement processes. Students study historical and technological concepts through lectures or seminars and interrogate these new concepts in studio-based design projects. At the end of this phase, students complete a comprehensive design project that demonstrates their ability to manage the myriad of technical issues as they express their intention through the manipulation of space and form. In the last phase of the curriculum, students conduct an in-depth study. Research topics are selected by the faculty and are selected from issues confronting contemporary society.

AREAS OF FOCUS AND RESEARCH

Focus

The Office of Community Design and Development (www.ocdd.lsu.edu) is a community outreach arm for the School. Its mission is to facilitate improvement in the quality of the physical environment through research, planning, design, and education. All OCDD projects involve students as a means to augment their academic curriculum with real-world experience. The Heritage Conservation Concentration study area promotes an integrated strategy encompassing design, historic preservation, and economic development essential to achieving community vitality. Students pursuing a Heritage Conservation Concentration are active in public service, research, and the educational issues that are fundamental to maintaining the integrity of historic communities.

Research

The School has achieved national and international recognition for research in historic preservation, sustainability and energy conservation, and community design studies. Research resources include: the Office of Community Preservation, the Office of Building Research, the LSU Construction Experiment Station, the Computer-Aided Design and Geographic Information System Lab (CADGIS) and the Office of Community Design and Development. These groups serve the research and outreach endeavors of the school, creating opportunities for student enrichment and specialization.

SPECIAL ACTIVITIES AND PROGRAMS

- Academic programs abroad — programs in Paris, London, Italy, and Mexico.
- Active student chapter of the American Institute of Architecture Students (AIAS).
- Annual O.J. Baker Design Competition and Awards program.
- Design Recruitment Day annual job interview and placement fair.
- A computing laboratory designated as an Intergraph Center for Excellence providing access to all Intergraph software products.
- Cooperative education opportunities.
- Guest lecture and exhibit series — ongoing program of invited distinguished designers and artists.
- LSU Construction Experiment Station — investigations of low-cost building systems.
- Office of Community Design and Development — joint student and faculty service learning opportunities.
- Office of Community Preservation — historic preservation, development and documentation (http://lhn.lsu.edu/).
- Student–professional mentorship program — a pairing of professional architects and students for career advising.
- Tau Sigma Delta — a local chapter of the national architectural and allied arts honorary society.

FACILITIES

The School of Architecture is housed in historic Atkinson Hall, centrally located on the primary campus quadrangle. In addition to computer network access from every studio workstation, the upgraded facility provides students with a research laboratory for computer-aided design, image processing and other computer applications associated with the arts and design. The School shares an outstanding workshop, a Design Resource Center, and a Visual Resource Library with other units in the College. The workshop provides equipment, workspace and technical assistance to students. The conveniently located Design Resource Center has over 13,000 volumes and supplements the University library. The Visual Resource Library's collection contains over 135,000 images.

SCHOLARSHIPS AND FINANCIAL AID

LSU awards scholarships in the form of full and partial tuition exemptions, cash stipends, and employment opportunities to students who meet certain academic qualifications. Scholarships and awards administered by the School of Architecture are reserved for upper division students. Graduate students are eligible for teaching and research assistantships. Contact the Graduate Program Coordinator for applications and application deadlines. In addition to scholarships, the Office of Student Aid and Scholarships administers several federally funded financial aid programs.

ADMINISTRATION

David L. Cronrath, AIA: Dean
Jori Erdman: Director
Chris Theis: Graduate Coordinator

LOUISIANA TECH UNIVERSITY

ADDRESS

MAIN
Louisiana Tech University
School of Architecture
P.O. Box 3147
305 Wisteria Rd.
Ruston, LA 71272
Tel.: 318.257.2816
Fax: 318.257.4687
www.arch.latech.edu

STUDENT AND FACULTY DEMOGRAPHICS

% of Female Students	61
% of International Students	2
% of Minority Students	18
% of Out-of-State U.S. Students	14
No. Full-Time Faculty	15
No. Part-Time Faculty	2
No. Full-Time Students	254
No. Part-Time Students	18

FINANCIAL INFORMATION

Main Source of University Funding	Public
Annual Tuition & Fees (graduate, resident)	$5,061
Annual Tuition & Fees (graduate, nonresident)	$9,966
Annual Tuition & Fees (undergraduate, resident)	$5,061
Annual Tuition & Fees (undergraduate, nonresident)	$10,470
% Students Receiving Federal Financial Aid	51
% Students Receiving University Financial Aid	31
% Students Receiving Departmental Financial Aid	5
% Students Receiving Scholarships (assistantships or fellowships)	8
Average Annual Scholarship for Department	$4,700

ACADEMIC SESSIONS

Fall Quarter/Trimester: September to November
Winter Quarter/Trimester: November to February
Spring Quarter/Trimester: February to May

Summer Session I: May to July
Summer Session II: July to August

ARCHITECTURE AND RELATED DEGREE PROGRAMS

Degree	Min. Yrs. to Complete	Professional Accreditation	# of FT Students	# of PT Students	# of First-Year Students	# of Degrees Conferred	Admissions Requirements
Architecture							
B.S. Arch	4		190		60	20	ACT
M. Arch	1	NAAB	6		6	6	Undergraduate Architecture Degree, Portfolio, Rec. Letters, Essay
Interior Design/Interior Architecture							
BID	4	CIDA/FIDER	48	0	20	10	

SPECIALIZATIONS

Architectural Design	Community Design	Interior Design/Architecture	Sustainability
Art and Design	Computer-Aided Design	Professional Practice	Tectonics
Building Technology/Env. Systems	Environment/Sustainability		

ARCHITECTURE PROGRAM SUMMARY

Recognizing that architecture is one of the basic or root arts in human culture, the primary mission of the School of Architecture is to provide an accredited professional degree program in architecture that is reflective of the architect's role as the primary shaper and steward of the built environment throughout the life cycle of its buildings and communities. Additionally, the School of Architecture acknowledges that the conscientious making of the built environment is a collaborative endeavor, and consequently its secondary mission is to provide accredited degree programs in allied fields of study that share responsibility for influencing and affecting the nature and quality of the built environment.

More specifically, this entails:

- Teaching architecture in a manner that places a premium on design excellence understood as transcending mere utility to meet the needs of the intellectual, aesthetic and spiritual.
- Teaching architecture with an emphasis on design excellence informed by ethics and an appreciation of the cultural, social and physical contexts.
- Teaching architecture by placing value on design excellence as the preservation of the environment, the maintenance of sustainable growth and change, and the embodiment of appropriate cultural patterns, values and forms.
- Teaching architecture through understanding the relationship between what has been and what could be, and investigating both the timeless and the topical as measures of design excellence.
- Teaching the critical theoretical framework and skills necessary to challenge current methods and paradigms of practice in architecture and its allied fields.
- Teaching architecture and its allied fields within the context of the liberal arts and sciences by stressing the integration of knowledge from other disciplines in a process of design comprised of analysis, synthesis and production.

UNIVERSITY SETTING

Located in the piney hills of north Louisiana, Louisiana Tech University (11,000 students) serves the educational needs of this population primarily through strong baccalaureate programs in a broad range of studies in the arts, humanities, liberal arts, and sciences and in professional areas including architecture. The University presently offers a choice of master's programs and doctoral programs. The city of Ruston is the home of Louisiana Tech and offers an idyllic, small-town setting for the university community.

SCHOOL PHILOSOPHY

We define Architecture as the art of giving physical shape and identity to the environmental aspiration of people, their communities and their culture. We regard architecture as a synthesis of both poetic and pragmatic concerns, and we educate architects to be experts at resolving the conflicting demands of contextual, operational, aesthetic and ideological forces inherent to all architectural problems. The method we teach is an interpretive and reconciliatory one. It stresses that the final, physical form of building is the result of a thoughtful and intentional manipulation of compound, interacting forces.

PROGRAM DESCRIPTION
Undergraduate Program

The first two years of the architecture curriculum focus on the acquisition of basic artistic and critical skills. We believe that building a vocabulary of formal and spatial imagery, acquiring a repertory of compositional strategies, developing a sensitivity to context, and, most importantly, learning to formulate incisive questions are the foundations of architectural education. As our students advance to the professional concentration of the program, the scale and complexity of architectural problems they encounter increase progressively. Beginning at the third year where our students address community-scale issues, and extending into the fourth year where they concentrate on urban issues, we expect our students to face the contextual complexity, cultural diversity, ethical ambiguities, and increasing technical and pragmatic demands inherent to real-world architectural problems. Through our curriculum, we emphasize that every architectural problem is issue oriented and that design is a knowledge-based process.

Graduate Program

In our graduate program, we invite our students to define their own, individual degree design projects. We expect degree design projects to not only demonstrate technical and professional competence, but also to exhibit an ethic, a social conscience, and the personal conviction necessary to make a difference in our physical environments.

AREAS OF FOCUS AND RESEARCH
Focus

The School of Architecture maintains a particular interest in the "art and craft" of building. From the first year of the program, students are engaged in the real, material consequences of design by working directly with the "stuff" of building (wood, concrete, metal, etc.). Additional opportunities to build projects at full-scale occur in the professional concentration level of the program in the forms of furniture design, sculpture, ceramics, as well as realizing design projects for the local and university communities. Acquisitions of CNC fabrication equipment (routers, plasma cutters, and milling center) will enhance the School's interest in thoughtful making and building, moving an exclusively "hands-on" approach into the digital realm.

SPECIAL ACTIVITIES AND PROGRAMS

The School offers a wide range of programs designed to enhance the educations of our students. Each year we organize field trips to various metropolitan areas within easy driving distance, such as, Houston, Dallas, New Orleans and San Antonio; and each year we offer one major field trip to a center of urban culture such as New York, Chicago and Los Angeles. Our faculty works hard to make the trips as affordable as possible for our students. Each year we sponsor a guest lecture series, which provides our students with direct exposure to nationally and internationally renown practitioners, thinkers, and teachers.

FACILITIES

Our 30,000 square feet of studio and classroom spaces are housed in Hale Hall (recently completed) and the Wyly Tower of Learning which also contains an auditorium and the university library. We share with the School of Art another 20,000 square feet of work space in a shop facility which houses woodworking, metal-working, sculpture, ceramics and print-making equipment. Our students enjoy secured access to our facilities and to their own, private desks in our studio spaces. Our studios and classroom spaces are fully networked, and we offer our students access to a wide range of electronic equipment, including scanners, printers and plotters.

Additionally, students have access to a newly constructed Fabrication and Assembly Shop adjacent to the Art and Architecture Workshop. At approximately 3,000 square feet, the facility provides the School's programs with a large floor plate/high ceiling space for large-scale construction projects, and secure storage for both materials and tools/equipment.

SCHOLARSHIPS AND FINANCIAL AID

In addition to the wider range of scholarships and financial aid which the University offers to qualified students, the School of Architecture offers numerous scholarships to our own majors. Please contact Assistant Professor Damon Caldwell at the School of Architecture for additional information.

ADMINISTRATION

Karl Puljak, AIA: Director

MASSACHUSETTS COLLEGE OF ART AND DESIGN

ADDRESS

Main
Massachusetts College of Art and Design
Department of Architecture
621 Huntington Avenue
Boston, MA 02115
Tel.: 617.879.7669
Fax: 617.879.7773
www.massart.edu

STUDENT AND FACULTY DEMOGRAPHICS

% of Female Students	60
% of International Students	3
% of Minority Students	19
% of Out-of-State U.S. Students	29
No. Full-Time Faculty	6
No. Part-Time Faculty	11
No. Full-Time Students	62
No. Part-Time Students	8

FINANCIAL INFORMATION

Main Source of University Funding	Public
Annual Tuition & Fees (graduate, resident)	
Annual Tuition & Fees (graduate, nonresident)	
Annual Tuition & Fees (undergraduate, resident)	$7,900
Annual Tuition & Fees (undergraduate, nonresident)	$23,000
% Students Receiving Federal Financial Aid	40
% Students Receiving University Financial Aid	60
% Students Receiving Departmental Financial Aid	
% Students Receiving Scholarships (assistantships or fellowships)	
Average Annual Scholarship for Department	

ACADEMIC SESSIONS

Fall Semester: September to December;
    Application Deadline: see online application
Spring Semester: January to May;
    Application Deadline: see online application

Summer Session I: June to August;
    Application Deadline: see online application

ARCHITECTURE AND RELATED DEGREE PROGRAMS							
Degree	**Min. Yrs. to Complete**	**Professional Accreditation**	**# of FT Students**	**# of PT Students**	**# of First-Year Students**	**# of Degrees Conferred**	**Admissions Requirements**
Architecture							
B.A. Architecture	4	NASAD	57	0	15	300	SAT, TOEFL, Portfolio, Rec. Letters, Essay
M. Arch	2	NAAB Candidate	5	5	5	0	Undergraduate degree, Undergraduate Architecture degree, TOEFL, Portfolio, Rec. Letters, Essay
Interior Design/Interior Architecture							
B.A. Interior Architecture	4	NASAD	57		15	300	SAT, TOEFL, Portfolio, Rec. Letters, Essay

SPECIALIZATIONS

Architectural Design	Computer-Aided Design	Housing	Sustainability
Art and Design	Energy	Interior Design/Architecture	Tectonics
Building Technology/Env. Systems	Environment/Sustainability	International/Regional Architecture	Theory/Criticism
Community Design	History	Professional Practice	Urban Planning and Design

ARCHITECTURE PROGRAM SUMMARY

The Architecture program at Massachusetts College of Art and Design is designed to provide a rigorous, accessible and affordable professional preparation for a variety of architecture careers in a world facing serious global challenges. The undergraduate pre-professional architecture program offers courses of study in architecture and interior architecture. Grounded in energy-conscious building and site design, studio coursework in the Master of Architecture program is designed to produce architects and designers skilled in the technical and formal aspects of building, who are realistically prepared to be skilled collaborators in a collective environment of students, educators and professionals in architecture, engineering and construction.

UNIVERSITY SETTING

Massachusetts College of Art and Design is centered in the city of Boston, an urban environment with a diverse urban population rich in historic traditions. The school is within walking distance of many cultural institutions, museums and historic neighborhoods. Boston is a unique city with an active harbor and waterfront, thriving business centers, close knit communities and neighborhoods, as well as a wide range of schools and universities. Outside of the greater Boston area are small towns that represent a range of communities and econnomic centers—industrial communities with histories of fabrication, fishing villages and harbors with active fleets, and small New England towns with a square defining the town center. The studio and design-build projects are typically situated in one of these neighborhoods, encouraging students to experience the city and these communities through their work while learning how to collaborate in diverse economic, social and political settings.

SCHOOL PHILOSOPHY

The Architecture program at Massachusetts College of Art and Design is designed to provide a rigorous, accessible and affordable professional preparation for a variety of architecture careers in a world facing serious global challenges. Grounded in energy-conscious building and site design, studio coursework promotes the practical application of learned theory in building systems, construction technology, ethical practice and cultural traditions in architecture. The curriculum combines professional requirements with hands-on design-build experience focused on community living and working spaces, so that students develop as socially aware artisan-architects who are versatile problem-solvers and skilled collaborators, dedicated to sustainable improvement of the built environment.

PROGRAM DESCRIPTION

Massachusetts College of Art and Design offers a 120-credit pre-professional Bachelor of Arts with a major in Architecture, and a 60-credit Master of Architecture degree. The program is designed to produce architects and designers skilled in the technical and formal aspects of building, who are realistically prepared to be skilled collaborators in a collective environment of students, educators and professionals in architecture, engineering and construction.

Studio courses in housing, urban design and community projects ranging in scale from details in materials to housing and urban site planning are integrated with instruction in structural design, and sustainable construction materials, building methods and services systems, so that learned theory is put directly into practice. Scale models and full scale mockups are used not merely as overall massing studies, but also as analogs for the building process so that model-building represents structural systems and connections with various infill systems, giving tactile three-dimensional understanding of two-dimensional representations.

Both state-of-the-art and traditional technologies are employed for 2D and 3D presentations. Students may make sophisticated computer representations of details or connections that they originally sketched by hand, then hand fabricated in our wood, metal or glass shops. Frequent constructive critiques by faculty and guest design/construction professionals assist students in refining designs: these discussions typically cover design and program issues for buiding and related site and neighborhood, materials and structural decisions, safety, accessibility and code concerns, legal and economic issues, and energy conservation.

Seminars in architectural history and the building traditions of different cultures widen the students' frame of reference, and introduce techniques that involve presentation, restoration and adaptive re-use of historical buildings or cultural districts.

The graduate program curriculum is offered in four intensive continuous semesters, starting and ending in a summer semester, the final semester devoted to the student's thesis—a design project founded in research and practice and relevant to both the students' experience, vision and practice of architecture. Use of summer semesters permits shop and construction experience in prime building season, so that all students develop experience with designing and crafting details and assembling materials.

AREAS OF FOCUS AND RESEARCH

We expect each student to develop a personal language of form and a responsible design ethic, from a study of current, visionary, historic and vernacular architecture, and experimentation with the intrinsic properties and geometries of materials and building systems. Through hands-on experience, students learn to appreciate the range of detail possibilities and expressive potential of building materials and structural systems.

A final thesis in both the pre-professional and graduate programs permits each student to focus in detail on a research topic or building project of particular personal interest. At the graduate level, the thesis is a culmination of a student's work grounded in research and practice, relevant to the student's experience and vision, with the intention to further the profession in a particular area.

SPECIAL ACTIVITIES AND PROGRAMS
- Summer Design-Build Program (graduate program)
- Collaborations with New England Foundation of the Arts (NEFA)

- Professional experience—through the internship program students may opt to work in a firm and/or elect to take courses in the program working directly with client groups in design and construction projects.
- Travel Options (Europe, South America) that incorporate programs in sustainable projects, history, artisanry, building/neighborhood documentation, and design-build collaborations.
- Outside lecturers woven into curriculum including architects, design professionals, fabricators, urban planners and alumni on a wide range of topics.
- Visiting Artists funded through Exhiibitions Department who come for a period of time to live on campus and work with students in their area of expertise.
- Curatorial opportunities within the college network of exhibition spaces.

FACILITIES

Facilities include personal wireless studio spaces, extensive professional shops (wood, cold and hot metal, cold and hot glass, fibers, ceramics), a model construction shop and spray booth, computer labs, a lending library including extensive online collections and a large slide library, critique space, exhibition space, classrooms, seminar rooms, and faculty and administrative offices. Our inner courtyard is frequently used for large fabrication work for classrooms and individuals. Additionally, students engaged in joint projects with students and faculty from other departments or schools may utilize collaborative project spaces for this work throughout the school or offsite.

The school has dormitories directly across Huntington Avenue from the main campus to house all freshman and then upperclass students as available. Dorms and the main campus include adjacent studio work/fabrication spaces for student work outside the classroom, a provisions store, cafes, food-court style cafeteria, and social spaces, as well as multiple exhibition spaces.

SCHOLARSHIPS AND FINANCIAL AID

In general, 60% of our population obtains loans from federal and state sources as well as private lending institutions. These federal and state loans including both secured and unsecured monies for a full-time student can be as high as $20,000 annually. In addition, funds for work–study are available in the undergraduate program. In the graduate program students may obtain course assistantships for the undergraduate studios and other work within the graduate department.

ADMINISTRATION

Patricia Seitz, AIA, LEED: Head Graduate Program
Paul Hajian, AIA: Coordinator Undergraduate Program
Margaret Hickey: Chair, Department of Environmental Design
Ellen Shortell, PhD: Chair Critical Studies Department

MASSACHUSETTS INSTITUTE OF TECHNOLOGY

ADDRESS

Main
Massachusetts Institute of Technology
School of Architecture and Planning
Dept of Architecture, Bldg. 7, 7-337
77 Massachusetts Avenue
Cambridge, MA 02139-4307
Tel.: 617.253.7791
Fax: 617.253.8993
darrenb@MIT.EDU
architecture.mit.edu

STUDENT AND FACULTY DEMOGRAPHICS

% of Female Students	48
% of International Students	25
% of Minority Students	6
% of Out-of-State U.S. Students	89
No. Full-Time Faculty	30
No. Part-Time Faculty	3
No. Full-Time Students	260
No. Part-Time Students	3

FINANCIAL INFORMATION

Main Source of University Funding	Private
Annual Tuition & Fees (graduate)	$36,140
Annual Tuition & Fees (undergraduate)	$34,986
% Students Receiving Federal Financial Aid	15
% Students Receiving University Financial Aid	0
% Students Receiving Departmental Financial Aid	80
% Students Receiving Scholarships (assistantships or fellowships)	
Average Annual Scholarship for Department	$18,070

ACADEMIC SESSIONS

Fall Semester: September to December
Spring Semester: January to May

ARCHITECTURE AND RELATED DEGREE PROGRAMS

Degree	Min. Yrs. to Complete	Professional Accreditation	# of FT Students	# of PT Students	# of First-Year Students	# of Degrees Conferred	Admissions Requirements
Architecture							
BS Arch Des	4		70	0	0	22	
M. Arch—2 years	2.5	NAAB	44	0	14	9	
M. Arch—2 years	3.5	NAAB	48	0	8	12	
MS Arch	2		52	0	27	16	
PhD	3		57	0	9	11	
Graphic Design							
MS Visual Studies	2		4	0	4	2	
Other							
MS Bldg Tech	1.5		3	0	2	6	
MS Real Estate	1		35	0	30	29	

SPECIALIZATIONS

Architectural Design
Building Technology/Env. Systems
Community Design
Computer-Aided Design

Energy
Engineering
Environment/Sustainability
Graphic Design

History
International/Regional Architecture
Photography
Professional Practice

Sustainability
Theory/Criticism
Urban Planning and Design

ARCHITECTURE PROGRAM SUMMARY

The Department of Architecture offers two undergraduate degree programs: Bachelor of Science in Art and Design (BSAD), Course IV, offered in one of five disciplines (Architecture Design; Building Technology; Computation; History, Theory and Criticism of Architecture and Art; and Visual Arts), and Bachelor of Science (SB), Course IV-B, an interdisciplinary program. The Department also offers five graduate degree programs: Master of Architecture (MArch); Master of Science in Architecture Studies (SMArchS) (in five research areas: Aga Khan Program for Islamic Architecture; Architecture and Urbanism; Building Technology; Design and Computation; History, Theory and Criticism of Architecture and Art), Master of Science in Building Technology (SMBT); Master of Science in Visual Studies (SMVisS); Master of Science Without Specification. The Doctor of Philosophy (PhD), offered in three research areas: Building Technology; Design and Computation; History, Theory and Criticism of Architecture and Art.

UNIVERSITY SETTING

Architecture students have access to the academic resources of the entire Institute. In addition to the professional curriculum, the department provides opportunities for study and research in urbanism, computation and design, visual arts, history, theory, and criticism of art and architecture, and building technology. Our sister department is Urban Studies and Planning. MIT maintains cooperative relationships with other area institutions, including Harvard. Boston, with its concentration of cultural and intellectual activities, is a major resource.

SCHOOL PHILOSOPHY

Our concern is for a humane environment supporting the needs of everyday life and satisfying the depths of human experience. We seek to explore all aspects of architecture and respond to the demands of a complex discipline. Faculty and students examine alternative ways of perceiving and designing and a range of technologies. Educational programs prepare students for practice, research, and further study on the frontiers of professions that determine the form and quality of the physical environment and shape environmental policies and opportunities. Students exercise a high degree of responsibility and initiative in formulating their career plans.

PROGRAM DESCRIPTION

Undergraduate Program

The department offers two undergraduate courses of study: Course IV leads to the Bachelor of Science in Art and Design; Course IV-B leads to the Bachelor of Science. Course IV offers a flexible program in four areas of concentration: architectural design; building technology (including structures, building process, energy systems, and environmental control); computation, history, theory, and criticism of art and architecture, and visual arts. Within a clear framework, students develop individual courses of study best suited to their needs and interests. Students who plan to continue their studies for the graduate degree, Master of Architecture, must apply for admission to the MArch program. Students who have fulfilled the requirements for the BS in Art and Design normally are able to satisfy the requirements for the professional degree in 2.5 or 2 years, if they include in their undergraduate program a sufficient number of professional subjects. Course IV-B is offered for students who find that their basic intellectual commitments fall within the Department of Architecture, but whose educational objectives cut across departmental boundaries. These students may, with department approval, plan a course of study that meets their individual need and interests, while including the fundamental areas within the department.

Graduate Program

The Master of Architecture (MArch) is an accredited program of 2.5 to 3.5 years combining intensive training in architectural design with other subjects providing preparation for certification and practice. Architectural design studios, the largest component of the MArch program, emphasize design processes linked by concerns for site, material factors, and a reciprocal relationship between use and the architectural propositions. Effort is made to coordinate learning in design with subjects in building technolgoy, visual arts, history and theory of architecture, and architecture studies including urban issues and computer technology. A thesis is required.

The Master of Science in Architecture Studies (SMArchS) is a two-year post-professional program based in research in architecture as a discipline and a practice. Students shape individual programs in accord with their interests, engaging faculty resources of the entire department. Four areas of inquiry are recognized: history, theory and criticism of art and architecture, design and computation, architecture and urbanism, and architecture and technology. A thesis is required.

Graduate degree areas are: building technology; city design (MCP joint with Department of Urban Studies and Planning); design and computation; history, theory and criticism of art and architecture (post-medieval Western and Islamic); and visual arts.

AREAS OF FOCUS AND RESEARCH

Focus

The department is organized into four discipline groups (architectural design including design and computation; visual arts; history, theory, and criticism of art and architecture; and building technology) which support the core studio-based professional degree program, but each also has a dedicated faculty group, research interests, and intellectual framework.

Research

Research is based in four discipline groups, yet ranges widely within and across their boundaries: architectural design (design and computation, graphics and representation, design inquiry, design strategies); visual arts (urban and architectural interventions, collective memory, body wear, nomadic devices); building technology (energy, indoor air quality, innovative structures and construction, sustainable design and materials); and history, theory, and criticism of art and architecture (social and physical context of built environment, the creative process). The Undergraduate Research Opportunities Program (UROP) supports research-based collaborations of MIT undergraduates with Institute faculty members.

SPECIAL ACTIVITIES AND PROGRAMS

- Aga Khan Program for Islamic Architecture
- Awards programs
- Career services programs
- Cross-registration with Harvard University and Wellesley College
- East Asian program
- International travel/study programs
- Internships for undergraduate and professional program students, including those with noted international practices
- Joint MCP degree program
- Lectures and exhibition programs
- Limited exchange programs with Hong Kong University and Delft University of Technology
- MIT/Japan Program
- *Pinup*, student newsletter
- Special Interest Group in Urban Settlements (SIGUS)
- *Thresholds*, critical journal

FACILITIES

- Berenice Abbott Photography Lab
- Bought Form (shop for drafting supplies)
- Building Technology Laboratory
- Distributed computer facilities
- Steam Café
- Model shop
- Rotch Library (269,764 volumes in art, architecture, planning)
- Rotch Library Visual Collections (386,617 slides)
- Visual Arts Computer Laboratory
- Wood and Metal shop
- Digital Fabrication Lab

SCHOLARSHIPS AND FINANCIAL AID

Financial support is available to graduate students through scholarships and hourly and salaried jobs. Incoming students predominantly receive partial tuition scholarships, which are awarded on the basis of merit and financial need. Scholarships for continuing students typically increase; additionally, many students receive research and teaching assistantships. Scholarships for undergraduates, and loans in general, are awarded from Institute funds through the MIT Student Financial Aid Office.

ADMINISTRATION

Adèle Naudé Santos: Dean
Yung Ho Chang: Department Head

MCGILL UNIVERSITY

ADDRESS

Main
McGill University
School of Architecture
815 Sherbrooke Street West
Macdonald-Harrington Building
Montreal, QC H3A 2K6
Canada
Fax: 514.398.7372
news.architecture@mcgill.ca
www.mcgill.ca/architecture

STUDENT AND FACULTY DEMOGRAPHICS

% of Female Students	64
% of International Students	17
% of Minority Students	
No. Full-Time Faculty	12
No. Part-Time Faculty	24
No. Full-Time Students	280
No. Part-Time Students	0

FINANCIAL INFORMATION

Main Source of University Funding	Public
Annual Tuition & Fees (graduate, resident)	C$3,211
Annual Tuition & Fees (graduate, nonresident)	C$6,625
Annual Tuition & Fees (undergraduate, resident)	C$3,252
Annual Tuition & Fees (undergraduate, nonresident)	C$6,584
% Students Receiving Federal Financial Aid	
% Students Receiving University Financial Aid	
% Students Receiving Departmental Financial Aid	
% Students Receiving Scholarships (assistantships or fellowships)	
Average Annual Scholarship for Department	

ACADEMIC SESSIONS

Fall Semester: September to December
Spring Semester: January to April

ARCHITECTURE AND RELATED DEGREE PROGRAMS

Degree	Min. Yrs. to Complete	Professional Accreditation	# of FT Students	# of PT Students	# of First-Year Students	# of Degrees Conferred	Admissions Requirements
Architecture							
BS Arch	3		162		55	55	TOEFL, Portfolio
Grad Diploma in Housing	1		0	0	0	0	Undergraduate degree, TOEFL, Portfolio, Rec. Letters, Essay
M. Arch — 1 years	1		38	0	21	34	Undergraduate degree, TOEFL, Portfolio, Rec. Letters, Essay
M. Arch — 1½ years	1.5	CACB	59	0	35	30	Undergraduate Architecture degree, TOEFL, Portfolio, Rec. Letters
PhD	3		33	0	6	1	TOEFL, Portfolio, Rec. Letters, Essay

SPECIALIZATIONS

Architectural Design
Community Design
Computer-Aided Design
Energy

Engineering
Environment/Sustainability
History
Housing

International/Regional Architecture
Professional Practice
Sustainability

Theory/Criticism
Urban Planning and Design
International Development

ARCHITECTURE PROGRAM SUMMARY

The School of Architecture at McGill University was founded in 1896. Our mission is to educate professionals who will contribute to the socio-economic and cultural development of Quebec, Canada and the broader global community through responsible participation in the process of the design, construction and interpretation of the built environment. The School offers professional programs, including B.Sc. (Arch.) and M.Arch. (Professional), and post-professional research programs, including M.Arch. (Post-professional), Graduate Diploma, and Ph.D.

UNIVERSITY SETTING

McGill University is situated in downtown Montreal (in the province of Quebec), a city noted for its cosmopolitan ambience, its social and cultural richness, and its bilingual (French and English) character. There is excellent public transport, and affordable housing within walking distance of the University. The School of Architecture is located in a 110-year-old greystone building in the central campus area, adjacent to the Faculty of Engineering.

SCHOOL PHILOSOPHY

The School's mission is to educate professionals who will participate responsibly in the process of the design, construction and interpretation of the built environment. Its objectives are to develop an effective and stimulating environment for teaching, learning and research in architecture; to maintain and continue to enrich a program providing professional education in architecture; to provide post-professional, research-based programs that advance the discipline of architecture; to engage in research and other professional and scholarly activities; to contribute to interdisciplinary and multi-disciplinary teaching and research programs within other McGill units and with other universities; and to serve the public toward the general improvement of the built environment.

PROGRAM DESCRIPTION

McGill's professional program in architecture is structured as a four-and-a-half-year, or nine-semester course of study divided into two parts. The first part, for students entering with the Diploma of Collegial Studies in Pure or Applied Science or the equivalent, is a six-semester design program leading to a non-professional degree, BSc (Arch). The second part, for students with BSc (Arch) degree, is a one-and-a-half-year, or three-semester program leading to the professional M Arch I degree. Undergraduate students receive a comprehensive background in engineering subjects such as Strength of Materials, Structures, Surveying, Mechanical and Electrical Services, and in architectural subjects such as History and Theory, Freehand Drawing, Civic Design, and Computer-Aided Design. The School does not subscribe to a single philosophy but, through the diversity of its teaching staff, exposes students to a variety of approaches to problem-solving.

AREAS OF FOCUS AND RESEARCH

Focus

- The scheduled time for the design studio at McGill varies from one to two full days per week and includes a two-hour lecture component. All design students (even in first year) are assigned a place in a studio and provided with a drafting table and reference desk.
- Emphasis is placed on the development of architectural drawings from the conceptual stage to detailed drawings.

Research

Research within the McGill School of Architecture falls into four domains: housing, history and theory of architecture, cultural landscapes, and urban design. Research activities include the following areas of specialization: vernacular architecture, history of housing, affordable housing, adaptable housing, reuse of existing buildings, construction materials, social and physical structures, computers in education, computer-aided design, theory of design, geometry in architecture, housing and human settlements in the developing world, energy efficiency, sustainability, medicine by design, material culture, women and architecture, post-war suburbs, architectural representation, history of architectural theories, philosophy of architecture, contemporary theory of architectural praxis (ethics and aesthetics).

SPECIAL ACTIVITIES AND PROGRAMS

- Summer studio abroad: annual supervised course in locations such as Greece and Venice
- Wilfred Truman Shaver Scholarship program: annual awards for supervised summer travel
- Annual summer sketching school outside Montreal
- Student exchange programs with Schools of Architecture in Austria, Belgium, France, Israel, Italy and Colombia
- The annual Charrette, a student-centered design competition organized by the Canadian Centre for Architecture, brings together staff and students from the Architecture, Landscape Architecture, Design and Urban Planning programs at McGill, Université de Montréal, Laval, Carleton, Université du Québec à Montréal, Concordia and Ryerson
- Visiting lecture and guest critic programs, with active participation in studio teaching by well-known practitioners from Canada and abroad
- Field trips to local sites and to other Canadian and American cities
- Architectural Undergraduate Society
- Habitat for Humanity

FACILITIES

- Architecture Slide Library, including 40,000 slides
- Blackader-Lauterman Library of Architecture and Art
- John Bland Canadian Architecture Collection, consisting of 140,000 plans and drawings, 25,000 photographs and slides, 100 models, as well as related business and personal papers of 19th- and 20th-century Canadian architects
- Photography and Multimedia Laboratory
- Access to School and Faculty of Engineering computer facilities
- School of Architecture Workshop, providing access to stations for working with wood and wood products, as well as laser cutting
- Architecture Cafe

SCHOLARSHIPS AND FINANCIAL AID

- $110,000 per year in scholarships to students in the professional program, awarded on the basis of academic merit
- $30,000 per year in fellowships to graduate students, in addition to other support in the form of fee waivers and teaching assistantships
- Also available is a loan and bursary fund
- McGill offers a number of entrance scholarships awarded in a university-wide competition

ADMINISTRATION

Michael Jemtrud: Director
Ricardo L. Castro, MRAIC:
    Associate Director (professional program)
Annmarie Adams, MRAIC:
    Associate Director (post-professional program)

MIAMI UNIVERSITY

ADDRESS

Main
Miami University
Department of Architecture & Interior
Design
101 Alumni Hall
Oxford, OH 45056
Tel.: 513/529-7210
Fax: 513/529-7009
www.fna.muohio.edu/architecture

STUDENT AND FACULTY DEMOGRAPHICS

% of Female Students	50
% of International Students	10
% of Minority Students	8
% of Out-of-State U.S. Students	50
No. Full-Time Faculty	17
No. Part-Time Faculty	20
No. Full-Time Students	325
No. Part-Time Students	

FINANCIAL INFORMATION

Main Source of University Funding	Public and Private
Annual Tuition & Fees (graduate, resident)	$11,267
Annual Tuition & Fees (graduate, nonresident)	$24,899
Annual Tuition & Fees (undergraduate, resident)	$11,443
Annual Tuition & Fees (undergraduate, nonresident)	$25,327
% Students Receiving Federal Financial Aid	
% Students Receiving University Financial Aid	
% Students Receiving Departmental Financial Aid	
% Students Receiving Scholarships (assistantships or fellowships)	
Average Annual Scholarship for Department	

ACADEMIC SESSIONS

Fall Semester: August to December
Spring Semester: January to May

ARCHITECTURE AND RELATED DEGREE PROGRAMS

Degree	Min. Yrs. to Complete	Professional Accreditation	# of FT Students	# of PT Students	# of First-Year Students	# of Degrees Conferred	Admissions Requirements
Architecture							
BA. Arch	4		210	0	55	50	
M. Arch II	2	NAAB	20	0	10	10	
M. Arch III	3.5	NAAB	24	0	8	8	
M. Arch I	1		1	0	1	1	
Interior Design/Interior Architecture							
B.F.A. Int. Design	4	CIDA	70	0	18	17	

SPECIALIZATIONS

Landscape Design   Urban Planning and Design

UNIVERSITY SETTING

Founded in 1809, Miami University is nationally recognized for its high quality of undergraduate teaching and its select programs of graduate study. With 20,000 students on three campuses, Miami has the character of a college but the advantages of a university. A strong honors program, the Center for American and World Cultures, the renowned Scripps Gerontology Center, and a full branch campus in Luxembourg are only a few of Miami's resources. The Architecture major is listed in the *Fiske Guide to Colleges 2007* as one of eight "strongest programs" at Miami.

SCHOOL PHILOSOPHY

The emphasis of the undergraduate program is to provide students with a broad understanding of architecture as a humanistic, technical, artistic, and professional endeavor. The program is decidedly interdisciplinary and exploratory. The Master of Architecture program has a principal goal of balanced professional preparation that integrates technical and material concerns with aesthetic and theoretical issues. Studios, lectures, seminars, and research require students to develop an overarching philosophical framework for design. A variety of studio experiences (some off-campus), and a rich array of scientific, computer mediated, and independent study options help students explore personal interests within the general curricular structure.

PROGRAM DESCRIPTION
Graduate Program

The mission of the Master of Architecture is to conduct architectural inquiry in the pursuit of new forms of knowledge and, through rigorous professional preparation, construct critical practices that empower students to interpret, engage and give form to the ideas and forces that impact their world. A centerpiece of the graduate program(s) is the thesis, which requires both a written document that is vetted in the form of a peer-reviewed conference paper, and a design thesis that explores ideas generated in the written paper. The Master of Architecture thus takes the intellectual lead in the department, while also benefiting from the array of undergraduate programming, including off-campus study, interdisciplinary partnerships, and research opportunities.

Undergraduate Program

The undergraduate program provides students with a broad understanding of architecture as a humanistic, technical, artistic, and professional endeavor. The first two years comprise a comprehensive interdisciplinary approach that introduces students to design, graphics, computer studies, history and theory, tectonics, urbanism, and landscape issues. The last two years encourage a more focused exploration of areas such as urban, landscape, interior, tectonic, or digital practices, as well as the development of deeper interests within the broader spectrum of architecture as a practice. Students are encouraged to study off campus for at least a semester or summer as a way of enhancing their educational experience and deepening their understanding of national and global community. Individually assigned faculty members counsel and advise students in the process of making all academic, curricular, programmatic, advanced degree, and career decisions. Supplemented by a concurrent professional major in Interior Design, by interdepartmental minors in landscape, urban design, and art and architectural history, by research opportunities, and by summer internships in architectural firms throughout the country and around the world, the four-year program in design provides a strong foundation for subsequent professional degrees at the graduate level in architecture, related design professions, or in areas of social, economic, business, and political process.

AREAS OF FOCUS AND RESEARCH
Focus

Special areas of focus include ongoing projects that address third-world countries, the inner-city core, and community planning issues through design and service-learning activities. The Ghana workshop is committed to improving the literacy rate of West African people through the design and construction of community buildings. The Center for Community Engagement renovates historic properties as low and middle-income rental units in Cincinnati's Over-the-Rhine neighborhood while studying the history and presence of its inhabitants. And ongoing community-based planning projects are coordinated through the department's Community Design Assistance Group.

Research

Twice recognized by the Ohio Board of Regents as an outstanding academic unit, the department supports a variety of research directions. The Center for Building Science Research, the Center for Community Engagement in Over-the-Rhine, and the Community Design Assistance Group offer diverse opportunities for research that complement ongoing research projects in history, theory, and digital media. Both undergraduate and graduate research opportunities are supported generously by departmental and university, as well as grant, funding and often permit students to conduct research abroad. Graduate students may pursue research in conjunction with a professional design firm during the summer prior to the thesis year.

SPECIAL ACTIVITIES AND PROGRAMS

The department operates the design-build workshop in Ghana, Africa; the interdisciplinary workshop in Italy in conjunction with Miami's Graphic Design major and prominent Italian design critics; a biannual workshop in London, the China workshop that partners with Miami alumni in Beijing and Shenzhen (partners in Urbanus); a traveling workshop in Turkey partnered with Yeditepe University in Istanbul, and a graphics workshop in New Mexico. The Miami University Center for Community Engagement in Over-the-Rhine (Cincinnati) renovates historic buildings and studies local urban culture. Since 2006, the Center has offered a semester-long residency experience, allowing students to live in, and take courses in, the Over-the-Rhine community. Each year, a number of students receive appointments as Undergraduate Summer Scholars to pursue independent research. These occur frequently in international locations, and students present research findings to the broader department in the form of gallery exhibits or as part of the departmental lecture series. The university maintains an active Honors Program that offers wide-ranging courses and academic experiences, including a senior-year independent project. Students enjoy intensive studio experiences with visiting critics and interaction with visiting speakers. Miami's Junior Scholars program is a six-week residential summer experience for qualified high school juniors.

FACILITIES

The Department of Architecture and Interior Design is housed in historic Alumni Hall, centrally located on the primary campus quadrangle. In addition to wireless computer access from every studio workstation, the upgraded facility provides students with a central high-end computer lab. The department enjoys an outstanding woodshop, including digital fabrication equipment. It houses the Wertz Art and Architecture Library (over 56,000 volumes, 400 periodicals), and shares a Visual Resources Library (over 150,000 images) with the Department of Art.

SCHOLARSHIPS AND FINANCIAL AID

Miami offers generous financial aid to all students. U.S. students, whether from Ohio or elsewhere, are eligible for need-based scholarships, grants, loans, and work-study packages. Financial aid for high ability students is usually merit based. The department offers scholarships to entering and continuing students including four full-tuition four-year renewable scholarships based principally on the creative portfolio. Over three-quarters of our graduate students hold assistantships, fee waivers, scholarships, and/or grants, and many benefit from other Graduate School awards for excellence.

ADMINISTRATION

John B. Weigand: Chair
John Reynolds: Director of Graduate Studies
Gulen Cevik: Director of Interior Design

MISSISSIPPI STATE UNIVERSITY

COLLEGE OF ARCHITECTURE

ADDRESS

Main
Mississippi State University
College of Architecture
P.O. Box AQ
Mississippi State, MS 39762-5541
Tel.: 662.325.2202
Fax: 662.325.8872
www.coa.msstate.edu

STUDENT AND FACULTY DEMOGRAPHICS

% of Female Students	42
% of International Students	1
% of Minority Students	17
% of Out-of-State U.S. Students	26
No. Full-Time Faculty	15
No. Part-Time Faculty	9
No. Full-Time Students	199
No. Part-Time Students	16

FINANCIAL INFORMATION

Main Source of University Funding	Public
Annual Tuition & Fees (graduate, resident)	$4,978
Annual Tuition & Fees (graduate, nonresident)	$11,469
Annual Tuition & Fees (undergraduate, resident)	$4,978
Annual Tuition & Fees (undergraduate, nonresident)	$11,469
% Students Receiving Federal Financial Aid	
% Students Receiving University Financial Aid	40
% Students Receiving Departmental Financial Aid	7
% Students Receiving Scholarships (assistantships or fellowships)	
Average Annual Scholarship for Department	$1,500

ACADEMIC SESSIONS

Fall Semester: August to December; Application Deadline: January 15
Spring Semester: January to May

Summer Session I: June to July
Summer Session II: July to August

ARCHITECTURE AND RELATED DEGREE PROGRAMS

Degree	Min. Yrs. to Complete	Professional Accreditation	# of FT Students	# of PT Students	# of First-Year Students	# of Degrees Conferred	Admissions Requirements
Architecture							
B. Arch	5	NAAB	200	16	45	30	Rec. Letters, Essay
Master of Science in Architecture	1.5		20	3	14	60	Undergraduate degree, GRE, TOEFL, Portfolio, Rec. Letters, Essay
Interior Design/Interior Architecture							
Interior Design Program	4	CIDA/FIDER	117		32	21	

SPECIALIZATIONS

Architectural Design   Building Technology/Env. Systems   Environment/Sustainability   Sustainability

ARCHITECTURE PROGRAM SUMMARY

The School of Architecture at Mississippi State University offers the Bachelor of Architecture degree. It is a five year professional program accredited by the National Architectural Accrediting Board (NAAB). The School of Architecture is the only NAAB-accredited architecture program in the state of Mississippi. The School of Architecture is situated within the broader context of the College of Architecture, Art and Design, providing interaction with the allied creative disciplines of fine arts, graphic design and interior design.

UNIVERSITY SETTING

Mississippi State University forms part of a cohesive town–university community with the growing agricultural-commercial-industrial town of Starkville. Away from urban complexities, the community enjoys many intellectual, cultural, and recreational advantages: lecture series, art exhibits, plays, recitals by local and visiting artists, public radio and public television programs, performances by popular musical groups of regional and national celebrity, frequent intercollegiate athletic events in modern facilities; and a variety of recreational opportunities on playing fields and courts, in neighboring forests, fields, and lakes.

Mississippi State University is a comprehensive, doctoral-degree-granting university with a diverse and capable student body of over 17,500 students. It is representative of the American Land-Grant tradition and distinctive in its own character and spirit. The University contributes to the world of knowledge through contributions in research, discovery, and application. It provides the state and its people a variety of expert services. Mississippi State University is accredited by the Commission on Colleges of the Southern Association of Colleges to award baccalaureate, master's, specialist, and doctoral degrees.

A faculty of over 1,300, drawn from the best institutions in all parts of the world, strives to demonstrate excellence in teaching, while producing significant research in their specialized studies. Thus they ensure for their students instruction that is in immediate touch with current knowledge and thought. A body of energetic researchers, both faculty and other, assisted by an effective research administration, places Mississippi State among the first one hundred universities in the nation in research and development in the sciences and engineering. The University's service agencies are similarly distinguished, earning the respect and support of their varied constituencies throughout the state, as well as in other states and in foreign countries.

SCHOOL PHILOSOPHY

The profession of architecture offers the student the opportunity to participate in improving the physical world, in solving problems of our society, and in giving form to the needs of modern culture. To meet these demands requires a highly trained profession composed of sensitive, dedicated men and women. The School of Architecture is the educational foundation of the profession in the state of Mississippi and provides for the development of the individual skills and understanding to prepare the student for his or her role in the practice of architecture. The College of Architecture offers an intense, carefully structured, and rich array of courses which constitute a solid foundation for architectural practice. While course work is comprehensive in scope, providing the students with an awareness of the diversity and complexity of today's professional world, each course has its own important role in developing the unique knowledge and abilities required of architects in a modern world.

PROGRAM DESCRIPTION

The School believes that architectural education can best be accomplished in an environment that stimulates the search for ideas by faculty and students. The size of the College and its small-town setting make possible a highly personal yet intense academic experience. Travel, visiting critics and lecturers, foreign exchange programs, symposia, and diverse student activities provide richness within a highly ordered educational setting. The College of Architecture offers an intensive, five-year course sequence leading to the professional Bachelor of Architecture degree. The program consists of four years of the professional program at the main campus with the final year at the facility in downtown Jackson, MS. In the fall, some 45 students enter the program as freshmen and are involved immediately in architecture studios. Required courses, with coordinated studio experiences each term, continue throughout the five-year undergraduate experience. Students not accepted into the first-year studio enter the pre-architecture curriculum and defer first-year design until the summer between their freshman and sophomore years. Pre-architecture and transfer students are accepted on a competitive basis into a summer design studio.

AREAS OF FOCUS AND RESEARCH

As the school of architecture for the state of Mississippi, and as an important force in the region, the School seeks to take advantage of the unique qualities of the state as a laboratory for architectural investigation. This includes rural, small towns and urban environments. The School has developed an outstanding visiting lecturer and critic program, bringing leaders in various fields to the campus, as well as a comprehensive program of travel to major urban centers. Fall semester housing studio works with Habitat for Humanity on design and construction projects. The focus areas of research include design, planning and economic development issues for communities and urban inner-city neighborhoods. A variety of housing issues, geospatial technologies, sustainability, educational-facilities design, and materials usage are other areas of faculty research included in the four School Research Centers. The Carl Small Town Center (CSTC) promotes a belief in the power of the physical environment to strengthen and empower our communities. The Gulf Coast Community Design Studio (GCCDS) is providing community planning and architectural design services to communities and rebuilding organizations on the Gulf Coast of Mississippi. The objective of the Jackson Community Design Center (JCDC) is to realize architectural projects that benefit the Jackson community. The Education Design Institute (EDI) is a collaborative initiative between the College of Education and the School of Architecture, charged with exploring changes in educational delivery and design. The Digital Research and Informatics Lab (DRIL) fosters an environment of exploring the role of computers in architecture as well as developing different computer visualizations and research agendas that deal with the broad issues of information technology.

SPECIAL ACTIVITIES AND PROGRAMS

- Summer Design Discovery Camp, an orientation to architecture as a profession for high school students and incoming freshmen
- The fifth-year program is located in downtown Jackson, MS

Student Organizations

- AIAS - American Institute of Architects Student Chapter
- NOMAS - National Organization of Minority Architecture Students
- Tau Sigma Delta National Honor Society in Architecture and the Allied Arts
- Dean's Council of Students

Enrichment Programs:

- School of Architecture Lecture Series
- Friday Forum Program sponsored by Tau Sigma Delta National Honor Society
- Beaux Arts Ball
- Annual Studio Field Trips
- Study Abroad opportunities
- Co-op work program

School of Architecture Research Institutes:

- The Carl Small Town Center (CSTC) allows students to work with communities in real and tangible ways through research and design.
- The Gulf Coast Community Design Studio (GCCDS) is providing community planning and architectural design services to communities and rebuilding organizations on the Gulf Coast of Mississippi.
- Jackson Community Design Center (JCDC) provides leadership and service to non-profit organizations in building fair and affordable housing, preserving historic structures, creating facilities for community assistance, and promoting public places.
- Educational Design Institute (EDI)
- Digital Research and Imaging Laboratory (DRIL) offers graphics computing/visualization.

FACILITIES

In 1977, the School of Architecture rehabilitated a 1930s livestock-judging pavilion, saving it from imminent destruction. A lantern-like symbol of architectural education at night, the renovation of the building houses the undergraduate design studios. In 1982, the School completed an award-winning addition which houses the first-year design studio, graduate studio, faculty and administrative offices, the library and gallery, jury room, and auditorium which supports music and film, as well as the architecture lecture series, computer docking stations, photographic studios, materials-testing facilities, a metal and woodworking shop, the Digital Research and Imaging Laboratory, and the Carl Small Town Center. The School of Architecture Fifth-Year Program and the Jackson Community Design Center is housed in a four story facility in downtown Jackson, MS.

SCHOLARSHIPS AND FINANCIAL AID

Mississippi State University awards approximately $16 million in financial aid each year. The University awards $500 to $8,000 annually in scholarships, along with waiver of out-of-state tuition, to students with ACT scores of 27 or higher. Approximately 40% of the class entering the School of Architecture in fall of 2007 had these scholarships, representing a sum of about $90,000. Within the College of Architecture, special design competitions and annual scholarships totaling $21,000 provide additional aid.

ADMINISTRATION

James L. West, AIA: Dean
David C. Lewis, PhD: Associate Dean
Larry Barrow, D.DES, AIA: Director, Grad Studies/Design Research & Informatics Lab
Caleb Crawford, AIA, LEED AP; Director, School of Architecture

MONTANA STATE UNIVERSITY

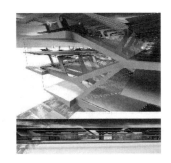

ADDRESS

Main
Montana State University
School of Architecture
160 Cheever Hall
P.O. Box 173760
Bozeman, MT 59717-3760
Tel.: 406.994.4255
Fax: 406.994.4257
architect@montana.edu
www.arch.montana.edu

STUDENT AND FACULTY DEMOGRAPHICS

% of Female Students	28
% of International Students	2
% of Minority Students	5
% of Out-of-State U.S. Students	41
No. Full-Time Faculty	19
No. Part-Time Faculty	6
No. Full-Time Students	508
No. Part-Time Students	48

FINANCIAL INFORMATION

Main Source of University Funding	Public
Annual Tuition & Fees (graduate, resident)	$5,222
Annual Tuition & Fees (graduate, nonresident)	$13,621
Annual Tuition & Fees (undergraduate, resident)	$5,749
Annual Tuition & Fees (undergraduate, nonresident)	$16,274
% Students Receiving Federal Financial Aid	64
% Students Receiving University Financial Aid	60
% Students Receiving Departmental Financial Aid	0
% Students Receiving Scholarships (assistantships or fellowships)	76
Average Annual Scholarship for Department	$1,000

ACADEMIC SESSIONS

Fall Semester: September to December
Spring Semester: January to May

Summer Session I: May to July
Summer Session II: July to August

ARCHITECTURE AND RELATED DEGREE PROGRAMS

Degree	Min. Yrs. to Complete	Professional Accreditation	# of FT Students	# of PT Students	# of First-Year Students	# of Degrees Conferred	Admissions Requirements
Architecture							
M. Arch	5	NAAB	60	8		70	SAT, GRE, TOEFL, Portfolio, Rec. Letters, Essay
Environmental Design							
BA Env Des	4		448	40	175	54	Portfolio

SPECIALIZATIONS

Architectural Design
Building Information Modeling
Building Technology/Env. Systems
Community Design

Computer-Aided Design
Energy
Environment/Sustainability
Graphic Design

Preservation
Professional Practice
Sustainability

Tectonics
Theory/Criticism
Urban Planning and Design

ARCHITECTURE PROGRAM SUMMARY

The School of Architecture at Montana State University continues to refine the vision of the school to respond to overarching trends in the profession of architecture with the ever increasing demand for **environmental stewardship, visualization, digital fabrication and integrated design**. The school believes that these trends will continue to evolve and redefine the face of the profession and will consequently continue to build the program around them.

The school has a strong tradition of fostering independent design-thinking in concert with independent research. Our award-winning faculty offer vigorous undergraduate and graduate educational programs. The multidisciplinary interests of our faculty and graduate students form the basis of exciting new research collaborations with a variety of other disciplines including the School of Agriculture, the School of Business and the School of Engineering. The School is currently collaborating with the non-profits Kohala Center (Big Island, Hawaii) and the Conscious Alliance (Boulder, Colorado) in addition to the North Face Research and Development Team to name a few.

UNIVERSITY SETTING

Montana State University, with 12,000 students, lies in the picturesque Gallatin Valley high in the Montana Rockies. The spacious campus is in the culturally rich, historic town of Bozeman, named All America City by the National Civic League in 2001. Yellowstone National Park, Big Sky and Bridger Bowl ski areas are all a short drive away from the campus. The School of Architecture is part of the College of Arts and Architecture, which also includes art, music, media and theater arts.

SCHOOL PHILOSOPHY

The MSU School of Architecture seeks to prepare students for a lifelong critical engagement in the art and science of architecture. Located in "the last best place" of the Northern Rockies we are in an extraordinary position to engage questions regarding the relationship between the natural and built environments. To that end, we teach and practice a moral, ethical and aesthetic responsibility to society and the natural world in the design of the built environment. It is in our design studios that this philosophy is most clearly demonstrated. Each studio is conceived to build upon the previous studio in a manner that develops a student's mastery of the science of architecture while at the same time exposing the student to the rich diversity of our faculty's philosophical beliefs.

Within a structured sequence of increasingly complex problems, emphasis is placed on teaching both an iterative design process and the visualization skills necessary to demonstrate the resultant design proposals. The science of architecture is continuously evolving and will do so over the life of every architect. We are committed to preparing our students to enter the profession with both the contemporary scientific knowledge and emerging technical expertise to further this evolution while at the same time ensuring that our graduates are grounded in the fundamental processes, composition and drawing skills that have been central to architecture throughout its history. In addition to the science of architecture we are equally committed to ensuring that our graduates acquire a critical philosophy with which they can engage the design of the built environment.

PROGRAM DESCRIPTION

The rigorous four-year Bachelor of Arts in Environmental Design program prepares students for a wide variety of career and educational options. Undergraduate education in environmental design is organized around an intense, design studio–based gradual emersion into architectural expertise. Each design studio is organized around a set of objectives, an emphasis, a scale, and complexity.

The first year is intended to encourage the greatest possible diversity of students to explore the opportunities and expectations of an environmental design education. Students acquire the fundamental math, science, writing, and design skills that are the foundation of their future learning. Particular emphasis is placed on conceptualization in the first year of the curriculum.

The second year requires that students complete their university core to ensure a broad perspective from which to engage their environmental design education. The design studio introduces fundamental strategies of precedent analysis, the organization of human activities and sustainability while applying the knowledge acquired in structures and graphics courses. Particular emphasis is placed on use & context during the second year of the curriculum.

Throughout the third year students develop the ability to design environmental control and integrated building construction systems as well as the ability to utilize advanced graphic communication strategies. A professional practice course provides students with an understanding of the strategies by which design concepts and business strategies are resolved. In the third

year, particular emphasis is placed on building tectonics within the curriculum.

Built upon the foundations of the first three years, the fourth year consists of one required studio course during one semester and a selection from one of the option studios in the other semester. Every student must complete a capstone studio emphasizing professional responsibility in which the student must synthesize program development, site development, structural systems, environmental controls systems, principles of sustainability and graphic communication. During the other semester—whether summer, fall or spring—all students choose between our foreign study program, completing an approved internship, working in the School of Architecture Community Design Center, or completing an approved off-campus program of study. With the satisfactory completion of the fourth year of study, students will receive a Bachelor of Arts in Environmental Design degree.

Students wishing to acquire the Masters of Architecture Degree must complete two semesters of graduate study. Throughout this graduate study, students will choose from a variety of architectural studios, craft studios, architectural seminars, and non-architectural electives intended to emphasize the development of a critical position with regard to the environment and architecture. A final comprehensive studio or thesis is required that demonstrates, through the development of an architectural project, the student's moral, ethical and aesthetic responsibility to society and the natural world.

AREAS OF FOCUS AND RESEARCH

Design is at the center of all we do with particular emphasis on the landscape, culture, sustainability and theory. Studios begin regionally and expand outwardly, with fourth-year field trips to Portland and Seattle. Graduate option studios have visited and worked on projects in places that have included Boston, Chicago, New York, San Francisco, Nepal, the Big Island of Hawaii and Yellowstone National Park.

The School has an outstanding tradition in service-learning. The School has developed strong connections with the state's cities, towns, national parks and tribes, including projects on the Crow and Blackfeet reservations and on-going work in Yellowstone National Park. The School's research reflects a diverse and wide-ranging faculty of committed practitioners of the profession of architecture. Several of the faculty have received national recognition for their work, ranging from the 2006 NCARB Prize, the ACSA Distinguished Professor, an AIA Honor Award for Urban Design and numerous AIA State and Regional Awards. The School has focused on areas of stewardship and visualization and is the current headquarters of the Design Communication Association. Faculty-led efforts include the application of sustainable design practice in rural regions, development of visually compelling tools to encourage smarter growth in the rapidly growing Rocky Mountain west, ongoing research in day-lighting with the integrated Design Lab, national and international competitions, community design workshops, historic preservation, and the application of both hand and digital drawing in the design process.

SPECIAL ACTIVITIES AND PROGRAMS

Our outstanding Lecture Series has included Glenn Murcutt, Daniel Liebeskind, Dan Rockhill, William Massie, and Antoine Predock just to name a few. During the fourth year of study, students may choose to participate in our foreign study program, professional internship, design-build studio or our Community Design Center. Each year, approximately half of fourth-year students study abroad for an entire semester, joined by two-to-four faculty members. The faculty develops study tours in various parts of the world, with the fall semester typically in Europe and the spring semester in Asia, Central America or South America. Alternatively, students may elect to spend the spring semester and summer as an intern in an architecture firm anywhere in the United States or abroad. The Community Design Center offers another option, in which students work directly with community-based clients all over Montana assisting public and non-profit groups in planning, programming, and conceptual design ideas. Students also may participate in the dB studio—a design-build program allowing students to explore innovate design ideas from concept to construction. During the graduate year students also select from a series of option studios including the Visiting Scholars Studio which brings visiting faculty or practitioners to the MSU campus to teach a graduate-level studio. In addition, the Advanced Architectural Studio, another graduate studio option, has explored issues of Historic Preservation and Planning in Yellowstone National Park, the design of sustainable agricultural communities in Hawaii and urban design throughout the United States.

FACILITIES

The School is within the College of Arts and Architecture complex, which includes our Creative Arts Library, replete with 25,000 volumes. Other facilities include a rapid prototyping room, laser cutting equipment, CNC milling machines, digital media room, photo studio, print room, and wood shop. The School is fully networked with each studio desk wired to the university's network system and has a full-time computer technician. All second-year students are required to have laptops, and the school provides fullcolor printing capabilities throughout the building and a full-time computer technician. Our Lecture Hall includes a state-of-the-art digital projection system.

SCHOLARSHIPS AND FINANCIAL AID

The School of Architecture offers a wide range of endowed and annual Scholarships, as well as two annual design competition scholarships totaling over $56,000. The selection criteria for each scholarship vary from outstanding capability, to promise of excellence and demonstration of financial need. Approximately twenty of our top graduate students are awarded Graduate Assistant Teaching Fellowships, which provides both tuition waivers and other incentives.

ADMINISTRATION

Susan Agre-Kippenhan: Dean
Heather Bentz: Assistant Dean
John C. Brittingham, AIA: Interim Associate Director
Steven Juroszek, AIA: Director

MORGAN STATE UNIVERSITY

ADDRESS

Main
Morgan State University
School of Architecture and Planning
2201 Argonne Drive
Montebello D103
Baltimore, MD 21251
Tel.: 443.885.3225
Fax: 443.885.8233
www.morgan.edu

STUDENT AND FACULTY DEMOGRAPHICS

% of Female Students	30
% of International Students	10
% of Minority Students	60
% of Out-of-State U.S. Students	20
No. Full-Time Faculty	20
No. Part-Time Faculty	10
No. Full-Time Students	310
No. Part-Time Students	92

FINANCIAL INFORMATION

Main Source of University Funding	Public
Annual Tuition & Fees (graduate, resident)	$6,480
Annual Tuition & Fees (graduate, nonresident)	$10,278
Annual Tuition & Fees (undergraduate, resident)	$3,219
Annual Tuition & Fees (undergraduate, nonresident)	$7,464
% Students Receiving Federal Financial Aid	
% Students Receiving University Financial Aid	
% Students Receiving Departmental Financial Aid	
% Students Receiving Scholarships (assistantships or fellowships)	
Average Annual Scholarship for Department	

ACADEMIC SESSIONS

Application Deadline: Fall Admission, June 30
Application Deadline: Spring Admission, November 30

ARCHITECTURE AND RELATED DEGREE PROGRAMS

Degree	Min. Yrs. to Complete	Professional Accreditation	# of FT Students	# of PT Students	# of First-Year Students	# of Degrees Conferred	Admissions Requirements
Architecture							
2 + 3 M.Arch	5	NAAB	16	0			Portfolio, Rec. Letters, Essay
M.Arch 60 Credit	2	NAAB	40	20	10	12	Undergraduate Architecture degree, Portfolio, Rec. Letters, Essay
M.Arch 90 Credit	3	NAAB	20	10	20	10	Undergraduate degree, Portfolio, Rec. Letters, Essay
Landscape Architecture							
MLA	3		17	8	10	2	
MS LA	1.5		0	0	0	0	
Planning							
M CRP	2	PAB	17	24	17	6	Undergraduate Degree
Other							
BS AED	4		200	92	60	20	

SPECIALIZATIONS

Architectural Design	Community Design	Sustainability	Urban Planning and Design
Building Information Modeling	Environment/Sustainability		

ARCHITECTURE PROGRAM SUMMARY

Architecture at Morgan offers many paths to an accredited professional degree in architecture. The Graduate Programs of the Department of Architecture awards an NAAB-accredited Master of Architecture degree to students from a wide variety of undergraduate fields of study. Students without any prior experience in architecture are placed in the 90-credit Master of Architecture degree program. Students with undergraduate study in architecture may be given advanced standing to enroll in the 60-credit Master of Architecture degree program. Student placement is based in part on an evaluation of a portfolio, prior academic experience, and additional information from the application process.

The most dynamic path to the professional degree is a "2 + 3" Master of Architecture degree program. This program awards the Master of Architecture degree after five years of intensive study for the high school graduate. This path is open to students with a two-year degree in architectural studies from a community college, and students with a two-year community college degree may receive the Master of Architecture degree after three years of full-time study. Application to this program is also open to students enrolled in the undergraduate BSAED program at Morgan State University, and to transfer students from other four-year undergraduate architectural programs. The enrollment in the "2 + 3 Master of Architecture" is competitive and highly selective.

Graduates from the BSAED program at Morgan State, and other undergraduate programs, who have not been selected for the "2 + 3" program are encouraged to apply to the 60/90 credit Master of Architecture programs, and are placed according to the quality of their undergraduate portfolios and academic records, and additional information from the application process.

The 90-credit Master of Architecture program is primarily designed for students without any academic background in architecture, and accepts students from many diverse fields of prior study.

The primary objective of Architecture at Morgan is preparation for the profession of architecture, with a special emphasis on mentorship of student populations that are underrepresented in the profession of architecture. The focus of architecture at Morgan is preparation for an increasingly complex profession, engaged with rapidly changing technologies in the materials, production, and representation of the built environment, in a world of diminished natural resources, degraded urban and suburban environments, and in a progressively more complicated social, cultural, economic and legal environment. A key objective is to mentor, to encourage, and to nurture students from diverse populations; including African American, women, and other minority students who are underrepresented in the profession of architecture with a curriculum and teaching pedagogy that is responsive to the needs of these students.

The faculty includes many registered architects with experience in the profession. The Department of Architecture has an active partnership with AIABaltimore, an urban component of the American Institute of Architects. The faculty includes a Senior Fulbright Scholar.

Prospective students should visit the School of Architecture and Planning website for the most current information on application deadlines.

UNIVERSITY SETTING

Morgan Sate University is located on 140 acres in a residential area of northeastern Baltimore just 20 minutes from the central business district and the famous Inner Harbor. Washington D.C. is 35 miles south. The university is an historically black institution with a diverse student body of about 5,500 undergraduate and 600 graduate students. Transfer students are encouraged to apply.

SCHOOL PHILOSOPHY

Education Mission: The School of Architecture and Planning (SAP) provides professional preparation for future Architects, Landscape Architects, and Planners. We provide access to all students, including those with less demonstrable preparation. Through our graduates, our programs advance sustainability and enrich and preserve cultural and built environments.

Research Mission: SAP embraces an interdisciplinary agenda that promotes sustainability in its broadest sense. It engages research that values design and practice leading to problem solving and theory building, which focus on urban core areas of the region.

Service and Outreach: SAP's service and outreach priority rests within our desire to support the neighborhoods of Baltimore. Service is provided to communities and non-profit organizations through collaborative ventures.

Diversity: SAP fosters knowledge and appreciation for the cultures and contributions of diverse segments of humanity and their environments. We promote the inclusion of students who have been traditionally excluded from the study of the built and natural environment.

PROGRAM DESCRIPTION
Undergraduate Program

The Bachelor of Science Degree in Architecture & Environmental Design is a pre-professional, undergraduate four-year program of study. Graduates can then attend Morgan's accredited programs in Architecture, Landscape Architecture or Community and Regional Planning. The specific aim of the program is to develop in students an understanding of the role of architecture, landscape architecture and planning in the design and planning of the built environment, to support human activities and improve the physical environment. Concentrations of study are offered: Architecture, Environmental Design and Community Planning. Students in the Pre-Professional Degree Program in Architecture & Environmental Design must complete 129 credit hours. The program requires 46 credits of general education, which includes English, math, philosophy, African-American studies, history and humanities. Required courses in the Architecture & Environmental Design sequence constitute 83 credits and include concepts and theory courses, built environment history, graphic communication skills, design studio, statics and strength of materials, systems design, office practice & management, site planning, urban development and sustainability.

AREAS OF FOCUS AND RESEARCH
Focus

Morgan's mission incorporates its designation as the state's urban-orientated university and service to the citizens of Maryland. The Center for Built & Natural Environmental Research (CEBNER) is a nonprofit clinic that integrates the academic, research, service and practice areas of architecture, landscape architecture, and city and regional planning. Programs are geared towards producing employable graduates. There is also an emphasis on interdisciplinary interactions in coursework.

Research

Multi-disciplinary research opportunities are fostered by the presence of the collateral Graduate Programs in Landscape Architecture and City and Regional Planning. The on-campus National Transportation Center offers unique research opportunities, for both faculty and students. Architecture faculty members are actively engaged in both creative practice endeavors and research, and these activities are cultivated to enrich the student's educational experience. Recent faculty research and practice have included urban design, sustainability, community design, educational facilities, religious centers, planning and housing, Main Street programs, gender and minority studies, transportation studies, and the historic preservation of the historic African-American built environment, specifically the historic black churches of Maryland and the nation.

SPECIAL ACTIVITIES AND PROGRAMS

Through the curriculum, lectures, seminars, construction site visits, field trips, and joint endeavors with other schools and departments at Morgan and other institutions, the education process engages students in academic, professional, and societal experiences. The architecture programs support active student chapters of the AIAS (American Institute of Architecture Students) and NOMA (National Organization of Minority Architects). Off campus, students participate in events of the Baltimore A.I.A., including the Baltimore AIA Spring Lecture Series; the Chesapeake Bay Chapter of the AIA (Annapolis, Maryland); activities of the Baltimore Architectural Foundation; and other regional professional associations. On campus, CEBNER (Center for Built & Natural Environment Research) sponsors practice clinics and student internships in community design initiatives. A mentorship program links individual students with area practitioners. Mentorship uniquely contributes to the development of student design projects, and to the professional growth of the individual student. Students can receive transfer credit for specified international study-abroad programs sponsored by other institutions, subject to University approval.

FACILITIES

The School of Architecture and Planning is located in the Montebello complex at the southern end of the Morgan campus. The program occupies 27,000 square-feet on three floors. Undergraduate studios and classrooms are on the lower level; faculty and administrative offices, the computer lab, a multimedia resource center, and jury space occupy the first floor; graduate studios and classrooms are housed on the second floor. Exhibit and display space is located throughout the three floors. Access to studios is 24 hours a day, 7 days a week, and off street parking is conveniently located adjacent to the building.

SCHOLARSHIPS AND FINANCIAL AID

To attract deserving students of high promise and to assist them in the prompt attainment of career objectives, the School of Graduate Studies and Research makes student aid available to qualified applicants on a competitive basis. Application forms may be available for the Spring Semester; application forms must be returned by November 1. No awards are made for summer sessions. Awards for the fall semester are usually announced in late May or early June. Paid internships are also available periodically to students desiring financial assistance and professional experience.

ADMINISTRATION

Mary Anne Akers, PhD: Dean
Ruth Connell, AIA: Chair, Architecture
Siddhartha Sen, PhD: Chair, City & Regional Planning
Glenn Smith: Chair, Landscape Architecture
Gabriel Kroiz: BSAED Director

NEW JERSEY INSTITUTE of TECHNOLOGY

ADDRESS

Main
New Jersey Institute of Technology
University Heights
Weston Hall, Room 320
Newark, NJ 07102
Fax: 973.596.8296
architecture@njit.edu
architecture.njit.edu

STUDENT AND FACULTY DEMOGRAPHICS

% of Female Students	24
% of International Students	7
% of Minority Students	32
% of Out-of-State U.S. Students	12
No. Full-Time Faculty	30
No. Part-Time Faculty	58
No. Full-Time Students	800
No. Part-Time Students	80

FINANCIAL INFORMATION

Main Source of University Funding	Public
Annual Tuition & Fees (graduate, resident)	$7,177
Annual Tuition & Fees (graduate, nonresident)	$9,857
Annual Tuition & Fees (undergraduate, resident)	$5,675
Annual Tuition & Fees (undergraduate, nonresident)	$10,041
% Students Receiving Federal Financial Aid	56
% Students Receiving University Financial Aid	34
% Students Receiving Departmental Financial Aid	14
% Students Receiving Scholarships (assistantships or fellowships)	35
Average Annual Scholarship for Department	

ACADEMIC SESSIONS

Fall Semester: September to December; Application Deadline: April 1
Spring Semester: January to May; Application Deadline: November 15

Summer Session I: May to June
Summer Session II: July to August

ARCHITECTURE AND RELATED DEGREE PROGRAMS

Degree	Min. Yrs. to Complete	Professional Accreditation	# of FT Students	# of PT Students	# of First-Year Students	# of Degrees Conferred	Admissions Requirements
Architecture							
B. Arch	5	NAAB	714	115	180	64	SAT, Rec. Letters
BS Arch	4		56	8	15	22	SAT, Rec. Letter
MS Arch (Academic)	1		2	8	6	1	Undergraduate degree, GRE, TOEFL, Rec. Letters, Essay
M. Arch	3	NAAB	66	15	24	31	Undergraduate degree, GRE, TOEFL, Portfolio, Rec. Letters, Essay
MS Arch (Post-Professional)	1		3	3	3	4	Prof. Architecture degree, GRE, TOEFL, Portfolio, Rec. Letters, Essay
Interior Design/Interior Architecture							
BA Interior Design	4	CIDA/FIDER	30	0	15		SAT
Industrial Design							
B.S. Industrial Design	4		45		15		SAT
Planning							
Master of Infrastructure Planning	1		5	10	8	6	Undergraduate degree, GRE, TOEFL, Portfolio, Rec. Letters, Essay

SPECIALIZATIONS

Architectural Design	Community Design	History	Sustainability
Art and Design	Computer-Aided Design	Housing	Tectonics
Building Information Modeling	Environment/Sustainability	Interior Design Architecture	Urban Planning and Design
Building Technology/Env. Systems			

ARCHITECTURE PROGRAM SUMMARY

The New Jersey School of Architecture at the New Jersey Institute of Technology is one of the largest architecture schools on the east coast and the largest in New Jersey. The School offers undergraduate and graduate degree programs in Architecture and Infrastructure Planning as well as a constellation of new programs beginning in fall 2008 which includes Fine Arts, Interior Design, Digital Design, and Industrial Design. The School has, historically, placed strong emphasis on both digital technology in the service of design and in the design of communities.

UNIVERSITY SETTING

Newark is a college town where 30,000 undergraduate and graduate students attend classes on University Heights at the City's four public institutions of higher learning. The NJIT campus consists of forty-five acres of self-contained pedestrian walkways across the street from Rutgers University and down the hill from University of Medicine and Dentistry of New Jersey. The University has a new Campus Center with multiple dining options, rooftop gardens, computer labs and a bowling alley as well as four on-campus, fully wired residence halls. Ninety-five student clubs and Greek organizations enrich student life here.

The School's location in Newark, New Jersey's largest city and its cultural and economic capital, provides an intense architectural laboratory, offering diverse settings for studio projects, building analysis and historical study. Recent work at the School of Architecture has drawn upon this diversity for studies of high density housing, urban planning and renovation, and waterfront development.

Newark is home to the state's most vibrant arts center, NJPAC, as well as Newark Symphony Hall. The Newark Museum, the state's largest museum, houses 80 galleries of world-class American, Asian, African and Classical art. The city boasts the Bears and Eagles Riverfront Stadium, where the NJIT baseball team plays its home games, and the Newark Arena, home to the New Jersey Devils hockey team. NJIT students enjoy the many small art galleries downtown, the historic Branch Brook Park designed by the firm of Frederick Law Olmsted, the Ironbound district, a neighborhood of Portuguese and Brazilian restaurants, bakeries, food markets, and shops.

The School's proximity to New York City, only ten minutes away from campus by subway, offers easy access to even more museums, galleries, film venues and lectures. New York provides cultural opportunities in the forms of theatre, music, and dance. The School of Architecture is able to draw much of its faculty from the many vibrant architectural firms located in the City. In turn, these same firms recruit from the School when looking to hire talented and well prepared young professionals, especially those skilled in design using digital media.

SCHOOL PHILOSOPHY

Undergraduate architecture is an intellectual adventure that combines inspiration, judgment, and informed decision-making. It requires not only technical expertise and creative vision but organizational skills and an understanding of the values of our civilization as revealed through art, literature, and other forms of cultural expression.

These factors come together in the design studio, the basic academic unit of the School, where students learn to analyze different kinds of information, synthesize it into a coherent design solution, and present the solution with clarity and conviction to reviewers from the school and the profession. This education provides the basis for a wide range of careers and teaches habits of mind and skills that are transferable to many human endeavors. The aim of the School is to educate a complete professional who is competent in the field of architecture, but who also grasps the role of the profession in its broader cultural context.

The New Jersey School of Architecture, born of the New Jersey Institute of Technology, is the largest architecture program on the east coast. It enjoys a legacy of technological innovation and was one of the first architecture schools in the nation to incorporate digital technology into the curriculum. Every architecture student designs with state of the art hardware and a constellation of up-to-the-minute software beginning on the first day of class. Building Information Modeling (BIM) has recently been introduced into the curriculum to reflect the emerging use of this technology in professional practice around the world.

PROGRAM DESCRIPTION

The New Jersey School of Architecture at NJIT has recently been expanded to include four new degree programs in fields relating to Architecture. A master plan provides for the creation of the College of Architecture and Design to include the existing New Jersey School of Architecture and the pending School of Art and Design. The architecture degrees are described below. Discriptions of other degrees offered by the School can be found on the website.

Bachelor of Architecture

The B Arch degree, the first professional degree, is a five year sequence consisting of a three-year core and a two-year vertical studio options program leading to licensure. The core program is guided by a specific focus for each of the first three years: visual literacy; technical literacy; and computer literacy. The vertical studio options program combines 4th- and 5th-year students and poses a series of design problems that test and apply basic skills and knowledge in a wide array of physical and intellectual contexts. The school offers a dual degree option for B Arch students, in association with the School of Management, leading to the additional Master of Science in Management degree.

Bachelor of Science in Architecture

The School of Architecture also offers a four-year nonprofessional undergraduate program leading to the BS in Architecture. The first two years of the BS Arch program are identical to the course of study for the B Arch program. In their third and fourth years, students tailor a program to their individual interests and abilities. The BS program is designed to lead into accelerated graduate degree programs or a professional graduate degree in architecture leading to licensure.

Master of Architecture

The professional M Arch is a 3.5 year program of study for applicants who have earned a BS, BA or a graduate degree in fields other than architecture. Applicants who have a pre-professional BS/BA in architecture or related field are reviewed for advanced placement. Candidates will complete a required core sequence in a minimum of 2 years. After completion of the core sequence, all graduate students enter the professional options sequence, in which design studios are offered as option choices in a vertical arrangement. Additional elective courses complete the minimum requirements of the program.

Master of Science in Architecture

The post-professional M Arch is a 1-year minimum continuing program of study for applicants who have previously earned a professional B Arch degree.

Master in Infrastructure Planning

The Master in Infrastructure Planning is a unique interdisciplinary program directed at students with previous degrees in architecture, landscape architecture, urban planning, or civil engineering. The program can be completed in three semesters of full-time study; part-time and dual degree options are individually arranged.

Either M Arch track offers the option of a dual degree program with the Master in Infrastructure Planning degree, allowing substantial overlap of coursework. Another dual degree program is offered by the Schools of Architecture and Management as an option involving the M Arch and a Master of Science in Management.

AREAS OF FOCUS AND RESEARCH

For many years the School of Architecture has had two major areas of focus; computer aided design and the design of communities. The School has continually transformed and recalibrated its curriculum to enhance these priorities. Most recently, building information modeling (BIM) has been introduced to reflect the use of this technology in practices around the globe. The design of communities has been carried on through ongoing relationships with cities and towns around the state such as Patterson, Jersey City, and Newark itself.

SPECIAL ACTIVITIES AND PROGRAMS

The School has many special ongoing programs which are enhanced each year. The following is a short list of some of these.

• Fall and Spring Lecture Series
• Visiting Lecturers and Critics Program
• Albert Dorman Honors College
• Visiting Professors
• Community involvement projects
• Siena Summer Studio
• Fall Student Exhibit
• Career Development Services
• Design Showcase featuring student and alumni work
• Second-Year Masonry Design Build Competition
• AIAS chapter and Graduate Student Association
• Mentors Program
• Collection and review of student work in the Kepler data archive system
• Student/Alumni receptions at local and regional architectural firms

FACILITIES

The School is housed in a 143,000 square-foot facility built in 1998. Conceived of as a "lantern on the hill" the glassy structure reveals to the public all its principle functions. The building, named Weston Hall, is open 24 hours a day and one can see students at work at all times of the day and night. In addition to studios, classrooms and lecture halls Weston Hall contains the Littman Architecture Library and the Architecture Science Research Center, and a digital fabrication lab for 3-D printing. New space continues to be added each year in order to accommodate the growth in the new School of Art and Design.

In 2006 the School launched an internet-based archiving and retrieval system called the Kepler System that allows students to store and retrieve all work from every project in every course. This allows for longitudinal assessment for faculty and administrations as well as easy access to digital portfolios for all students.

SCHOLARSHIPS AND FINANCIAL AID

Financial aid and scholarship applications are available through the University Financial Aid Office. The School of Architecture currently has a variety of scholarships and grants available. Scholarships have been awarded to 3rd-, 4th-, and 5th-year undergraduate students from the New Jersey Society of Architects Scholarship Foundation, as well as part-time college work-study programs. Graduate students are similarly supported by the AIA New Jersey and are eligible for teaching and graduate assistantships through NJIT. State and federal financial aid programs are available through NJIT. Work experience in architecture firms in the New York/New Jersey area can be obtained through the Office of Cooperative Education. Part-time college work-study programs and graduate assistantships are also available. Additionally, the School of Architecture has established an endowed scholarship program and a great number of individually funded annual scholarships.

ADMINISTRATION

Urs Gauchat, RA: Dean

NEW YORK INSTITUTE OF TECHNOLOGY

ADDRESS

Main
New York Institute of Technology
School of Architecture & Design
Education Hall
Old Westbury, NY 11568
Tel.: 516.686.7659
Fax: 516.686.7921
fmruk@nyit.edu
iris.nyit.edu/architecture

STUDENT AND FACULTY DEMOGRAPHICS

% of Female Students	26
% of International Students	17
% of Minority Students	27
% of Out-of-State U.S. Students	
No. Full-Time Faculty	28
No. Part-Time Faculty	79
No. Full-Time Students	853
No. Part-Time Students	162

FINANCIAL INFORMATION

Main Source of University Funding	Private
Annual Tuition & Fees (graduate)	$39,895
Annual Tuition & Fees (undergraduate)	$21,498
% Students Receiving Federal Financial Aid	
% Students Receiving University Financial Aid	
% Students Receiving Departmental Financial Aid	
% Students Receiving Scholarships (assistantships or fellowships)	
Average Annual Scholarship for Department	

ACADEMIC SESSIONS

Fall Semester: September to December
Winter Quarter/Trimester: January to January
Spring Semester: January to May

Summer Session I: May to June
Summer Session II: July to August

ARCHITECTURE AND RELATED DEGREE PROGRAMS

Degree	Min. Yrs. to Complete	Professional Accreditation	# of FT Students	# of PT Students	# of First-Year Students	# of Degrees Conferred	Admissions Requirements
Architecture							
B. Arch	5	NAAB	110	51		64	2.75 cum - portfolio acceptance
BS Arch Tech	4		672	106	278	52	SAT - 1000 combined
M. Arch — 2 years	1.5		12	2	6	5	
Interior Design/Interior Architecture							
B.F.A. Int. Design	4	CIDA/FIDER	75	1	29	21	
Other							
Assoc. Appl. Science in Arch. Tech.	2						
BS Arch Tech Advanced CAD	4						
BS Arch Tech Const Mgmt	4						
BS Arch Tech Energy Mgmt	4						
Bus Admin BS Arch Tech/ MS Energy Mgmt	5						

SPECIALIZATIONS

Computer-Aided Design
Energy

Environment/Sustainability
History

Theory/Criticism

Urban Planning and Design

ARCHITECTURE PROGRAM SUMMARY

The School of Architecture and Design offers degrees in architecture and interior design. Four architecture degrees are offered:

1. Associate in Applied Science in Architectural Technology Degree (A.A.S.)
2. Bachelor of Science in Architectural Technology (B.S.A.T.)
3. Bachelor of Architecture (B.Arch.)
4. Master of Architecture in Urban and Regional Design (M.Arch.)

The B.Arch. degree is recognized as a first professional degree and is fully accredited by the National Architectural Accrediting Board (N.A.A.B.). The M.Arch. is a post-professional degree.

The school also offers a Bachelor of Fine Arts in Interior Design (B.F.A.), a professional degree accredited by the Council for Interior Design Accreditation (C.I.D.A.).

UNIVERSITY SETTING

NYIT's three campuses offer a rich variety of alternative academic environments to the student. In New York City, the Metropolitan Center provides the opportunity to study in an urban environment located on Broadway, near Central Park. On Long Island, campuses are located in park-like suburban settings at Old Westbury and Central Islip. Student residence halls are located at Central Islip. All three campuses feature open-access computer labs, wood shops and exhibit facilities.

SCHOOL PHILOSOPHY

Architecture is regarded as the "mother" of all the arts. As an art, the act of making architecture requires the use of the eye, the mind and the hand, in addition to a commitment to passion, precision and learning. Unlike the other arts however, architecture has a functional task in that it must provide built environments for human activity. Through design and construction, architecture addresses form and space making, as well as the interrelated physical, social, economic and cultural values prevailing in a particular place and time. The School maintains that an emphasis on design within the curriculum best prepares students for effective participation in the profession and for rendering service to the public. The intentions of the program are summarized as follows: (1) To stimulate artistic sensitivity and creative power. (2) To strengthen intellectual ability and self-confidence. (3)To teach technical expertise for the practice of architecture and interior design. Architecture today, operating in a changing world, must address diverse practical considerations such as energy management, ecological well-being and cost effectiveness while responding to fast-paced changes in contemporary society. The curriculum prepares the student by presenting a broad range of considerations occurring within and outside of the design profession. In response to the emergence of computers in the profession, the curriculum is committed to keeping up with change and anticipating the future.

PROGRAM DESCRIPTION
Undergraduate Program

Entering architecture students must complete a two-year core curriculum that includes design studios and architectural history courses, in addition to course work in math, physics and English. After successful completion of the two-year common core curriculum, students may continue in the four-year Bachelor of Science in Architectural Technology program or apply for admission into the five-year Bachelor of Architecture program, which provides the successful candidate with a first professional degree accredited by the National Architecture Accrediting Board. The B.S.A.T. is a non-professional degree offering. Admission to the B. Arch. program requires the submission of a portfolio of student work that is reviewed by a faculty committee. Following acceptance, the student can gain admission to the B. Arch. program if his or her cumulative grade average meets a minimum of 2.75 for all courses undertaken at NYIT or 3.00 for courses in architecture.

With the B. Arch. degree, the successful student may proceed with the professional internship that leads to eligibility for certification from the National Council of Architectural Registration Board (NCARB). All architecture students are required to complete four semesters of core design studios. Students accepted into the B. Arch. program are required to complete six additional studios.

Design Fundamentals, in the first year, introduces the student to the basic principals of three-dimensional design. In the second year, more demanding problems and building analysis projects are undertaken. In the third year, students are required to solve architectural problems involving larger building programs. Urban design and building design solutions requiring inventive structural systems are emphasized in the fourth year. In the fifth and final year of the five-year program, students undertake a two-semester terminal thesis project.

In the fourth and final year of the B.S.A.T. program, the student is required to complete a capstone Project Integration Studio where all aspects of a building design and architectural technology are fully coordinated. Historical analysis as a tool is presented in a sequence of architecture history seminars that introduce the student to the great architectural monuments and cities. History is introduced not only as a chronology of dates and events, but as a body of knowledge that serves the design process. Technical competence is taught with a curriculum that covers all aspects of building materials, structure, mechanical and electrical systems, as well as the procedures of professional practice.

Undergraduate Program in Interior Design

Interior Design as a profession has greatly changed. In the past, it was regarded primarily as the activity of decorating space. Today's interior designers must know how to enhance the quality and efficiency of working and living environments, as well as make aesthetic decisions. The fully-accredited Interior Design program prepares the student for this. Following the completion of two semesters of Design Fundamentals studios and an architecture history course undertaken with architecture students, the student may proceed in the Interior Design program. The Interior Design program is based at the Old Westbury campus. Upon graduation and the completion of two years of Interior Design internship, the candidate becomes eligible to sit for the National Council of Interior Design Qualification (NCIDQ) exam.

AREAS OF FOCUS AND RESEARCH
Focus

Those students who choose to undertake the B.S.A.T. program may gain a degree minor in either Advanced Computer Aided Design (CAD) or in Construction Management. With a minor in Advanced CAD, the B.S.A.T. candidate undertakes upper-level courses focusing on the use of computers in areas such as the preparation of CAD construction drawings and three-dimensional visual representations. Upper-level courses in areas such as contract management, construction supervision, and real estate fundamentals make up the course work of the B.S.A.T. with a minor in Construction Management.

SPECIAL ACTIVITIES AND PROGRAMS

The School enjoys an international reputation for its Summer Studies Abroad programs. Open to all architecture and interior design students, the faculty-directed programs travel each summer to architecturally rich destinations such as China, Egypt, Spain, Germany, Italy and France. Course work undertaken on a Summer Studies Abroad program provides credits that can be applied toward the various degrees. In addition to the summer abroad programs, the School of Architecture and Design has established formal exchange programs with the Tongji University School of Architecture in Shanghai China, and with the Politecnico di Milano in Milan Italy.

Technology is a passion shared by all students at NYIT as evidenced by NYIT's participation in the last two consecutive Solar Decathlon competitions. Students designed and constructed two "state of the art" Solar Homes which were shipped to Washington D.C. for the International Competition. This truly interdisciplinary effort successfully produced the innovative "Open House,"an open source residence and "America's First Solar Hydrogen Home."

SCHOLARSHIPS AND FINANCIAL AID

Merit Scholarships are available for all qualified high school graduates and transfer students. Approximately 90% of all students enrolled at NYIT receive financial assistance in the form of federal, state, and institutional grants or direct student loans. Upper-level students participate in local and national AIA scholarship programs. A variety of professionally-sponsored portfolio and design competitions offer the student the chance for additional financial support.

ADMINISTRATION

Judith DiMaio: Dean
Frank Mruk: Associate Dean
Martha Siegel, ASID: Chair, Interior Design
David Diamond, RA: Chair, Manhattan Architecture
William Palmore: Chair, Old Westbury Architecture

NEWSCHOOL OF ARCHITECTURE & DESIGN

ADDRESS

Main
NewSchool of Architecture & Design
1249 F Street
San Diego, CA 92101
Tel.: 619.235.4100 x200
Fax: 619.235.9893
saltman@newschoolarch.edu
www.newschoolarch.edu

STUDENT AND FACULTY DEMOGRAPHICS

% of Female Students	42
% of International Students	8
% of Minority Students	37
% of Out-of-State U.S. Students	38
No. Full-Time Faculty	16
No. Part-Time Faculty	48
No. Full-Time Students	379
No. Part-Time Students	95

FINANCIAL INFORMATION

Main Source of University Funding	Private
Annual Tuition & Fees (graduate)	$19,500
Annual Tuition & Fees (undergraduate)	$19,500
% Students Receiving Federal Financial Aid	55
% Students Receiving University Financial Aid	25
% Students Receiving Departmental Financial Aid	0
% Students Receiving Scholarships (assistantships or fellowships)	10
Average Annual Scholarship for Department	$5,000

ACADEMIC SESSIONS

Fall Quarter/Trimester: October to December
Winter Quarter/Trimester: January to March
Spring Quarter/Trimester: April to June

Summer Session I: July to September
Summer Session II: July to August
Summer Session III: August to September

ARCHITECTURE AND RELATED DEGREE PROGRAMS

Degree	Min. Yrs. to Complete	Professional Accreditation	# of FT Students	# of PT Students	# of First-Year Students	# of Degrees Conferred	Admissions Requirements
Architecture							
B. Arch	5	NAAB	241	55	67	32	TOEFL, Essay, grade average of 2.5 or higher
BA	4		1	2	0	2	TOEFL, Essay
M. Arch — 2 years	2	NAAB	26	4	15	5	Undergraduate degree, Undergraduate Architecture degree, TOEFL, Portfolio, Essay, grade average of 2.7 or higher
M. Arch — 3 years	3	NAAB	110	31	37	38	Undergraduate degree, TOEFL, Portfolio, Essay, grade average of 2.7 or higher
MS Arch—post-professional and non-professional	1		1	3	1	1	

SPECIALIZATIONS

Art and Design
History

Professional Practice
Tectonics

Theory/Criticism

Urban Planning and Design

ARCHITECTURE PROGRAM SUMMARY

NewSchool offers the first Professional Degree in its undergraduate and graduate programs, as well as bachelor and master degrees for those who wish to study architecture but who do not wish to pursue licensure. From its downtown San Diego location, the School takes advantage of its urban location through projects and participation in the city, itself a dynamic and growing community. The School schedules classes in the afternoon and evening to enable students to work and study at the same time. The faculty are drawn from the profession, building upon its core full-time faculty, themselves with significant experience in the field, with talented practitioners who bring current issues, problems and solutions into the classroom for analysis and learning. This blending of instructors provides a rich, interactive environment where students are exposed to best practices, are nurtured to perform at high levels and who will become responsible professionals in the future. NewSchool offers international program opportunities for study abroad, and welcomes students from diverse backgrounds and geographies to facilitate learning from one another.

UNIVERSITY SETTING

NewSchool is an intimate, professional college of architecture located in downtown San Diego. We enjoy a small student body of individuals, including students straight from high school, college transfer students and working and mid-career students of diverse backgrounds, experiences and ages that make for a very exciting learning environment. Our students get much individual attention, which is virtually impossible to get at large schools, from professors who are experienced, practicing professionals from the community.

SCHOOL PHILOSOPHY

NewSchool's mission is to nurture and develop technically competent, aesthetically sensitive, socially responsible professionals for a changing, global society. NewSchool believes that individuals can find reward and fulfillment in the study of architecture. The instructional program nurtures the artistic passion into professional excellence. Students are challenged with rigorous advancement standards. The faculty includes experienced architects and practicing professionals who develop creative mentorships. NewSchool subscribes to the "learn by doing" educational philosophy. The urban San Diego community is seen as an ideal laboratory for architectural innovation. Students are encouraged to intern as soon as their abilities and circumstances allow.

PROGRAM DESCRIPTION

Undergraduate Program

The First Professional Bachelor of Architecture degree program (B.Arch.) at NewSchool, in conjunction with the mission statement of the school, pursues objectives that best support the continuously evolving demands of practice and simultaneously recognizes the needs for consistency, as well as change, in architectural instruction. The curriculum, with a comprehensive view of architecture, focuses on the development of the necessary skills for the effective communication of ideas, development of individual design abilities that effectively integrate technology, function and aesthetics, and development of an enlightened sense of urban design, professional ethics and beliefs in architectural practice. The five-year program consists of focusing, in the first and second years, on the necessary skills and knowledge for design and practice, in the third year on tectonics and design, in the fourth year on urban design, and in the fifth year on integration of research methodology and programming in design through an individual thesis design project. Throughout the five-year program, in order to have a broader point of view, students are obligated to select a minor from one of five categories: Art & Design, History & Theory, Professional Practice, Technology or Urban Studies.

Graduate Program

The M. Arch. program is a First Professional Degree program for students who hold the baccalaureate degree. The three-year program is designed for students who do not have any prior background in architecture. The two-year program is available for students who have previous design and architectural preparation but who do not hold the professional degree. Both programs provide the necessary skills and abilities for effective contributions to the field as well as satisfying initial licensure requirements. Students in the graduate program may also participate in the School's international programs. In order to ensure that students have an opportunity to develop some specific foci, the program requires an Area of Concentration to be completed from one of the following: Art & Design, History & Theory, Professional Practice, Technology or Urban Studies.

AREAS OF FOCUS AND RESEARCH

Focus

Directed research and study in specific areas of concentration develop specialized conceptual and methodological skills. Students must declare a minor and successfully complete a minimum of fifteen units from one of the following areas of concentration:

- Art & Design
- History & Theory
- Professional Practice
- Technology
- Urban Studies

Research

Student research is encouraged throughout the curriculum, with emphasis placed on the final year of both the professional and graduate degrees. Each student is required to produce a research thesis, which is the final graduation requirement. The thesis process is an integration of work done in the Research course with work produced in the final year Studio sequence. The Thesis Integration course guides students through the thesis-assembly process. All fourth-year B.Arch. students are required to take an upper-division Communications course to prepare them for the language requirements needed for the research year.

SPECIAL ACTIVITIES AND PROGRAMS

NewSchool offers a Summer Exploratory Program each July affording individuals of all ages the opportunity to "taste" the field of architecture. The Summer Exploratory Program is a five-week session that exposes students to the fundamentals of the field and introductions to the study of architecture.

Another special program opportunity is the School's international programs. Each Summer, students have the opportunity to participate in an international overseas program, opting to study architecture and urban design in Copenhagen, Rome or other global destinations.

We have a Career Services Office where students receive career counseling and job placement assistance for internships and after graduation. We participate in awards programs for talented students in conjunction with CSI, San Diego Regional Energy Office, the Lumberman's Association and national competitions such as Steel Tube Institute and ACSA competitions. Cartouche, NewSchool's student publication, is a forum of ideas and display of student, faculty and community work from the San Diego design community.

FACILITIES

Classes are held in an 83,500 square-foot facility located in the East Village section of the San Diego Arts District. NewSchool has permanent exhibit areas of approximately 2,000 square-feet; a Library housing approximately 12,000 volumes, periodicals, slides and videos, all listed in a computerized database; a Project Lab for model and furniture making; two Computer Labs with the latest computer-aided design software; a wireless broadband network, a centralized Print Center, an archive of student work maintained in a permanent display area; a student lounge; and individual studio spaces for each student taking design courses. The facilities and equipment comply with federal, state and local ordinances.

SCHOLARSHIPS AND FINANCIAL AID

NewSchool is approved to participate in Title IV and state programs including: Cal Grant, Federal Pell Grant, Federal SEOG, Federal Family Education Loan Program, Subsidized and Unsubsidized Federal Stafford Loan & Federal College Work Study Program. NewSchool also provides scholarships to continuing and new students who demonstrate high scholastic and design achievement. Teaching assistantships are also available.

ADMINISTRATION

Steven Altman, PhD: President
Gilbert Cooke, AIA: Dean
Kurt Hunker, AIA: Chair/Graduate Dept.
Mitra Kanaani, AIA, ICBO, SBSE:
    Chair/Undergraduate Dept

NORTH CAROLINA STATE UNIVERSITY

ADDRESS

Main
North Carolina State University
College of Design
School of Architecture
Campus Box 7701
Raleigh, NC 27695-7701
Tel.: 919.515.8350
Fax: 919.515.7330
architecture_design@ncsu.edu
www.design.ncsu.edu

Undergraduate Admissions
North Carolina State University
203 Peele Hall
Campus Box 7103
Raleigh, NC 27695-7103

Graduate Admissions
North Carolina State University
1575 Varsity Drive, Flex Lab Module 6
Campus Box 7102

STUDENT AND FACULTY DEMOGRAPHICS

% of Female Students	47
% of International Students	4
% of Minority Students	14
% of Out-of-State U.S. Students	11
No. Full-Time Faculty	14
No. Part-Time Faculty	23
No. Full-Time Students	221
No. Part-Time Students	9

FINANCIAL INFORMATION

Main Source of University Funding	Public
Annual Tuition & Fees (graduate, resident)	$5,636
Annual Tuition & Fees (graduate, nonresident)	$17,684
Annual Tuition & Fees (undergraduate, resident)	$5,118
Annual Tuition & Fees (undergraduate, nonresident)	$17,316
% Students Receiving Federal Financial Aid	65
% Students Receiving University Financial Aid	49
% Students Receiving Departmental Financial Aid	31
% Students Receiving Scholarships (assistantships or fellowships)	31
Average Annual Scholarship for Department	$1,724

ACADEMIC SESSIONS

Fall Semester: August to December
Spring Semester: January to May

ARCHITECTURE AND RELATED DEGREE PROGRAMS

Degree	Min. Yrs. to Complete	Professional Accreditation	# of FT Students	# of PT Students	# of First-Year Students	# of Degrees Conferred	Admissions Requirements
Architecture							
B. Arch	5	NAAB	22	0	22	19	Undergraduate Architecture degree, Portfolio, Rec. Letters, Essay
BEDA	4		133	3	43	33	SAT, Portfolio, Essay
M. Arch Track 1	2	NAAB	18	1	7	8	Undergraduate Architecture degree, TOEFL, Portfolio, Rec. Letters, Essay
M. Arch Track 2	1.5		0	0	0	2	Professional Architecture degree, TOEFL, Portfolio, Rec. Letters, Essay
M. Arch Track 3	3.5	NAAB	48	5	18	14	Undergraduate degree, GRE, TOEFL, Portfolio, Rec. Letters, Essay
Other							
PhD in Design	3		15	0	4	1	

SPECIALIZATIONS

Architectural Design
Building Technology/Env. Systems
Community Design
Computer-Aided Design

Energy
Environment/Sustainability
History
International/Regional Architecture

Preservation
Professional Practice
Sacred Spaces
Sustainability

Tectonics
Theory/Criticism
Urban Planning and Design

ARCHITECTURE PROGRAM SUMMARY

The School of Architecture at NC State provides two means of achieving a professional degree in architecture: (1) We offer the **Bachelor of Environmental Design in Architecture** (BED-A), followed by an independent fifth year **Bachelor of Architecture** (B.Arch) degree. *The fifth year B.Arch is open to applicants from any four year pre-architecture degree (BED, BS Arch, BA Arch, etc).* (2) We offer a **2-year first-professional Master of Architecture** (M.Arch) degree for graduates from pre-architecture porgrams; a **3.5-year first professional M.Arch** for students from any undergraduate background; and a **1-year post-professional M.Arch** for students with a B.Arch or M.Arch who wish to develop a specialization and undertake research. The College of Design at NC State also offers a **Ph.D in Design**.

UNIVERSITY SETTING

NC State University — the largest in the sixteen-campus University of North Carolina System — is a Research 1 university with the depth and breadth of resources to provide an intellectually stimulating setting for professional education in architecture. It has an enrollment of 32,000 students representing every state in the United States and 90 foreign countries. Raleigh is the state capital and the cultural focus of the "Research Triangle" region — a prosperous metropolitan area of over one million inhabitants.

SCHOOL PHILOSOPHY

The School of Architecture is the largest component of a dynamic, multidisciplinary College of Design, which also contains undergraduate and graduate programs in landscape architecture, industrial design, graphic design, art and design, and a Ph.D. in Design. With a permanent faculty of 14 and a large cadre of adjunct faculty, the School is richly endowed with teachers and scholars dedicated to the advancement of architecture as a discipline and to the betterment of society. By instilling in our students experimental and ethical attitudes in their approach to design, we seek to make architecture a supple instrument for enhancing the physical environment.

PROGRAM DESCRIPTION
Undergraduate Program

The Bachelor of Environmental Design in Architecture program gives priority to the education of the individual student. Students are challenged to employ their intelligence, imagination, and sense of responsibility in an intense pursuit of knowledge and in the development of creative skills. The discipline of architecture offers the primary framework for this process of intellectual and creative development, but the curriculum recognizes the critical contributions that the larger university environment, as well as the culture of the state, nation and world, make to the student's growth as an individual and citizen.

The BEDA program comprising eight semesters of design studio, professional core courses, and a broad general education component serves as the foundation for advanced study in professional degree programs. The School of Architecture offers two accredited degree

programs: a one-year Bachelor of Architecture and the two-year Master of Architecture, both of which satisfy the educational requirements for licensure.

The Bachelor of Architecture curriculum is a 30-credit hour program which focuses on preparation for architectural practice through an intensive design studio program supported by required and elective courses in history, theory, building systems, and legal and practice processes. Applications to the B.Arch. program are invited from graduates of pre-professional programs in architecture.

Graduate Program

The Master of Architecture prepares students to assume responsible roles in a variety of settings including private and public practice, education, and research. The focus of graduate study is the design studio, where students explore and evaluate design principles through direct experience with real and hypothetical projects. Studios are supplemented by a wide variety of architecture elective courses in history, theory, technology, and methodology. The primary goal of the program is to develop and nurture individuals who seek excellence in their professional, intellectual, and creative pursuits.

The School offers three tracks to the M. Arch degree: Track 1 is a two-year program for holders of the Bachelor of Environmental Design in Architecture or an equivalent pre-professional degree; Track 2 is a three-semester second professional degree for holders of the five-year Bachelor of Architecture degree; and Track 3 is a three-and-one-half-year program for students with degrees in fields other than architecture.

Three curricular choices are available to Track 1 and Track 3 students in their final two years of graduate study. The first is the Studio Option, the second is the Independent Final Project Option, and third is the Research Project Option for students contemplating doctoral study.

The PhD in Design program is aimed at preparing graduate students for careers in research, scholarship, public service and teaching. It provides opportunities to investigate important research issues related to architecture, graphic design, industrial design, and landscape architecture. It has links to academic resources in the university and neighboring institutions at UNC-Chapel Hill and Duke University.

AREAS OF FOCUS AND RESEARCH
Focus

While the primary emphasis of the professional programs is the development of the individual student toward becoming a broadly educated and skilled graduate, ready to assume a responsible, professional role, the School possesses a depth of resources and learning opportunities which also enable students to develop a level of expertise in individualized areas of interest. These include: Campus Design, Urban Design, Community Design and Assistance, Universal Design, Architectural Conservation, Architectural Technology, and Sustainable Design.

Research

Faculty research, scholarship, and critical practice are given a high priority in the School of Architecture. Recent examples include experimentation in long-span

structures, innovations in masonry construction, urban form and growth, "the modern site," daylighting, sustainable communities, suburban space and identity, transforming workplaces, designing responsive schools, typological theory, and vernacular architecture. In addition, a number of faculty are actively engaged in innovative and award-winning architectural practices. Other opportunities for student participation are available in the Ph.D. in Design program.

SPECIAL ACTIVITIES AND PROGRAMS

- Design Camp is a summer program which introduces high school students to design.
- Foreign Study Opportunities include semester-long exchange programs with architecture schools in Istanbul (Turkey), Manchester (England), San Sebastian (Spain), Stuttgart (Germany), semester-long study at the College of Design Prague Institute (Czech Republic), and links to many other international study and travel programs.
- Public lectures and exhibitions featuring internationally recognized practitioners, scholars, critics and cutting edge design work play a significant role in enriching the classroom experience of architecture students.
- Field trips to architectural offices, buildings and construction sites, and major centers of architectural interest are regular features of the program.
- Student organizations include AIAS, Design Council, Tau Sigma Delta, African-American Design Students Association, and Architecture Graduate Students Association.

FACILITIES

The College of Design, which includes the School of Architecture, is housed in the complex of Brooks, Kamphoefner, and Leazar Halls containing dedicated studio space for 700 students, instructional labs, classrooms, galleries, research centers, shops and library. Among the noteworthy facilities are the Harrye B. Lyons Design Library; the Multimedia Lab; the Belk Rotunda and Gilbert Gallery, providing well-appointed spaces for project review and exhibitions; the Materials Lab; and the state-of-the-art Burns Auditorium.

SCHOLARSHIPS AND FINANCIAL AID

The School provides more than $50,000 in merit-based scholarships and fellowships annually. Students may also qualify for merit and need-based university scholarship programs and grants. A number of current architecture students have won coveted Park Scholarships and Caldwell Fellowships which provide all academic and living expenses for four years. In addition, more than two dozen teaching assistantships and research assistantships valued at $2,000 per semester are awarded to qualified graduate students. Students may also qualify for national AIA/AAF Scholarships.

ADMINISTRATION

Marvin J. Malecha, FAIA, DPACSA,
   AIA/ACSA Topaz Laureate: Dean
Robin Fran Abrams, PhD., AIA, ASLA: Head
David Hill: Director of Graduate Program

NORTH DAKOTA STATE UNIVERSITY

ADDRESS

Main
North Dakota State University
NDSU Downtown
650 NP Avenue
Fargo, ND 58102
Tel.: 701.231.5789
Fax: 701.231.7342
www.ndsu.edu/arch

STUDENT AND FACULTY DEMOGRAPHICS

% of Female Students	40
% of International Students	5
% of Minority Students	5
% of Out-of-State U.S. Students	65
No. Full-Time Faculty	21
No. Part-Time Faculty	4
No. Full-Time Students	600
No. Part-Time Students	0

FINANCIAL INFORMATION

Main Source of University Funding	Public
Annual Tuition & Fees (graduate, resident)	$5,975
Annual Tuition & Fees (graduate, nonresident)	$14,346
Annual Tuition & Fees (undergraduate, resident)	$5,013
Annual Tuition & Fees (undergraduate, nonresident)	$13,384
% Students Receiving Federal Financial Aid	135
% Students Receiving University Financial Aid	
% Students Receiving Departmental Financial Aid	
% Students Receiving Scholarships (assistantships or fellowships)	
Average Annual Scholarship for Department	

ACADEMIC SESSIONS

Fall Semester: August to December; Application Deadline: August 15
Spring Semester: January to May; Application Deadline: January 1

ARCHITECTURE AND RELATED DEGREE PROGRAMS

Degree	Min. Yrs. to Complete	Professional Accreditation	# of FT Students	# of PT Students	# of First-Year Students	# of Degrees Conferred	Admissions Requirements
Architecture							
M. Arch	5	NAAB	215	0	300	50	TOEFL
Landscape Architecture							
Bachelor of Landscape Architecture	5	LAAB	70	0	40	15	
Environmental Design							
B.S. Environmental Design	4						

SPECIALIZATIONS

Architectural Design
Art and Design
Building Technology/Env. Systems
Community Design

Computer-Aided Design
Environment/Sustainability
History
International/Regional Architecture

Landscape Design
Preservation
Professional Practice

Sustainability
Theory/Criticism
Urban Planning and Design

ARCHITECTURE PROGRAM SUMMARY

NDSU offers a 5-year, professionally oriented Master of Architecture program housed primarily in a beautifully restored historic industrial building in downtown Fargo, which has emerged as an exciting, student-oriented urban district. Entry into the first, pre-professional year is open to any student admitted to NDSU. Admission to the professional program, beginning in the second year of study, is competitive and based on performance in first-year courses. Curriculum includes field trips to cities across the country and is supported by a professionally-staffed wood shop, digital media labs, and laser cutter for model-making. Both traditional and digital means are emphasized. An optional semester abroad, plus foreign study tours during summers, are offered.

UNIVERSITY SETTING

NDSU is a campus of 13,000 students set in a supportive, friendly metropolitan area of approximately 170,000 people in eastern North Dakota and western Minnesota. Within this community, NDSU is one of three colleges comprising a consortium that offers a rich variety of coursework, extensive library holdings, and a wide range of student activities. NDSU offers excellent opportunities to develop a strong foundation for a professional career in architecture through close personal interaction with faculty and an energetic student body. Transfer students cannot generally be accepted with advanced standing.

SCHOOL PHILOSOPHY

NDSU prepares students to enter the profession of architecture with a strong self-image, a global perspective, and the understanding that they have the capacity to help people find imaginative solutions to problems. The program begins by stimulating students' imagination and curiosity while building respect for others, for the environment, and for education. These fundamentals are followed by developing professional skills, self-confidence, and a framework for lifelong learning. NDSU's architecture program offers students the chance to study architecture as members of a small, close-knit group whose members are selected for their academic and professional promise.

PROGRAM DESCRIPTION

During the first year of the program, students take introductory courses in environmental design, foundation studies, and freehand drawing, in addition to general education requirements of the curriculum with courses in English, math, and behavioral sciences. In recent years, approximately 300 students have enrolled in the department at the beginning of the first year. After a minimum of two semesters on campus, 54 students are selectively admitted from those who apply to advance into the second-year professional program, based on academic merit and professional promise demonstrated in their first year of study. The next three years integrate coursework in technical systems, history, and theory with design work in the studio. Because faculty

studio critics also teach courses in history, theory, and technology, the opportunity for integrative learning is stressed. At the end of the third year, students may apply for the accredited Master of Architecture degree program, which requires two additional years of study for a total of five years to degree. Or students may remain in the undergraduate Bachelor of Science in Environmental Design program and receive their degree at the end of the fourth year of study.

The graduate program emphasizes specific aspects of professional practice, architectural theory, history, design, and research, and culminates in an individual design thesis that integrates all previous learning. The design thesis is exhibited before the public and university community, and is presented to a faculty jury. Upon successfully completing the fifth year, a student earns the Master of Architecture professional degree; completing the academic phase of training for the profession of architecture.

AREAS OF FOCUS AND RESEARCH

In addition to the basic curriculum, which endeavors to give students exposure to the broadest range of architectural issues, each student undertakes an individualized concentration of elective courses from related disciplines like landscape architecture, art, construction management, interior design, or business administration. Individual faculty have also developed areas of specific, focused interest which they share with students through graduate seminar courses, special independent study courses, and continuing education or international study offerings. Individual faculty maintain research agendas oriented toward design practice, environmentally sustainable design, urban design, architectural history, historic preservation, digital visualization and computer-aided design, community design, Great Plains regional issues, and other areas.

Occasionally these research undertakings provide opportunities for students to become involved as research assistants. Faculty share their research and creative scholarship by participating in national and international conferences. Through the Center for Community Planning and Design, students also engage in research that contributes to helping communities and non-profit organizations visualize design opportunities for community development. Fifth-year graduate students become intensively involved in research that is relevant to their specific design thesis topic by working with a faculty critic to develop a detailed program of project requirements.

SPECIAL ACTIVITIES AND PROGRAMS

Active student organizations include the American Institute of Architecture Students and the national honor society Tau Sigma Delta. Student organizations serve their members with activities during the school year including participation in the national student Forum conference, outreach to public school students to generate interest in architecture, and sponsoring guest speakers and competitions, and organizing the annual Beaux-arts Week each spring. This week-long

celebration of architecture includes special speakers, demonstrations, workshops, and social activities that culminate in an awards ceremony and the annual Beaux Arts ceremony. Many NDSU architecture students participate in either a North American or international study program for academic credit. In recent years, students have traveled to England, France, Italy, Spain, Germany, the Czech Republic, Denmark, Sweden, Finland, Greece, and Turkey. Field trips to cities in North America (Chicago, Las Vegas, Minneapolis, San Francisco, Washington DC, Winnipeg) are a regular part of the studio curriculum. Academic exchange programs enable NDSU students to complete a semester of architectural study abroad in several countries while receiving corresponding credit under the NDSU curriculum. Students may also participate in the university's cooperative education program by spending a year off campus as full-time employees in an architectural firm while maintaining full-time student status with NDSU. After completing the third-year of architectural study, students can count their internship experience toward becoming eligible to take the architectural registration exam.

FACILITIES

Architecture at NDSU is housed entirely in two buildings in downtown Fargo, which has emerged as an exciting, student-oriented urban core. One of the two buildings is a LEED-certified, Historic Tax Act project that transformed a 100-year-old, 4-story industrial building into art and architecture studios. Facilities include a professional wood shop with a full-time wood shop manager, two dedicated computer labs for architegture and landscape architecture, also professionally staffed, a high-end laser cutter, and a gallery for display of student work. The Architecture and Landscape Architecture Library, a branch of the main university research library, is housed in our building. Classrooms and studio spaces throughout the department are networked to provide excellent support for the laptop computers each student obtains in the second year of the professional program. Many students take advantage of additional studio, darkroom, and gallery facilities of the Art Department, with which we share one building.

SCHOLARSHIPS AND FINANCIAL AID

Conventional federal grant and loan programs and a modest number of assistance, recognition, and support programs are available to students based on merit or need. The American Institute of Architects provides scholarships from the national Architecture Foundation (AAF) and from statewide chapters in both North Dakota and South Dakota. Students are regularly selected for scholarships from national organizations like the Association for Women in Construction and Construction Specifications Institute.

ADMINISTRATION

Paul H. Gleye: Chair

NORTHEASTERN UNIVERSITY

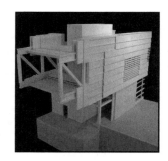

ADDRESS

Main
Northeastern University
School of Architecture
360 Huntington Avenue
151 Ryder Hall
Boston, MA 02115
Tel.: 617.373.4637
Fax: 617.373.7080
architecture@neu.edu
www.architecture.neu.edu

STUDENT AND FACULTY DEMOGRAPHICS

% of Female Students	50
% of International Students	10
% of Minority Students	10
% of Out-of-State U.S. Students	60
No. Full-Time Faculty	10
No. Part-Time Faculty	25
No. Full-Time Students	450
No. Part-Time Students	0

FINANCIAL INFORMATION

Main Source of University Funding	Private
Annual Tuition & Fees (graduate)	$31,360
Annual Tuition & Fees (undergraduate)	$33,320
% Students Receiving Federal Financial Aid	74.3
% Students Receiving University Financial Aid	66.4
% Students Receiving Departmental Financial Aid	0
% Students Receiving Scholarships (assistantships or fellowships)	48.2
Average Annual Scholarship for Department	$6,000

ACADEMIC SESSIONS

Fall Semester: September to December; Application Deadline: February 1
Spring Semester: January to April

Early Action: November 1
Regular Decision: January 15

ARCHITECTURE AND RELATED DEGREE PROGRAMS

Degree	Min. Yrs. to Complete	Professional Accreditation	# of FT Students	# of PT Students	# of First-Year Students	# of Degrees Conferred	Admissions Requirements
Architecture							
BS Arch	5		400	10	95	65	HS Diploma, SAT, and University Admissions requirements
M. Arch — 1 year	1	NAAB	34	0	34	32	Undergraduate Studio Architecture degree or Prof. Architecture degree, TOEFL, Portfolio, Rec. Letters, Essay
M. Arch — 2 years	2	NAAB	16	0	8	8	Undergraduate Studio Architecture degree, TOEFL, Portfolio, Rec. Letters, Essay

SPECIALIZATIONS

Architectural Design
Building Information Modeling
Building Technology/Env. Systems
Community Design

Computer-Aided Design
Energy
Environment/Sustainability
History

Housing
International Development
Landscape Design
Professional Practice

Sustainability
Tectonics
Theory/Criticism
Urban Planning and Design

UNIVERSITY SETTING

Northeastern University is located in the heart of Boston, one of the country's oldest and most architecturally rich cities. The University is one of the largest in the region, and a national leader in co-operative education, or the formal linkage of academic and practical learning. The School of Architecture encourages students to take advantage of related courses in the College of Arts and Sciences, the Center for Urban and Regional Policy, College of Engineering, and the College of Business.

SCHOOL PHILOSOPHY

The School of Architecture at Northeastern focuses on urban building and its ramifications. The program seeks to bring the critical and inventive capabilities of the architect to bear on the real problems of contemporary cities; especially Boston. The School is home to a number of important outreach programs in urban housing, new urban school prototypes, mapping initiatives, and new urban design strategies for post-industrial sites. The mission of the School of Architecture assumes architecture to be the context of civic life, and seeks opportunities for public imagery in an increasingly privatized urban landscape.

PROGRAM DESCRIPTION

The undergraduate program is by far the largest part of Northeastern's School of Architecture. It offers a pre-professional Bachelor of Science degree (BS Arch), but is also the prerequisite for the one-year professional Master's degree program (M.Arch). It is a five year program that includes four years of academic study and two six-month periods of professional work periodically inserted into the curriculum. Students begin their studies directly in the School of Architecture with related courses in the core curriculum within the College of Arts and Sciences, and their relationship with that college remains throughout their education. Design Studio work begins with a strong foundation in both manual and digital representation, followed by design studios dealing with urban types and basic composi-

tion in urban settings. The history sequences includes a full-year survey course covering world architecture and is followed by more detailed courses in 19th and 20th century architecture and urbanism. Upper-level studios address urban design, the challenges of building in cities and suburbs, housing, and tectonics. Computer technology is introduced at very beginning of the curriculum along with the basics of drawing and thinking about architectural topics. Building technology courses are coordinated with the sequence of design studios to create integration of design and building technology thinking.

AREAS OF FOCUS AND RESEARCH

The School of Architecture engages the discipline and profession of architecture by bringing critical attention to the practical problems of urban housing, the problems associated with integrating 1960s urbanism with the contemporary city, new technologies and their integration with building design, and new planning methods. The faculty is very active in research, and was recently ranked 11th in the nation in this area.

The School of Architecture also focuses on the relationship of architecture to urban design and planning. By addressing the larger issues of the "new geography of urban design" in the design studio, students learn new techniques for linking the architecture of individual projects to larger aims. The discussion of different modes of agency allows these new techniques to be evaluated against the effectiveness in a complex urban environment.

SPECIAL ACTIVITIES AND PROGRAMS

Perhaps the foremost special opportunity for the architecture student at Northeastern is simply Boston itself. The city and its environs offer outstanding examples of architecture from the past 350 years. Students visit regional architectural sites of interest, including the work of Bullfinch, Richardson, Wright, Le Corbusier, Saarinen, Aalto, Kahn, Moneo, and Machado and Silvetti. The School also has a professional co-operative education

advisor whose responsibility is to help students find professional work in architecture and related fields during their "co-op periods" in the curriculum. The School has a mandatory semester abroad in Rome, Italy. There is an extensive public lecture and exhibition series every year, which is supplemented by additional outstanding offerings from Harvard, MIT, another area institutions. The students also run a chapter of the American Institute of Architecture Students (AIAS).

FACILITIES

The School of Architecture is situated at the heart of the University's newly reinvented urban campus. Dedicated studios are located in the Ruggles MBTA Station. The School offices, slide library, and classrooms are located in Ryder Hall. Students are housed in campus housing or city apartments. The campus is served by two of Boston's major public transit lines, both of which have stops on campus.

At Northeastern the city is more than the location of the campus. Boston serves as a laboratory for addressing the complexities of successful post-industrial cities. It offers students a chance to see the workings of the city up-close, and to learn by participating in its ongoing transformation. Students regularly travel from campus to project sites around the city, using the "T" and other transportation options.

SCHOLARSHIPS AND FINANCIAL AID

Both merit-based, and need-based financial aid is available from the University as a whole. The College of Arts and Sciences itself offers a few modest awards based on annual reviews of academic success.

ADMINISTRATION

George Thrush, FAIA: Director
Peter Wiederspahn, AIA: Graduate Program Director
Danielle Walquist: Office Manager
Lynn Burke: Co-op Coordinator
Mary Hughes: Media Librarian

NORWICH UNIVERSITY

ADDRESS

Main
Norwich University
Architecture Program
Chaplin Hall
158 Harmon Drive
Northfield, VT 05663-1035
Fax: 802/485-2623
archart@norwich.edu
www.norwich.edu/academics/art

STUDENT AND FACULTY DEMOGRAPHICS

% of Female Students	40
% of International Students	5
% of Minority Students	10
% of Out-of-State U.S. Students	85
No. Full-Time Faculty	10
No. Part-Time Faculty	10
No. Full-Time Students	147
No. Part-Time Students	1

FINANCIAL INFORMATION

Main Source of University Funding	Private
Annual Tuition & Fees (graduate)	$24,000
Annual Tuition & Fees (undergraduate)	$24,000
% Students Receiving Federal Financial Aid	92
% Students Receiving University Financial Aid	80
% Students Receiving Departmental Financial Aid	0
% Students Receiving Scholarships (assistantships or fellowships)	0
Average Annual Scholarship for Department	$20,000

ACADEMIC SESSIONS

Fall Semester: August to December
Spring Semester: January to May

Summer Session I: May to July
Summer Session II: May to August

ARCHITECTURE AND RELATED DEGREE PROGRAMS

Degree	Min. Yrs. to Complete	Professional Accreditation	# of FT Students	# of PT Students	# of First-Year Students	# of Degrees Conferred	Admissions Requirements
Architecture							
BS Arch Studies	4		76	1	45	2	
M. Arch — 1.5 years	1.5	NAAB	17	0	17	15	

UNIVERSITY SETTING

As the only professional program in Northern New England, Norwich, which has a small and intimate student body of about 1,900 students, appreciates a special relationship with the profession as a regional center for education, information, and discourse. The school's location near Montpelier, the capital of Vermont, also affords direct contact with the policymakers in the fields of environmental issues, regional planning, and education, concerns for which citizens of Vermont have been recognized as national leaders.

SCHOOL PHILOSOPHY

Reflecting the aspirations of Alden Partridge, founder of Norwich University, our program offers many opportunities for experiential learning. Both in and outside of class, one finds our students designing and building playgrounds in surrounding communities, framing houses for Habitat for Humanity, or crafting furniture in our shop. However, experiential learning goes beyond merely skills development: reflection is the other critical part of this learning process; in other words, the program explores in many dimensions the meaning of making and the making of meaning. Our faculty, who have been drawn from a range of social, educational, artistic and practical backgrounds, reflects this specificity.

PROGRAM DESCRIPTION
Undergraduate Program

The professional architecture program is a five-and one-half year curriculum primarily designed for high school graduates and transfer students. The first four years of this program lead to a pre-professional BS in Architectural Studies degree. In addition to establishing a strong foundation in general education and the basic professional knowledge of architecture, this curriculum is structured to allow undergraduate students to pursue a minor in another field. Our setting in a state renown for its pristine landscapes, remarkably preserved villages, and traditional values for craftsmanship and the arts serves as a unique laboratory for studying the role of architecture in the making of place. Our program stresses the importance of developing leadership and teamwork skills both in and out of the classroom. Each student is expected to be active in the program, the university, and the community. Reflecting the aspirations of Alden Partridge, the curriculum also emphasizes a balance between conceptual and experiential learning through such offerings as the design/build studio, technical workshops, and community service projects. Pedagogically, Norwich actively seeks to explore the varying philosophical positions within architecture. We believe that students should explore the diversities that enrich the profession and the contentions that spice it.

AREAS OF FOCUS AND RESEARCH
Focus

President Kennedy said, "leadership and learning are indispensable to each other." Norwich students are encouraged to develop both an understanding of individual responsibility and teambuilding skills. Small class size, a broad exposure to architectural traditions and involvement in community projects, such as urban design workshops, facilitates this development. Through lecture courses, seminars and design studios, students gain an appreciation and understanding for the environment and its diverse cultures. A strong emphasis on creativity, integrity and service prepare them for leadership roles within the design profession as well as thoughtful, contributing roles in society and in the 'global village.'

Research

As a program with an emphasis on the art and craft of making and its resultant and intended meaning, a significant portion of the faculty's research interests involves participatory investigations in creative endeavors (photography, painting, drawing, installation, furniture, cabinetry, etc.) as well as professional practice. In addition, the relationship of building in landscape and townscape, as well as the pedagogy of community action is stressed. The School participates in a university-wide faculty development program consisting of representatives from all areas of the University who review and recommend funding of research proposals.

SPECIAL ACTIVITIES AND PROGRAMS

Norwich supports students in developing choices that make each experience in school unique. Our students have taken part in various study abroad programs throughout the world. Our students enjoy the capability of studying in Berlin, Germany. We also offer workshops jointly with the Preservation Institute of Historic Windsor, and we have a very strong relationship with the Yestermorrow Design/Build School in Warren, Vermont. The School sponsors a lecture and exhibit series to bring guests. In order to experience the work of renowned architects and artists, the School also has field trips to cities such as Boston, New Haven, New York, Washington, and Montreal. The Norwich Chapter of AIAS (American Institute of Architecture Students), hosts activities such as lectures, movies, and program gatherings. Student representatives visit other schools and attend national AIAS meetings throughout the country. Our strongest students academically are members of the Architecture Honor Society, and sponsor our student mentorship program, competitions, scholarships, and awards.

FACILITIES

The School of Architecture and Art occupies Chaplin Hall, formerly the university library. Thoroughly renovated to house the architecture program, the building is exemplary of the adaptive reuse of an historic structure. Spacious design studios, classrooms, offices, and gallery provide excellent flexibility of use with an abundance of natural light. Students in the architectural design studio sequence have their own desk/work area. Also included are computer and digital imaging laboratories, a photography studio and darkroom, a materials laboratory, a woodworking and model shop, slide and video libraries, and student lounge. The architectural book and periodical collections are housed in the Kreitzberg Library.

SCHOLARSHIPS AND FINANCIAL AID

Norwich offers a vast array of Merit Scholarships in addition to needs-based financial aid. Norwich will automatically award students one of the Academic Scholarships if they are in the top 10% to 20% of their high school class. Students should complete the Financial Aid Form of the College Scholarship Service. In addition to university-wide scholarships, the program grants a growing number of architecture-specific awards, including one from the Vermont Chapter of the AIA.

ADMINISTRATION

Arthur Schaller, RA: Head of Department
Kirsten van Aalst: Program Director

THE OHIO STATE UNIVERSITY

ADDRESS

Main
The Ohio State University
Austin E. Knowlton School of
Architecture
275 W. Woodruff Avenue
Columbus, OH 43210
Tel.: 614.292.1012
Fax: 614.292.7106
knowlton.osu.edu

STUDENT AND FACULTY DEMOGRAPHICS

% of Female Students	33
% of International Students	8
% of Minority Students	9
% of Out-of-State U.S. Students	22
No. Full-Time Faculty	16
No. Part-Time Faculty	18
No. Full-Time Students	282
No. Part-Time Students	10

FINANCIAL INFORMATION

Main Source of University Funding	Public
Annual Tuition & Fees (graduate, resident)	$10,800
Annual Tuition & Fees (graduate, nonresident)	$25,662
Annual Tuition & Fees (undergraduate, resident)	$8,679
Annual Tuition & Fees (undergraduate, nonresident)	$21,918
% Students Receiving Federal Financial Aid	
% Students Receiving University Financial Aid	
% Students Receiving Departmental Financial Aid	
% Students Receiving Scholarships (assistantships or fellowships)	
Average Annual Scholarship for Department	

ACADEMIC SESSIONS

Fall Quarter: September to December
Winter Quarter: January to March

Spring Quarter: April to June

ARCHITECTURE AND RELATED DEGREE PROGRAMS

Degree	Min. Yrs. to Complete	Professional Accreditation	# of FT Students	# of PT Students	# of First-Year Students	# of Degrees Conferred	Admissions Requirements
Architecture							
BS Arch	4		211	8	84	72	Prerequisite courses, portfolio submission at end of first year
M. Arch — 2 years	2	NAAB	26	3	12	13	Undergraduate Architecture degree, GRE, TOEFL, Portfolio, Rec. Letters, Essay
M. Arch — 3 years	3	NAAB	36	3	15	13	Undergraduate degree, GRE, Portfolio, Rec. Letters, Essay
Master of Architectural Studies	1.3		3	1	0	1	Undergraduate degree, Undergraduate Architecture degree, Prof. Architecture degree, GRE, Rec. Letters, Essay

SPECIALIZATIONS

Architectural Design
Computer-Aided Design

History

Theory/Criticism

Urban Planning and Design

ARCHITECTURE PROGRAM SUMMARY
Bachelor of Science in Architecture

Bachelor of Science in Architecture leads to a four-year pre-professional undergraduate degree. The curriculum combines a general liberal arts education with concentrated studies in architecture. As such, students receive a rigorous intellectual training in the sciences, the humanities, and the arts, as well as a direct, hands-on approach to synthesizing this knowledge in the architectural design studios. The Bachelor of Science in Architecture instills a broad cultural awareness and, most significantly, the ability to act upon this awareness. The undergraduate degree provides the student with a strong educational foundation for not only the profession itself but also for the other arts, business, and public service. Students who desire professional architectural registration will be required to study for an additional two years to receive a National Architectural Accrediting Board (NAAB) accredited Master of Architecture degree. Admission to the program is selective.

Master of Architecture 3-Year Program

The Master of Architecture program culminates in a National Architectural Accrediting Board (NAAB) accredited professional degree for students with an undergraduate degree in a field other than architecture. It is assumed that the student's undergraduate education will have provided the intellectual training necessary to undertake a rigorous, accelerated graduate curriculum. The focus of the curriculum is the development of the student's critical, technical, and inventive ability in an architectural discourse.

Master of Architecture 2-Year Program

The two-year program is advanced placement in the Master of Architecture program for students who have strong design skills and hold an undergraduate pre-professional degree that is part of an NAAB accredited program. Design studios and theory courses focus on the broader cultural implications of architecture while courses in technology and professional practice prepare the student for the realities of architectural practice. The curriculum is supplemented by the distinguished visiting faculty of the Baumer Seminar, exhibitions and presentations of the Wexner Center for the Arts, and KSA travel programs and lecture series. The central goal of the program is to prepare students to engage in the cultural project of architecture with critical ability, inventive curiosity, and technical facility.

Master of Architectural Studies

The Master of Architectural Studies program is a four-quarter curriculum that culminates in a non-professional degree for students with either an undergraduate or a master's degree in architecture or related disciplines. The program is geared toward students who have previously studied architecture, design, or the arts, and are primarily interested in exploring one of the offered areas of study in intensive detail.

The Master of Architectural Studies in Criticism aims to advance techniques and genres of critical writing through intensive workshops and publication studios.

UNIVERSITY SETTING

The Ohio State University offers 7,000 courses in 202 academic areas and a computerized library system accessing 3.7 million volumes. Located in Columbus, Ohio, the university is within 600 miles of two-thirds of the population of the United States. Columbus offers a strong professional architectural community, the

Wexner Center for the Arts, the Ohio Historical Society, the Columbus Museum of Art, the Columbus Symphony Orchestra, and a range of contemporary and historical architecture.

SCHOOL PHILOSOPHY

Architecture is not simply a professional service, it is also a cultural practice. The undergraduate program in architecture offers a strong curriculum in architectural design, theory, and technology within the larger framework of a liberal arts education. The graduate program focuses these investigations in preparation for a student's entry into the profession. In both cases, the emphasis is placed on design and how it is influenced by theory and technology. Instruction focuses on the cultural implications of architecture to strengthen intellectual growth, to stimulate creative and analytical powers, and to foster the development of the skills necessary for significant performance within the profession.

PROGRAM DESCRIPTION
Undergraduate Program

The undergraduate architectural curriculum provides a liberal arts education for the pursuit of knowledge and the beginning of a professional education for the practice of architecture. The freshman year is comprised of general education courses and introductory and prerequisite courses for architecture. The sophomore and junior years focus on a design studio sequence with integrated courses in architectural history/theory, graphics, structures, and construction. The senior year is devoted to selective studios, elective seminars, and general electives within the university. All studios have a 12:1 student-to-faculty ratio and allow the investigation of design from a broad range of methodologies; the seminars permit an in-depth study of specific architectural issues; and the general electives encourage the development of relationships to other disciplines. The goal is to provide an education in which a sophisticated cultural investigation of architecture is combined with a general education in the humanities and sciences. It is a liberal arts education that a student must engage intellectually and pursue creatively —it is a liberal arts education which a student must act upon.

AREAS OF FOCUS AND RESEARCH
Focus

The program focuses on advanced strategies of architectural design, fabrication, and criticism. The permanent faculty, the Baumer symposia and Seminars, the Lecture Series, and the Wexner Center for the Arts all combine to provide students with a unique and intimate vision of the cultural potential of architecture. Extensive woodshop and computer facilities coupled with the Advanced Center for Computer Aided Design afford students a vast array of tools for creative exploration. Students are engaged with the profession and community through mentoring initiated by Professional Associateships and internships at the Columbus Design Center.

Research

The faculty offer diverse perspectives but share a common expectation of rigor in the pursuit of meaningful architectural form. Faculty engage in critical writing, exhibition curating, and creative practice. Critical writings explore the persistence of formal typologies as well as the emergence of new form catalyzed by the digital realm and new materiality. Curatorial efforts are

advanced at both the school gallery and the renowned Wexner Center for the Arts. Creative practice ranges from international competition entries to local residential construction. In all cases, faculty advance the discipline of architecture through a spirited engagement with persistent and emerging critical ideas.

SPECIAL ACTIVITIES AND PROGRAMS

- The Baumer Symposia and Baumer Seminars have afforded the participation of Thom Mayne, Zaha Hadid, Bernard Tschumi, Steven Holl, and Jacques Herzog.
- The Lecture Series brings noted architects such as Frank Gehry, Greg Lynn, Foreign Office Architects, Bernard Tschumi, MVRdV.
- The Wexner Center for the Arts has an ongoing program of architectural exhibitions: Louis Kahn, Rem Koolhaas, Eric Own Moss, Coleman Coker, Peter Eisenman, and Le Corbusier.
- Study Abroad programs offer students the opportunity to enroll in study tours to Europe with an annual spring tour of Italy and occasional summer tours of Vienna.
- Student organizations encourage greater camaraderie and student initiative: the section has strong student chapters of the American Institute of Architects and Alpha Rho Chi.
- An honors program is available for qualified ungraduates.

FACILITIES

Dedicated in 2004, Knowlton Hall is an award-winning facility designed by the architects Mack Scogin and Meril Elam that houses architecture, landscape architecture and city and regional planning, enabling fruitful interaction between disciplines. At the base of Knowlton Hall sits the materials and digital fabrication lab, a state-of the art facility where technology and craft, experimentation and precision meet. The top floor holds the library, a contemplative, cerebral space with a collection of over 30,000 volumes. Sandwiched between the lab and the library are the studios—the heart of the school where thinking and making converge. Their continuous buzz suffuses the building with the palpable energy of intellectual inquiry. Here, the physical intersection of spaces spawns a creative intersection of thinking, making, writing, fabricating, debating and drawing, providing an incredibly fertile ground for the future of the discipline to be practiced.

SCHOLARSHIPS AND FINANCIAL AID

The department awards undergraduate scholarships of $1,000–$4,000 each year and the university provides student loans, grants, and scholarships. Graduate students are eligible for University Fellowships with monthly stipends and full tuition and fee waivers, professional associateships or teaching assistantships with monthly stipends and partial or full tuition and fee waivers, and other departmental scholarships and university student loans. Application for graduate financial aid is integral to the application process (January 1 deadline.)

ADMINISTRATION

Ann Pendleton-Jullian: Director
Ashley Schafer: Head of Architecture
John McMorrough: Grad Chair
Michael Cadwell: Undergraduate Chair

OKLAHOMA STATE UNIVERSITY

ADDRESS

MAIN
Oklahoma State University
School of Architecture
101 Architecture
Stillwater, OK 74078-5051
Tel.: 405.744.6043
Fax: 405.744.6491
randy.seitsinger@okstate.edu
architecture.ceat.okstate.edu

STUDENT AND FACULTY DEMOGRAPHICS

% of Female Students	27
% of International Students	15
% of Minority Students	15
% of Out-of-State U.S. Students	17
No. Full-Time Faculty	17
No. Part-Time Faculty	0
No. Full-Time Students	326
No. Part-Time Students	2

FINANCIAL INFORMATION

Main Source of University Funding	Public
Annual Tuition & Fees (graduate, resident)	$5,489
Annual Tuition & Fees (graduate, nonresident)	$16,220
Annual Tuition & Fees (undergraduate, resident)	$6,201
Annual Tuition & Fees (undergraduate, nonresident)	$16,556
% Students Receiving Federal Financial Aid	20
% Students Receiving University Financial Aid	70
% Students Receiving Departmental Financial Aid	
% Students Receiving Scholarships (assistantships or fellowships)	
Average Annual Scholarship for Department	

ACADEMIC SESSIONS

Fall Semester: August to December
Spring Semester: January to May

ARCHITECTURE AND RELATED DEGREE PROGRAMS							
Degree	Min. Yrs. to Complete	Professional Accreditation	# of FT Students	# of PT Students	# of First-Year Students	# of Degrees Conferred	Admissions Requirements
Architecture							
B. Arch	5	NAAB	261	2	90	30	
Engineering							
B Arch Eng	5	ABET	65	0	0	15	

UNIVERSITY SETTING

Oklahoma State University, with an enrollment of approximately 20,000, is a modern comprehensive land grant university that serves the state, national and international communities by providing its students with exceptional academic experiences, by conducting scholarly research, and by disseminating knowledge to the people of Oklahoma and throughout the world. OSU is located in Stillwater, Oklahoma which is approximately 65 miles from both Tulsa and Oklahoma City, the state's two major urban centers.

SCHOOL PHILOSOPHY

The fundamental mission of the School is to focus its unique combination of accredited programs in architecture and architectural engineering to prepare and inspire students for the vital professional leadership roles and responsibilities required to shape the physical environment and positively impact the social, economic and cultural qualities of life in Oklahoma, the nation and the world. The School is dedicated to providing the highest-quality program of education to students whose career goals are to enter the professional practice of architecture and architectural engineering.

PROGRAM DESCRIPTION
Undergraduate Program

The undergraduate programs are professional degree granting programs leading to either the Bachelor of Architecture or Bachelor of Architectural Engineering degree. The individual programs are each five years in length, or they may be combined for a dual-degree in six years. The two programs are accredited by NAAB and ABET, respectively. The first two years of each program are virtually identical, allowing the student to become familiar with each field of study before making a final choice between programs. The architecture program places strong emphasis on applied conceptual design skills, with the design studio as the central focus around which are organized courses in history, theory,

practice, management, technical, and general education subjects. The architectural engineering program places strong emphasis on creative structural analysis and design skills, with a combination of design studio and technical analysis courses as the program core, supported by courses in environmental controls, advanced structural systems, mathematics, sciences, technical, and general education course offerings. All students meeting the general entrance requirements of the university are accepted into the first two-year segment of the program. Admission into the upper division of the program is based upon academic selection criteria established by the school.

AREAS OF FOCUS AND RESEARCH
Focus

The school maintains a sharp focus on professional education in both architecture and architectural engineering. In the Architecture program the design studio is emphasized for its synthesizing nature of combining theory, technology, and a strong focus on problem-solving. AIAS students have developed a nationally recognized K-12 program (ASTEC) for integrating architecture into mainstream public education.

Research

The faculty, in keeping with the school's professionally oriented program, has distinguished educational and professional experience, as well as diverse professional and public service backgrounds. The majority are licensed architects or engineers with national or international experience. Many of the faculty are active and in leadership roles in the various professional societies. Many have received recognition for their teaching excellence and many maintain active and innovative architectural practices.

SPECIAL ACTIVITIES AND PROGRAMS

A nine-week summer European Study program based in Paris is offered to students in the professional programs. Other special programs include a distinguished

lecture series, three student organizations (AIAS, CSI, and AEI), summer and graduate job assistance programs, and collaboration with practicing architects and architectural engineers, statewide and regionally, as visiting jury critics and lecturers. A studio focused on national and international student architectural design competitions is offered. Over the past 15 years, over 100 OSU architecture students have won or placed in national and international design competitions.

FACILITIES

The School is currently constructing a new and renovated facility which will be complete in the fall of 2009, which will coincide with the School's 100th anniversary. The new Donald W. Reynolds School of Architecture Building will include 78,000 sf of space, which is more than double the school's previous size. The facility will include state of the art classrooms, an auditorium, studios, gallery spaces, computer labs, an administrative suite, a vastly expanded architectural library, shop space, and a daylighting lab.

SCHOLARSHIPS AND FINANCIAL AID

Oklahoma State University has many opportunities for scholarships available for incoming freshmen and continuing students. In addition, the School of Architecture administers numerous fellowships and scholarships for architecture and architectural engineering students. These scholarships are mostly focused to upper-division students and are mostly merit based. Upper division and graduate students are eligible for teaching and administrative assistantships, including non-resident tuition waiver grants.

ADMINISTRATION

Randy Seitsinger, AIA: Head
Suzanne Bilbeisi: Academic Advisor

PARSONS THE NEW SCHOOL FOR DESIGN

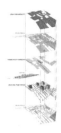

ADDRESS

Main
Parsons The New School for Design
School of Constructed Environments
25 East 13th Street
New York, NY 10003
Tel.: 212.229.8955
Fax: 212.229.8937
aidl@newschool.edu
www2.parsons.edu/sce

STUDENT AND FACULTY DEMOGRAPHICS

% of Female Students	54
% of International Students	45
% of Minority Students	26
% of Out-of-State U.S. Students	14
No. Full-Time Faculty	4
No. Part-Time Faculty	40
No. Full-Time Students	141
No. Part-Time Students	0

FINANCIAL INFORMATION

Main Source of University Funding	Private
Annual Tuition & Fees (graduate)	
Annual Tuition & Fees (undergraduate)	
% Students Receiving Federal Financial Aid	42
% Students Receiving University Financial Aid	8
% Students Receiving Departmental Financial Aid	57
% Students Receiving Scholarships (assistantships or fellowships)	
Average Annual Scholarship for Department	$6,481

ACADEMIC SESSIONS

Fall Semester: September to December; Application Deadline: February 1

Spring Semester: January to May

ARCHITECTURE AND RELATED DEGREE PROGRAMS							
Degree	Min. Yrs. to Complete	Professional Accreditation	# of FT Students	# of PT Students	# of First-Year Students	# of Degrees Conferred	Admissions Requirements
Architecture							
BFA Arch. Design	4		42	0	0	0	
M. Arch—1.5 years	1.5		2	0	0	0	Prof. Architecture degree, GRE, TOEFL, Portfolio, Rec. Letters, Essay
M. Arch—3 years	3	NAAB	65	0	22	20	Undergraduate degree, GRE, TOEFL, Portfolio, Rec. Letters, Essay
M.Arch/MFA Design & Technology	4		2	0	0	0	
Other							
MA Lighting Design	1		37	3	0	0	

SPECIALIZATIONS

Community Design
Computer-Aided Design

Energy
Environment/Sustainability

History
Interior Design/Architecture

Theory/Criticism
Urban Planning and Design

ARCHITECTURE PROGRAM SUMMARY

The unique position of the Master of Architecture Program at Parsons resides in its particular manner of engagement with current architectural issues, its community of committed faculty and talented students, and its location in downtown New York City. The Parsons graduate program is renowned for its commitment to smart integrated design from the scale of the singular architectural object to that of the city. Integrating theory, analysis, experimentation and speculation with the logics of building, the graduate program sees such contemporary architectural issues as the activation of site and programmatic forces, the social commitment of design, tectonic and material methodologies, infrastructural and natural systems in design thinking, and digital and sustainable technologies, among others, as fields of potential for architectural investigation.

UNIVERSITY SETTING

New York City has the greatest resources for art, entertainment, commerce and cultural diversity in the world, making it an exceptional place to live and to study architecture and design. Faculty members are successful professionals and use the City as an extension of the classroom. Manhattan's architecture and public spaces are sources of research and inspiration. Parsons' main campus is located in Greenwich Village, near residential neighborhoods, multimedia companies and design studios.

SCHOOL PHILOSOPHY

The Department of Architecture emphasizes the study of architecture as a cultural practice. Using the urban environment of New York as a laboratory, the school teaches students a way of thinking about the built environment in all of its complex forms. It examines the designed world in multiple scales: landscape, furniture, as well as multiple social practices: cities to performance space. Student's interdisciplinary training and digital expertise provide them with a range of career opportunities in the design world. Lighting design is integral to architecture, interior design, product design and theater, contributing to the success of these professions.

PROGRAM DESCRIPTION
Bachelor of Fine Arts in Architectural Design

This interdisciplinary training teaches students a way of thinking about the built environment in all of its complex forms. A rigorous design curriculum prepares students for careers in many possible fields including architecture, interior architecture, exhibition design, lighting design, and information design. Students graduating from this program can apply for admission to the M.Arch program and can complete this professional degree in two years.

Pre-Architecture Studies

This custom-designed, semester-long or year-long program introduces a student to architectural design. It is intended for liberal arts graduates or exchange students who want to focus on design, drawing and portfolio preparation in preparation for applying to graduate study in architecture. An applicant is not required to submit a portfolio. Fall entry only.

AREAS OF FOCUS AND RESEARCH
Focus

In the spring of a student's second year, students from both the M.Arch and BFA programs enroll in the Design Workshop, a two-semester studio in which they follow a project from design to construction. Following the design team model. The Design Workshop emphasizes the important notion that architectural projects are collective efforts realized by many talents with different roles and responsibilities. The Design Workshop is the only design/build program in the New York metropolitan area.

Research

The Michael Kalil Center for research into technological and natural systems was initiated in the 2001-2002 academic year. The center provides research, grants, and scholarship funding for faculty professionals and students interested in the intersection between technology and the natural world. Issues of ecology, new technologies, sustainability, and architectures that focus on these areas are supported. The design workshop is the metropolitan area's only design program and focuses on the capacity to detail and material to mediate social space. Research in new materials and construction techniques, particularly in their relationship to social practices, is supported.

SPECIAL ACTIVITIES AND PROGRAMS
Summer Intensive Studio in Architecture

This six-week design studio is for students from high school and up who are interested in drawing/portfolio preparation for an architecture education.

Lectures, Symposia and Exhibitions

Each semester the department sponsors a rich and diverse series of public events. The department also cosponsors events with the Van Alen Institute including: The Harbor is a Public Realm; Four Times Square: Manhattan's Green Giant-Robert F. Fox Jr., Fox and Fowle Architects; River Projects Exhibition; and New York Waterfront Design Workshop.

FACILITIES

The heart of the Architecture department is the studio, a large, open loft where students develop design projects while they interact with faculty and peers. The materials and lighting libraries, model shop, and computer lab are located adjacent to the studio. The department's computer facilities are augmented by a variety of satellite computer labs. Macintosh, PC and Silicon Graphics workstations provide access to industry-standard software. The Adam and Sophie Gimbel Design Library is an art and design resource supporting the art, architecture and design programs offered by Parsons School of Design. The library's collections contain more than 195,000 books, serials, slides, pictures and videos.

SCHOLARSHIPS AND FINANCIAL AID

Parsons offers eligible students a wide range of financial aid programs, including school-supported scholarships and grants, government and private grants, and various loan programs. All applicants for admission may, and should, apply for financial aid consideration if they feel they have a need for it. Information is available upon request from the University Financial Aid Office, 212/229-8930, or e-mail: financialaid@newschool.edu.

ADMINISTRATION

David Leven: Director of Graduate Architecture
Henry Smith-Miller: Director MArch Program
Joanna Merwood: Associate Chair
Laura Briggs: BFA Architectural Design Director

PENNSYLVANIA STATE UNIVERSITY

ADDRESS

Main
Pennsylvania State University
School of Architecture and Landscape
Architecture
Department of Architecture
121 Stuckeman Family Building
University Park, PA 16802
Tel: 814.865.9535
Fax: 814.865.3289
www.arch.psu.edu

STUDENT AND FACULTY DEMOGRAPHICS

% of Female Students	48
% of International Students	4
% of Minority Students	10
% of Out-of-State U.S. Students	29
No. Full-Time Faculty	19
No. Part-Time Faculty	9
No. Full-Time Students	271
No. Part-Time Students	0

FINANCIAL INFORMATION

Main Source of University Funding	Public
Annual Tuition & Fees (graduate, resident)	$13,948
Annual Tuition & Fees (graduate, nonresident)	$25,150
Annual Tuition & Fees (undergraduate, resident)	$13,282
Annual Tuition & Fees (undergraduate, nonresident)	$24,272
% Students Receiving Federal Financial Aid	
% Students Receiving University Financial Aid	
% Students Receiving Departmental Financial Aid	11
% Students Receiving Scholarships (assistantships or fellowships)	$20,453
Average Annual Scholarship for Department	$660

ACADEMIC SESSIONS

Fall Semester: August to December
Spring Semester: January to May

ARCHITECTURE AND RELATED DEGREE PROGRAMS

Degree	Min. Yrs. to Complete	Professional Accreditation	# of FT Students	# of PT Students	# of First-Year Students	# of Degrees Conferred	Admissions Requirements
Architecture							
B. Arch	5	NAAB	271	0	74	36	Undergraduate Architecture degree, SAT, ACT
BS Arch	4		0	0	0	0	Undergraduate Architecture degree, Prof. Architecture degree, SAT, ACT
M. Arch — 2 years	1		14	0	0	1	Prof. Architecture degree, GRE, TOEFL, Portfolio, Rec. Letters

SPECIALIZATIONS

Architectural Design
Art and Design
Building Technology/Env. Systems

Community Design
Computer-Aided Design

International/Regional Architecture
Sustainability

Theory/Criticism
Urban Planning and Design

UNIVERSITY SETTING

The Pennsylvania State University occupies a beautiful campus in State College, in a rural area of central Pennsylvania that is within convenient travel distance of major metropolitan centers. Students take courses in related departments such as art, art history, landscape architecture, and engineering. The Department shares the award winning "green" (LEED Gold Rating) Stuckeman Family Building with the Department of Landscape Architecture. Facilities include a state-of-the-art shop, an outdoor building yard, digital fabrication equipment and an Immersive Environments Lab for 3D visualization. Transfer students are admitted upon portfolio and transcript review. Students also benefit from the innumerable opportunities for diverse educational, cultural, and recreational activities that a large and comprehensive state university provides. The relatively small size of the program encourages intense and informal interaction between students and a committed, energetic faculty. The studio is often the setting for such interaction. Studio facilities are available on a 24-hour basis. Each student is assigned a permanent workstation in the facilities, which are centrally located on the campus.

SCHOOL PHILOSOPHY

Undergraduate Philosophy

The objectives of the Department of Architecture are to provide excellence in professional, resident instruction in the field of architecture and opportunities for exploration and research related to the areas of theory and practice in architecture community and urban digital design and fabrication, advanced visualization, sustainability, and architectural theory. The focus is on the content of design, namely the acquisition of knowledge and skills through studio education and the acquisition of professional values, perspectives, and attitudes.

Graduate Philosophy

Penn State offers a post-professional graduate pro-gram leading to a Master of Architecture degree. The Master of Architecture program provides individuals who hold a baccalaureate degree in architecture (B.Arch) the opportunity to expand their knowledge of architectural design and architectural and urban theory.

PROGRAM DESCRIPTION

The first four years of the professional degree program provide courses in foundation core of design, introductory studies in architecture and environmental design at various scales, programming and implementation techniques, architectural computer systems applications, architectural theories in design and methodologies, and research. Students are admitted into the five-year professional program leading to the bachelor of architecture degree. Students are reviewed at the end of the fourth semester for retention in the program. A portfolio of architecture design work examples is required. A review will be based on criteria that evaluate growth over the four-semester period and architectural design competence as evidenced in the work presented. A positive review permits continuation. At the end of the fourth year, students are reviewed for retention in the five-year B. Arch program. This review evaluates a student's performance by reviewing the overall university grade-point average, which must be a minimum of 2.50, and the student's performance in architectural design studio courses, where the minimum must be 2.67 on the 4.00 scale. In cases where either of these minimums is not met, a portfolio of design work examples will be requested. In cases where retention is not permitted, students having already completed Bachelor of Science requirements will be given a "change of major" and awarded the BS in Architecture degree. The post-professional Master of Architecture program offers three distinct options for graduate-level studies: students interested in architectural and urban design or digital visualization may study within the fields of community and urban design or digital design, while students interested in architectural and urban theory may focus on culture, society, and space. All three courses of study offer an engagement with faculty who are recognized leaders in their field, and all three programs are housed within a brand new state-of-the-art Stuckeman Family Building recently awarded the "green" (LEED Gold Rating) by the U.S. Green Building Council.

SPECIAL ACTIVITIES AND PROGRAMS

- Internship program with practicing architects
- Semester abroad in Rome, Italy
- Annual Visiting Lecturer Series
- Field trips
- Awards programs
- Summer course for interested students (non-majors)
- Professional societies' Annual Beaux Arts Ball
- American Indian Housing Initiative
- Solar Decathlon project

FACILITIES

- Digital Fabrication Facilities
- Model shop
- Individual work stations for every student
- Departmental library
- Hamer Center for Community Design
- 3D Immersive Environment Lab
- Rome, Italy studios and classrooms

SCHOLARSHIPS AND FINANCIAL AID

A number of loans, grants, and scholarships are available through university loan programs and PHEAA grant programs. The department annually awards five half-time and three quarter-time graduate assistantships to candidates for the M.Arch degree. A number of department scholarships are awarded each year based on academic excellence and/or financial need.

ADMINISTRATION

Daniel Willis, RA: Head

PHILADELPHIA UNIVERSITY

ADDRESS

Main
Philadelphia University
School of Architecture
School House Lane & Henry Avenue
Philadelphia, PA 19144-5497
Tel.: 215.951.2828
Fax: 215.951.2110
BuegeD@PhilaU.edu
www.philau.edu/architecture

STUDENT AND FACULTY DEMOGRAPHICS

% of Female Students	40
% of International Students	1
% of Minority Students	9
% of Out-of-State U.S. Students	59
No. Full-Time Faculty	12
No. Part-Time Faculty	60
No. Full-Time Students	352
No. Part-Time Students	7

FINANCIAL INFORMATION

Main Source of University Funding	Private
Annual Tuition & Fees (graduate)	
Annual Tuition & Fees (undergraduate)	$25,386
% Students Receiving Federal Financial Aid	78
% Students Receiving University Financial Aid	96
% Students Receiving Departmental Financial Aid	0
% Students Receiving Scholarships (assistantships or fellowships)	93
Average Annual Scholarship for Department	$7,312

ACADEMIC SESSIONS

Fall Semester: August to December;
   Application Deadline: Rolling Admissions
Spring Semester: January to May;
   Application Deadline: Rolling Admission

Summer Session I: May to June
Summer Session II: July to August
Summer Session III: May to August

ARCHITECTURE AND RELATED DEGREE PROGRAMS

Degree	Min. Yrs. to Complete	Professional Accreditation	# of FT Students	# of PT Students	# of First-Year Students	# of Degrees Conferred	Admissions Requirements
Architecture							
B. Arch	5	NAAB	352	7	103	55	SAT/ACT, TOEFL (Rec. Letters, Essay Optional)
BS Architectural Studies	4		67	3	21	17	SAT/ACT, TOEFL (Rec. Letters, Essay Optional)
Landscape Architecture							
BLA	5	LAAB Candidate	35	0	10	3	SAT/ACT, TOEFL (Rec. Letters, Essay Optional)
Interior Design/Interior Architecture							
BS Interior Design	4	CIDA/FIDER	193	3	55	45	SAT/ACT, TOEFL (Rec. Letters, Essay Optional)
Other							
MS Sustainable Design	1.5		0	11	10	0	Undergraduate degree, GRE, Portfolio, Rec. Letters, Essay

SPECIALIZATIONS

Architectural Design	Computer-Aided Design	International/Regional Architecture	Preservation
Building Information Modeling	Environment/Sustainability	Landscape Design	Sustainability

ARCHITECTURE PROGRAM SUMMARY

Philadelphia University provides a unique opportunity to study architecture on a tranquil campus in close proximity to a great urban center. The Architecture program is the largest program on this small campus where almost 60% of the undergraduates study one of the design professions. The Program emphasizes materiality and sustainability in projects at all levels of the curriculum and the in-depth exploration of new material and tectonic possibilities in the upper levels of the program.

UNIVERSITY SETTING

Since 1884, Philadelphia University has offered professional education in a variety of fields. The university's signature blending of the liberal arts and sciences with professional studies prepares graduates for successful careers in areas that include architecture, interior design, landscape architecture, graphic design, industrial design, digital design, fashion design, textile design, business, health, and science. The university (undergraduate enrollment of 2,600 full-time students) attracts students from 38 states and 42 countries, offering graduate and undergraduate degree programs in more than 40 areas of study.

SCHOOL PHILOSOPHY

In considering the diverse and changing context of the practice of architecture, the School of Architecture recognizes that design professionals require an indepth understanding of economic, technical, and aesthetic issues within a complex social, cultural, and environmental framework. Building on the university's goal to provide a liberal professional education, the mission of the School is to prepare students to be creative, independent thinkers and innovative problem solvers. Emphasis is placed on creative excellence, balanced with the fundamental knowledge and skill required for meaningful contributions to professional design practice. Four different undergraduate career options (architecture, interior design, landscape architecture, and architectural studies) are offered in an intimate collegiate setting and cooperative faculty/student learning environment. A Master of Science in Sustainable Design is available for students with non-professional or professional undergraduate degrees.

PROGRAM DESCRIPTION

The professional architecture program is a five-year undergraduate program leading to the NAAB accredited Bachelor of Architecture (B.Arch.) degree. The primary goal of the B.Arch. program is to provide a comprehensive professional education that will develop the knowledge, skill, and vision necessary for the student to understand contemporary global issues and address the varied needs of society. The program is committed to an interdisciplinary approach at all levels of the curriculum and shares an integrated curriculum with Interior Design and Landscape Architecture. In the professional architecture program, the design studio is the focus of activity where liberal arts and professional course work

and creativity are synthesized. The curriculum is based on recognition of local, regional, and world views of architecture, while emphasizing the forces that shape design and the process of making buildings and places. During the first year, foundation studios are conducted in an interdisciplinary environment, introducing principles, values, and the common vocabulary necessary for effective professional teamwork. In the second year, studios continue teaching the building blocks of design with an emphasis on environmental and urban issues. During the third, fourth, and fifth years, the more advanced technical and professional courses are added to the curriculum, supporting studio design projects of increasing complexity and scope. In the fourth year, an elective design studio is available; options include topical architecture studios, design studios offered by the other programs on campus, and studios set in study-abroad programs. In the fifth year, systems synthesis is emphasized in addressing complex urban and theoretical problems. Studio instruction emphasizes independent research, programming, and critical analysis in establishing the theoretical basis for design work. A thesis option, requiring an approved thesis proposal, is offered during the final year.

AREAS OF FOCUS AND RESEARCH

In addition to providing a comprehensive professional education, the School has developed a number of areas of focus that allow students to explore and develop special interests. The University offers minor concentrations in numerous areas including sustainability, multimedia and visualization, photography, construction management, historic preservation, business, and psychology. Through elective options, students can also develop area concentrations in any of the design disciplines offered at the University; interior or landscape design, graphic design or industrial design, fashion or textile design, sustainable or community design. The Program has developed a special design/build elective studio at the fourth year that provides students with the opportunity to design and build houses for Habitat for Humanity and other community groups in Philadelphia.

The majority of the full-time and part-time faculty in the School practice in the design professions. They hold positions in firms that range in size from two to several hundred employees. Their work comprises a comprehensive accumulation of contemporary projects. All faculty members who practice are encouraged to share their experience and work with students and other faculty members in discussions, tours, critiques, and lectures. A number of faculty members are active in historical/theoretical research and applied research in areas of sustainable materials, fabric structures, composite systems, digital fabrication, etc., exposing students to the multitude of options and functions that shape practice and the profession.

SPECIAL ACTIVITIES AND PROGRAMS

Fourth and fifth year students have the opportunity to study at the Engineering and Design Institute, where they work with faculty who are doing research in ex-

perimental materials and structures, especially those with a foundation in composite textiles. The School has been initiating a number of opportunities for students to investigate architectural theory and practice beyond the University campus. These include the "Great American Cities" urban program, and a highly regarded interdisciplinary visiting lecture series. The School has an established Study-Abroad Program with the American University of Rome in Italy. Students are also encouraged to arrange individualized study-abroad opportunities during their fourth year. Students have frequently studied at the Danish Institute for Study Abroad and at NABA Academy of Arts and Design in Milan, and individual students have recently studied in Hong Kong, Tokyo, Barcelona, Paris, Glasgow, and the Dominican Republic. The University sponsors the International Leadership Program, which takes selected sophomores and faculty from all disciplines for 10 days of summer study to non-traditional destinations such as Beijing, Johannesburg, Buenos Aires, Istanbul and Tunis.

FACILITIES

The University has dedicated five campus facilities for use by the Architecture, Landscape and Interior Design programs. The Architecture & Design Center provides an exciting studio environment for students and faculty to work. The A&D Center includes space for 200 dedicated studio workstations for upper level students in a wireless environment. It also provides space for review and exhibition, state-of-the-art computer labs, archives, a materials resource library, and faculty offices. Ravenhill Studios provide teaching and workspace for foundation studios. Weber Hall provides space a for comprehensive model shop (woodworking/metal and work/digital fabrication) and Smith House provides additional teaching and workspace for foundation studios, classrooms for seminars and technology instruction, computer labs, and faculty offices. The Engineering and Design Institute, in the exciting Main Street environment of nearby Manayunk, provides 50 dedicated fully networked studio workstations for upper-level and graduate students, as well as research, laboratory, and workshop space for the exploration of Textiles and Material Technology.

SCHOLARSHIPS AND FINANCIAL AID

The University believes that no student should be denied the opportunity for post-secondary education solely because of lack of adequate financial resources. In keeping with this philosophy, the Financial Aid Office provides information to students about financial planning and distributes financial aid resources to qualified students. The amount of financial aid available to any student is based on academic performance, need, and the availability of funds. Students should apply for financial aid by April 15.

ADMINISTRATION

Vini Nathan, PhD: Dean
David J. Buege: Director

POLYTECHNIC UNIVERSITY OF PUERTO RICO

ADDRESS

Main
Polytechnic University of Puerto Rico
School of Architecture
Box 192017
San Juan, PR 00919-2017
Tel.: 787.622.8000
Fax: 787.767.0607
www.pupr.edu

STUDENT AND FACULTY DEMOGRAPHICS

% of Female Students	41
% of International Students	4
% of Minority Students	
% of Out-of-State U.S. Students	
No. Full-Time Faculty	16
No. Part-Time Faculty	35
No. Full-Time Students	272
No. Part-Time Students	426

FINANCIAL INFORMATION

Main Source of University Funding	Private
Annual Tuition & Fees (graduate, resident)	
Annual Tuition & Fees (graduate, nonresident)	
Annual Tuition & Fees (undergraduate, resident)	$8,015
Annual Tuition & Fees (undergraduate, nonresident)	$8,015
% Students Receiving Federal Financial Aid	69.1
% Students Receiving University Financial Aid	6.8
% Students Receiving Departmental Financial Aid	0
% Students Receiving Scholarships (assistantships or fellowships)	0
Average Annual Scholarship for Department	$0

ACADEMIC SESSIONS

Fall Quarter/Trimester: August to October; Application Deadline: May
Winter Quarter/Trimester: November to February; Application Deadline: August

Spring Quarter/Trimester: March to May

ARCHITECTURE AND RELATED DEGREE PROGRAMS

Degree	Min. Yrs. to Complete	Professional Accreditation	# of FT Students	# of PT Students	# of First-Year Students	# of Degrees Conferred	Admissions Requirements
Architecture							
B. Arch	5	NAAB	272	426	201	134	Minimum GPA = 2.5

UNIVERSITY SETTING

ARQPOLI, the School of Architecture at the Polytechnic University of Puerto Rico, joined the undergraduate program in 1995. Housed in a compact urban campus in San Juan, UPPR is the largest Hispanic-serving engineering school in the United States, with more than 5,000 Puerto Rican, foreign and transfer students. The extended architectural legacy of the Caribbean has been an invaluable resource for the architecture program, but it is the refocusing of the Caribbean from a geographical location to a translocal cultural condition that drives the school's current development.

SCHOOL PHILOSOPHY

ARQPOLI encourages individuals to acquire the knowledge, skills and social responsibility fundamental to a discipline concerned with the betterment of the human condition and the physical environment. By expounding an understanding of historical processes, examining the Caribbean as a paradigm of dynamic order and contesting technology as scaled down to culture, students relate architecture to ever-present social predicaments. The School empowers students to exercise their potential for service, collaboration, productivity, leadership and civic engagement by validating design and research as interdependent activities, promoting an interdisciplinary interest in related fields, rendering the profession as an accessible goal, and articulating pedagogical strategies accordingly. Today, the School revalidates its ongoing experiment with the unusual, openly assuming its primary goal of bringing a critical edge to the local architectural practice and discourse.

PROGRAM DESCRIPTION
Undergraduate Program

With its five-year professional degree as the main offering, the School is fully committed to an undergraduate curriculum that challenges traditional alternatives. Pedagogical sedimentation—simultaneous and continued exposure to all areas related to architecture—begins at the freshman level and continues throughout the length of the program. Concurrency of learning grants students a more integrated experience. With the design sequence as datum, each year becomes an opportunity to address a wide variety of problems at a deeper level. The first-year curriculum allows students a glimpse of different areas of concern: Design, History, Theory, Technology, and Architectural Representation. The second year integrates issues of programming as a design tool, transformation through composition and typological assessment of informal spatial patterns. The history/theory sequence includes an introductory course that exposes students to cultural, compositional, technological and symbolic aspects of architecture, and a series of courses focusing on subjects like the history of architectural theory, the condition of modernity and modern architecture, the Caribbean context from a sociological and cultural-studies perspective, historiography and the neo-avant-gardes. A mid-career research, an investigation focused on a freely chosen topic, is a requirement in the third year. Issues of conservation and sustainability are explored in third-year design courses. The fourth year addresses urban concerns and housing with a scope that spans from regional considerations to contemporary strategies of infill. A fifth year capstone project synthesizes theoretical, design, technological and representation dexterity. The curriculum profits specifically from the conflicting contexts of North and South America, and the tangible tensions in both historical and contemporary architecture that are an important part of the Caribbean condition. Discussions on technological development, the legal context of architecture and the management infrastructure of a design firm are covered in the design and technology/practice sequences of the curriculum.

AREAS OF FOCUS AND RESEARCH
Focus

The relationship between design and research is at the heart of the School's multilayered pedagogical mission. An increasing dissatisfaction with the country's prevailing patterns of development, erratic use of land, and the pervasive commodification of architecture (with the most banal results) has radicalized education at ARQPOLI. Very often, architects seem to be part of the problem instead of the enlightened professionals that would deliver solutions. If the concept of legacy, as it is used in architectural conservation discourse has been an important part of the school's approach toward history and architects' social responsibility, it is the acknowledgment and discussion of current pathologies and dysfunctions in both the built environment and the profession itself that characterizes the school's current focus.

Research

At ARQPOLI, the early emphasis on research as a learning tool engages undergraduate students in investigation while simultaneously expanding the traditional subject matters of architecture. Specific topics not previously investigated charter future architects into the creation of new knowledge. Myriad methodological procedures and agile taxonomical skills become key training objectives. Five different components frame the research work of both faculty and students: the Center for Urban Studies, the Media Lab, the Architectural Conservation Laboratory, the Materials Workshop, and Ciudadlab, a course where faculty and students research a foreign city from without and from within as they travel to it. Recent destinations have been as diverse as Orlando, Florida and Moscow, Russia. These experiences have resulted in a redirection from the expected interest in the architectural object toward an interdisciplinary study of emerging subjectivities and the role of the architectural imagination in contemporary culture.

SPECIAL ACTIVITIES AND PROGRAMS

Design studios and workshops have taken students to Italy, France, Spain, Greece, Venezuela, Argentina, Mexico, Panama, Cuba, Russia, and diverse American cities like New York, Savannah and Orlando. Since the school's inception, collaboration agreements with diverse universities have enriched the program and its faculty composition; recently, agreements with *Instituto Torcuato Di Tella* in Buenos Aires and *Instituto de Arquitectura Avanzada de Cataluña* in Barcelona have facilitated study-abroad programs in these cities. An agreement with Museo del Barrio in New York was crucial for establishing a summer program in New York, oriented toward analyzing the experience of the historical "El Barrio" and the urban transformations induced by migratory patterns such as the Puerto Rican Diaspora. In addition, year-round international lecture series and exhibitions complement academic initiatives, while ongoing collaborations with community-based groups expose students to diverse social needs, confronting the ubiquitous self-importance of the profession with issues of social responsibility. In an effort to reach out to and attract prospective candidates, a summer Architecture Workshop is offered for high school students.

Finally, to complement the university's counseling programs, the School's Director of Academic Affairs offers advising services to architectural students in the interest of insuring curricular compliance, as well as local and international educational and career opportunities.

FACILITIES

Located at the university's multi-purpose building, design studios occupy a full floor, along with the computer laboratory, photography laboratory, administrative offices and review spaces. The dynamic interior, with one studio flowing into another, is facilitated by an open plan. Students are assigned a personal workspace with 24-hour controlled access. A second floor includes classrooms, faculty offices, the Media Lab, the Materials Workshop, the Architectural Conservation Laboratory, and a 125-seat auditorium. The Media Lab and the campus library have extensive resources relevant to international architecture, with focus on the development of the Hispanic Antilles and Latin America.

SCHOLARSHIPS AND FINANCIAL AID

The Financial Aid Office assists students in defraying university cost, which for the average student (living at home) is calculated at $23,193 per year. Several scholarship funds and loan programs are available to architecture students: Federal Student Financial Aid (Pell Grant), Stafford Loan Program (SLP), Parent Plus Loans (PPL), Supplemental Educational Opportunity Grants (SEOG), Student Private Loans (SPL), and Institutional Honor Awards (IHA), among others. In addition, there are federal college work/study programs and similar institutional programs.

ADMINISTRATION

Miguel Rodriguez: Dean
Nadya Nenadich: Associate Dean

PORTLAND STATE UNIVERSITY

ADDRESS

Main
Portland State University
Department of Architecture
235 Shattuck Hall
P.O. Box 751
Portland, OR 97207-0751
Tel.: 503.725.8405
Fax: 503.725.8318
www.pdx.edu/architecture

ACADEMIC SESSIONS

Fall Quarter: September to December;
   Application Deadline: February 1st
Winter Quarter: January to March

Spring Quarter: March to June
Summer Session I: June to August

STUDENT AND FACULTY DEMOGRAPHICS

% of Female Students	33
% of International Students	7
% of Minority Students	22
% of Out-of-State U.S. Students	19
No. Full-Time Faculty	5
No. Part-Time Faculty	15
No. Full-Time Students	167
No. Part-Time Students	76

FINANCIAL INFORMATION

Main Source of University Funding	Public
Annual Tuition & Fees (graduate)	Under review
Annual Tuition & Fees (graduate, nonresident)	Under review
Annual Tuition & Fees (undergraduate, resident)	$1,722
Annual Tuition & Fees (undergraduate, nonresident)	$5,106
% Students Receiving Federal Financial Aid	51
% Students Receiving University Financial Aid	14
% Students Receiving Departmental Financial Aid	0
% Students Receiving Scholarships (assistantships or fellowships)	8
Average Annual Scholarship for Department	

ARCHITECTURE AND RELATED DEGREE PROGRAMS

Degree	Min. Yrs. to Complete	Professional Accreditation	# of FT Students	# of PT Students	# of First-Year Students	# of Degrees Conferred	Admissions Requirements
Architecture							
B.A/B.S. Architecture	4		167	76	80	29	SAT, ACT, TOEFL
M. Arch	2	NAAB Candidate	50		25		Undergraduate Architecture degree, GRE, TOEFL, Portfolio, Rec. Letters, Essay

SPECIALIZATIONS

Architectural Design	Environment/Sustainability	Landscape Design	Tectonics
Art and Design	History	Sacred Spaces	Theory/Criticism
Community Design	International/Regional Architecture	Sustainability	Urban Planning and Design

ARCHITECTURE PROGRAM SUMMARY

Portland State University is Oregon's largest public university and is located in downtown Portland. The Department of Architecture offers a 4-year undergraduate major in architecture integrated with a 2-year Master of Architecture degree currently in candidacy for professional accreditation with NAAB. Architecture programs focus on urban, issue-led design investigations through creative making, hands-on material exploration and fabrication, in a context of sustainable practices.

UNIVERSITY SETTING

Portland State University, a nationally acclaimed leader in community-based learning, is situated in the Portland metropolitan region with a population of approximately 2 million. The University was established as the Vanport Extension Center in 1946 to serve returning World War II GIs. In 1955, the Vanport Extension Center

became Portland State College, a four-year, degree-granting institution. Graduate studies were added in 1961, doctoral programs began in 1968, and the institution was granted university status in 1969.

At the beginning of the 2008-09 academic year Portland State University had over 27,000 enrolled students. The University's position in the heart of Oregon's economic and cultural center enables PSU students and faculty to exercise scholarly investigation in the context of multiple business and community organizations. Portland State's eight colleges and schools offer over 120 undergraduate, master, and doctoral degrees, as well as graduate certificates and continuing education.

The PSU campus is a cityscape occupying a 49-acre area centered on the South Park Blocks. At the edge of campus, the University merges into downtown Portland. The areas immediately surrounding the cam-

pus contain private student housing, shops, student services, and restaurants.

The University's motto, 'Let knowledge serve the city,' is comprehensively embodied by a continuing record of civic engagement through its educational programs and research. In particular PSU has embarked on an institution-wide focus on sustainability fostered, in part, by a $25 million grant from the Miller Foundation to support the creation of a Center for Sustainable Processes and Practices that will energize inter-disciplinary research collaborations between the Department of Architecture and the internationally recognized PSU urban studies and engineering programs.

SCHOOL PHILOSOPHY

The PSU Architecture program engages students in the fascinating creative questions that pertain to the making of architecture. The program develops the creative identity of each student while nurturing civic responsibility, critical judgment and the representational and technical ability to translate ideas into plausible architectural works. This lies at the core of an educational experience that provides a rich initiation into the world of architectural practice and preparation for a career as a licensed professional. The heart of the program resides in the architecture design studio and is nourished by the accompanying lecture and seminar courses that bring focused study in the humanities, technology, and the profession. Alongside a progressive attitude to design process and theoretical speculation, the program participates in the advancement of knowledge in contemporary issues and technologies of sustainable urban living and environmental stewardship.

The educational emphasis of the department encourages students to recognize the value of creative engagement with the prevailing realities of the city as a primary means of cultural transformation, and to perceive Portland as an 'urban laboratory' for experimental investigations of contemporary human issues. This takes place through interaction and dialogue with the communities at large and by continual acts of interpretive making with diverse media at multiple scales, including full-size fabrication.

In giving place to human situations architecture bears the responsibility of being the most public of the arts and it cannot be practiced meaningfully without a conversation with the community at large. At PSU the studio classes, in particular, are sustained by an engagement beyond the university to the life-world shared with urban cohabitants, including direct interaction with the architectural practice community through adjunct professors, critics, guest speakers and advisers. This fosters imaginative responses to the challenge of 'what ought to be' in the face of 'what is.'

The final year of the Master of Architecture enables students to engage deeply with the cultural ramifications of urban situations through an individually developed study agenda leading to a sustained exercise in discursive and creative research and culminating in the Graduate Design Thesis.

PROGRAM DESCRIPTION
The Department of Architecture offers a 4-year BA/BS Major in Architecture and a 2-year Master of Architecture degree within an integrated 4+2 model. Students completing the full 4+2 professional program track would receive two degrees: (1) either a Bachelor of Arts or Science, Major in Architecture and (2) a Master of Architecture. The curriculum is structured in three primary educational segments:
- 2 Introductory Years—An introduction to architecture through a six-quarter sequence of lecture and studio classes, plus general education classes. At the conclusion of this study students would seek formal admission into the professional track by Portfolio Review.
- 2 Intermediate Years—Initiation of the professional degree track in a six-quarter sequence of architectural and general education classes. During the fourth year students decide whether to complete their studies at the BA/BS level or apply for competitive admission to graduate studies at PSU or elsewhere.
- 2 Graduate Years—Continuation of the professional degree track in a six-quarter sequence of studios and seminars, culminating in a Graduate Design Thesis project. Students would complete

a total of 254 credits (180 undergraduate credits plus 74 graduate credits) for graduation.

The undergraduate program is for students who will pursue the two-year Master of Architecture degree required for licensing as an architect. It is also an excellent foundation for students who will enter other related fields, including design, planning, and construction.

The graduate program is intended for students who have completed a pre-professional undergraduate degree in architecture, from PSU or elsewhere, and who intend to become licensed architects. The program is in Candidacy status for professional accreditation with the National Architectural Accrediting Board (NAAB).

AREAS OF FOCUS AND RESEARCH
In both pedagogy and research the Department or Architecture has established a reputation in three main areas of exploration:
1. the communicative potential of material and the poetics of making
2. urbanism and the metropolitan condition
3. civic engagement and the interpretation of collective identity

The fundamental questions of environmental stewardship and sustainability underpin the academic ethos of the Department and this is fostered by direct faculty involvement in a university-wide, cross-disciplinary research hub, The Center for Sustainable Processes and Practices.

The educational objectives of the program are also enriched by the specialist areas of knowledge and expertise of faculty, and include the following:

The cultural meanings of architectural representation understood through investigations of the phenomenology of the human body, an architecture of experience, and the cultural value of metaphoric work.

Urban design history and theory and the creative renaissance of public spaces for meaningful collective experiences, with investigations of the spatial and cultural relationships between cities and rivers.

A hands-on approach to exploring materials, detailing, and building assembly through fabrication and the practical application of tectonic theory.

European modernism with particular reference to intervention in historic urban environments and the adaptive reuse of the existing built fabric as a critical avenue for a responsible sustainability.

Creative investigation of abandoned industrial landscapes towards the mitigation or celebration of their qualities, in particular territories associated with forms of transportation such as disused railroad yards, and land abandoned amidst freeway development.

The 'Basic Initiative' program, a multi-disciplinary fieldwork program that challenges students to apply their design education in service of marginalized communities, promoting sustainable architecture and community design in the developing world for both not-for-profit organizations and governmental and international agencies.

SPECIAL ACTIVITIES AND PROGRAMS
Praxis Lecture Series
Portland architects are regularly invited into the school to informally discuss current work in the design or construction phases.
Loacker Architecture Lecture
Internationally distinguished guest presenters are invited annually in this donor-sponsored event, now in its third year. The first and second Loacker presenters were Brian McKay-Lyons and Stephen Kieran.

Guest Speakers
Nationally and internationally known architects frequently present their work at the school to students and local design professionals. Recent visitors to the school have included: Alberto Perez-Gomez, Aaron Betsky, Ken Yeang, Peter Cook, Tom Kundig, Eric Parry, Jennifer Siegal, Michael Rotondi, Sarah Graham, David Leatherbarrow, Wes Jones, Ben Van Berkel, Perry Kulper, Alex Lifshutz.
International Study Opportunities
Current programs include summer trips to Barcelona offering in-depth study of one of the world's most vibrant architectural settings. Students are encouraged to visit other countries through connections with other schools, including the Danish International School in Copenhagen.
Graduate Certificate in Urban Design
The Department of Architecture participates in this program in joint delivery with the Toulan School of Urban Studies and Planning.

FACILITIES
The Department of Architecture occupies Shattuck Hall, a beautiful red brick 1915 elementary school, extensively remodeled and upgraded in 2008. The first floor is conceived as a media exploration center accommodating the Materials Lab consisting of multiple shops dedicated to wood working, model making, metal working (including a foundry), and concrete/plaster casting; and a Digital Lab consisting of software, scanning, printing and plotting facilities. In process is a digital milling suite to complement the existing labs. The second floor houses the Department reception/reading room, gallery, and faculty offices. The third floor accommodates an open-plan, split-level interior landscape encompassing all studios, wrapped around an accessible open-air roof terrace. The third floor includes a Resource Room overseen by the Architecture Students Association. Adjacent to the main building is the Annex, a large, double-height, multi-purpose space accommodating major presentations, critiques and events in Architecture and the other departments of the School of Fine and Performing Arts. PSU's main library, the Millar Library, has holdings of more than 1.3 million books and over 16,000 serial subscriptions (with nearly 70,000 journals accessible electronically). The library holds over 5,400 titles in the NA classification alongside access to 69 journals. PSU also participates in the Summit alliance that currently provides access to over 28 million items from 34 college and university libraries throughout Oregon and Washington.

Portland State University offers a unique college experience providing all the amenities expected of a major university, such as housing, health services, recreation facilities, and student clubs and associations, all interwoven within the very livable, walkable, and tight urban grain of downtown Portland.

SCHOLARSHIPS AND FINANCIAL AID
The department currently awards a traveling fellowship, overall achievement scholarships, and an excellence in drawing award. A number of graduate research and teaching assistantships providing tuition remission and a stipend are available for students in the graduate program.

ADMINISTRATION
Clive Knights: Department Chair

PRAIRIE VIEW A&M UNIVERSITY

ADDRESS

Main
Prairie View A&M University
School of Architecture
P.O. Box 519, Mail Stop 2100
University Dr. @ L.W. Minor St.
Prairie View, TX 77446-4207
Tel: 936.261.9800
Fax: 936.261.9826
arch@pvamu.edu
https://www.pvamu.edu/architecture

STUDENT AND FACULTY DEMOGRAPHICS

% of Female Students	25
% of International Students	2.39
% of Minority Students	91
% of Out-of-State U.S. Students	10
No. Full-Time Faculty	17
No. Part-Time Faculty	8
No. Full-Time Students	335
No. Part-Time Students	41

FINANCIAL INFORMATION

Main Source of University Funding	Public
Annual Tuition & Fees (graduate, resident)	$5740
Annual Tuition & Fees (graduate, nonresident)	$12,460
Annual Tuition & Fees (undergraduate, resident)	$6,120
Annual Tuition & Fees (undergraduate, nonresident)	$14,460
% Students Receiving Federal Financial Aid	50
% Students Receiving University Financial Aid	85
% Students Receiving Departmental Financial Aid	8
% Students Receiving Scholarships (assistantships or fellowships)	10
Average Annual Scholarship for Department	$1,500

ACADEMIC SESSIONS

Fall Semester: August to December
Spring Semester: January to May

Summer Session I: May to June
Summer Session II: July to August

ARCHITECTURE AND RELATED DEGREE PROGRAMS

Degree	Min. Yrs. to Complete	Professional Accreditation	# of FT Students	# of PT Students	# of First-Year Students	# of Degrees Conferred	Admissions Requirements
Architecture							
BS Arch	4		331	15	97	47	
M. Arch — 2 years	1	NAAB	32	2		10	
Construction Management/Technology							
BS Construction Science	4	ACCE	48	5	15	5	
Other							
Master of Community Development	1		14	19		10	

ARCHITECTURE PROGRAM SUMMARY

The School of Architecture, with programs in Architecture, Construction Science and Community Development and Art, is dedicated to accomplishing our mission by preparing graduates for leadership roles in rebuilding America's cities and improving the quality of the built environment. By offering a diverse curriculum led by an accomplished faculty in a comprehensive studio and classroom environment, the School of Architecture programs will educate students for significant roles as practitioners, developers and leaders in architecture, construction, community planning and community development. Students in the programs of the School will be challenged to develop their abilities in problem solving, creative thinking and informed decision making as a focus of their professional education. They will accomplish this in a nurturing and student centered environment that fosters personal development and professional excellence.

UNIVERSITY SETTING

Prairie View A&M University is the second-oldest public university in the State of Texas, located in a rural, small-town setting, with many new dormitories and educational buildings including a new student center, and a new school of architecture facility. The campus of over 8,500 students is just 40 miles northwest of Downtown Houston, a living museum of modern architecture and a source of all the amenities one might require. This location offers an opportunity for students to enrich their learning experience through access to the greater architectural and construction community of the region with its many employment opportunities in the field.

SCHOOL PHILOSOPHY

The School of Architecture is committed to providing a well-protected, student-centered, technology-intensive learning environment that will lead to graduating well-prepared students who will continue in the profession and become licensed architects. The school is dedicated to preparing students to play a leadership role in changing America's built environment for future generation. This is done through technology-assisted learning opportunities, giving a comprehensive view of problems facing the future architect, supported by a well-rounded faculty, focused on the technical and human aspects of settlement.

PROGRAM DESCRIPTION

The Bachelor of Science degree (pre-professional program) provides the common ground for studies in architecture. It is intended to cover the basic content for the preparation of an educated practitioner and to lead to professional studies at the graduate level.

The Bachelor of Science in Architecture degree has two tracks; Program A, the Professional Track, leads directly to the Master of Architecture professional degree. Program B, the Non-professional Track, provides a basic education in architecture with the opportunity to study a broad range of elective opportunities. Both tracks consist of 132 credit hours of undergraduate courses.

Master of Architecture Professional Program

The Master of Architecture, as a professional program, prepares students for roles in the profession of architecture by building on the content of the pre-professional program through intensive and focused advanced studies in the field of architecture practice and design. A major objective of this program is preparing graduates to obtain their professional architecture registration. The Master of Architecture degree program, consisting of an undergraduate curriculum of 132 credit hours and a graduate curriculum of 36 credit hours, is the accredited program at Prairie View A&M University.

AREAS OF FOCUS AND RESEARCH

Focus

The central focus of the program is the comprehensive design of building in their community and urban text. The laptop intensive environment of the program also leads to a commitment to advanced student development in computer technologies and applications. Degree programs in community development and construction science provide opportunities for specialized and advanced studies in those areas.

Research

Research and community service are conducted through the community, the Urban and Rural Enhancement Service Center, and the Texas Institute for Preservation of History and Culture both of which are located within the school. Together these activities document the history and culture while providing research, service learning and community service encompassing the physical and infrastructure needs of communities large and small throughout the State of Texas. Previous research activities within the school have involved development, design and construction of a community center. Other endeavors include small town revitalization studies, remodeling and additions studies for a wide range of users, transportation studies and space habitat studies with NASA.

SPECIAL ACTIVITIES AND PROGRAMS

The school supports a number of active student groups including American Institute of Architecture Students, National Organization of Minority Architecture Students, Tau Sigma Delta honor society, Women in Architecture Students, Construction Specification Institute Students, National Association of Home Builders Students, and Agency for General Contractors Students. There is an annual speakers' series bringing architects and other professionals to the campus who lecture on relevant topics. In the summer 2005, the school initiated an annual study abroad program with its first course offered in Italy. Students actively participate in local, state and national competitions and are annually involved with local, state and national activities of the American Institute of Architects and other related organizations. The school offers the Architectural Concepts Institute summer program for well prepared high school students wishing to accelerate their studies in architecture and another special intensive design program for transfer students who are trying to catch up with their studies in architecture. Students may also obtain a second degree or a minor in construction science by completing the required prescribed courses

FACILITIES

The Construction of a new 105,000 square foot facility to house and support the programs of the School of Architecture was completed in the fall of 2005. The widely published and award wining building was designed by Michael Rotondi, FAIA, of Roto Architects from L.A. and HKS of Dallas. The building, which is named for Nathelyne Archie Kennedy (the first African-American P.E. in the State of Texas), includes a state of the art computer lab, model shop, reference library, studio and study spaces. The school also has lecture rooms, a reference library, gallery as exhibit space, lounge and offices for faculty, staff and students organizations.

SCHOLARSHIPS AND FINANCIAL AID

All financial aid is administered through the university financial aid offices. There are need-based and merit scholarships available along with loans and work-study opportunities. For graduate students, there are a number of competitive and merit scholarships and graduate assistant positions available for the last years of study.

ADMINISTRATION

Dr. Ikhlas Sabouni: Dean
Dr. Bruce F. Bockhorn, AIA: Director of
    Construction Science
Dr. Rick Baldwin: Director of Community Development
Professor Clarence Talley, MFA: Director of Arts

PRATT INSTITUTE

ADDRESS

Main
Pratt Institute
School of Architecture
200 Willoughby Avenue
Brooklyn, NY 11205
Tel.: 718.399.4305
Fax: 718.399.4315
pgill@pratt.edu
www.pratt.edu/arch

STUDENT AND FACULTY DEMOGRAPHICS

% of Female Students	50
% of International Students	15
% of Minority Students	20
% of Out-of-State U.S. Students	75
No. Full-Time Faculty	20
No. Part-Time Faculty	160
No. Full-Time Students	655
No. Part-Time Students	150

FINANCIAL INFORMATION

Main Source of University Funding	Private
Annual Tuition & Fees (graduate)	$32,000
Annual Tuition & Fees (undergraduate)	$32,000
% Students Receiving Federal Financial Aid	50
% Students Receiving University Financial Aid	75
% Students Receiving Departmental Financial Aid	30
% Students Receiving Scholarships (assistantships or fellowships)	30
Average Annual Scholarship for Department	$8,000

ACADEMIC SESSIONS

Fall Semester: September to December
Spring Semester: January to April

Summer Semester: May to August

ARCHITECTURE AND RELATED DEGREE PROGRAMS

Degree	Min. Yrs. to Complete	Professional Accreditation	# of FT Students	# of PT Students	# of First-Year Students	# of Degrees Conferred	Admissions Requirements
Architecture							
B. Arch	5	NAAB	550	5	130	85	
M. Arch	3	NAAB	150	0	50	50	
MS Arch	1.5		30	0	15	15	
Planning							
MS CRP	2	PAB	0	60	20	15	
Urban Design							
MS UD	1.5		9	0	9	8	
Construction Management/Technology							
BS Const Mgmt	4		0	70	15	20	
MS Facilities Mgmt	2	IFMA	0	15	8	5	
Historic Preservation							
MS HP	2	NCPE	25	0	12	12	

SPECIALIZATIONS

Preservation

ARCHITECTURE PROGRAM SUMMARY

The School of Architecture's mission is to educate the future leaders of the design disciplines in the professional fields of architecture, urban design, city and regional planning, construction and facilities management, and historic preservation. This effort builds upon a strong context of professional education within an art and design institute that stresses the relationship between intellectual development and creative activity. The school provides a broad cultural and analytical base in the liberal arts and sciences, while providing the specialized knowledge unique to individual disciplines. The importance of independent learning is emphasized through studio-based curricula and research-oriented thesis programs.

UNIVERSITY SETTING

Pratt Institute is a specialized university with 4,000 students in undergraduate and graduate programs in the fine arts, design, fashion, architecture, and information and library science. The main campus is on 25 acres near downtown Brooklyn. Many of the design and architecture programs are very highly ranked within their professional discipline.

SCHOOL PHILOSOPHY

The School of Architecture offers degree programs in Undergraduate Architecture, First-Professional and Post-Professional Graduate Architecture, Urban Design, City and Regional Planning, Construction and Facilities Management and Historic Preservation. All of these programs focus on design and stress the relationship between theory and practice within their respective discipline. This philosophy is built upon the dynamic culture of New York City, as well as the primary mission of Pratt Institute to educate students in productive and artistic disciplines.

PROGRAM DESCRIPTION

Undergraduate Architecture is a five-year B.Arch program that prepares students with an early interest in architecture to become leading professional practitioners. The five-year design sequence offers a thorough foundation in architecture, integrating critical thinking, design, technology, building, representation, and social responsibility. Firmly committed to contemporary material practices, the program is currently developing initiatives to integrate new technologies into the curriculum.

Graduate Architecture offers two different degrees in architecture: a first professional Master of Architecture for students with a four-year bachelor's degree in any field; and a post-professional Master of Science in Architecture for students with a five-year professional undergraduate architecture degree. The first-professional program is six semesters and allows students to attain professional status upon graduation. The post-

professional architecture program is three semesters and allows students to pursue research at an advanced level. The Graduate Architecture and Urban Design program offers a Master of Science in Architecture and Urban Design. The program is three semesters and is open to students holding a five-year, or equivalent, professional undergraduate degree in architecture. The Graduate Architecture and Urban Design programs are focused on contemporary practice, new technologies, global urbanism and advanced design approaches to sustainability and performative building systems.

The Graduate Center for Planning and the Environment (GCPE) is a four-semester graduate program focusing on community-based planning with an increasing emphasis on sustainable planning practices. Concentrations within the GCPE include community planning, environmental planning and physical planning. Environmental Planning and Historic Preservation are two specialized graduate degree programs within the GCPE offering contemporary approaches to the urban problems of sustainable design and the preservation of urban context and buildings.

The Construction Management program is a four-year undergraduate program which prepares students for careers in the construction industry. The program offers a thorough education in all aspects of construction and, through its broad alumni network in the New York area, extensive opportunities for internships during the academic year. The Facilities Management program is a two-year graduate program preparing students for careers in Facilities Management, Real Estate Management and related construction and management fields.

AREAS OF FOCUS AND RESEARCH

Focus

The focus of all the graduate and undergraduate programs is to provide the best possible professional preparation for students in their respective fields. In the architecture and urban design programs creative design thinking with advanced technologies serves as the basis for an understanding of contemporary practices. The Planning, Environmental and Preservation programs emphasize the importance of community based planning with special emphasis on the relationship between policy, social justice and the empowerment of communities. Sustainable planning and design are common threads in all of the architecture and planning programs and shape both the intellectual and professional discourses across all curricula.

Research

Research activities in the School of Architecture take place both within the school in the form of independent faculty work as well as in dedicated research centers. Research is concentrated in the areas of building technology and computation as well as sustainable

and contemporary urbanism. Corporate donors sponsor research studios in the areas of building skins, lighting control, skylighting, new materials and structural systems including carbon fiber and nano-technology. The Kullman Center for Industrialized Construction is a research center focused on prefabricated high-rise housing. The Center for Experimental Structures examines new structural typologies based on genomics in consultation with private industry partners. The Pratt Center for Community and Environmental Design conducts research for both communities and government including the city of New York, the Ford Foundation and the city of New Orleans in the aftermath of Hurricane Katrina.

SPECIAL ACTIVITIES AND PROGRAMS

The Undergraduate Architecture department maintains a study-abroad program in Rome for students in their fourth year of study, and a six-week summer program in Beijing. The Graduate Architecture program has an intensive six week study program at the Rome campus as well as travel opportunities in conjunction with design studios. The school publishes an annual journal, *inprocess*, and has a distinguished lecture series of internationally renowned architects and designers.

FACILITIES

The School of Architecture maintains Brooklyn and Manhattan facilities. The Brooklyn facility is a 110,000 square-foot Romanesque loft building that is an historical landmark with a contemporary addition building with a 250 seat auditorium, dedicated gallery and state-of-the-art studios. The Manhattan facility is a seven-story newly renovated loft building on 14th Street in lower Manhattan and houses the Construction and Facilities Management programs.

SCHOLARSHIP AND FINANCIAL AID

The School of Architecture students benefit from financial aid packages based on merit and need. Students receive aid in the amount of 25% to 100% of their tuition costs.

ADMINISTRATION

Thomas Hanrahan: Dean
Evan Douglis: Chair, Undergraduate Architecture
William MacDonald: Chair, Graduate Architecture and Urban Design
John Shapiro: Chair, The Graduate Center for Planning and the Environment
Harriet Markis: Chair, Construction Management and Facilities Management
Eric Allison: Director, Graduate Historic Preservation

PRINCETON UNIVERSITY

ADDRESS

Main
Princeton University
School of Architecture
S-110 Architecture Building
Princeton, NJ 08544-5264
Tel: 609.258.3741
Fax: 609.258.4740
soa@princeton.edu
www.princeton.edu/soa

STUDENT AND FACULTY DEMOGRAPHICS

% of Female Students	43
% of International Students	17
% of Minority Students	20
% of Out-of-State U.S. Students	
No. Full-Time Faculty	12
No. Part-Time Faculty	32
No. Full-Time Students	129
No. Part-Time Students	0

FINANCIAL INFORMATION

Main Source of University Funding	Private
Annual Tuition & Fees (graduate)	$34,050
Annual Tuition & Fees (undergraduate)	$34,290
% Students Receiving Federal Financial Aid	10
% Students Receiving University Financial Aid	55
% Students Receiving Departmental Financial Aid	
% Students Receiving Scholarships (assistantships or fellowships)	63
Average Annual Scholarship for Department	$24,000

ACADEMIC SESSIONS

Fall Semester: September to January; Application Deadline: December 1
Spring Semester: February to June

ARCHITECTURE AND RELATED DEGREE PROGRAMS

Degree	Min. Yrs. to Complete	Professional Accreditation	# of FT Students	# of PT Students	# of First-Year Students	# of Degrees Conferred	Admissions Requirements
Architecture							
AB	4		30	0	19	12	SAT
M. Arch — 1.5 years	1.5		14	0	8	6	Prof. Architecture degree, GRE, TOEFL, Portfolio, Rec. Letters, Essay
M. Arch — 3 years	3	NAAB	36	0	17	22	Undergraduate degree, GRE, TOEFL, Portfolio, Rec. Letters, Essay
PhD	5		17	0	4	3	Undergraduate degree, GRE, TOEFL, Rec. Letters, Essay

ARCHITECTURE PROGRAM SUMMARY

Princeton University's School of Architecture promotes a synthetic approach to architecture, drawing upon design innovation, in-depth studies in the history and theory of architecture, as well as the emerging cultures of computation and building technology. Architecture at Princeton has always been taught in this broad cultural context. Our design studios and technical courses are rigorous and demanding; they prepare our graduates to practice effectively in a competitive environment. Our history and theory curriculum, with its strong interdisciplinary ties, encourages the critical intelligence necessary to make sense of a changing world. Moreover, the School's small size enables us to integrate design

and theory as no other school can, taking advantage of the overlaps and intersections between studio work and a rich culture of research and intellectual speculation. The School's programs and facilities are being constantly upgraded: this year we welcome new faculty, revamped programs, and a significant new expansion to the School of Architecture building itself.

Architecture and education both require a profound commitment to a better future. As architects, we design buildings, landscapes and cities for a society whose ideas and technologies will inevitably change; as educators, we teach new generations of students who will practice in a world more global, more urban, more technologically complex, and more

open to change. The only certainty is change itself, and our first obligation is to equip all students with the practical and intellectual tools necessary to invent new practices for the new century.

UNIVERSITY SETTING

Students at the School benefit from its small size and thorough integration with the University community. Approximately 65 graduate and 50 undergraduate students are enrolled. Both programs share faculty, courses, and facilities, fostering close relationships among all students. Because many courses are cross-listed with other departments, students pursue their education through a wide range of related disciplines, including art and archaeology, civil and environmental engineering, history, English, sociology, American studies, and European cultural studies.

SCHOOL PHILOSOPHY

Architecture is a collective art-form, involving the expertise of many different fields. The School is committed to a culture of collaboration involving architecture, urbanism, landscape and media. Architecture is constantly enriched by the traffic between theory and practice. At Princeton, we are confident that our long history of a productive dialogue between academic research and practical design work will produce a new generation of architects prepared to transform our complex world in previously unimagined ways.

Although the School of Architecture has expanded its facility, faculty, and student body over the years, it retains a small size that encourages close contact between faculty members, graduate students, and undergraduates. From the beginning, the School of Architecture's curriculum has always responded to changes in the profession and in architectural education, providing students with courses that reflect contemporary and emerging issues in architecture. Within this flexible academic framework, the School of Architecture has remained committed to its original goals: providing undergraduates with a well-rounded liberal arts education and a strong basis for additional studies in architecture, and offering graduate students a comprehensive education in design, technology, and the history and theories of architecture.

PROGRAM DESCRIPTION

The undergraduate program in architecture offers an opportunity for in-depth study of architecture within the context of a liberal arts education. The program of study emphasizes the complex relationship between architectural form, culture and society considered through an in-depth exploration of architectural design, history and theory of architecture, building technology, urbanism, and landscape architecture. Particular attention is paid to the social and political aspects of architecture's urban setting, and its impact on the natural environment.

The undergraduate program at the School of Architecture is known for its rigorous and interdisciplinary approach to pre-professional education. The four-year undergraduate program leads to an A.B. with a concentration in architecture. In addition to architectural design and the history and theory of architecture and urbanism, undergraduates study a range of disciplines that contribute to an architect's knowledge and vision, including courses in architectural analysis, representation, computing, and building technologies. Such a broad academic program also prepares students for a graduate program in architecture and other related disciplines such as landscape architecture, urban planning, civil engineering, art history, and the visual arts. In addition, the B.S.E. program in architecture and engineering is offered through the School of Engineering and Applied Science.

The Master of Architecture degree (M.Arch.), accredited by the National Architectural Accrediting Board (NAAB), is intended for students who plan to practice architecture professionally. It qualifies them to take the state professional licensing examination after completing the required internship. Students are eligible for admission to the graduate program whether or not they have had undergraduate work in architecture. The typical duration of the program is three years; students with an undergraduate architecture background may be eligible for advanced standing. The master's degree program is structured around a rigorous sequence of design studios. Studio work is complemented by courses in technology, history, theory, and analysis and representation. Each student constructs an individual program of study to meet course and distribution requirements. Students are also eligible to take elective courses in the School and in other departments of the University.

AREAS OF FOCUS AND RESEARCH

Teaching and research at Princeton is focused around three complementary areas: urbanism; technology and new media; and the intersection of architecture and the creative arts.

Urbanism

The School's long-standing commitment to examining the interplay between architecture and urbanism, and the culture of cities more generally, has recently been consolidated around two new programs: an Undergraduate Certificate Program in Urban Studies, headed up by Prof. Christine Boyer, and at the graduate level, a Research Center devoted to Architecture, Urbanism and Infrastructure, directed by Prof. Mario Gandelsonas. The Center was recently awarded the second annual Latrobe Fellowship, given by the College of Fellows of the American Institute of Architects.

Media and Technology

Digital design technologies have been fully integrated into the design teaching of the school, and these programs are supported by a full complement of equipment, software and technical support. More importantly, Princeton's faculty has been in the forefront of those thinking critically about the role of these new technologies in architecture, and their potential convergence with the 'hard' technologies of building. Faculty have recently been added in this area, and through programs such as Prof. Beatriz Colomina's Program in Media and Modernity, the School will continue to take a leadership role in this area.

Art and Architecture

The School of Architecture has a prominent place in the University-wide Creative Arts initiative. Building on the School's strong interdisciplinary tradition, many faculty at Princeton have strong connections with the creative arts. Previous programs have included School of Architecture participation in exhibitions, theatrical productions and conferences. This new focus will result in collaborative teaching and research, cross-disciplinary exchanges and shared programs with the Department of Art and Archaeology and the Program in Visual Arts.

SPECIAL ACTIVITIES AND PROGRAMS

The School sponsors a wide variety of lectures, conferences and symposia throughout the year, inviting speakers to lecture on topics related to architecture. Conferences have included:

Retracing the Expanded Field: A Conference on Art and Architecture: April 20/21, 2007; "THE Matter of Facts: architecture and generation of design information": March 28, 2008.

The exhibition Clip, Stamp, Fold: The Radical Architecture of Little Magazines, 196x to 197x, organized by PhD students, opened at the Storefront for Art and Architecture, and traveled to various venues.

Princeton students participated in the 2007 Rotterdam Biennial, completing a research project on cities and urban spaces in New Jersey, which was published in *Visionary Power: Producing the Contemporary City* (Rotterdam, Berlage Institute, 2007).

The School has an active publications program. Upcoming publications include the inauguration of a new series, *Point*, conference proceedings from recent events, and a series of studio publications. *306090, a Journal of Emergent Architecture and Design*, begun in 2002, was produced initially by a student editorial board and introduces the work of promising students and young professionals whose cross-disciplinary projects, ideas, buildings, and other media offer innovative directions for the growth of architecture. *PIDGIN*, an interdisciplinary journal edited, designed, and published by current students, including essays, projects and works in progress by both students and faculty.

The School is active in a number of international programs. A formal exchange program with Chinese universities began in the fall of 1996, and continues to the present. Students and faculty from the Department of Architecture, University of Hong Kong, and the School of Architecture, TongJi University participate in these joint design studios. Princeton students travel to Shanghai for a week of exchange and discussion. The School recently established an ongoing Tokyo Studio supported by a bequest from Jack Curtis, '51. Students travel to Tokyo, where the design project is sited. At a time when the practice of architecture is global in its reach, this studio offers an unparalleled educational opportunity for our students.

FACILITIES

Most of the School's facilities are in the Architecture Building, located on McCosh Walk near the center of campus, which is home to undergraduate and graduate design studios, seminar rooms, Betts Auditorium, an exhibition gallery, faculty and administrative offices, the School of Architecture Library, the Visual Resources Collection, the Computer-Aided Design and Imaging Facility, and the Architecture Laboratory.

SCHOLARSHIPS AND FINANCIAL AID

Princeton provides aid to undergraduate students who make satisfactory progress toward a degree and continue to demonstrate financial need. The amount and type of aid students receive is reviewed annually. Princeton offers fellowships to graduate students. Fellowships enable outstanding students to pursue their graduate studies and require no service in return. Fellowships applied to tuition are nontaxable; stipends are taxable according to present law. Financial aid applications are included with the application for admission.

ADMINISTRATION

Stan Allen, AIA: Dean
Paul Lewis: Director of Graduate Studies,
   M.Arch. Programs
Beatriz Colomina: Director of Graduate Studies,
   Ph.D. Program
Cynthia Nelson: Administrator

RENSSELAER POLYTECHNIC INSTITUTE

ADDRESS

Main
Rensselaer Polytechnic Institute
School of Architecture
Greene Bldg
110 8th Street
Troy, NY 12180-3590
Tel.: 518/276-6466
Fax: 518/276-3034
www.arch.rpi.edu

STUDENT AND FACULTY DEMOGRAPHICS

% of Female Students	51
% of International Students	24
% of Minority Students	2
% of Out-of-State U.S. Students	58
No. Full-Time Faculty	28
No. Part-Time Faculty	11
No. Full-Time Students	357
No. Part-Time Students	6

FINANCIAL INFORMATION

Main Source of University Funding	Private
Annual Tuition & Fees (graduate)	$36,950
Annual Tuition & Fees (undergraduate)	$36,950
% Students Receiving Federal Financial Aid	25
% Students Receiving University Financial Aid	93
% Students Receiving Departmental Financial Aid	0
% Students Receiving Scholarships (assistantships or fellowships)	93
Average Annual Scholarship for Department	$0

ACADEMIC SESSIONS

Fall Semester: August to December
Spring Semester: January to May
Summer Session I: May to August

Summer Session II: May to June
Summer Session III: July to August

ARCHITECTURE AND RELATED DEGREE PROGRAMS

Degree	Min. Yrs. to Complete	Professional Accreditation	# of FT Students	# of PT Students	# of First-Year Students	# of Degrees Conferred	Admissions Requirements
Architecture							
B. Arch	5	NAAB	292	0	60	37	SAT, Portfolio, Essay
M. Arch	3.5	NAAB	4			4	Undergraduate degree, GRE, TOEFL, Portfolio, Rec. Letters, Essay
MS Architectural Sciences Concentrations in Acoustics, Built Ecologies, Lighting	1		38			13	Undergraduate degree, GRE, TOEFL, Portfolio, Rec. Letters, Essay
MS Lighting	2		12		7	4	Undergraduate degree, GRE, TOEFL, Portfolio, Rec. Letters, Essay
PhD Architectural Sciences Concentrations in Acoustics, Built Ecologies, Lighting			14		13		GRE, TOEFL, Portfolio, Rec. Letters, Essay

SPECIALIZATIONS

Architectural Design
Building Technology/Env. Systems
Building Information Modeling

Computer-Aided Design
Energy
Environment/Sustainability

International/Regional Architecture
Professional Practice
Sustainability

Tectonics
Urban Planning and Design

ARCHITECTURE PROGRAM SUMMARY

Significant changes are occurring within the discipline and profession of architectue in the areas of globalization, interdisciplinary teamwork, and emerging technologies.

UNIVERSITY SETTING

Rensselaer's historic main campus sits on a bluff overlooking the city of Troy, NY., and the Hudson River. The area offers a relaxed lifestyle with many cultural and recreational opportunities, with easy access to several major metropolitan centers. The School of Architecture is housed in the Greene Building, located in the center of Rensselaer's campus.

SCHOOL PHILOSOPHY

There has never been a better time to consider becoming an architect; architecture is constantly in the public eye and is called on, not only to enhance the quality of life through the creation of the built environment, but also to do so in a manner that is beneficial, appropriate and responsive to the natural environment. The architect of the future needs to balance creative ambition with knowledge of the world, a disciplined understanding of new materials technologies, and the ability to approach increasingly complex problems. The School of Architecture embraces these challenges with a determination to consider how our enterprise and graduates will change the profession with an emphasis on critical thinking and the development of diverse tools and techniques, both analog and digital. The School believes firmly in the transformative power of computing and digitization and sits within a culture of architectural sciences—Built Ecologies, Architectural Acoustics, and Lighting that are unequalled nationally. Our goal is to cultivate each distinct imagination and to find pleasure in conceptual thought and the satisfaction of leaving a permanent and beneficial mark on society.

PROGRAM DESCRIPTION

The School of Architecture offers a five-year Bachelor of Architecture (B.Arch.), a professional degree accredited by the National Architecture Accrediting Board. A visit to the School of Architecture, and a faculty interview are encouraged as part of the application process. To schedule a visit with the School of Architecture go to our web site: http://www.arch.rpi.edu/visit.htm. Architecture candidates are asked to submit a creative portfolio with their application. Students with unusually strong academic profiles may be reviewed without the portfolio, however, such cases are exceptionally rare; we prefer that all applicants submit a portfolio. (Portfolio req: http://www.arch.rpi.edu/about_directions.htm) Students may also apply for transfer from other schools in architecture or related programs of study. Transfer students are placed at an appropriate level in the program after a review of transcript, course descriptions, and portfolio of work.

The School of Architecture offers both professional and research degrees at an advanced level. The Master of Science and PhD in science and architectural sciences degrees are research-oriented programs with concentrations in Built Ecologies, Architectural Acoustics, and Lighting. These advanced programs are founded on the position that the increasing demands for effective building performance both perceptually and technically can only be addressed adequately through research. The School of Architecture offers the Doctor of Philosophy degree in Architectural Sciences to candidates who are prepared to undertake innovative and substantive research that adds to the body of knowledge drawn on by the design disciplines. The Sciences in this context refer to those disciplines that support and shape our understanding and production of the built environment including its physical, biological, social, cognitive and cultural contexts. The Ph.D. is an inherently interdisciplinary degree in which concentrations can be elected in Architectural Acoustics, Built Ecologies, and Lighting. A distinguished faculty within the School and across the Institute provides support for research projects that are informed by both disciplinary depth and trans-disciplinary integration. For more information: http://www.arch.rpi.edu/grad_phd.htm.

AREAS OF FOCUS AND RESEARCH

Architectural Acoustics Research Facilities, Innovations and Initiative offers advanced facilities in this area including a testing room with hemi-anechoic chamber, a coupled-room telepresence laboratory, several binaural listening test stations, equipment for ultrasonic physical scale modeling, software for auralization and other forms of computational acoustics. The faculty are highly regarded for their scholarly achievement in the international acoustics community and for their acoustic consulting expertise in room acoustics. With a focus on the fundamental theories underlying room acoustics and applied design applications, graduates from our program can pursue post–entry-level consulting positions as well as advanced research in acoustics. Current research areas focus on: Acoustics of Performance Venues and Classrooms, Acoustics of Offices, Studis and Other Small Rooms, Auralization & Applicatons of Comutational Room Acoustics, Electronic Enhancement of Acoustical Communication over Large Distances, Room Tuning, Novel Measurement Techniques for Room Acoustics & Sound Quality, Telepresence & Synthetic Environments, and Interdisciplinary Research.

The Center for Architectural Sciences (CAS) has a unique educational and research collaboration between Rensselaer Polytechnic Institute and Skidmore, Owings and Merrill (SOM). CAS seeks to address the global need for accelerated innovation and implementation of radically improved, energy-efficient, sustainable built environments. Using actual building projects as demonstration sites, Rensselaer is leading interdisciplinary research teams with seasoned building professionals to expedite the application of critical emerging advances in multiple fields such as Biotechnology, Material Science and Information Technology. Current research areas focus on next-generation building systems that make substantial advances in urgently needed areas such as clean, on-site energy generation, fresh indoor air and water resources for urban areas through the integration of ecological methods. CAS is uniquely placed to hasten the implementation of emerging materials that will substantially after the environmental impact of urban buildings.

The Lighting Research Center (LRC), with funding from the U.S. Department of Energy, conducted extensive research to identify and to seek ways of reducing the barriers limiting the wide acceptance and use of energy-efficient lighting systems. Our research teams include experts in experimental psychology, vision, photobiology, engineering, physics, architecture, photometry, optics, and design. This expertise is why the world often looks to the LRC for objective answers to its lighting questions. We operate the only independent lighting research laboratory accredited by the National Voluntary Laboratory Accreditation Program (NVLAP) to test lamps and lighting equipment. Research facilities include a fully equipped photometry laboratory, climate-controlled lamp and electrical testing laboratories, human factors research space, and the equipment necessary to produce fully functional prototypes and models. The current areas of research focus on: Application & Design, Automotive & Street Lighting, Aviation Lighting, Controls, Daylighting, Energy & Environment, Health & Vision, LEDs, Outdoor Lighting, Product Testing, Residential Lighting, Security Lighting, Technologies, and Technology Transfer.

SPECIAL ACTIVITIES AND PROGRAMS
Summer College Programs for High School Students

The School of Architecture offers an Introductory Architecture Career Discovery Program for rising high school juniors and seniors. This program is two weeks in length. The program provides an opportunity for career discovery to decide whether a design education in architecture is appropriate. Studio work can be used to develop a portfolio of creative work. For further information contact Outreach Program at 518-276-8351 or visit www.summer.rpi.edu.

International study is a defining aspect of architectural education at Rensselaer. The School of Architecture offers semester-long programs of study in four world cities that will challenge and help to define the future of architecture. The programs are open, by competitive application, to second-year students selected on the basis of academic accomplishment. The programs are directed by Rensselaer faculty members and supplemented by adjunct faculty in the host city or institution and there is a program fee for participation. Italy: The Italy program involves a design studio, an examination of the architectural development of Rome, courses in Italian language and culture, and travel throughout Italy. The program seeks to deepen appreciation of a city and the layers of its culture that have played a seminal role in the development of the West. India: The program is based in the School of Architecture CEPT at Ahmedabad, India, a highly respected school for the study of architecture and urbanism. It offers students the opportunity to travel, study and apply the lessons learned from Indian architecture and Indian history and theory within the context of a major research center. China: The semester in Shanghai is based in the School of Architecture at Tongji University, a preminent institution of higher learning in China. In addition to joint studios in design with Chinese faculty and students, the program offers courses in Chinese history and culture augmented by guided travel through central China. NYC: The semester in New York City offers study together with the Built Ecologies graduate program students at Skidmore, Owings & Merrill facilities, one of the world's leading architecture firms. Studio work addresses design and integration of multiple building systems. Courses taken with graduate students include Topics in Built Ecologies, Urban Ecologies, New York Explorations, and Topics in Computation Design.

FACILITIES

The School of Architecture at Rensselaer is committed to providing world-class facilities outfitted with the most current information and technology resources. The technology labs include laser cutting systems, rapid prototyping devices, and a 3axis router/mill etc. in support of digital fabrication processes. Computational design and visualization techniques are complemented by binaural listening and auralization test station, the Lighting Research Center (the world's largest university-based research and educational institution dedicated to light and lighting in all its forms), and an Acoustics research lab.

SCHOLARSHIPS AND FINANCIAL AID

Rensselaer offers financial assistance to undergraduate students in the form of scholarships, loans, and employment. This assistance is based on the family's financial need as demonstrated by the Financial Aid form of the College Scholarship Service. Graduate financial aid is available in the form of tuition scholarships and teaching assistantships; graduate aid is awarded on the basis of merit.

ADMINISTRATION

Mark Mistur: Acting Dean

RHODE ISLAND SCHOOL OF DESIGN

ADDRESS

Main
Rhode Island School of Design
Division of Architecture & Design
Two College Street
Providence, RI 02903
Tel.: 401.454.6281
Fax: 401.454.6299
archdept@risd.edu
www.risd.edu/architecture.cfm

STUDENT AND FACULTY DEMOGRAPHICS

% of Female Students	50
% of International Students	24
% of Minority Students	20
% of Out-of-State U.S. Students	90
No. Full-Time Faculty	12
No. Part-Time Faculty	35
No. Full-Time Students	235
No. Part-Time Students	0

FINANCIAL INFORMATION

Main Source of University Funding	Private
Annual Tuition & Fees (graduate)	$35,000
Annual Tuition & Fees (undergraduate)	$35,000
% Students Receiving Federal Financial Aid	80
% Students Receiving University Financial Aid	100
% Students Receiving Departmental Financial Aid	20
% Students Receiving Scholarships (assistantships or fellowships)	85
Average Annual Scholarship for Department	$5,000

ACADEMIC SESSIONS

Fall Semester: September to December; Application Deadline: March of previous year
Winter Quarter/Trimester: January to February
Spring Semester: February to May

ARCHITECTURE AND RELATED DEGREE PROGRAMS

Degree	Min. Yrs. to Complete	Professional Accreditation	# of FT Students	# of PT Students	# of First-Year Students	# of Degrees Conferred	Admissions Requirements
Architecture							
B. Arch	5	NAAB	150	0	45	55	
M. Arch	3.2	NAAB	90	0	35	15	

SPECIALIZATIONS

Architectural Design	Building Technology/Env. Systems	Graphic Design	Sustainability
Art and Design	Environment/Sustainability	International Development	Tectonics

126

ARCHITECTURE PROGRAM SUMMARY

RISD is one of the few accredited architecture programs in the US in the context of a broadly conceived art and design education. Graduate and undergraduate students share courses, facilities and teachers in the primary areas of architecture and design (landscape architecture, interior architecture, graphic design, industrial design, furniture design, apparel design), in the fine arts (including film and animation, ceramics, glass, textiles, painting, illustration, sculpture) and in arts education. Separate divisions of graduate studies, digital media, liberal arts and foundation studies complete RISD's course offerings. All Brown University courses can also be taken by RISD students, providing university-level access to many other areas of study.

UNIVERSITY SETTING

Established more than a century ago, RISD is an art and design school within the urban environment of Providence, Rhode Island. It has approximately 2,000 students majoring in a variety of disciplines from architecture, apparel and industrial design, to painting, sculpture, and jewelry, among others. First-year students from all disciplines follow a common set of courses in the visual arts that constitutes the foundation for a shared culture and rich interaction among all the areas of the school. Major offerings in liberal arts, several programs of study abroad, cross-registration with Brown University, and the RISD Museum create a vital environment for an education in architecture. The studio sequence is the central educational experience for the architecture student at RISD. It begins with a series of coordinated core studios—Design Principles, Architectural Design, and Urban Design Principles—that engages students in critical and instrumental design practices, and progressively introduces issues of form, construction, scale, space, program, and context. Following this core, students are encouraged to develop and follow more particular interests; to that effect, each term the department offers a variety of advanced elective studios (6 to 8 per term) that address different issues, approaches, and scales of architectural inquiry; these studios rely on regular and visiting faculty. In the final term, students are required to develop an independent Degree Project with the assistance of a faculty advisor. Course size and format are central to the nature and quality of the education in the Department of Architecture at RISD. Studios are at the core of the curriculum, with students working together in a common environment. The size of each section—between 12 and 14 students—and the intensity of two (almost) full-day meetings a week establishes a close and individual relationship between student and instructor. Other courses balance the general delivery of instruction with forms of participatory discussion, alternating (or in some cases combining) lecture courses (60 to 100 students) with seminar or workshop formats (15 to 25 students). These courses also balance survey-like syllabi with integrative approaches. The offerings of the department rely on various connections with other areas of the school. All students in the department are expected to have an education in the fundamentals of the visual arts provided by the Foundation year; transfer and graduate students without an education in the visual arts are required to enroll in Summer Session (equivalent to Foundation courses). Undergraduates take the required distribution in Liberal Arts. Particularly important is the relation among the "three architectures" (Architecture, Interior, and Landscape) that are located in the same building, have common courses and studios, and share a variety of activities and undertakings.

SCHOOL PHILOSOPHY

Within the context of an art and design school, the Department of Architecture at RISD understands architecture as a cultural discipline and the education of architects as a process of inquiry and experimentation. While the program trains students for the practice of architecture, it does not conceive the discipline in a narrow instrumental way, choosing instead to understand architecture as a cultural discourse subject to the complexities of action and interpretation prevalent in the fields of art and design. At RISD education in architecture is part of a culture of hands-on material sensibility and intellectual speculation.

PROGRAM DESCRIPTION

The Department intertwines the five-year Bachelor of Architecture and the three-year Master of Architecture programs in the studio curriculum, providing an inspiring and diverse environment for critical thinking and creativity. The hands-on tradition of RISD as a whole is expressed in the program by a deep interest in the physical world, and in construction as a social act; digital fabrication and visualization tools are equally engaged in the students' work.

AREAS OF FOCUS AND RESEARCH

Research focuses on the realization of construction projects in three venues: low energy-impact, high-tech solutions in the Northeastern United States (collaboration with the Brown University Department of Engineering); low energy-impact, socially conscious proposals for developing economies (to date, projects in Mexico and Costa Rica); and low-cost, high-design projects in the Providence area (collaboration with HousingOperative). Additional research areas are supported by individual faculty members.

SPECIAL ACTIVITIES AND PROGRAMS

Wintersession at RISD, a six-week long course of study offered to all students, is a unique opportunity at RISD to pursue non-major activities and to participate in academically framed travel. Current courses include travel to northern India, Switzerland (to study the work of Le Corbusier), Italy (to study underground architecture) and Costa Rica, in the context of a bamboo-based design/build project.

FACILITIES

Please see the RISD Department of Architecture website for current information on facilities.

SCHOLARSHIPS AND FINANCIAL AID

Please contact the Office of Student Accounts at RISD for current information on financial aid.

ADMINISTRATION

Lynnette Widder: Department Head

RICE UNIVERSITY

ADDRESS

Main
Rice University
School of Architecture
6100 Main Street
Houston, TX 77005-1892
Tel.: 713.348.4864
Fax: 713.348.5277
arch@rice.edu
www.arch.rice.edu

STUDENT AND FACULTY DEMOGRAPHICS

% of Female Students	53
% of International Students	35
% of Minority Students	8
% of Out-of-State U.S. Students	70
No. Full-Time Faculty	15
No. Part-Time Faculty	21
No. Full-Time Students	210
No. Part-Time Students	

FINANCIAL INFORMATION

Main Source of University Funding	Private
Annual Tuition & Fees (graduate)	$24,330
Annual Tuition & Fees (undergraduate)	$28,400
% Students Receiving Federal Financial Aid	
% Students Receiving University Financial Aid	
% Students Receiving Departmental Financial Aid	85
% Students Receiving Scholarships (assistantships or fellowships)	
Average Annual Scholarship for Department	$15,000

ACADEMIC SESSIONS

Fall Semester: August to December; Application Deadline: January 2nd

ARCHITECTURE AND RELATED DEGREE PROGRAMS

Degree	Min. Yrs. to Complete	Professional Accreditation	# of FT Students	# of PT Students	# of First-Year Students	# of Degrees Conferred	Admissions Requirements
Architecture							
B. Arch	6	NAAB	41	0	22	21	Undergraduate Architecture degree, Portfolio, Essay
B.A. in Arch.	4		87	0	23	25	SAT, ACT, Portfolio, Rec. Letters, Essay
M. Arch (Option 3)	1.5		12	0	8	4	Prof. Architecture degree, GRE, TOEFL, Portfolio, Rec. Letters, Essay
M. Arch. (Option 1)	3.5	NAAB	40	0	9	11	Undergraduate degree, GRE, TOEFL, Portfolio, Rec. Letters, Essay
M. Arch. (Option 2)	2.5	NAAB	30	0	13	5	Undergraduate Architecture degree, GRE, TOEFL, Portfolio, Rec. Letters, Essay
D. Arch			0	0	0	0	

SPECIALIZATIONS

Architectural Design
Building Information Modeling
Building Technology/Env. Systems
Community Design

Computer-Aided Design History
Energy
Environment/Sustainability
International Development

International/Regional Architecture
Professional Practice
Sustainability
Tectonics

Theory/Criticism
Urban Planning and Design

PROGRAM DESCRIPTION
Undergraduate Program
The undergraduate programs are intended to provide an intensive preparation in fundamental aspects of architectural theory and professional practice consistent with the broader objectives of a liberal arts education. The school adheres to no single design approach, but rather is process oriented and endeavors to maintain balanced diversity within its faculty and student body. Students are encouraged to pursue individual interests and to undertake independent study with faculty guidance where appropriate. The undergraduate program in architecture is designed around a basic professional framework allowing options for individual student growth and exploration. The first four years are structured to serve the needs of both students who wish to study for an undergraduate professional degree in architecture, and those who intend to earn a graduate professional degree. However, options exist for those students who may decide to pursue a general education and an emphasis on architecture, with the Bachelor of Arts as a terminal degree.

Students in the undergraduate program pursuing a Bachelor of Arts degree can choose between two majors during their second year of study: architecture or architectural studies. Architecture is a pre-professional program of concentration with four years of design studios, related lecture courses, a liberal component of free electives that use the resources of the entire university.

Architectural studies offers early concentration in architecture for two-and-a-half years followed by a wide selection of free electives, allowing the student a broadly based education with a possible second major. Students who have successfully completed the four-year program with a major in architecture may apply for the first professional degree program, leading to a Bachelor of Architecture degree. This is a two-year program with the first year spent in the Preceptorship Program, which places students in the offices of leading architects and planners for one academic year of practical experience. A tuition of $200 is charged during this year.

SPECIAL ACTIVITIES AND PROGRAMS
- Sophomore field trip
- Preceptor program (two-semester practicum in leading architectural offices for approved students who have received the BA in Architecture from Rice)
- School lecture series
- Rice Design Alliance lecture series at the Museum of Fine Arts, Houston
- CITE, quarterly review of architecture and design of the Rice Design Alliance
- Jury week (fall and spring)
- Traveling fellowships
- Special visiting critics studios at both the graduate and undergraduate levels
- Architectural Exhibitions in the Farish Gallery
- Student Council
- *Architecture at Rice*, school publication

FACILITIES
The school occupies quarters renovated and expanded by James Stirling, Michael Wilford and Associates in 1981. These include an advanced computer graphics laboratory, a well-equipped wood shop, and the Farish Gallery. The school is adjacent to the Alice Pratt Brown Art and Architecture Library, completed in 1986, which consolidates the university's holdings in art history, architecture, city planning, landscape, and classical archaeology.

SCHOLARSHIPS AND FINANCIAL AID
The financial aid program at Rice University seeks to provide assistance as needed to all students who are admitted. Through low-interest loans, fellowships, campus work opportunities, or a combination of these programs, Rice attempts to give students sufficient aid to meet educational expenses. Approximately 85 percent of architecture graduate students receive some kind of financial aid from the university, in the form of either scholarship or a stipend.

ADMINISTRATION
Lars Lerup: Dean
John J. Casbarian, FAIA: Associate Dean

ROGER WILLIAMS UNIVERSITY

ADDRESS

Main
Roger Williams University
School of Architecture, Art
and Historic Preservation
1 Old Ferry Road
Bristol, RI 02809-2921
Tel.: 401.254.3605
Fax: 401.254.3565
saahp@rwu.edu
www.rwu.edu/Academics/
Academic+Programs/
School+of+Architecture

STUDENT AND FACULTY DEMOGRAPHICS

% of Female Students	45
% of International Students	3
% of Minority Students	3
% of Out-of-State U.S. Students	60
No. Full-Time Faculty	23
No. Part-Time Faculty	22
No. Full-Time Students	375
No. Part-Time Students	0

FINANCIAL INFORMATION

Main Source of University Funding	Private
Annual Tuition & Fees (graduate)	$27,384
Annual Tuition & Fees (undergraduate)	$27,384
% Students Receiving Federal Financial Aid	
% Students Receiving University Financial Aid	60
% Students Receiving Departmental Financial Aid	0
% Students Receiving Scholarships (assistantships or fellowships)	10
Average Annual Scholarship for Department	$8,000

ACADEMIC SESSIONS

Fall Semester: August to December; Application Deadline: February 1
Winter Quarter/Trimester: January to January
Spring Semester: January to May

Summer Session I: June to July; Application Deadline: May 1
Summer Session II: July to August; Application Deadline: May 1
Summer Session III: June to August; Application Deadline: May 1

ARCHITECTURE AND RELATED DEGREE PROGRAMS

Degree	Min. Yrs. to Complete	Professional Accreditation	# of FT Students	# of PT Students	# of First-Year Students	# of Degrees Conferred	Admissions Requirements
Architecture							
B. Arch	4		315	0	95	60	SAT, ACT, TOEFL, Portfolio, Rec. Letters, Essay
M. Arch I	2	NAAB	61	0	30	18	Undergraduate Architecture degree, TOEFL, Portfolio, Rec. Letters, Essay
Historic Preservation							
BS in Historic Preservation	4		40	0	10	8	SAT, ACT, TOEFL, Rec. Letters, Essay
Other							
BA in Art and Architectural History	4		25	0	6	12	SAT, ACT, TOEFL, Rec. Letters, Essay
BA in Visual Arts Studies	4		30	0	10	8	SAT, ACT, TOEFL, Portfolio, Rec. Letters, Essay

SPECIALIZATIONS

Computer-Aided Design
International/Regional Architecture

Preservation

Sustainability

Urban Planning and Design

UNIVERSITY SETTING

Roger Williams University is a co-educational liberal arts institution offering undergraduate, professional, graduate and continuing education programs. The University's Core Values guide degree programs designed to encourage the development of critical and independent thought and a commitment to service, while preparing students for careers and lifelong learning. The faculty and coursework reflect an unusual combination of the elements and scale of a traditional liberal arts college, with professional and graduate degree programs in architecture, business, law, justice studies, education, public administration and construction management often found only in larger institutions. Transfer applications are encouraged.

SCHOOL PHILOSOPHY

The School of Architecture, Art and Historic Preservation is a multidisciplinary community committed to balance between creation and conservation, aesthetic and technical pursuits, national and international perspectives, individual exploration and community involvement in a period of environmental challenges. We work to achieve this balance through a variety of teaching situations that engage students, faculty and those active in the field in close relationships. All courses are taught by faculty, with no teaching assistants. We serve a continuum of students in undergraduate and professional degree programs, High School Career Discovery, post-professional and continuing education opportunities. The School extends itself most fully by bringing people together around topics and works of international significance in public events, professional conferences, and community initiatives.

PROGRAM DESCRIPTION

Architecture at Roger Williams focuses on the development of design solutions that operate in context at the scales of site, space and detail. We provide students with a strong sense of design, a balanced awareness of technology, history/theory, social, environmental and practice issues, and the breadth of a liberal arts education in the four year Bachelor of Science in Architecture + NAAB-accredited 1.5–2-year Master of Architecture sequence.

Architecture students pursue parallel Architecture and University Core Curriculum studies in the first 2-1/2 years, followed by an academic and portfolio review. Students are encouraged to assume increasing responsibility for the choice and direction of their inquiry and career path over time, and to expand their studies into various studio options and topical areas of study at advanced levels. Students are also encouraged to participate in semester-long off-campus learning opportunities in Florence, and Summer Amsterdam or China programs. These provide meaningful contact with significant urban settings and cultural resources.

Graduate studies focus on design excellence in studios led by prominent Visiting Faculty and Visiting Teaching Firms in Residence, complemented by advanced coursework that can be combined into internal concentrations within and beyond the school in Digital Media, Historic Preservation, Sustainable Design, Construction Management, and other areas. Students complete a graduate design thesis as a culminating experience.

AREAS OF FOCUS AND RESEARCH

The School is committed to interdisciplinary, local/global and campus/community connections through various means including at the undergraduate level in required 5-course Core Concentrations in a second area of study, graduate-level M.Arch. Concentration options, the Community Partnerships Initative, and the Center for Macro Projects and Diplomacy. The Community Partnerships Initiative links faculty and student research with community interest and need in the NE region and internationally. The Center for Macro Projects and Diplomacy fosters the interdisciplinary formulation, design, demonstration and debate of large scale project proposals that can contribute to human progress through the improvement of world habitat, through the Macro Studio and Conferences. Faculty research is pursued as it contributes to the advancement of teaching excellence, RWU's primary mission. Areas of faculty interest include regions such as North America, Latin America, the Islamic world, non-Western architecture and culture, transit-oriented development, digital design and manufacturing, sustainable design and development, and historic preservation.

SPECIAL ACTIVITIES AND PROGRAMS

- Public and Special Events Series—12–15 lectures, 4–6 exhibitions, and one major conference annually bring important practitioners and leaders to the School.
- Summer Academy—4-week Career Discovery program for high school students
- Summer Studies in Architecture, Art and Historic Preservation for 80+ undergraduate and graduate students in Architecture, Art and Historic Preservation in multiple studio options
- Visiting Critics Program brings more than 200 practitioners each year for design studio reviews
- Visiting Professor and Teaching—Firm-in-Residence Programs bring leading national and international educators, practicners and firms for semester long studios and seminars
- International Fellows Program brings mid-career professionals together for 2-day Summer conferences with renowned architects and preservationists
- Off-Campus Study Programs in Florence: 20–25 students per semester; Amsterdam or China Programs: 20–25 students in alternate summers
- Career counseling and placement through the School's Futures Access Network (FAN) bringing firms for day-long recruitment visits
- Annual IDP Forum in conjunction with the AIA

Rhode Island, NCARB, and the RWU AIAS chapter.
- Professional Honorary Society/Social Organizations—American Institute of Architecture Students, Art Society, Historic Preservation Club, Tau Sigma Delta Honor Society in Architecture and Allied Arts
- Studio Culture and Inclusive Excellence initiatives develop a remarkable study environment of the school

FACILITIES

Dedicated architecture facilities are provided in Bristol, RI and Florence, Italy. Bristol facilities are housed in an NEA-sponsored original building (1987) containing undergraduate studios and seminar/review spaces, 35-station computer lab, darkroom, workshop, student lounge, and Architecture library containing 11,000 volumes, 70,000 slides, extensive periodicals and consortium access. Building expansion (2005) included graduate studios, Lecture Theater, Exhibition Gallery, Digital Manufacturing Lab, satellite computer areas, and review and seminar spaces located on the main university quadrangle. Florence facilities include classroom and seminar rooms at the Palazzo Rucellai (designed by Alberti), with architecture studio, computer lab, seminar spaces and at the Villa Alammani.

SCHOLARSHIPS AND FINANCIAL AID

Undergraduate Merit-based Presidential, Deans and Transfer Scholarships are available for entering students. Applicants are evaluated based on academic excellence, portfolio and extracurricular activities. Selected freshmen participate in the University Honors Program. Transfer Scholarships are available to graduates of 2-year colleges. Need-based aid includes grants-in-aid, loans, federal work study and University employment opportunities. Graduate merit-based aid includes up to 20 Graduate Assistantships per entering graduate class, in addition to loan opportunities.

The School has multiple endowed scholarships for returning undergraduate and graduate students, including the Paul Arris, Saksena and Shapiro Memorial Scholarships for academic excellence, international students, and Study Abroad. Kaestle Boos Associates and S/L/A/M Collaborative Scholarships are awarded for design excellence and leadership. Students receive numerous annual scholarships from the AIA Rhode Island Forum scholarship fund. The School's Annual Student Honors & Awards provide multiple awards for each of the school's academic programs. Pre-college support includes two full tuition, room and board scholarships awarded annually for high school students enrolled in the 4-week Summer Academy in Architecture.

ADMINISTRATION

Stephen White, AIA: Dean
Okan Ustunkok, PhD: Associate Dean

RYERSON UNIVERSITY

ADDRESS

Main
Ryerson University
Department of Architectural Science
350 Victoria Street
Toronto, Ontario M5B 2K3
CANADA
Tel.: 416/979-5000 x1-6510
Fax: 416.979.5353
www.ryerson.ca/arch

STUDENT AND FACULTY DEMOGRAPHICS

% of Female Students	50
% of International Students	4
% of Minority Students	50
% of Out-of-State U.S. Students	0
No. Full-Time Faculty	27
No. Part-Time Faculty	12
No. Full-Time Students	600
No. Part-Time Students	0

FINANCIAL INFORMATION

Main Source of University Funding	Public
Annual Tuition & Fees (graduate)	
Annual Tuition & Fees (graduate, nonresident)	
Annual Tuition & Fees (undergraduate, resident)	C$6,000
Annual Tuition & Fees (undergraduate, nonresident)	C$13,500
% Students Receiving Federal Financial Aid	
% Students Receiving University Financial Aid	
% Students Receiving Departmental Financial Aid	
% Students Receiving Scholarships (assistantships or fellowships)	
Average Annual Scholarship for Department	

ACADEMIC SESSIONS

Fall Semester: September to December
Winter Quarter/Trimester: January to April

ARCHITECTURE AND RELATED DEGREE PROGRAMS

Degree	Min. Yrs. to Complete	Professional Accreditation	# of FT Students	# of PT Students	# of First-Year Students	# of Degrees Conferred	Admissions Requirements
Architecture							
Bachelor of Architectural Science	4		600	0	112		Undergraduate degree, Portfolio, Essay
Masters of Architectural Science	2	CACB Candidate	50	0	21		Undergraduate Architecture degree, Portfolio, Rec. Letters
Construction Management/Technology							
Masters of Building Science	2		24	0	24		Portfolio, Rec. Letters, Essay

SPECIALIZATIONS

Architectural Design
Building Technology/Env. Systems

Computer-Aided Design
Environment/Sustainability

International Development
Landscape Design

Professional Practice
Sustainability

ARCHITECTURE PROGRAM SUMMARY

Founded in 1948 and housed in a Ron Thom-designed facility located in the heart of downtown Toronto, the Department of Architectural Science features a diverse, multidisciplinary faculty dedicated to the pursuit of integrated, more sustainable approaches to the design and development of the built environment. The Department offers a pre-professional degree with options in Architecture, Building Science, and Project Management, and graduate programs in Architecture (M.Arch) and Building Science (MBSc/MASc).

UNIVERSITY SETTING

Ryerson University is located in downtown Toronto, where the skyline is constantly changing. Students witness this progress by taking field trips to notable sites and buildings. The dynamic and multicultural urban setting provides tremendous access to community partners, potential clients, practicing professionals, seminars, conferences and trade shows.

SCHOOL PHILOSOPHY

The Department of Architectural Science provides education for a wide range of professional roles in the design, construction and management of the built environment by developing, enhancing and maintaining undergraduate, graduate and certification programs of applied study, and research in the areas of design, building science, project management and landscape. The program prepares professionals for leadership roles in the AEC industry in the Toronto area, Canada, and internationally by focusing on the development of fundamental skills, knowledge and critical judgment necessary for effective participation in a complex, collaborative, cross-disciplinary workplace. The programs foster a comprehensive vision of architecture as a social, technical, political, and cultural practice in the context of sustainability and evolving environmental and societal needs, and to utilize our combined expertise for the benefit of the larger community. The department cultivates an environment conducive to lifelong learning and the pursuit of scholarly, research and creative activity by faculty and students.

The M.Arch program believes that in addition to possessing strong technical skills, today's practitioners must be strong, independent, critical thinkers, who nonetheless are comfortable acting in an increasingly collaborative industry. By focusing on a critical study of architectural practice, both in its contemporary forms and in its future potential, Ryerson's program provides students with the opportunities for intellectual growth needed to develop these leadership faculties in the profession and society.

PROGRAM DESCRIPTION

The goal of the Bachelor of Architectural Science (B. Arch.Sci) program is to educate students for a wide range of professional roles in the construction industry. The program emphasizes studies in design theory, technology, and management. The long-standing reputation of the program rests in part on this unique emphasis of the curriculum. The first three years of the program (in the *revised* curriculum) provide students with a common foundation. The final year offers three different options, Architecture, Building Science and Project Management. The initial years place students in a position to make informed choices of option, and they are encouraged to do so as early as possible. The *revised* curriculum is structured around four themes: introduction and context, preparation (tools and elements), integration and concentration/specialization/transition. The first semester provides students with an introduction and sets the context for their education in architectural science. Semesters two, three and four prepare students for advanced studies through an exploration of the tools and elements necessary for further studies. Semesters six and seven provide a comprehensive integration of the multiple components of an undergraduate education in architectural science. In the final two semesters, students select from one of the three options available—architecture, building science or project management—and undertake intensive work in their chosen specialization.

In addition, the program requires a number of courses in liberal studies, as well as a range of professional electives, offered by the Department and other Departments at the University and the application of this knowledge to the solution of a wide range of architectural and environmental problems. The architectural science program promotes an integrated approach to architectural science, through studio and lecture courses. Students have the opportunity to apply theory learned in the lecture courses to studio projects which engage with real-life problems in design, construction, management and the environment. As enrollment in each program option may be limited, placement of students in fourth year program options, is determined by academic performance to best suit their career goals and academic strengths.

AREAS OF FOCUS AND RESEARCH

Architectural Science faculty members are known nationally and internationally for their research expertise, and they bring their specialized knowledge into the classroom. There are five primary areas of research in the department.

Sustainability and Building Technologies: Faculty members have expertise in the area of performance evaluation and building envelope systems for residential buildings. Other areas of interest are architectural acoustical modeling and noise control. Several faculty members are internationally known in energy efficient housing, the benefits of thermal mass, and the reuse of building materials, along with research into areas of green roofing, and the performance and durability of envelope components. Other faculty members study building services engineering, building automation and management, simulation of building systems, structural design and material durability.

New Media and the Virtual World: Several faculty members explore representation pertaining to seeing and thinking through digital and analog media exploration. This area of research experiments with new and emerging digital technologies and investigates relationships between media and design process.

Conducting the Construction Project: The department offers optional studies in project construction management. The faculty members' expertise and renown extends to building economics and productivity assessment, construction project management, construction site layout, and dynamic systems modeling.

Innovative and Collaborative Architectural Practice: Our faculty members bring expertise of the profession of architecture into their teaching with award winning architectural practice. They explore the built environment through aspects of practice and project management, and architectural design through competitions and housing strategies. These researchers explore materials and methods of construction, the role of glass and sound in architecture, and the future of practice with the study of innovative and collaborative practice.

Globalization and Culture: Numerous faculty members have widely respected research into the history, theory, and criticism of architecture. Several study conservation and preservation pertaining to the heritage and culture of communities, the relationships between housing and urbanism, pedagogy and design process, contemporary and postwar Canadian architecture, architectural models and sketches, and historical Brazilian architecture.

SPECIAL ACTIVITIES AND PROGRAMS

The department participates in an exchange program with the Fochhochschule in Frankfurt-am-Main, and other study tours to Israel, Europe and Pakistan. Additionally, the fourth year option studio provides opportunities for study in other foreign locations. The graduate program requires a spring/summer research studio comprised of either foreign or Canadian travel. The student chapters of the Architecture Course Union, American Institute of Architecture Students, the Ryerson Student Chapter of the Project Management Institute, and the Ontario Institute of Quantity Surveyors are particularly active. The department regularly encourages design/build construction projects and the publication of the student magazine, *325*. Regularly students travel on field trips to cities such as Montreal, New York City and areas in the Toronto region to study contemporary and historic architecture.

FACILITIES

The Department of Architectural Science has occupied its present building on the Ryerson University campus, designed by the Thom Partnership, since 1984. The building holds studios, a computer lab, a workshop for wood and metals, a digital fabrication lab, building science lab, REALab, spaces for research and simulation, Resource Center, classrooms, and faculty member and administrative offices.

SCHOLARSHIPS AND FINANCIAL AID

OSAP is based on financial need as determined through an assessment of your application. Educational costs and the resources OSAP expects you (and your family, if applicable) to contribute, are taken into consideration.

ADMINISTRATION

Colin Ripley: Graduate Program Director, M.Arch.
Kendra Smith: Chair

SAVANNAH COLLEGE OF ART AND DESIGN

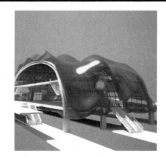

SCAD

ADDRESS

Main
Savannah College of Art and Design
School of Building Arts
229 Martin Luther King Blvd.
PO Box 3146
Savannah, GA 31402-3146
Tel.: 912.525.6861
www.scad.edu

STUDENT AND FACULTY DEMOGRAPHICS

% of Female Students	42
% of International Students	14
% of Minority Students	9
% of Out-of-State U.S. Students	72
No. Full-Time Faculty	28
No. Part-Time Faculty	3
No. Full-Time Students	356
No. Part-Time Students	75

FINANCIAL INFORMATION

Main Source of University Funding	Private
Annual Tuition & Fees (graduate)	$24,840
Annual Tuition & Fees (undergraduate)	$24,390
% Students Receiving Federal Financial Aid	
% Students Receiving University Financial Aid	
% Students Receiving Departmental Financial Aid	
% Students Receiving Scholarships (assistantships or fellowships)	
Average Annual Scholarship for Department	

ACADEMIC SESSIONS

Fall Quarter/Trimester: September to November; Application Deadline: Rolling deadline
Winter Quarter/Trimester: January to March; Application Deadline: Rolling deadline

Spring Quarter/Trimester: March to May; Application Deadline: Rolling deadline
Summer Session I: June to August; Application Deadline: Rolling deadline

ARCHITECTURE AND RELATED DEGREE PROGRAMS

Degree	Min. Yrs. to Complete	Professional Accreditation	# of FT Students	# of PT Students	# of First-Year Students	# of Degrees Conferred	Admissions Requirements
Architecture							
BFA in Architecture	4		300		35	55	SAT, ACT, TOEFL
M. Arch	2	NAAB	102			24	Undergraduate Architecture degree, Portfolio, Rec. Letters, Essay
Interior Design/Interior Architecture							
BFA in Interior Design	4		216	0	12	24	SAT, ACT, TOEFL
MFA in Interior Design	2		55			22	Undergraduate degree, TOEFL, Portfolio, Rec. Letters, Essay
Historic Preservation							
BFA Historic Preservation	4		80		5		SAT
M.A. in Historic Preservation							
Urban Design							
Master of Urban Design	2		17			8	Undergraduate Architecture degree, Prof. Architecture degree, TOEFL, Portfolio, Rec. Letters, Essay

SPECIALIZATIONS

Architectural Design
Art and Design
Building Information Modeling
Building Technology/Env. Systems

Computer-Aided Design
Environment/Sustainability
Interior Design Architecture

International/Regional Architecture
Preservation
Professional Practice

Sustainability
Tectonics
Urban Planning and Design

ARCHITECTURE PROGRAM SUMMARY

The Savannah College of Art and Design is a private, nonprofit, accredited institution with locations in Savannah, Atlanta, and in Lacoste, France. SCAD's School of Building Arts includes the departments of architecture, interior design, and historic preservation. The school is committed to global awareness and creative excellence in design. SCAD offers a pre-professional BFA, a professional M. Arch., and post-professional architecture degrees. Off-campus programs are held in major international cities and at the SCAD campus in

Lacoste, France. The college provides a unique opportunity to pursue minors in electronic design, urban design, architectural history, historic preservation, cultural landscape, and interior design.

UNIVERSITY SETTING

SCAD exists to prepare talented students for professional careers, emphasizing learning through individual attention in a positively oriented university environment. The goal of the college is to nurture and cultivate the unique qualities of each student through an inter-

esting curriculum, in an inspiring environment, under the leadership of involved professors. SCAD offers 38 majors and minors and awards Bachelor of Fine Arts, Master of Architecture, Master of Arts, and Master of Fine Arts degrees. The international faculty and student body have come from each of the 50 U.S. states and from more than 80 countries. Class sizes at SCAD are kept small to allow each student to receive individual attention from the faculty. Located in the Southeast coastal region of the United States and served by the Savannah-Hilton Head international airport, SCAD Savannah Campus is in close proximity to natural and historic sites and landscapes, yet well connected to major metropolitan areas. The semi-tropical conditions of the region provide mild climate and rich vegetation, which contribute to the unique built environment of the city of Savannah. The urban campus of SCAD in historic Savannah is composed mostly of renovated buildings that are fully integrated with the city's pedestrian friendly fabric. The architecturally rich setting of Savannah's Historic District is an ideal living laboratory for architecture and design students. The city streets, squares, and residential and public places are based on one of the most admired urban plans in the world. Because students experience the architecture and the city plan directly, they develop an intuitive understanding of the built environment. The college has been a recognized leader in restoring and adaptively reusing many of the city's architectural treasures.

SCAD's School of Building Arts includes the departments of architecture, interior design, and historic preservation which offer both undergraduate and graduate degree programs in the three fields in addition to courses in urban design, electronic design, and cultural landscape.

SCHOOL PHILOSOPHY

Architectural education at SCAD continues to be responsive to the challenges posed by architecture as a discipline and as a profession in the United States and around the world. The architecture department remains agile and flexible to face global environmental, economic, technological, social, and cultural realities of the 21st century.The school is committed to design excellence—to build a nationally recognized scholarship agenda in art and design, digital technology and design, sustainable design and interdisciplinary design.

The school mandates global awareness—to educate our students to establish a humanistic understanding of architecture and related disciplines and their relationship to a broader global perspective.

The school demands critical thinking—to facilitate and foster our students' ability to engage in multiple modes of thinking through their architectural education and apply such thinking to a wide range of challenges and opportunities.

The school advances ethical values—to commit to a holistic education which encompasses honoring of a social contract to advance basic human values. It includes life-long learning and the application of that knowledge to a richer, fuller life for our students as future practitioners and professionals.

The school builds on communication skills— to prepare our students with the necessary means, methods, and attitudes to be effective communicators while pursuing many spheres of creative activity.

The school promotes leadership—to provide a strong and instrumental relationship with the profession to educate our students for leadership roles in future practice.

PROGRAM DESCRIPTION

The architecture programs at the Savannah College of Art and Design offer pre-professional, professional, and post-professional architectural education with a core emphasis on creative design. The architecture department adopts a philosophy that encourages diverse approaches to design within a comprehensive and well-structured sequence of studio courses. This philosophy is supported by academically and professionally diverse faculty members who, in turn, bring diversity to the design studio and to the department as a whole. Each

studio instructor develops a unique approach to design, and utilizes his or her own special expertise in architectural theory, practice, or research. The professional and academic background of the faculty covers a wide range of activities in major architectural firms and in prominent educational and research institutions around the United States and in many other countries. Students are encouraged to diversify their learning experience by taking studio courses with a different instructor each academic term.The five-year professional architecture program is accredited by NAAB and leads to the professional M. Arch. degree. Students begin with a strong foundation of core courses in art, design, and liberal arts. They continue with major program courses in architectural theory, structures, construction technology, environmental control, computer-aided design, and architectural practice. The M. Arch. curriculum has the design studio sequence at its core. A series of architectural design studio courses allows students to produce projects of increasing complexity and scope. Each studio has an emphasis on an interrelated set of theoretical issues that gradually lead to a comprehensive design studio experience. Students engage in realistic problem solving and investigate theoretical issues in a variety of environmental and urban settings, ranging from the unique historic city of Savannah to major urban and natural settings around the world. As a culmination of their graduate course of study, students devise and solve their own architectural design thesis project.

The post-professional Master's program is designed to fulfill the needs of students with professional degrees in architecture or an equivalent professional and academic background. The program provides opportunities for these students to develop a special focus in architecture such as electronic design. The power of the computer as an analytical tool is a key component of graduate education in architecture.

AREAS OF FOCUS AND RESEARCH

The post-professional program at SCAD is intended to expand its mission beyond the satisfaction of typical professional architectural education to embrace computation technology and building information modeling (BIM). Students explore the role of this relatively new technology in architectural design and practice. And, while architectural theory and design remain the core of the program, the role of electronic design tools and information technology in architectural education, research, and practice is carefully considered. Students are expected to go beyond learning about the computer as a design and communication tool to explore how the age of information technology can help in making more informed design decisions.

Graduate seminars focus on architectural research in a broad sense and how it relates to architectural design and practice. The seminars also explore the theoretical aspects of information technology as they relate to the discipline and profession of architecture in a digital society.

SPECIAL ACTIVITIES AND PROGRAMS

The Savannah College of Art and Design offers off-campus programs in major cities in the United States, Canada, Europe, Asia, and Australia. SCAD also offers periodic building arts courses at the SCAD campus in Lacoste, France. The college provides a unique opportunity to pursue a minor in electronic design or an additional degree in architectural history, historic preservation, or interior design to strengthen the architecture student's credentials. Architecture student organiza-

tions include the American Institute of Architecture Students, Tau Sigma Delta honor society, and the American Society of Heating, Refrigeration and Air Conditioning Engineers. Architecture students also work with the college chapter of Habitat for Humanity, the Savannah chapter of the US Green Building Council, the AIA Young Architects group, and with various community organizations.

The office of career planning and placement provides career development and professional job search assistance to both students and alumni, advertising job openings, scheduling on-campus interviews with employers, and placing students in campus work-study positions. A strong English-as-a-Second-Language program and dedicated international student–services staff assist international students. Rising Star, a unique five-week residential summer program for rising high school seniors, allows qualified students to earn 10 hours of college credit that may be applied toward a baccalaureate degree at the Savannah College of Art and Design or at other colleges and universities.

FACILITIES

The Savannah College of Art and Design architecture department is housed in Eichberg Hall, a three-story Romanesque-style building built in 1887. The building and attached sheds contain approximately 70,000 square-feet of space and feature high ceilings, loft offices, tall windows with stained glass, and red brick and terra cotta ornamentation. The college has carefully restored the former Central of Georgia Railroad building, adapting it to contain spacious studios and state-of-the-art instructional classrooms and laboratories. A client/server network system connects a large number of PCs configured with a diverse range of electronic design software, including AutoCAD, Revit, Microstation, 3D Studio-Viz, and Adobe Photoshop and InDesign CS3. A fully integrated and wireless intranet system offers on-line help, downloadable supplemental material, and other information. Black Board software provides online instruction to support classroom teaching. The CIAD computer laboratory network serves all design studios, which are also served by a Laser-cutting-equipped model making shop and a project photography room.

SCHOLARSHIPS AND FINANCIAL AID

The Savannah College of Art and Design offers a comprehensive financial aid program, as well as undergraduate scholarships and graduate fellowships. United States citizens and legal residents may apply for financial aid by first completing an application for admission to the college. Financial aid options include federal grants, state grants, federal loans, federal college work-study earned funds, and veterans educational benefits. Undergraduate scholarships are offered based on SAT/ACT scores, competitions, and other criteria such as portfolio strength. Scholarships are also offered to high school valedictorians, National Merit finalists or semifinalists, Governor's Honors or Governor's Schools participants, and Congressional Art Competition for High School Students participants, upon acceptance to SCAD. Graduate fellowships are offered based on GRE scores and portfolio presentation. In addition, two specific architecture scholarships are offered, one based on grade point average and the other on portfolio excellence.

ADMINISTRATION

Brian Wishne: Dean
Scott R. Singeisen: Department Chair

SCHOOL OF THE ART INSTITUTE OF CHICAGO

ADDRESS

Main
School of the Art Institute of Chicago
Department of Architecture, Interior
Architecture, and Designed Objects
36 S. Wabash Ave. #1257
Chicago, IL 60603
Tel.: 312.629.6650
Fax: 312.578.0960
www.saic.edu

STUDENT AND FACULTY DEMOGRAPHICS

% of Female Students	50
% of International Students	4
% of Minority Students	4
% of Out-of-State U.S. Students	80
No. Full-Time Faculty	13
No. Part-Time Faculty	20
No. Full-Time Students	80
No. Part-Time Students	4

FINANCIAL INFORMATION

Main Source of University Funding	Private
Annual Tuition & Fees (graduate)	$32,550
Annual Tuition & Fees (undergraduate)	
% Students Receiving Federal Financial Aid	70
% Students Receiving University Financial Aid	70
% Students Receiving Departmental Financial Aid	0
% Students Receiving Scholarships (assistantships or fellowships)	30
Average Annual Scholarship for Department	

ACADEMIC SESSIONS

Fall Semester: August to December;
Application Deadline: February 1

Spring Semester: January to May;
Application Deadline: February 1

ARCHITECTURE AND RELATED DEGREE PROGRAMS							
Degree	**Min. Yrs. to Complete**	**Professional Accreditation**	**# of FT Students**	**# of PT Students**	**# of First-Year Students**	**# of Degrees Conferred**	**Admissions Requirements**
Architecture							
M. Arch with Emphasis in Interior Architecture Option II	2	NAAB Candidate	6	0	4	0	Undergraduate Architecture degree, TOEFL, Portfolio, Rec. Letters, Essay
M. Arch with Emphasis in Interior Architecture	3	NAAB Candidate	40	2	14	0	Undergraduate degree, TOEFL, Rec. Letters, Essay
M. Arch	3	NAAB Candidate	40	0	14	0	Undergraduate degree, TOEFL, Rec. Letters, Essay
M. Arch Option II	2	NAAB Candidate	6	0	3	0	Undergraduate Architecture degree, TOEFL, Portfolio, Rec. Letters, Essay
Interior Design/Interior Architecture							
Bachelor of Interior Architecture	4		75	5	20	10	Portfolio, Rec. Letters
Master of Fine Arts, Emphasis in Emerging Technologies	2		12	1	6	6	Undergraduate Architecture degree, Prof. Architecture degree, TOEFL, Portfolio, Rec. Letters, Essay
Historic Preservation							
Master of Science in Historic Preservation	2		28	2	14	14	Undergraduate degree, Portfolio, Rec. Letters, Essay
Industrial Design							
Master of Design In Designed Objects	2		26	2	14	12	Undergraduate degree, Undergraduate Architecture degree, TOEFL, Portfolio, Rec. Letters, Essay

SPECIALIZATIONS

Architectural Design	Community Design	History	Sustainability
Art and Design	Computer-Aided Design	Interior Design/Architecture	Theory/Criticism
Building Information Modeling	Environment/Sustainability	Photography	Urban Planning and Design
Building Technology/Env. Systems	Graphic Design	Preservation	

ARCHITECTURE PROGRAM SUMMARY

The School of the Art Institute of Chicago offers students the chance to study architecture and design within the context of a major urban fine arts museum school. Trans-disciplinary work is the norm at SAIC, leading to a very wide array of full-scale making activities and theoretical investigations.

UNIVERSITY SETTING

SAIC's Department of Architecture, Interior Architecture, and Designed Objects is located at the geographic center of Chicago, at State and Madison Streets, with brand-new studios and shops on the top floor of the historic, recently renovated 1896 Schlessinger and Meyer store by Louis Sullivan. Two state of the art studio dormitories are located within one block of the studios, and the world famous Burnham and Ryerson Libraries are located in the Museum of the Art Institute two blocks east. Buildings of the famous first and second Chicago School of Architecture form a spectacular panorama right outside the wide Chicago windows under Sullivan's beautiful cantilevered terra cotta cornice.

SCHOOL PHILOSOPHY

Students are encouraged to take chances, to work on things that might seem impossible, and ultimately develop individual voices that can offer the value of design and architecture to a wide and diverse population. We expect engagement with the most trying issues of the day, deep innovative research, and a willingness to work with partners offering leverage and opportunity.

Our goal is to take design and architecture out into the world where they can offer hope in the face of environmental and political crisis.

PROGRAM DESCRIPTION

The School of the Art Institute offers four specific professional Master of Architecture tracks, all of which have official NAAB candidacy status as of 2007:
1. Emphasis in Architecture (3 years).
2. Emphasis in Interior Architecture (3 years).
3. Emphasis in Architecture Option II (2 years, requiring a pre-professional bachelor's degree).
4. Emphasis in Interior Architecrture Option II (2 years, requiring a pre-professional bachelor's degree).

AREAS OF FOCUS AND RESEARCH

Students choose the School of the Art Institute for their professional architectural studies because of the school's world-class fine arts facilities, including a general emphasis in sustainable design, and highly accessible faculty members with every expertise imaginable. Historic Preservation, Interior Architecture, Emerging Technologies, and the urban landscape arts are among the many areas of focus particular to the professional study of architecture at the School of the Art Institute of Chicago. A certificate in Historic Preservation can be earned at the same time as a Master of Architecture degree.

SPECIAL ACTIVITIES AND PROGRAMS

The Motorola-endowed GFRY studio offers advanced students a dedicated studio and funds to make functional prototypes in the fields of architecture and design, and then take them out into the world of commerce and industry for manufacture and marketing. Recent GFRY studios have sent students and their realized projects to the ICFF in New York (Best in Show) and the Salon di Mobile, and Industreale in Milan.

Bruce Mau's Design's Center for Massive Change offers SAIC students the chance to work in teams on projects that will directly affect the design of new sustainable urban systems, and the climate of desire that will encourage citizens of Chicago to adopt them.

FACILITIES

Students of Architecture, Interior Architecture, and Designed Objects work side by side in dedicated graduate studios. Students use personal Macintosh Powerbook Pros with a standard school template of both Mac and Windows operating systems, and a variety of specialized architectural software programs. A large, brand-new, and fully equipped furniture shop is on the same floor as the studios, including a CNC router, a vacuformer, a lost-wax mold maker, an ABS rapid prototyper, 2 laser cutters, large-scale 2D and 3D scanners, and 36" wide color and black and white printers.

ADMINISTRATION

Hennie Reynders: Department Chair
Anders Nereim, AIA: Program Director

SOUTHERN CALIFORNIA INSTITUTE OF ARCHITECTURE

ADDRESS

Main
Southern California Institute of
Architecture
960 E. Third Street
Los Angeles, CA 90013
Tel.: 213.613.2200
Fax: 213.613.2260
admissions@sciarc.edu
www.sciarc.edu

STUDENT AND FACULTY DEMOGRAPHICS

% of Female Students	40
% of International Students	31
% of Minority Students	30
% of Out-of-State U.S. Students	68
No. Full-Time Faculty	0
No. Part-Time Faculty	80
No. Full-Time Students	500
No. Part-Time Students	0

FINANCIAL INFORMATION

Main Source of University Funding	Private
Annual Tuition & Fees (graduate)	$22,690
Annual Tuition & Fees (undergraduate)	$22,690
% Students Receiving Federal Financial Aid	80
% Students Receiving University Financial Aid	
% Students Receiving Departmental Financial Aid	
% Students Receiving Scholarships (assistantships or fellowships)	
Average Annual Scholarship for Department	

ACADEMIC SESSIONS

Fall Semester: September to December
Spring Semester: January to April

Summer Session I: May to August

ARCHITECTURE AND RELATED DEGREE PROGRAMS

Degree	Min. Yrs. to Complete	Professional Accreditation	# of FT Students	# of PT Students	# of First-Year Students	# of Degrees Conferred	Admissions Requirements
Architecture							
B. Arch	5	NAAB	260	0	50		SAT, ACT, TOEFL, Portfolio, Rec. Letters, Essay
M. Arch 1	3	NAAB	157	0	50		Undergraduate degree, GRE, TOEFL, Portfolio, Rec. Letters, Essay
M. Arch 2	2	NAAB	72	0	38		Undergraduate Architecture degree, GRE, TOEFL, Portfolio, Rec. Letters, Essay
Other							
Master of Design Research, Specialization in Media	1		10	0	10		Undergraduate degree, TOEFL, Portfolio, Rec. Letters, Essay
Master of Design Research, Specialization in Urban Research	1		10	0	10		Undergraduate degree, TOEFL, Portfolio, Rec. Letters, Essay

UNIVERSITY SETTING

With its location in the intensely urban Artist District in Downtown Los Angeles, SCI-Arc provides students with a uniquely inspiring environment in which to study architecture. SCI-Arc's home in a renovated, quarter-milelong railway freight depot is set in the cultural hub of a city with a tradition of architectural experimentation. The school is distinguished by the vibrant atmosphere of its studios, where students and faculty work together in a fluid, nonhierarchicial manner, re-examining assumptions and exploring and testing new ideas through making. The school is an integral part of downtown L.A.'s emerging cultural center, which includes the Museum of Contemporary Art (MOCA), the Japanese American Museum, and the Geffen Contemporary, as well as major new works of architecture, such as Rafael Moneo's new cathedral and the Disney Concert Hall by Frank Gehry.

SCHOOL PHILOSOPHY

The pedagogical focus of the undergraduate and graduate programs at SCI-Arc is not on any single style, technique, or method of design, but on a comprehensive and flexible approach to the practice of architecture. Students develop a framework with which to test both their own intellectual and design convictions, and the limits of the architectural profession. This framework of inquiry, experimentation, and making is developed as students advance through a series of core studios that are integrally linked to critical courses in history and theory, the humanities, technology, professional practice, and the visual arts.

PROGRAM DESCRIPTION
Undergraduate Program

SCI-Arc's undergraduate program is structured to educate students to practice architecture at the highest level. It is recognized nationally and internationally for its breadth and substance, as well as its experimental approach to architectural design. The five-year, first-professional Bachelor of Architecture (B.Arch) program is accredited by the Western Association of Schools and Colleges (WASC) and the National Architectural Accreditation Board (NAAB). The program is built around an integrated core of design studio, visual studies, history and theory, and technology courses, into which interdisciplinary seminars in the arts, sciences, and humanities are woven. Following the core sequence are upper-division courses in professional practice and building technology, advanced specialized studios, and a final comprehensive design project. Over five years of study, students become familiar with digital environments as well as the material and physical worlds. SCI-Arc students are prepared and confident upon graduation to participate in leading architectural practices, independent practice, as well as in other design-related fields.

Students entering the program come from various backgrounds: transfer students enter the school from other two- or four-year colleges, while graduated high school students enter the first year of the program. The undergraduate student body is a diverse population ranging in age, education, and professional background.

Graduate Program

SCI-Arc's graduate studies foster the school's open-ended spirit of inquiry, responding to shifts in society, technology and culture with a constantly evolving learning environment in which faculty and advanced-level students work together to move toward the next generation of the architectural discipline. The programs are led by a faculty of practitioners and scholars actively engaged in contemporary architectural discourse and production worldwide, working in fields ranging from design and engineering, to visual and cultural studies. Through the feedback they provide from their own practices, the graduate curriculum is continuously and dynamically shaped in a manner only available to an institution entirely devoted to architecture. The graduate programs promote cross-pollination from other fields of study in a critical manner, with a practice that derives from an emphasis on process and a synthesis of thinking, inquiry and execution. With a diverse and international student body, the graduate programs at SCI-Arc provide a rigorous architectural education that promotes experimentation and creative freedom, and is at once global and local, comprehensive and current. In pursuit of these goals, the graduate programs offer four study options: the three-year M.Arch 1 program, the two-year M.Arch 2 program and the one-year SCIFI and MediaSCAPES programs.

AREAS OF FOCUS AND RESEARCH

SCI-Arc has sought opportunities to engage the various communities within and surrounding downtown Los Angeles by spearheading a number of tactical, action-based projects, which enable students to collaborate directly with community agencies, and undertake design/build projects. Each project deals with some form of practical and urgent problem-solving circumstance. Drawing upon the professional expertise of architects, urban planners, computer designers, visual artists, social scientists, cultural theorists, and others, SCI-Arc faculty and students have demonstrated a powerful capacity to impact specific social problems, working intentionally with short lead-times and reacting quickly to address immediate conditions. Whether coordinating with local government, city or community agencies, private industry, educational or philanthropic institutions, or local residents, SCI-Arc's Community Programs are known for applying solutions that are at once uniquely innovative and personally felt.

SPECIAL ACTIVITIES AND PROGRAMS

The school offers students the opportunity to travel and study in foreign countries and other parts of the United States by participating in travelling studios, faculty lead field trips, and international exchange programs. In addition, students have the opportunity to participate in SCI-Arc's European Program (SCI-Arc: Vico) taught in Switzerland that offers an intensive study of architecture under teachers and architects form Europe and the United States.

Making + Meaning is a rigorous five-week summer workshop where students develop essential architectural skills and sensitivities through studio projects, seminars, lectures, field trips, and discussions.

The SCI-Arc Lecture Series invites an eclectic selection of lecturers from multiple disciplines including architects, artists, engineers, theoreticians, and performers. The SCI-Arc Gallery exhibits unique, site-specific installations by architects, and provides a space where practitioners, professionals, faculty, students, and the public can learn about and experience provocative architecture.

FACILITIES

SCI-Arc offers facilities that encourage research, exploration, and experimentation. The Information Technology Department includes three computer labs and a print center. Our Wood and Metal Shop is equipped with hand and power tools and includes a machining room, a model-making shop, bench room, metalworking area, assembly space, a laser cutter, Computer Numeric Control (CNC) milling machines, and 3-D printers. The Kappe Library and Media Center maintains a collection of 30,000 books, a slide collection of 35,000 historic architectural images, and an archive of student work, and includes nine computer workstations used for scanning and video transfer. The SCI-Arc Supply Store, a student-developed project, sells architecture and art supplies, textbooks and readers, and a wide selection of model-making materials and structural shapes.

SCHOLARSHIPS AND FINANCIAL AID

Need-based financial assistance in the form of grants and/or loans is available to qualified students who are citizens or permanent residents of the United States. Eligible international students may apply for private educational loans. A limited number of scholarships are awarded to entering students with exceptional academic backgrounds and who demonstrate potential to excel at SCI-Arc. After completing two semesters of study at the school, continuing students are eligible to apply for internal scholarships.

ADMINISTRATION

Eric Owen Moss: Director
Hsin-Ming Fung: Graduate Program Head

SOUTHERN ILLINOIS UNIVERSITY

ADDRESS

Main
Southern Illinois University
School of Architecture
410 Quigley Hall MC 4337
875 S. Normal Avenue
Carbondale, IL 62901-4303
Tel.: 618-453-3734
www.siuc.edu/~arc_id

STUDENT AND FACULTY DEMOGRAPHICS

% of Female Students	26
% of International Students	4
% of Minority Students	18
% of Out-of-State U.S. Students	8
No. Full-Time Faculty	15
No. Part-Time Faculty	7
No. Full-Time Students	256
No. Part-Time Students	11

FINANCIAL INFORMATION

Main Source of University Funding	Public
Annual Tuition & Fees (graduate)	$6,125
Annual Tuition & Fees (graduate, nonresident)	$13,187
Annual Tuition & Fees (undergraduate, resident)	$4,907
Annual Tuition & Fees (undergraduate, nonresident)	$10,138
% Students Receiving Federal Financial Aid	44
% Students Receiving University Financial Aid	70
% Students Receiving Departmental Financial Aid	10
% Students Receiving Scholarships (assistantships or fellowships)	20
Average Annual Scholarship for Department	$4,118

ACADEMIC SESSIONS

Fall Semester: August to December; Application Deadline: March 1
Spring Semester: January to May; Application Deadline: NA

Summer Session I: June to August; Application Deadline: NA

ARCHITECTURE AND RELATED DEGREE PROGRAMS

Degree	Min. Yrs. to Complete	Professional Accreditation	# of FT Students	# of PT Students	# of First-Year Students	# of Degrees Conferred	Admissions Requirements
Architecture							
BS in Architectural Studies	4		256	11	63	33	ACT
M. Arch	1	NAAB Candidate	17	0	17	8	Undergraduate degree, Undergraduate Architecture degree, TOEFL, Portfolio, Rec. Letters, Essay

SPECIALIZATIONS

Architectural Design
Building Technology/Env. Systems
Community Design

Computer-Aided Design
Energy
History

Interior Design/Architecture
Preservation

Professional Practice
Urban Planning and Design

ARCHITECTURE PROGRAM SUMMARY

Through our cultural heritage, environmental context and the tradition of integrating emerging technology and innovative practice, the Architecture faculty and students explore, create and develop architecture as a synthesis of design excellence, artistic expression, technology and community involvement.

UNIVERSITY SETTING

From its humble beginnings as the state's second teachers college—founded in 1869 with a dozen academic departments and an inaugural class of 143—Southern Illinois University Carbondale now ranks among Illinois' most comprehensive public universities. Each year, we welcome students from all 50 states and more than 100 countries who take advantage of outstanding academic programs as they pursue associate, bachelor's, master's, doctoral and professional degrees in law, medicine, and architecture.

SCHOOL PHILOSOPHY

The School of Architecture provides design education and vision from three perspectives, Architecture, Fashion Merchandising and Design, and Interior Design. Three undergraduate programs and a professional master's program in Architecture are constituted to provide the framework for study. While these three disciplines are closely related, each affects the environment differently: in fashion, the immediate or clothing environment; in interior design, the spaces that we live in and use on a daily basis; and in architecture, the buildings and places that give breath and substance to our lives and the cultures they create.

Our faculty is committed to challenging students in the diverse aspects of design and fabrication as appropriate to the disciplinary focus of the careers housed in the School. In addition, we all strive to be responsive to the region of the world we inhabit, the Mississippi River Delta, a unique, powerfully important, culturally distinctive, economically diverse place, in effect, the torso of the nation, with the river as its spine. We are especially attuned to the needs and desires of the people of our region. We know, as we address their aspirations through study and important work as faculty and students, we will positively impact other such regions of the nation and world that are similar in context.

This is our commitment, and it is coupled with our promise to prepare students for a challenging and rewarding career.

PROGRAM DESCRIPTION

The four-year curriculum in architectural studies offers the beginning level of education for those who intend to pursue a career in the profession or a related field. A structured sequencing of courses is included which provides for a gradual interactive development of required knowledge and skills. This pre-professional preparation is combined with the core curriculum courses to provide a comprehensive scholarly foundation for advancement. Graduates are prepared to immediately become productive employees or to pursue graduate degrees.

AREAS OF FOCUS AND RESEARCH

The faculty in the School of Architecture is as diverse as the student body. Representing three continents and with more than 300 years of combined teaching experience, the faculty will teach you to think critically about the built environment and architecture. Seventy percent of the faculty members are licensed architects and they hold advanced degrees in architecture and other disciplines as well.

Particular interests of the faculty focus on the architecture of the Heartland River Delta Region, Non-Western architecture and the development and implementation of technology in architecture. Opportunities to work with faculty from other disciplines including Interior Design and Fashion Design are readily available.

SPECIAL ACTIVITIES AND PROGRAMS

Architecture and Interior Design majors can take advantage of this unique opportunity that encourages student interaction and provides a living and studying environment focused on similar interests and study habits. Students on these floors have access to common study areas, a limited number of drafting tables, and a small reference library.

Currently the student organizations include the American Institute of Architecture Students, Illuminating Engineers Society, Precast Concrete Institute, and the Construction Specifications Institute. These organizations provide students the opportunity to pursue leadership roles, develop contacts with the profession and take advantage of various activities which include field trips, guest speakers and workshops.

Support services include career services, disability support services, tutoring services for first-year students and mentoring programs. Additional activities include the University Honors Program, travel study programs, workshops, guest lectures, co-op and extern opportunities.

FACILITIES

Dedicated studios located in Quigley Hall are provided for all sophomores, juniors and seniors in the program. Students are issued 24-hour building passes and a studio key. The large open space studios encourage student interaction and provide informal jury presentation space. Quigley Hall is equipped with wireless internet access.

The program's resource library/exhibition area is located in Quigley Hall. The resource library supplements Morris Library, the main campus library. It contains a collection of reference books, manufacturers' catalogs, magazines, and material samples. It also contains computer stations that provide access to the internet, inter-library searches and design-related data warehouses. The exhibition area displays current student work.

The program's computer graphics lab is a modern well-equipped facility. It provides access to an array of peripheral equipment that includes printers, scanners, and plotters. Our software subscription provides access to the latest releases of a full range of profession-related software applications.

The program's model and furniture shop is located in the "Blue Barracks," which is a short distance from Quigley Hall. This facility is equipped with a wide variety of power and hand tools.

SCHOLARSHIPS AND FINANCIAL AID

A number of scholarships are available to students in the architectural studies program at Southern Illinois University, Carbondale. The university awards many scholarships at the President's, Chancellor's, and Dean's level. Other scholarships are awarded by the College of Applied Sciences and Arts and still others by the architectural studies program.

The College of Applied Sciences and Arts (ASA) offers a partial tuition waiver to students in any of its programs. The amount of the tuition waiver varies from year to year. In 2006, the waivers were $1,000 each. Applications for the awards are made available every year on the first Friday of the spring semester. The application is available at the Dean's office in the ASA Building, at the college's seven department offices (located throughout campus), and from the ASA Scholarship Chair's office at 410 Quigley Hall. Applications are always due in the Dean's office no later than 4:00 pm on the Friday before spring break. Full details of the terms of the awards are provided on the application. A final note, this award is available only to those who are continuing students in ASA programs; it is not available to new students in those programs. Additional information is provided on the ASA web site.

The ASA Alumni Scholarship is available to those students who are a relative of an SIUC graduate, with preference being given to those who are relatives of ASA or College of Technical Careers (CTC) alumni. Applications are due by May 1 for the fall semester and by October 1 for the spring semester. No awards are made for the summer semester. Applications are available from the ASA Dean's office. Full details of the terms of the awards are provided on the application. Additional information is provided on the ASA web site.

ADMINISTRATION

Walter Wendler: Director

John K. Dobbins: Head of Graduate Programs
in Architecture

SOUTHERN POLYTECHNIC STATE UNIVERSITY

ADDRESS

Main
Southern Polytechnic State University
School of Architecture
1100 South Marietta Parkway
Marietta, GA 30060-2896
Tel.: 770.528.7253
Fax: 770.528.7228
dayala@spsu.edu
www.spsu.edu/home/academics/
architecture.html

STUDENT AND FACULTY DEMOGRAPHICS

% of Female Students	34
% of International Students	13
% of Minority Students	41
% of Out-of-State U.S. Students	9
No. Full-Time Faculty	18
No. Part-Time Faculty	14
No. Full-Time Students	471
No. Part-Time Students	138

FINANCIAL INFORMATION

Main Source of University Funding	Public
Annual Tuition & Fees (graduate, resident)	$3,482
Annual Tuition & Fees (graduate, nonresident)	$11,722
Annual Tuition & Fees (undergraduate, resident)	$4,232
Annual Tuition & Fees (undergraduate, nonresident)	$13,220
% Students Receiving Federal Financial Aid	58
% Students Receiving University Financial Aid	2
% Students Receiving Departmental Financial Aid	0
% Students Receiving Scholarships (assistantships or fellowships)	34
Average Annual Scholarship for Department	0

ARCHITECTURE AND RELATED DEGREE PROGRAMS							
Degree	Min. Yrs. to Complete	Professional Accreditation	# of FT Students	# of PT Students	# of First-Year Students	# of Degrees Conferred	Admissions Requirements
Architecture							
B. Arch	5	NAAB	276	12	150	21	

ARCHITECTURE PROGRAM SUMMARY

Building on its strong history of excellence, the Architecture Program at Southern Polytechnic State University continues to create an environment supportive of a collaborative and multidisciplinary hands-on approach to learning, creativity, scholarship, application, and engagement. We believe that these components are integral to a strong educational foundation, the creation of an environment that fosters our student's drive to achieve excellence and to contribute to their profession and their communities, and which encourages a greater appreciation of architecture and good design.

SCHOOL PHILOSOPHY

The Architecture Department at SPSU attracts and retains a strong faculty committed to professional excellence and recruits and supports qualified students who desire to learn, achieve and excel in their field. The mission of the Architecture Program is to be a prominent leader in architectural education at the national and international levels. It fulfills this mission via a strong commitment to:

- Creating and continuously improving a multidisciplinary curriculum that nurtures critical thinking; embraces new technologies and encourages creativity and innovation through the integration of the theory, art, technology and science of the built environment.
- Applied learning methods that emphasize hands-on exploration designed to provide the student with the knowledge, skills, and experiences necessary to be productive, contributing leaders in the architectural profession and civic community.
- Encouraging outreach programs designed to maintain vital connections with the architectural community, improve effective communication, support continued professional development and build future leaders of the profession.
- Advocating an appreciation of good design and the benefits of responsible architecture through the education of its students and the civic community.

PROGRAM DESCRIPTION

The Architecture Program is committed to foster invention, creativity, and craft through "hands-on" exploration that is the foundation of technology since its inception in 1964. Moreover, the knowledge of cultural diversity, communication, history, and criticism is inseparable from the application of technology. This process is *"the making of architecture."*

The Architecture Program assures interdependent academic relationships with allied fields of Civil Engineering Technology and Construction Management Programs within the School of Architecture and with other programs in the campus to diversify collaborative learning of our students.

"The Vision being the Mission" is the paradigm to guide the Architecture Program into the 21st century of technologically expressive architecture. This is not to be confused with "High Tech", that is a style. Technologically expressive architecture is not a style; it is a tool and a philosophy—the essence of what we call "making."

AREAS OF FOCUS AND RESEARCH

Hands-on and integrative approach to design and research: history, theory and criticism, design communication, urban design & redevelopment, sustainability, design pedagogy and housing.

SPECIAL ACTIVITIES AND PROGRAMS

Furniture/product design, community outreach projects (urban design, redevelopment and adaptive re-use), spatial morphology, sustainability, comprehensive design

FACILITIES

Building M: Environmental Tech Lab (3200 square feet facility). This lab is equipped with a high-end computer facility to support digital and BIM simulations with other supporting, environmental technology simulation programs besides structures.

SCHOLARSHIPS AND FINANCIAL AID

Architecture students at Southern Polytechnic have a variety of options for financial assistance. The Architecture Program offers various merit and need-based scholarships besides regular state and federal financial assistance programs:

The Jimmy Goldgeier Scholarship
The James G. Fausett Education Fund
AIA Scholarship Awards
Architect's Foundation of Georgia John D.
Mulford Memorial Scholarship
Architecture Foundation of Georgia Dorothy P.
Spence Memorial Scholarship
Lance Linscott Scholarship

ADMINISTRATION

Wilson C. Barnes, PhD, Dean: School of Architecture
Ameen Farooq, PhD: Chair

SOUTHERN UNIVERSITY AND A&M COLLEGE

ADDRESS

Main
Southern University and A&M College
School of Architecture
P.O. Box 11947
Baton Rouge, LA 70813
Tel.: 225.771.3015
Fax: 225.771.4709
www.subr.edu/academic/architecture

STUDENT AND FACULTY DEMOGRAPHICS

% of Female Students	33
% of International Students	3
% of Minority Students	99
% of Out-of-State U.S. Students	26
No. Full-Time Faculty	10
No. Part-Time Faculty	5
No. Full-Time Students	94
No. Part-Time Students	0

FINANCIAL INFORMATION

Main Source of University Funding	Public
Annual Tuition & Fees (graduate, resident)	
Annual Tuition & Fees (graduate, nonresident)	
Annual Tuition & Fees (undergraduate, resident)	
Annual Tuition & Fees (undergraduate, nonresident)	
% Students Receiving Federal Financial Aid	81
% Students Receiving University Financial Aid	23
% Students Receiving Departmental Financial Aid	
% Students Receiving Scholarships (assistantships or fellowships)	
Average Annual Scholarship for Department	$1,132

ACADEMIC SESSIONS

ARCHITECTURE AND RELATED DEGREE PROGRAMS

Degree	Min. Yrs. to Complete	Professional Accreditation	# of FT Students	# of PT Students	# of First-Year Students	# of Degrees Conferred	Admissions Requirements
Architecture							
B. Arch	5	NAAB	85	0	38	12	Portfolio, Rec. Letters, Essay

UNIVERSITY SETTING

Southern University School of Architecture is located on the Baton Rouge campus of Southern University and A&M College on the bluffs of the Mississippi River. The university is a publicly supported, co-educational, land grant, historically black institution opened in 1879. The Baton Rouge Campus has over 9,000 students and offers baccalaureate, master's and doctoral degrees. Transfer students from other colleges and universities may be accepted into the program following evaluation by the School of Architecture.

SCHOOL PHILOSOPHY

The Mission of the School of Architecture is "to prepare graduates for leadership roles, support the historic mission of the University by advocating for African-American voices in the profession of architecture, and to engender in graduates a commitment to service the community and its built environment". To accomplish this mission, the School of Architecture is focused on creating and nurturing an active learning community where teachers and students work together in an educational environment which fosters individual responsibility, academic excellence, and an appreciation of intellectual, ethical and aesthetic values. Individual success is celebrated as community achievement.

PROGRAM DESCRIPTION

The School of Architecture at Southern University offers a fully accredited five-year program of study leading to the first professional degree of Bachelor of Architecture. The curriculum consists of a professional studies core of architectural design studios and supporting courses in architectural drawing and modeling (traditional and computer), building technology, and architectural history and theory. The professional core is augmented with studies in the arts, humanities, sciences and social sciences. The curriculum is organized into two distinct segments. During the first two years, students concentrate on basic studies in architecture and supporting courses. At the end of the second semester of the second year, students must complete the matriculation process which evaluates their ability to succeed in the final three years of the program. The academic concentration of the third, fourth and fifth years focuses on a manner of designing and building driven by the process of integration into the studio of all of the various academic components of the program. Work in the community design center educates students to become visionary leaders through working in everyday, down-to-earth, face-to-face relationships with members of the community.

AREAS OF FOCUS AND RESEARCH

Areas of Focus

The Community Design and Research Center (CDRC) offers a special opportunity for students in the third and fourth years of the program to engage studio projects in communities. For these projects, students work with community members in all disciplines focusing on activities which enhance the community. Student experience at the CDRC, coupled with internships in professional offices, gives the student a multi-faceted 'real life' experience of the professional world. The school also liaises with several high schools in the area (one of which is a magnet program in Architecture and Environmental Design) to the benefit of all parties.

Research

Over the past five years, Southern University School of Architecture has held over one million dollars in research grants for studies in areas of: community design in neighborhoods adjacent to the campus (US Department of Housing and Urban Development); integration of a professional practice component in the curriculum (US Department of Education Fund for the Improvement of Post Secondary Education); and energy conservation studies (US Department of Energy). Students have either been direct beneficiaries or participants in the projects. The Community Design and Research Center coordinates research projects in historic preservation, energy conservation, sustainability, rural/urban design, and community revitalization.

FACILITIES

Southern University School of Architecture houses its own library which contains the majority of the university's excellent collection of books on architecture. The library also houses collections of videotapes, slides, and architectural drawings. The school has three computer labs equipped with architectural graphics and modeling software, as well as internet service, plotters and printers. The modelbuilding workshop is also equipped for full scale wood construction. The construction resource center contains materials samples and catalogues to supplement construction courses. The School of Architecture is located within easy walking distance of the Student Union, gymnasia, football and basketball stadia, dormitories and cafeterias.

SCHOLARSHIPS AND FINANCIAL AID

The School of Architecture awards 15 full scholarships annually to qualified students who major in architecture. Scholarships in the school are supported by the Southern University Academic Scholarship Awards Program. Awards are renewed each semester following the review of the student's academic performance at satisfactory levels. The School of Architecture Scholarship Committee selects the recipients. In addition to these, students hold scholarships from various sources. Several of these are offered by the Honors College, which provides an enhanced educational experience for students who have exceptionally strong academic records. The Office of Student Financial Aid administers a program designed to help students meet their college expenses. Financial assistance in the form of scholarships, loans, grants and employment is available to all students who complete the application process and qualify prior to established deadline dates.

ADMINISTRATION

Lonnie Wilkinson: Dean

SYRACUSE UNIVERSITY

ADDRESS

Main
Syracuse University
School of Architecture
201 Slocum Hall
Syracuse, NY 13244-1250
Tel.: 315.443.2256
Fax: 315.443.5082
soa.syr.edu

STUDENT AND FACULTY DEMOGRAPHICS

% of Female Students	48
% of International Students	10
% of Minority Students	32
% of Out-of-State U.S. Students	69
No. Full-Time Faculty	30
No. Part-Time Faculty	15
No. Full-Time Students	444
No. Part-Time Students	0

FINANCIAL INFORMATION

Main Source of University Funding	Private
Annual Tuition & Fees (graduate, resident)	$20,460
Annual Tuition & Fees (graduate, nonresident)	$20,460
Annual Tuition & Fees (undergraduate, resident)	$33,450
Annual Tuition & Fees (undergraduate, nonresident)	$33,450
% Students Receiving Federal Financial Aid	17.1
% Students Receiving University Financial Aid	78.6
% Students Receiving Departmental Financial Aid	10
% Students Receiving Scholarships (assistantships or fellowships)	See *
Average Annual Scholarship for Department	See *

* Please contact the school directly for more information

ACADEMIC SESSIONS

Fall Semester: August to December; Application Deadline: January 1
Spring Semester: January to May; Application Deadline: No mid-year transfers

Summer Session I: May to June
Summer Session II: July to August

ARCHITECTURE AND RELATED DEGREE PROGRAMS							
Degree	Min. Yrs. to Complete	Professional Accreditation	# of FT Students	# of PT Students	# of First-Year Students	# of Degrees Conferred	Admissions Requirements
Architecture							
B. Arch	5	NAAB	444	0	100	75	
M. Arch less than 2 yrs.	1		3	0	3	3	
M. Arch multiple paths	2 - 3.5	NAAB	90	0	30	30	

ARCHITECTURE PROGRAM SUMMARY

Architecture is a complex discipline that organizes diverse human needs and interests, ranging from the pragmatic to the visionary. The Syracuse University School of Architecture offers a professional education that is disciplinary and rooted in a humanistic tradition. This intellectual rigor enhances the understanding of the formative interaction between buildings and culture. The School's intent is to educate broadly and to approach skill and technique with the same vitality as a comprehensive knowledge of the world. The studio experience, which is at the core of both undergraduate and graduate programs, focuses on the intense exploration of the creative process, supported by the most challenging approaches to history and theory in the context of the technologies that inform the future practice of our field. Students benefit from extensive one-on-one communication with dedicated faculty, in both formal reviews and informal interactions. As part of its curriculum, the School of Architecture offers a series of lectures, symposia, and exhibitions featuring leading practitioners, critics, and scholars. Situated in a major liberal arts university, students in the School also have access to a wide variety of courses throughout the campus and are encouraged to participate in the life outside the boundaries of the studio, in other academic units, in the city of Syracuse, and beyond.

UNIVERSITY SETTING

Syracuse University is in the center New York State in a metropolitan area of 500,000 inhabitants, approximately four to six hours from Toronto, Montreal, Boston, New York and Philadelphia. The area is rich in outdoor activities, significant historical and architectural sites, and cultural offerings such as Syracuse Stage and the Syracuse Symphony. The University has approximately 12,000 undergraduates and 6,000 graduate students. Transfer students are accepted into both the undergraduate and graduate programs.

SCHOOL PHILOSOPHY

The Syracuse University School of Architecture offers fully accredited programs leading to a Bachelor of Architecture or a Master of Architecture as a first-professional degree. This is a design-oriented program that focuses on the study of the built environment and its constituent elements, through the use of analysis, speculation, and design as a means of inquiry. The activity of design is seen as bringing together issues of history and criticism, technology, structures, drawing, and computers into a process of architectural representation. The programs focus on synthesizing the innumerable aspects that go into a built environment with the goal of elevating the "facts" of mere building into the realm of art, and ultimately enriching life.

PROGRAM DESCRIPTION

The broad goal of the School's curriculum is to develop each student's ability to think critically and give each individual the tools to express ideas through drawing, modeling, and writing. The necessary technical and aesthetic skills are learned through a carefully structured curriculum that stresses creativity, research, and problem solving. Student work and personal point of view are enriched through rigorous and frequent dialogue between faculty and fellow students. The highly integrated curriculum also includes opportunities to explore individual interests. The five-year program consists of 162 credits (most courses are 3 or 6 credits). Of these, 120 credits are in professional architecture courses, 36 in arts and sciences. In the first three years, the architecture program is sequentially organized and principally skills-oriented, including visual and architectural design studios and required technical design, structures, and history courses. The fourth year is intended as a year of choice, providing opportunities to broaden the student's interests and experiences by participation in the school's Florence, London, and NYC programs. For those remaining on campus, special design studios are available, and a first-semester advanced design studio of the student's choice usually with a distinguished visiting architect/educator. The fifth and final year includes a course in the legal aspects of professional practice and a summary course in technologies. During the last semester, the entire program culminates in a senior thesis, almost always in the form of a major design project.

AREAS OF FOCUS AND RESEARCH

Focus

The Syracuse University School of Architecture offers one of the most distinguished programs in the nation leading to a professional degree. Founded in 1873, the School provides a comprehensive and intellectually challenging approach to the design of the built environment. It is a course of study that recognizes the mix of art and technology, and responds to the changing demands of the profession and society. The design studio sequence is at the core of the program and is unique to architectural education. It is here that students begin to understand the fundamentals of design, working alongside their classmates.

Graduates may be found in all the leading practices in the United States, particularly in New York, Boston, and Washington, DC, Europe, and Asia. Given the faculty's strong interest in urban design, a close pedagogical connection is made with our overseas programs in Florence and London, which almost all students attend. The School has a particularly rich availability of courses in architectural history and theory in Syracuse, Florence, London, and NYC.

Research

Research is carried out at several levels, particularly within the School's visiting critic studios, individual students' theses and via UPSTATE, the School's interdisciplinary center for design, research, and real estate which engages in innovative design and development practices; addresses environmental and economic challenges; and strengthens the impact of planning and architecture in the city of Syracuse and the region. In addition, the School engages in interdisciplinary studies in environmental building technology and evaluation with the College of Engineering and the Center of Excellence in Environmental and Energy Systems.

SPECIAL ACTIVITIES AND PROGRAMS

- Semester in Florence, Italy, London, England, NYC
- Summer programs abroad: Italy, England, Spain, Portugal
- Summer sessions in Syracuse
- Pre-Architecture Florence, Italy
- Visiting studio critics program
- School lecture, exhibition, and Technology Talks
- Student publications

FACILITIES

Slocum Hall, the School of Architecture's campus home, was constructed in 1918 and is listed on the National Register of Historical Places. The recent redesign, by the New York firm of Garrison Architects, has enhanced and restored the five-story building's original qualities while updating it technologically, functionally, and aesthetically. The renovation includes the re-creation of the central atrium space, the addition of a new auditorium and gallery, as well as expanded studio, research, and office space. The completed renovation has yielded an ideal environment for teaching, research, and production, and incorporated new technology in the studio environment, expanded research facilities, and adequate faculty offices. Public review spaces, an exhibition gallery, the architecture reading room, faculty offices, and the café are located along the perimeter of these atria in order to encourage collaboration and exchange. This renovation is a compelling opportunity to integrate the school's facilities with its pedagogical priorities. Computing/plotting and woodshop/fabrication facilities are state-of-the-art.

The School maintains a downtown Syracuse presence at The Warehouse in Armory Square, located in one of the most vital, pedestrian-oriented parts of the city. The Warehouse serves as headquarters for UPSTATE: A Center for Design, Research, and Real Estate as well as selected visiting critic studios. It is the perfect setting for students to understand the intricate relationships among architecture, design, and the public realm. Students look out from the floors of the former furniture warehouse and see most of the city, and the low-lying hills to the south.

SCHOLARSHIPS AND FINANCIAL AID

For undergraduate information, please visit www.syracuse.edu. For graduate financial aid information, visit soa.syr.edu.

ADMINISTRATION

Mark Robbins: Dean
Katryn Hansen: Assistant Dean
Jonathan Massey: Chair, Undergraduate Program
Mark Linder: Chair, Graduate Program

TEMPLE UNIVERSITY

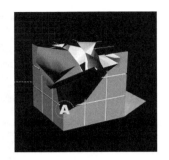

ADDRESS

Main
Temple University
Tyler School of Art
Architecture Department
1947 N. 12th Street
Philadelphia, PA 19122-6077
Tel.: 215.204.8813
Fax: 215.204.5481
www.temple.edu/architecture

STUDENT AND FACULTY DEMOGRAPHICS

% of Female Students	30
% of International Students	12
% of Minority Students	26
% of Out-of-State U.S. Students	38
No. Full-Time Faculty	12
No. Part-Time Faculty	21
No. Full-Time Students	290
No. Part-Time Students	23

FINANCIAL INFORMATION

Main Source of University Funding	Public
Annual Tuition & Fees (graduate, resident)	
Annual Tuition & Fees (graduate, nonresident)	
Annual Tuition & Fees (undergraduate, resident)	$10,748
Annual Tuition & Fees (undergraduate, nonresident)	$19,660
% Students Receiving Federal Financial Aid	85
% Students Receiving University Financial Aid	
% Students Receiving Departmental Financial Aid	
% Students Receiving Scholarships (assistantships or fellowships)	
Average Annual Scholarship for Department	

ACADEMIC SESSIONS

Fall Semester: September to December;
  Application Deadline: March 1
Spring Semester: January to May;
  Application Deadline: November 1

Summer Session I: May to July
Summer Session II: July to August

ARCHITECTURE AND RELATED DEGREE PROGRAMS

Degree	Min. Yrs. to Complete	Professional Accreditation	# of FT Students	# of PT Students	# of First-Year Students	# of Degrees Conferred	Admissions Requirements
Architecture							
B. Arch	5	NAAB	107	10	0	35	Portfolio, Rec. Letters, 2.75 GPA
BS Arch.	4		136	3	70	22	SAT

SPECIALIZATIONS

Architectural Design
Building Technology/Env. Systems

Community Design
Computer-Aided Design

International Development

Theory/Criticism

ARCHITECTURE PROGRAM SUMMARY

The mission of the Department of Architecture of the Tyler School of Art at Temple University is to educate design professionals relevant to the contemporary world by constructing an environment where general, architectural and urban issues are investigated in depth. While acquiring the fundamental skills and knowledge base of the discipline, students are taught to think critically about architecture, as a situated physical, spatial and social practice, and to engage in environmentally responsible ways with the opportunities and dilemmas presented to it by contemporary transformations in society, culture, technology and materials.

UNIVERSITY SETTING

The Architecture Department is part of the Tyler School of Art, of Temple University an institution of profound accomplishment, relevance and promise. Temple has the most diverse student body in the nation and epitomizes what it means to be an urban public research university: creating knowledge, improving lives and serving the community. Temple University as a whole, the Tyler School of Art and the Architecture Department are in an exciting period of tremendous transformation. Advancements in academics, research, faculty recruitment and residential campus life are being noticed nationwide. We are located on Broad Street in North Philadelphia, at the northernmost point of the Avenue of the Arts, where we tap into the energy of a major city, while offering the ambience of a college campus. The architecture department offers the advantage of a being a small learning community while providing the advantages afforded by a large comprehensive research institution.

SCHOOL PHILOSOPHY

Temple University is located in Philadelphia, one of America's great cities, long globally acknowledged and connected. It and architectural practice within it are currently being transformed by forces of global restructuring in ways comparable with that of other mid-sized post-industrial cities around the world. Pedagogy and research are framed by this urban and professional condition. It is used as a primary laboratory for deep critical engagement, architectural investigation and operative transformation in environmentally responsible ways.

Central to work in the department is the recognition of architecture as a material practice, in which acts of design and acts of making extend into one another. These include drawing, model building, fabrication and building. This locates the department's laboratories—studios, woodshop, digital and fabrication labs and a materials library—and the relationship between thinking and making, at the heart of the department's ethos and pedagogy. The department promotes Investigations into architecture's material and technical properties as a basis for environmentally sustainable design and research. These include conventional materials and technologies as well as investigations into emerging materials and new computational and fabrication technologies.

The department espouses a position that architecture is a social practice. It investigates the complex socio-economic, cultural and political dynamics of the contemporary, post-industrial city and explores these as opportunities for design. These include forces of migration, crime, fear, religion, climate change, etc.—phenomena, which have shaped the modern metropolis since its beginning but have taken on additional urgency under the impact of globalization, as well as more traditional forces of commercial capital and politics.

Fundamental to architecture is design, a speculative practice that operates on the real, to know and transform it. The design studio, from foundation level where students learn basic design and representational skills to advanced-level comprehensive and urban studios provide a critical environment for architectural speculation. These are supported by the study of theoretical, historical, technical and professional phenomena relevant to design practice in the metropolis of tomorrow.

The department operates from the position that architecture is a collaborative practice. Collaborations with other centres of excellence in the university for teaching and research are encouraged. Pedagogy and research are connected to real conditions through partnerships or collaborations with other urban agents (e.g., planners, developers, political activists, researchers, fabricators, artists and other professionals). In this way, architectural education ensures its relevance to the transforming world of practice. Applied research and consultancy are encouraged.

PROGRAM DESCRIPTION

The Architecture Department currently offers two undergraduate degrees—the Bachelor of Science in Architecture (B.S.Arch, four years) and the Bachelor of Architecture (B.Arch, five years, professionally accredited). It has NAAB approval to begin offering a Master of Architecture degree, which it hopes to initiate in Fall 2010.

The two undergraduate programs share a common two-year basic studies program. Upon successful completion of this preparatory program, students either may continue in the B.S.Arch curriculum path or may apply for acceptance to the B.Arch professional curriculum path.

The five-year B.Arch prepares students for the practice of architecture in entry-level positions, part of an intern development program which leads to professional registration. This curriculum is designed to enable students to learn theories and methodologies of architectural design as well as to understand the social, economic, political, and technological forces which shape the built environment. The principal educational component of the curriculum is a coordinated series of studio courses in which creative design talents and management skills are developed. The B.Arch curriculum is accredited by the National Architectural Accrediting Board (NAAB). Holders of this degree may, upon completion of postgraduate apprenticeship, be admitted to the architectural licensing examination offered in each state, through which they may become registered architects.

The four-year B.S.Arch program is designed to develop a strong base in architectural technology and practice upon which students may develop additional areas of special competence based upon individual goals. Minors in other disciplines (e.g. business / art history / geography and urban studies) are possible. Graduates are qualified for a variety of positions in architecture and related fields for which a professional degree and registration are not requirements for advancement. Additionally, holders of this degree may qualify for architectural education at the graduate level.

Transfer students are sometimes admitted to Temple's architecture programs with advanced standing. Students who already hold a bachelor's degree and certain other upper-level transfer students may be eligible for consideration for participation in various options for acceleration. Placement is based upon prior architectural education, not merely the number of credits earned at another institution. All transfer students must consult directly with the Department after admission but well in advance of registration.

AREAS OF FOCUS AND RESEARCH

The department's areas of focus and research are under development and being shaped by its mission statement and core values. It is currently focusing on two broad areas: site, settlement and territorial studies, and material studies.

The department has a history of focusing its pedagogy and research on the neighbourhoods of North Philadelphia that surround it. This is ongoing, but being extended to other sites, settlements or territories around the world subject to political, economic, or ecological transformation, including the ancient village at the Pueblo of Acoma, Route 66 towns, ancient Islamic sites in Jerusalem, Johannesburg South Africa, the Balkans and informal settlements around the world. Methodologies are currently eclectic and subject to ongoing debate.

A number of faculty are focusing their research on emerging material technologies and in the potential that material and fabrication advancements offer in enhancing process-based desires in design. Further to this, research into the instructional logic of repetitious systems is including experiments with field manipulations, digital planer fabrication techniques, animation and mapping techniques. Central to this research is the global mandate for sustainability and environmentally conscious design.

SPECIAL ACTIVITIES AND PROGRAMS

Study in Temple's Rome program and on Temple Japan's campus is offered to selected students in both the fall and spring of the third or fourth year of both undergraduate programs.

FACILITIES

The Architecture Department is accommodated on three floors of the College of Engineering and Architecture building on Temple's main campus, which also houses the architecture library. It has its own well equipped woodshop, computer laboratories and plot room and is currently fundraising for a digital fabrication laboratory. The department maintains a small exhibition gallery and shares review and jury space with the College of Engineering. It has its own seminar room for smaller classes. Students are allocated dedicated desk space for studio courses. The design studios, limited to a maximum of 15 students per section, are housed in large, open-studio areas sub-divided by low partitions with electrical and computer internet points. Thesis students are assigned to smaller shared studios. All studios are also covered by Temple's wireless service. In addition to this, the department makes use of the lecture rooms in university's Tuttleman Learning Center and the 75,000 square feet, 700-computer, state-of-the-art Tech Center, the largest of its kind in the nation.

SCHOLARSHIPS AND FINANCIAL AID

Loans and scholarships available to students include national direct student loans, college work-study program grants, Supplemental Educational opportunity Grants and Pell Grants. In addition, Temple University offers a number of competitive grants. Direct application to the Financial Aid Office is required to obtain information about these.

The department awards two scholarships to senior-level students: the Knowles Scholarship, which enables students to undertake a semester of study abroad in Rome and the Olivieri Scholarship, a one-year scholarship to a student in the final year of study who has shown commitment to the program. Further information about these can be obtained from the Senior Associate Dean, Professor Brigitte Knowles.

ADMINISTRATION

Brigitte Knowles, AIA: Senior Associate Dean
Lindsay Bremner: Chair
Laurie Duffy: Director of Academic Services

TEXAS A&M UNIVERSITY

ADDRESS

Main
Texas A&M University
Department of Architecture
Langford Building A - Room 411
College Station, TX 77843-3137
Tel.: 979.845.1015
Fax: 979.842.1571
gmills@archmail.tamu.edu
archone.tamu.edu/College

STUDENT AND FACULTY DEMOGRAPHICS

% of Female Students	32
% of International Students	17
% of Minority Students	31
% of Out-of-State U.S. Students	4
No. Full-Time Faculty	114
No. Part-Time Faculty	22
No. Full-Time Students	1688
No. Part-Time Students	294

FINANCIAL INFORMATION

Main Source of University Funding	Public
Annual Tuition & Fees (graduate, resident)	$7,000
Annual Tuition & Fees (graduate, nonresident)	$16,000
Annual Tuition & Fees (undergraduate, resident)	$7,844
Annual Tuition & Fees (undergraduate, nonresident)	$16,274
% Students Receiving Federal Financial Aid	
% Students Receiving University Financial Aid	5
% Students Receiving Departmental Financial Aid	16
% Students Receiving Scholarships (assistantships or fellowships)	16
Average Annual Scholarship for Department	$1,889

ARCHITECTURE AND RELATED DEGREE PROGRAMS

Degree	Min. Yrs. to Complete	Professional Accreditation	# of FT Students	# of PT Students	# of First-Year Students	# of Degrees Conferred	Admissions Requirements
Architecture							
Bachelor of Environmental Design	4		531	42	89	125	SAT Competitive
Doctor of Philosophy in Architecture	3		35	18	10	5	Prof. Architecture degree
M. Arch	2	NAAB	42	2	5	20	Undergraduate Architecture degree
M. Arch	3.5	NAAB	48	1	14	20	Undergraduate degree
Master of Science in Architecture	1.5		7	1	0	0	Undergraduate Architecture degree
Landscape Architecture							
Bachelor of Landscape Architecture	5		139	11	21	22	SAT
Master of Landscape Architecture	2		25	3	5	5	Undergraduate degree
Master of Science in Land Development	1.5		34	3	11	21	Undergraduate degree, Undergraduate Architecture degree
Construction Management/Technology							
Bachelor of Science in Construction Science	4	ACCE	495	168	72	206	SAT
Master of Science in Construction Science	1.5		121	5	64	46	Undergraduate degree, Undergraduate Architecture degree
Other							
Bachelor of Science in Urban and Regional Science	4		51	0	18	0	
Doctor of Philosophy in Urban and Regional Science	3		35	11	5	4	

ACADEMIC SESSIONS

Fall Semester: August to December   Spring Semester: January to May   Summer Session I: May to June   Summer Session II: July to August

SPECIALIZATIONS

Architectural Design	Computer-Aided Design	International/Regional Architecture	Sacred Spaces
Art and Design	Environment/Sustainability	International Development	Sustainablility
Building Information Modeling	Graphic Design	Landscape Design	Theory/Criticism
Building Technology/Env. Systems	History	Preservation	Urban Planning and Design
Community Design	Housing	Professional Practice	

ARCHITECTURE PROGRAM SUMMARY

The College of Architecture at Texas A&M University is located in the Langford Architecture Center on the university's main campus in College Station, Texas, which is adjacent to the city of Bryan. The two cities are sometimes referred to interchangeably or together as Bryan/College Station and have a combined population of approximately 120,000 residents. Easterwood Airport, located in College Station, is served by Continental and American Airlines with connecting flights to and from Houston and Dallas.

UNIVERSITY SETTING

The College of Architecture is one of ten colleges in a university of some 45,000 students, including 8,300 graduate students. The college houses Departments of Architecture, Construction Science, Landscape Architecture and Urban Planning, and Visualization. There is a strong commitment to student advising and mentoring along with student organizations and programs in athletics, operating and performing arts societies, theater productions, and public radio and television stations.

SCHOOL PHILOSOPHY

The educational intent of the Department of Architecture is to develop and disseminate knowledge about architecture. To realize this goal, faculty members have made a commitment to build on their diverse experiences and backgrounds and to work together to establish a climate in which scholarship and creativity can flourish. Within such an academic climate, there is a clear recognition of the relative importance of goals at all levels of academic activity, including:
- An innovative architecture and environmental design curriculum;
- A creative and supportive architectural culture;
- A supportive research infrastructure;
- An effective infrastructure for service, outreach and marketing, and
- Mechanisms for continuous assessment.

PROGRAM DESCRIPTION

Undergraduate Program

The Department of Architecture offers a four-year, 120-semester-credit-hour curriculum in environmental design leading to a Bachelor of Environmental Design degree. The curriculum has the shaping of space for human activity as its backbone and provides opportunities to study the professional disciplines which plan and develop the built environment and manage the interface between people and their buildings. It prepares the student for the pursuit of a professional master's degree in architecture and makes them aware of a range of career opportunities in related academic or professional programs. The curriculum is intended to develop students who understand the interrelationships between the parts of a building, who can analyze and

solve complex problems, and who are capable of responding to changing social and cultural needs, technologies and globalization. The students learn skills and acquire knowledge in programming, problem analysis, communications, structures, mechanical equipment systems, materials, computer technology, history, design, and in a chosen elective, studies in a variety of disciplines. In design studios they learn to synthesize these skills and knowledge.

Graduate Program

The Master of Architecture professional degree program requires 52 credit hours for completion and includes a core of professional course work supported by specialized study in one of the several areas of emphasis and exploration topics offered by the Department of Architecture. The Master of Science in Architecture is an advanced, multidisciplinary, 32-credit hour thesis program of graduate study designed to provide highly qualified students with a traditional academic foundation in theoretical concepts and research methods.

The doctoral program in architecture focuses primarily on expanding knowledge and research capacity of the highest order. Students are expected to enter this program with strong professional experience and a defined special interest, and complete 64 credit hours beyond a master's degree, including a research dissertation.

The College of Architecture offers six cross-disciplinary advanced certificate programs in:
- Environmental Hazard Management
- Facility Management
- Health Systems and Design
- Sustainable Urbanism
- Historic Preservation
- Transportation Planning

archone.tamu.edu/College/Academics/certificates/html

AREAS OF FOCUS AND RESEARCH

The college's research centers include the:
- Center for Hazard Reduction and Recovery
- Center for Housing and Urban Development
- CRS Center
- Center for Health Systems and Design
- Center for Heritage Conservation

SPECIAL ACTIVITIES AND PROGRAMS

The College of Architecture provides many special programs and activities to support and enhance its educational goals and enrich the experiences of its students. These include:
- Study abroad sites in China, Germany, India, Italy, Spain and Turkey
- Internship programs for credit for undergraduate and graduate students;
- Student organizations such as AIAS, Tau Sigma Delta, DBIA, FMIAD, ASHRAE, and more;

- Professional exam workshops and NCARB design test simulations;
- The Global Symposium;
- The Graduate Student Research Symposium;
- The Rowlett Lecture Series, and
- The Department of Architecture Lecture Series.

FACILITIES

The architecture program is housed primarily in the Ernest Langford Architecture Center, a three-building complex which, in addition to classroom and studio spaces, contains the following support facilities: the Technical Reference Center, Media Center, Woodworking Shop, computer labs equipped with high-quality workstations and peripherals and Architecture Ranch eequipped with plasma cutters and a CNC router. The college's research facilities include: the Visualization Lab and the Environmental Psychophysiology Lab.

Classrooms, labs and studio spaces are equipped with network and power connections.

SCHOLARSHIPS AND FINANCIAL AID

Texas A&M University administers a large number of competitive scholarships rewarding academic achievement, scholarly promise, and leadership excellence to incoming freshmen and currently enrolled students without regard to financial need. Also, financial aid is available in the form of grants, loans, part-time employment, and the College Work Study Program. The Department of Architecture administers competitive scholarships for undergraduate and graduate students based on financial need, scholastic ability, and promise of professional potential. Graduate teaching and research assistantships are also available.

ADMINISTRATION

Jorge Vanegas, PhD: Interim Dean
Walter G. Peacock, PhD: Interim Exec. Associate Dean
Louis G. Tassinary, PhD, JD: Associate Dean for Research, Director of Graduate Studies
Leslie H. Feigenbaum, MS: Assistant Dean for Undergraduate Programs
Elton D. Abbott, AIA DED: Assistant Dean for Special Projects
Glen Mills, PhD: Department Head
Michael O'Brien, RA, M.Arch: Associate Department Head
Richard R. Davison, MFA: 1st & 2nd year B.E.D. Coordinator
Marcel Erminy, Architect: 3rd & 4th year B.E.D. Coordinator
Ward Wells, AIA: M.Arch Coordinator
Phillip J. Tabb, PhD, AIA: Coordinator for MS Arch & PhD

TEXAS TECH UNIVERSITY

ADDRESS

Main
Texas Tech University
College of Architecture
Box 42091
Lubbock, TX 79409-2091
Tel.: 806.742.3136
Fax: 806.742.2855
Arch.admin@ttu.edu
www.arch.ttu.edu

STUDENT AND FACULTY DEMOGRAPHICS

% of Female Students	3
% of International Students	1
% of Minority Students	3
% of Out-of-State U.S. Students	1
No. Full-Time Faculty	40
No. Part-Time Faculty	6
No. Full-Time Students	743
No. Part-Time Students	73

FINANCIAL INFORMATION

Main Source of University Funding	Public
Annual Tuition & Fees (graduate, resident)	$8,284
Annual Tuition & Fees (graduate, nonresident)	$16,738
Annual Tuition & Fees (undergraduate, resident)	$6,784
Annual Tuition & Fees (undergraduate, nonresident)	15,214
% Students Receiving Federal Financial Aid	33
% Students Receiving University Financial Aid	1
% Students Receiving Departmental Financial Aid	0
% Students Receiving Scholarships (assistantships or fellowships)	1
Average Annual Scholarship for Department	$70,000

ACADEMIC SESSIONS

Fall Semester: September to December
Spring Semester: January to May

Summer Session I: June to July
Summer Session II: July to August

ARCHITECTURE AND RELATED DEGREE PROGRAMS

Degree	Min. Yrs. to Complete	Professional Accreditation	# of FT Students	# of PT Students	# of First-Year Students	# of Degrees Conferred	Admissions Requirements
Architecture							
Bachelor of Architecture	4		509		509		
M. Arch	5	NAAB	119			70	Prof. Architecture degree, GRE, Portfolio, Rec. Letters, Essay
Master of Science	2						Undergraduate degree, GRE, Portfolio, Rec. Letters

SPECIALIZATIONS

Community Design

Graphic Design

Preservation

ARCHITECTURE PROGRAM SUMMARY

The College of Architecture educates students for future design practice and advances knowledge of the dicipline for the benefit of society.

UNIVERSITY SETTING

Texas Tech University is composed of twelve colleges. Architectural studies have been offered on the campus since 1927. In 1996, the College of Architecture became the first national institution to offer a five-year Master of Architecture first professional degree. Campus resources include: the Museum, Ranching Heritage Center, Library including The Southwest Collection and the Vietnam Archives. The College of Architecture has a branch library with a collection totaling over 30,000 volumes.

SCHOOL PHILOSOPHY

The College will be an international learning community; engaging in exemplary architectural teaching, research, scholarship, creative endeavor, and service. The College of Architecture will: educate its students for effective practice in architecture; supplement sound training by nurturing the whole person within an understanding of architecture as a broad humanistic and scientific discipline; produce leaders able to meet the demands of a changing profession and whose technical skills will be complemented by personal vision, ethical persuasiveness and entrepreneurial drive.

PROGRAM DESCRIPTION

Those students not admitted, or choosing not to proceed to the Master of Architecture program, may elect to complete the required undergraduate credits and receive the Bachelor of Science in Architecture non-professional degree. The 4-year BS Arch consists of 131 credit-hours at the undergraduate level. This degree gives students knowledge and opportunities in the development of the building industry and related fields, as well as the possibility to continue in graduate education.

The Master of Architecture requires an additional 27-credit hours. Requirements for this program include completion of all academic course work in the first three years and a threshold score on the Admission Criteria Rating System. The threshold score is based on a sliding scale of GRE, GPA and portfolio scores.

The Master of Science is a 38-credit hour graduate degree focused on research and specialization in three different focus areas: Historic Preservation, Visualization and Comunity Development.

AREAS OF FOCUS AND RESEARCH

Focus

The College's interdisciplinary design studio brings together elements of architectural design, landscape design and interior design. Students majoring in each of these academic disciplines participate in the integrated studio at the fourth-year level. In conjunction with the Community Development Studio, the College regularly sponsors planning symposia, making available to students and area professionals the ideas of noted national and international experts in the field of community design and urban renewal. Additionally, the CDS provides assistance to rural communities in revitalization of economic development. The College's historic preservation emphasis allows students to work in tandem with the University's Ranching Heritage Center as an on-site research entity, as well as the National Park Service projects.

Research

The Architecture Research and Design Center facilitates research and service activities within the College, serves as an interface with other research and service centers and institutes at Texas Tech and University Health Sciences Center academic units, and provides research services to the wider public realm. The following major interest areas encourage collaborative research projects: community and urban design, international architecture, preservation/history/vernacular architecture, and visualization. The Center also facilitates the provision of feasibility and preliminary design services to area and regional municipalities on a for-fee basis through the Community Development Center.

SPECIAL ACTIVITIES AND PROGRAMS

- Counseling sessions occur each summer for entering freshmen and transfer students.
- The overseas summer studios for which scholarships are available study design, drawing, photography, historic preservation and urban design. These are offered in Montreal, Canada; Seville, Spain; Pueblo, Mexico; Paris, France; Brussels, Belgium and Verona, Italy. Additionally, Practicum+Studio opportunities are available in Houston, Dallas, San Antonio and El Paso.

- ARCHITOUR, a spring break, ten-day field trip, visits significant architectural and urban places in the U.S. and Canada.
- The Intern Program places students in offices across the United States. The Historic American Buildings Survey/Historic/American Engineering Record (HABS/HAER) summer programs are also available.
- The college's Lecture Series is complemented by international, national and local exhibitions.
- Student organizations include chapters of AIAS and Tau Sigma Delta, and internally the Knights of Architecture and Women in Architecture. Students arrange job fairs, portfolio workshops, help in recruiting and mentoring, and work with Habitat for Humanity and other community projects.

FACILITIES

The College of Architecture is located in its own building on the Texas Tech campus, and houses all design and visual communications studios, computer instruction laboratories, workshops and most lecture rooms, a branch library, wood metal and model shops and administrative, staff/faculty offices. Students have a lounge and gallery at their disposal. There are beginning and advanced computer instructional laboratories, a construction documents studio, and materials reference collection. The studios are equipped with Pentiums, plotters and printers. There are two audiovisual lecture rooms and one multimedia classroom. The college also has an Audio/Visual Lab equipped with backdrop, special lighting, and cameras.

SCHOLARSHIPS AND FINANCIAL AID

Scholarships are available on a competitive basis at both the undergraduate and graduate levels. Eligibility depends upon student enrollment in both fall and spring semesters and maintaining a minimum of a 3.0 GPA. Approximately $72,500 in scholarships are awarded annually by the college through support by various professional, business, and alumni organizations.

ADMINISTRATION

Andrew Vernooy, AIA: Dean
Michael G. Peters, AIA: Associate Dean for Academics
Brian T. Rex: Chair

TULANE UNIVERSITY

ADDRESS

Main
Tulane University
School of Architecture
Richardson Memorial Hall
New Orleans, LA 70118-5671
Tel.: 504.865.5389
Fax: 504.865.6722
tsarch@tulane.edu
www.tulane.edu/~tsahome/

STUDENT AND FACULTY DEMOGRAPHICS

% of Female Students	51
% of International Students	8
% of Minority Students	10
% of Out-of-State U.S. Students	85
No. Full-Time Faculty	19
No. Part-Time Faculty	19
No. Full-Time Students	351
No. Part-Time Students	5

FINANCIAL INFORMATION

Main Source of University Funding	Private
Annual Tuition & Fees (graduate)	$37,700
Annual Tuition & Fees (undergraduate)	$37,700
% Students Receiving Federal Financial Aid	80
% Students Receiving University Financial Aid	80
% Students Receiving Departmental Financial Aid	20
% Students Receiving Scholarships (assistantships or fellowships)	80
Average Annual Scholarship for Department	

ACADEMIC SESSIONS

Fall Semester: August to December;
  Application Deadline: February 15
Spring Semester: January to May

Summer Session I: June to July
Summer Session II: July to August

ARCHITECTURE AND RELATED DEGREE PROGRAMS

Degree	Min. Yrs. to Complete	Professional Accreditation	# of FT Students	# of PT Students	# of First-Year Students	# of Degrees Conferred	Admissions Requirements
Architecture							
M. Arch—5 years	5	NAAB	274	0	90	60	SAT, Rec. Letters, Essay
M. Arch—2 years	2	NAAB	26	0	8	8	Undergraduate Architecture degree, GRE, TOEFL, Portfolio, Rec. Letters, Essay
M. Arch—3.5 years	3.5	NAAB	36	0	12	10	Undergraduate degree, GRE, TOEFL, Portfolio, Rec. Letters, Essay
Historic Preservation							
Master of Preservation Studies	1		15	5	8	8	Undergraduate degree, Undergraduate Architecture degree, Prof. Architecture degree, GRE, Rec. Letters, Essay

SPECIALIZATIONS

Architectural Design
Building Information Modeling

Community Design
Environment/Sustainability

Preservation
Sustainablility

Theory/Criticism

ARCHITECTURE PROGRAM SUMMARY

The School of Architecture received a full six-year term in 2002 and recently went through positive reaccreditation review. Since Hurricane Katrina, both the School and the University have successfully rebounded and indeed surpassed all stated goals in the Tulane Renewal Plan. Under the aegis of the Tulane City Center, new programs have included URBANbuild, CITYbuild and GREENbuild, all of which have resulted in award-winning projects. With the appointments of a new dean, Kenneth Schwartz, a new associate dean, Elizabeth Burns Gamard, and Scott Bernhard as director of the City Center, 2008-09 promises continued success. New Orleans itself has in large part recovered and stands to reclaim its reputation as one of the exceptional and exciting cities in the world.

UNIVERSITY SETTING

The School of Architecture at Tulane University enjoys the advantages of two worlds, liberal arts study and professional education. As part of the larger community, the school takes advantage of the strong liberal arts curriculum and resources of this mid-size private research university. The low faculty-to-student ratio (1:12 in studio) allows nearly all students and faculty to become well acquainted, and there is a prevailing spirit of mutual challenge and support.

SCHOOL PHILOSOPHY

Within the constraints of a professional degree program, the school recognizes and represents the pluralistic character of architectural education and architectural practice. The presence of a diverse faculty, team teaching in the required studio sequence, a wide range of course offerings, and the frequent participation of visitors with a broad range of perspectives, exposes students to both past tradition and current diversity. The school today is characterized by energetic creative exploration and intellectual inquiry; it is an environment supportive of high standards, challenge, and growth.

PROGRAM DESCRIPTION
Undergraduate Program

The Master of Architecture program includes required courses and electives in order to give students thorough professional preparation opportunities for study in the liberal arts, and opportunities for advanced study in architecture. First-year courses include required study in architectural design, technology, and introductory architectural analysis, in addition to English and two semester electives, chosen from among forty subject areas offered throughout the university's undergraduate divisions. Second- and third-year courses include the majority of program requirements with elective opportunities. Intensive studio work in architectural design is complemented by study in architectural history and theory, structures, and building technology. The fourth and fifth-year curricula stress advanced architectural design that addresses diverse topics through elective studio courses called "platforms": these platform studios incorporate architectural theory, thesis research, and finally, the thesis design semester. In addition to academic-year studies, students are required to spend two summers working in architecture firms in order to gain an understanding of architecture as a profession. Transfer students with previous college work but without any background in architecture may take an intensive summer program as the equivalent of first-year. For these students, the master of architecture as a first undergraduate degree may then be obtained in four additional years.

SPECIAL ACTIVITIES AND PROGRAMS

Each year a number of well-known architects, architectural historians, theorists, and critics participate in a public lecture series, as well as in reviews, individual criticism, or informal discussions. Each year the student government sponsors Architects' Week, a week of activities, lectures, competitions, workshops, and other activities organized around a common theme or topic. Other student-organized events include Friday afternoon social gatherings and the annual Beaux Arts Ball. To augment the regular curriculum offerings, the school sponsors programs of study, research, and travel, usu-ally of six to ten weeks in duration, during the summer. The Newcomb-Tulane Junior Year Abroad Program (JYA) offers qualified students the opportunity to spend a full academic year abroad. In addition, there is a semester-long Rome Program, as well as multiple travel programs in settings such as Japan, Brazil, France and Central Europe.

FACILITIES

The School of Architecture is particularly fortunate to have the entire use of Richardson Memorial Hall. Designed in 1907 to house the Tulane Medical College, Richardson Memorial is located on the oldest and most beautiful quadrangle on the Tulane campus, near New Orleans prestigious St. Charles Avenue. Every student in the school is assigned a desk with storage in one of these studios each semester. The School of Architecture computer facilities equipment include, microcomputers configured for computer aided design and visualization with high-quality large-format printers, laser cutters, and rapid prototyping equipment. State-of-the-art three-dimensional modeling, rendering, and imaging capabilities are being utilized both for student projects and architectural research.

SCHOLARSHIPS AND FINANCIAL AID

Tulane University and the School of Architecture seek to offer educational opportunities to qualified students regardless of their current ability to meet expenses. Toward this end, the university extends financial aid, the basis of need and merit, through scholarships, grants, loans, and campus employment. In 2008, over three-quarters of incoming students were financial aid recipients. On- and off campus employment assistance is available through the Career Services Center. The Financial Aid Office has information covering aspects of student financial aid, including the brochure, Financing an Education.

ADMINISTRATION

Kenneth Schwartz, FAIA: Dean
Elizabeth Burns Gamard: Associate Dean

ADDRESS

Main
Tuskegee University
Department of Architecture
Room # 115
Willcox C Building
Tuskegee, AL 36088
Tel.: 334.727.8329
Fax: 334.724.4196
www.tuskegee.edu

STUDENT AND FACULTY DEMOGRAPHICS

% of Female Students	32
% of International Students	10
% of Minority Students	85
% of Out-of-State U.S. Students	75
No. Full-Time Faculty	10
No. Part-Time Faculty	1
No. Full-Time Students	150

FINANCIAL INFORMATION

Main Source of University Funding	Private & Public
Annual Tuition & Fees (graduate, resident)	
Annual Tuition & Fees (graduate, nonresident)	
Annual Tuition & Fees (undergraduate, resident)	$14,240
Annual Tuition & Fees (undergraduate, nonresident)	$14,000
% Students Receiving Federal Financial Aid	
% Students Receiving University Financial Aid	
% Students Receiving Departmental Financial Aid	
% Students Receiving Scholarships (assistantships or fellowships)	
Average Annual Scholarship for Department	

ARCHITECTURE AND RELATED DEGREE PROGRAMS							
Degree	Min. Yrs. to Complete	Professional Accreditation	# of FT Students	# of PT Students	# of First-Year Students	# of Degrees Conferred	Admissions Requirements
Architecture							
B. Arch	5	NAAB Candidate	120	0	50	15	

UNIVERSITY SETTING

One of the key features of the program at Tuskegee University is its relatively small size, which fosters a very personal and professional approach to professional training. The Department of Architecture has 10 full-time faculty members and an average enrollment of 150 students per year. The students hail from all geographical areas of the country, with the majority coming from the southeast. Alabama residents constitute approximately 25 percent of the total enrollment. Approximately 10 percent of the student body are foreign students and 32 percent are women. Tuskegee University is located in Tuskegee in eastcentral Alabama. Interstate 85 provides convenient access. Tuskegee is a two-hour drive from both Atlanta and Birmingham and a 40-minute drive from the capital of the state, Montgomery. Architectural and environmental design in the region ranges from complex urban architecture to stately antebellum structures. Tuskegee University's campus is designated as a national historic park site, with three buildings that are historic landmarks. Tuskegee is a technical, scientific, and professional institution with an average enrollment of 3,500 students per year. Instruction is organized under five major units: College of Engineering, Architecture & Physical Sciences; College of Agricultural, Environmental & Natural Sciences; College of Business, Organization & Management; College of Liberal Arts/Education; and College of Veterinary Medicine, Nursing & Allied Health. The Department of Architecture is one of the seven departments in the College of Engineering, Architecture & Physical Sciences. The other departments are: aerospace science engineering, chemical engineering, electrical engineering, mechanical engineering, physics and computer science. The Department of Architecture offers degrees in two disciplines: architecture and construction science and management (CSM). The department's faculty possess expertise in a variety of disciplines, including architectural design, architectural practice, urban design, city and regional planning, civil engineering, construction management, and graphic design.

PROGRAM DESCRIPTION

The five-year B Arch program offered at Tuskegee provides a broad architectural training focused on the practice of architecture. The program is a well-rounded liberal education integrated with professional studies. Students are also exposed to other areas of expertise that are related to the environmental design profession. This serves to provide an awareness of the influence that other disciplines have on the physical environment and of career options that may be pursued following receipt of the professional degree.

PROGRAM DESCRIPTION

The curriculum is organized as a five-year Bachelor of Architecture program, based on a 2+3 format. The first two years constitute pre-architecture, and the last three, professional program. Admission to the professional program is granted by the departmental admissions committee based on the successful completion of the prearchitecture program with minimum CGPAs (2.25 overall and 2.5 in architecture courses) and a portfolio review.

Pre-Architecture Program (1st/2nd Years)

The first year covers a study of visual design elements, color, texture, light, scale, etc., as well as a general examination of architecture and the built environment. Also included are the development of visual, graphic, and verbal communication skills, and mathematical understanding. The second year brings an introduction to problem-solving and decision-making techniques, procedures and factors, and a study of physical environmental (qualitative and quantitative) phenomena and their impact upon design. Visual, graphic, and verbal communication skill development are continued.

Professional Program (3rd/4th/5th Years)

In the third year, development of programming and design skills are stressed, together with an increased understanding of the interface between spatial-movement, structural/ mechanical, and site/landscape considerations in building design. Emphasis is given to a resolution of social, economic, and physical user needs. Influence(s) of architectural theory, history, and site/urban context in the building design process is introduced. In addition, quantitative structures and mechanical studies are included. The fourth year provides a more in-depth study of programming and the relating of the user social, economic, and physical needs with the other considerations in the architectural design process that include construction, materials, structures, HVAC, etc. There is a continuation of the examination of architectural theory, history, site/urban context etc. and their impact on architectural design and urban development. Elective study in general subjects is also provided. In the final fifth year, the students examine complex architectural problems in a semi-independent design studio. This studio allows the student to apply all knowledge gained from the preceding four years. In addition, each student completes a terminal project involving the research, programming, and design of an architectural project chosen by the student. The students also take courses in building economics, professional practice, construction, and management.

SPECIAL ACTIVITIES AND PROGRAMS

- Summer internships
- Faculty and student exchange program with University of Illinois at Chicago (UIC)
- Visiting lecturer series
- Annual field trips
- Student awards program
- Student professional and honor societies
- Community service projects with student involvement

FACILITIES

The Department of Architecture is centrally located on the campus in historically significant Wilcox A and B buildings. Together, they provide approximately 30,000 square feet for the Architecture and Construction Science and Management (CSM) Programs. Also, being a part of the College of Engineering, Architecture & Physical Sciences, the Department of Architecture has access to the School of Engineering building and its facilities. The department has the following key facilities: design studios, jury room, computer laboratory, dark room, model shop, and architecture library.

SCHOLARSHIPS AND FINANCIAL AID

Tuskegee's extensive Financial Assistance Program includes university and professional scholarships, Basic (Pell) and Supplemental Educational Opportunity Grants, National Direct Student Loans, fellowships, and work-study programs. The program's scope is broad, and the majority of Tuskegee students receive some type of assistance. Additional information and application forms are available from the Financial Aid Office, Tuskegee University, Tuskegee, AL 36088.

ADMINISTRATION

Legand L. Burge, Jr.: Dean
Richard Dozier, D. Arch, AIA, NOMA: Associate Dean

UNIVERSIDAD DE PUERTO RICO

ADDRESS

Main
Universidad de Puerto Rico
P.O. Box 21909, UPR Station
Rio Piedras, PR 00931
Tel.: 787.250.8581
Fax: 787.763.5377
prrp.upr.edu/archweb

STUDENT AND FACULTY DEMOGRAPHICS

% of Female Students	55
% of International Students	
% of Minority Students	
% of Out-of-State U.S. Students	
No. Full-Time Faculty	25
No. Part-Time Faculty	15
No. Full-Time Students	253
No. Part-Time Students	44

FINANCIAL INFORMATION

Main Source of University Funding	Public
Annual Tuition & Fees (graduate, resident)	
Annual Tuition & Fees (graduate, nonresident)	
Annual Tuition & Fees (undergraduate, resident)	
Annual Tuition & Fees (undergraduate, nonresident)	
% Students Receiving Federal Financial Aid	
% Students Receiving University Financial Aid	
% Students Receiving Departmental Financial Aid	
% Students Receiving Scholarships (assistantships or fellowships)	
Average Annual Scholarship for Department	

ARCHITECTURE AND RELATED DEGREE PROGRAMS							
Degree	Min .Yrs. to Complete	Professional Accreditation	# of FT Students	# of PT Students	# of First-Year Students	# of Degrees Conferred	Admissions Requirements
Architecture							
BS Arch	4	NAAB	207	30	80	38	
M. Arch—2 years	2	NAAB	46	14	27	5	

UNIVERSITY SETTING

The Universidad de Puerto Rico, established in 1903, is the major institution of higher education on the island. The language of instruction is Spanish. The School of Architecture is located on the Río Piedras Campus in San Juan, and has an extensive ensemble of buildings that represent various stylistic manifestations of Puerto Rican architecture, ranging from an original Spanish Revival academic quadrangle (listed in the National Register of Historic Places) to outstanding examples of tropical modernism.

SCHOOL PHILOSOPHY

The School of Architecture aims to educate architects in the spirit of a university environment that propitiates humanistic attitudes and a genuine desire for intellectual growth. Students develop aesthetic sensibilities, reinforce their social conscience and cultivate the highest ethical values for the eventual practice of the profession. The goal is to capacitate the student's ability to understand and to incite the discovery and the creation of knowledge through investigation and creative activities.

PROGRAM DESCRIPTION

Undergraduate Program Through an interdisciplinary program with emphasis on the humanities, the pre-professional Bachelor of Environmental Design (BED) provides a sound general education and a foundation in the fundamental principles of architecture. Students are prepared with the skills needed to enter advanced professional degree programs in architecture, as well as other related fields. They are expected to learn the basics of architectural design technology, structures, and architectural theory and history, and be able to contribute constructively to the creation of a better environment. The first two years of the program combine introductory design studio experiences with basic courses in the arts and sciences. The third and fourth years provide intermediate studio work in architectural design, as well as courses in structures, architectural technology, and architectural history and theory. Elective courses are encouraged in historic preservation, technology, research, and other areas, as well as international exchange opportunities emphasizing Latin America. Studio courses stress the identification, analysis, and solution of real-life problems and the development of decision-making in the design process. Tropical climatology, urban and rural issues, and the special environmental concerns of islands in development are focal areas. The BED degree requires 138 credit hours with a 2.0 grade point average.

AREAS OF FOCUS AND RESEARCH

Focus

The unique culture, geography and history of Puerto Rico facilitate linkages to both English-and Spanish-speaking cultures. Connections to the Americas are sustained through visiting faculty and lecturers, study abroad opportunities, joint research projects, and participation in international student organizations. The design studio is a strength of both the undergraduate and graduate programs and stresses the solution of real-world problems on the Island. This is reinforced in history and technology courses and support by the research goals of the School. A Community Design Center offers students opportunity to combine learning with service, interacting with under represented and economically disadvantaged communities.

Research

The unique archive of the School, Archivo de Arquitectura y Construcción de la UPR (AACUPR), promotes research in the history of Puerto Rican architecture. The many award-winning publications of AACUPR and the journal, InFormA, provide a vehicle for dissemination of faculty and student research. Other centers focus on investigation in technology areas, especially acoustics and biotropical architecture. Research areas include: architectural history and theory, Puerto Rican and Caribbean architecture, acoustics, professional practice, building technology, community design, bioclimatic design, historic preservation, structures, and culture. The University is a Doctoral/Research - Intensive institution as defined by the Carnegie Foundation.

SPECIAL ACTIVITIES AND PROGRAMS

Students are encouraged to participate in relevant social and urban issues through the Community Design Center, which works extensively with economically disadvantaged and under represented communities. Participation is encouraged in local and international design competitions, as well as courses created in specialized subjects. Activities and programs include the following: prearchitecture summer studios; visiting lecturers and faculty; special exhibits on the architectural heritage of Puerto Rico; school newsletter - DeArquitectura and journal - InFormA; and travel programs and summer studios. The school is active in academic and professional organizations, such as the Association of Collegiate Schools of Architecture (ACSA), the American Institute of Architecture Students (AIAS) and the Student Council. Strong affiliations are maintained with organizations in Latin America, such as the Conferencia Latinoamericana de Escuelas y Facultades de Arquitectura (CLEFA) and the Conferencia Latinoamericana de Estudiantes de Arquitectura (CLEA). Academic exchanges with institutions in those areas are encouraged. A Student Affairs Office serves counseling and academic advising needs.

FACILITIES

By spring 2004, a new architecture building will be completed that includes library, archives, exhibition gallery, design studios, classrooms, offices, and specialized areas, which will also serve the university and professional communities. There will be areas dedicated to architectural acoustics, computers, bioclimatic design, digital photography, and model construction. The school has the only specialized architectural library and slide collection in Puerto Rico, with over 30,000 volumes and 100,000 slides, as well as the most extensive architecture and construction archives in Latin America, a repository of documents and a source of research pertaining to Puerto Rican architecture and architectural history.

SCHOLARSHIPS AND FINANCIAL AID

The government of Puerto Rico promotes public higher education through reasonable tuition costs. Federal and local scholarship funds available include: Pell Grants, BEOG, work/study programs, guaranteed loans, honor student grants, and graduate teaching assistantships, among others. The school offers several scholarships in collaboration with the CAAPPR (e.g., Dan-El Viera Scholarship), as well as specific awards such as the Jaime Cobas Prizes and the Juan Marques travel fund.

ADMINISTRATION

Luis Irizarry-Ramirez: Associate Dean
Javier Isado: Director, Undergraduate Program

UNIVERSITÉ DE MONTRÉAL

ADDRESS

Main
Université de Montréal
École d'architecture
Pavillon de la Faculté de l'aménagement
C.P. 6128 Succursale Centre-Ville
Montréal, QC H3C 3J7
Canada
Tel: 514.343.6007
Fax: 514.343.2455
archi@ame.umontreal.ca
www.arc.umontreal.ca

Admissions
Université de Montréal
C.P. 6205, succursale Centre-ville
Montréal, QC H3C 3T5
CANADA

STUDENT AND FACULTY DEMOGRAPHICS

% of Female Students	61
% of International Students	5
% of Minority Students	
% of Out-of-Country	
No. Full-Time Faculty	15
No. Part-Time Faculty	4
No. Full-Time Students	386
No. Part-Time Students	18

FINANCIAL INFORMATION

Main Source of University Funding	Public
Annual Tuition & Fees (graduate, resident)	C$2,280
Annual Tuition & Fees (graduate, nonresident)	C$12,894
Annual Tuition & Fees (undergraduate, resident)	C$2,268
Annual Tuition & Fees (undergraduate, nonresident)	C$12,882
% Students Receiving Federal Financial Aid	
% Students Receiving University Financial Aid	
% Students Receiving Departmental Financial Aid	
% Students Receiving Scholarships (assistantships or fellowships)	
Average Annual Scholarship for Department	C$70,000

ACADEMIC SESSIONS

Fall Quarter/Semester: September to December
  Application Deadline: February 1

Winter Quarter/Semester: January to April
  Application Information: www.etudes.umontreal.ca

ARCHITECTURE AND RELATED DEGREE PROGRAMS

Degree	Min. Yrs. to Complete	Professional Accreditation	# of FT Students	# of PT Students	# of First-Year Students	# of Degrees Conferred	Admissions Requirements
Architecture							
B. Sc., Architecture	3		234	13	92	71	*DEC or equivalent
Maîtrise en architecture	1.5	CACB	152	5	70	59	Undergraduate Architecture degree, Portfolio

* DEC = Diplôme d'études collégiales (Québec education system) or equivalent

All courses are given in French. Students whose native language is not French may be required to pass a French language proficiency test.

SPECIALIZATIONS

Architectural Design	History	Photography	Tectonics
Computer-Aided Design	Housing	Preservation	Theory/Criticism
Engineering	International Development	Professional Practice	Urban Planning and Design
Environment/Sustainability	International/Regional Architecture	Sustainability	

UNIVERSITY SETTING

Université de Montréal is the main French-speaking university in North America. The University Campus and the School of Architecture are both located in Montréal, the second largest city in Canada. They are situated on the north side of Mount Royal, ten minutes from Montréal's vibrant downtown. The University offers numerous services, one of which is the CEPSUM, an excellent sport facility (http://www.cepsum.umontreal.ca/) home to the University's sport teams, "Les Carabins" (www.carabins.umontreal.ca) and other programs such as The Anglophone Student Support Program (http://www.futuretudiants.umontreal.ca/prospective/angl_stud_supp_progr/overview.html).

The School of Architecture resides in the Pavillon de la Faculté de l'aménagement, which was renovated and expanded after 1994 using the competition's winning submission drafted by well-known Saucier + Perrotte / Menkes Shooner Dagenais architectes. The University's Exhibition Center, including its extensive collection (http://www.expo.umontreal.ca/), the Institut d'urbanisme, the École d'architecture de paysage and the École de design industriel are also located within this pavilion.

Montréal has an exceptional architectural heritage that begins with French and British colonial architectures, it includes the finest examples of the international style, and features some more recent award-winning projects. Montréal offers a variety of architectural lectures, exhibitions, and activities, many of these presented by the internationally renowned Canadian Centre for Architecture (CCA) (http://www.cca.qc.ca/). Furthermore, Montréal is well known for its thriving cultural life, and its numerous museums and galleries.

SCHOOL PHILOSOPHY

The School originated as part of the École des Beaux-Arts and subsequently joined the University in 1965. An important shift of paradigms, from Beaux-Arts to Modernism, led the School to conform to the reformist and problem-solving attitudes of the time. During the 1980s, the School was widely known as the École de Montréal's birthplace, a movement that conjured a typo-morphological approach and the preservation of its architectural heritage. In recent years, the School has assigned a greater emphasis on the design process. Open to advanced technologies, the School's goal is to uphold a strong studio culture. The «Atelier d'architecture», the studio, is a critical learning environment providing knowledge and experience in the process of integrated design, as well as an introduction to research by design.

PROGRAM DESCRIPTION

The School offers both undergraduate and graduate degrees, the later being a professional degree.

The undergraduate B. Sc. Arch. is a three-year program that offers a general instruction in architecture. Its main focus is on design and representation, architecture and construction, and history and theory. Students having obtained this degree have the option to apply either to the architectural professional master's degree or to graduate studies in other fields of study, such as project management, preservation, and urban studies. The B.Sc. Arch. prepares graduates to work as assistants in architectural and design offices. During their third and final year, the students are given the opportunity to select a studio class of their choice, as well as some of their theory courses. Transferring students are not accepted, however applicants from other schools may obtain an advanced standing.

The year and a half Maîtrise en architecture is a professional degree. Candidates must have completed a pre-professional degree in architecture in order to be admitted. The master's program offers six different orientations: conservation of built environment, computer-aided design, industrialization and construction, project management, urban design and exploration in architectural design.

AREAS OF FOCUS AND RESEARCH

The School of Architecture seeks to establish and maintain a synergy between research and education.

Students may join research teams and laboratories as remunerated research assistants. The School benefits from the presence and contribution of guest teachers and adjunct professors, most of them practitioners in the Montréal area. The transfer of practical knowledge is of utmost importance and thus insures a healthy association between the School and the professional milieu. Research is based on and structured by teams and laboratories, joining professors and their associates. These include: Groupe de recherche en conception assistée par ordinateur (GRCAO, http://www.grcao.umontreal.ca), Groupe de recherche Industrialisation Forum (GRIF, http://www.grif.umontreal.ca), Groupe de recherche en architecture urbaine (GRAU), MedialabAU (http://www.medialabAU.umontreal.ca), Groupe de recherche en conservation de l'environnement bâti (GRCEB), Laboratoire d'étude de l'architecture potentielle (LEAP, http://www.leap.umontreal.ca).

The Canada research chair on built heritage (Chaire de recherche du Canada en patrimoine bâti, www.patrimoinebati.umontreal.ca) is also part of the School's research groups.

Furthermore, the School is part of l'Institut de recherche en histoire de l'architecture's (IRHA) consortium including McGill University, and the Canadian Centre for Architecture (CCA). The School has obtained grants and funds from all the major research agencies in Québec and Canada, and some from the private sector.

SPECIAL ACTIVITIES AND PROGRAMS

Conferences and exhibitions are organized on a regular basis, and students are encouraged to benefit from the numerous activities hosted and organized by the Centre Canadien d'Architecture (CCA). The School has an exchange program for third-year students wishing to study abroad. Agreements have been made with schools in France, Belgium, Germany, Switzerland, Italy, Mexico, Brazil and USA. Furthermore, the School frequently organizes design studios abroad that were, in the past few years, held in Mexico, Barcelona, Los Angeles, and Paris. Every year, the students are presented with two week-long charrettes. The first is the CCA's charrette that reaches students of all Québec schools; the other is themed on sustainable built environment. The school also organizes advanced-studies seminars on different theoretical and critical subjects, where eminent international scholars are invited to participate.

FACILITIES

The Faculty Library owns more than 65,000 books and has a great selection of periodicals, all in the fields of architecture, landscape architecture, industrial design and town planning. Computer laboratories, such as the Apple Design and Modeling Center and the PC Center are available for student use. Furthermore, students have access to several workshops equipped with various electrical power tools for the construction and production of their design models.

SCHOLARSHIPS AND FINANCIAL AID

Scholarships are available from the University's graduate faculty. Furthermore, the School offers many scholarships each year, most of them contributions from donators within the professional community. Extensive information can be obtained on the school's, the faculty's and the university's web sites.

ADMINISTRATION

Anne Cormier, OAQ; Directrice
Giovanni De Paoli, PhD; Doyen,
    Faculté de l'aménagement
Georges Adamczyk; Admissions, B.Sc.Arch.

UNIVERSITÉ LAVAL

ADDRESS

Main
Université Laval
École d'Architecture
1, côte de la Fabrique
Québec, QC G1K 7P4
Canada
Tel.: 418.656.2543
Fax: 418.656.2785
arc@arc.ulaval.ca
www.arc.ulaval.ca

Admissions
Bureau du Registraire
2440 Pavillono J.-C.-Bonenfant
Université Laval
Québec, QCG1K 7P4
Canada
Tel: 418.656.3080
Fax: 418.656.5216
reg@reg.ulaval.ca
www.ulaval.ca/reg

STUDENT AND FACULTY DEMOGRAPHICS

% of Female Students
% of International Students
% of Minority Students
No. Full-Time Faculty
No. Part-Time Faculty
No. Full-Time Students
No. Part-Time Students

FINANCIAL INFORMATION

Main Source of University Funding	Public
Annual Tuition & Fees (graduate)	C$2,928
Annual Tuition & Fees (undergraduate)	C$2,928
% Students Receiving Federal Financial Aid	
% Students Receiving University Financial Aid	
% Students Receiving Departmental Financial Aid	
% Students Receiving Scholarships (assistantships or fellowships)	
Average Annual Scholarship for Department	

ACADEMIC SESSIONS

Fall Semester: September to December
    Application Deadline: Undergraduate: March 1, Graduate: flexible

Spring Semester: January to May

ARCHITECTURE AND RELATED DEGREE PROGRAMS

Degree	Min. Yrs. to Complete	Professional Accreditation	# of FT Students	# of PT Students	# of First-Year Students	# of Degrees Conferred	Admissions Requirements
Architecture							
M Sc Arch	2						Undergraduate degree
M. Arch	1.5	CACB					
PhD	3						
Urban Design							
M Sc UD	1.5						Undergraduate Architecture degree, Prof. Architecture degree

UNIVERSITY SETTING

As the oldest French-speaking university in North America, with over 35,000 students, Université Laval is firmly established as a leader among large universities worldwide. Located in the heart of Old Québec, in the walls of the Seminary, a 17th-century architectural landmark, the School of Architecture offers a rich physical and cultural environment. The School is well-served by public transport and numerous services. Students can find housing nearby or lodge in the campus residences.

SCHOOL PHILOSOPHY

The School of Architecture offers its students a balanced education so that they can become knowledgeable and creative architects capable of yielding innovative solutions to complex architectural problems and asserting rigorous judgments on professional and ethical matters. As a design and research center, the School is dedicated to culturally and environmentally responsive architecture that contributes to quality of life. Students and faculty are invited to participate in the university's substantial International Profile and are actively involved in projects in developing countries, as well as with native communities.

PROGRAM DESCRIPTION
Undergraduate Program

Since September 2000, in order to gain access to the profession, students must complete a Bachelor of Architecture and a Master of Architecture, followed by a three-year training period. The undergraduate program aims at raising students' awareness of ideas and values affecting architectural practice, as well as the balanced development of theoretical, technical and methodological skills. Teaching is structured around studios addressing realistic and contemporary architectural and urban design problems.

Students seeking this degree take a total of 96 credits in a three-year curriculum. Mandatory courses take up 69 credits, while electives comprise the 27 remaining credits. A minimum of five studios is required. Advanced studios are offered with associated theory classes, allowing for in-depth training and important and/or emerging practice fields. Undergraduate students are encouraged to study abroad through the university's International Profile. This program depends on reciprocal agreements, which means the School of Architecture plays host to a contingent of foreign students as large as the one it sends to partner institutions in France, Mexico, Switzerland, Denmark, Lebanon, Vietnam, etc. Participants benefit from a unique opportunity to broaden intellectual horizons, gain intercultural awareness and comprehend a second, or even third language.

Graduate Program

Students enrolled in the Master of Architecture program, fulfilling the requirements for obtaining a professional degree in architecture, must choose two of the following concentrations: Construction and Design, Environment Control Systems, Architectural Conservation, Programming and Design, Virtual Architecture, Urban Design and Habitat and Cultures. Courses relating to architectural practice are taught at this level.

This program aims at developing social responsibility and ethical bases, providing reflective and analytical tools, as well as testing participatory design methods. A strong focus is placed upon research-based design.

Master of Science (Architecture-essay): This program offers seminars, labs and project-oriented coursework in the field of Urban Design. The curriculum is organized around a core studio where case studies (local, national or international) with real clients and participatory design methods are favored. Students must produce an urban design project and an essay as their final assignment. Master of Science (Architecture-thesis): Training in research and development is open to all candidates with a relevant undergraduate degree in three broad fields of study where faculty are actively involved: Housing and Urban Form, Computer Simulation for CAD, and Environment Control Systems and Construction Theory. A Ph.D. program is in the process of being approved by the University.

AREAS OF FOCUS AND RESEARCH
Focus

FocusRegularly, undergraduate and graduate studio work is based on real community projects, competitions and/or research projects. For instance, as part of a Construction and Design studio (2001–2002), two Laval teams were bestowed with Excellence Awards in the ACSA/STI Hollow Structural Sections Design and Engineering Challenge (Airport: Gateway to the City).

Also, many important research groups, where faculty and students work in collaboration, are firmly established at the School: Groupe de Recherche en Ambiances Physiques (environment control systems), Centre de Recherche en Aménagement et Développement (planning), Groupe Interdisciplinaire de Recherche sur la Banlieue (suburbs) and "Projet Vietnam" (population density in Hanoi).

Research

The School of Architecture offers three major research fields at the graduate level: Housing and Urban Form where courses on the following subjects are offered: history, morphogenesis and cultural aspects of urban form, architectural conservation, typomorphology, urban design and cooperation in developing countries; Environment Control Systems and Construction Theory in which thermal controls, lighting, acoustics, psychological and physical comfort, architectural theory, as well as materials and tectonics are studied; and Computer Simulation for CAD where 3D modeling and rendering techniques, knowledge representation and computer interface, and CAD simulation and visualization are examined.

SPECIAL ACTIVITES AND PROGRAMS

A conference series is offered every year with lectures from renowned architects from Québec and other Cana-

dian provinces, as well as from the United States and Europe. Lunch debate series are also held to encourage exchanges between students and local practitioners. Off-campus study programs are offered through exchange programs with architecture schools in France, Mexico, Switzerland, Belgium, Denmark, Lebanon and Vietnam. Annual academic visits to various destinations are organized, such as California, Chicago, Boston, Toronto and other East coast locations. Participation in design activities, such as charrettes, and contests is encouraged and regularly attended by students of the School of Architecture. In addition to the activities listed above, graduate students are invited to present papers at local, national and international conferences and are encouraged to participate in existing research teams working in Québec, Mexico and Vietnam.

FACILITIES

Completely renovated, the School of Architecture is constantly adapting its facilities, laboratories and equipment to fit the changing needs of its students, faculty and mission. The School is equipped with the latest computer technology, providing every studio workstation with highspeed network capabilities and CAD software. The School offers various types of laboratories: computer, infographic, acoustic and climatology. Students also have access to a model workshop, an architectural library, and a construction and materials electronic library. Also, a Café and an Architectural Supply Store are managed by students.

SCHOLARSHIPS AND FINANCIAL AID

Students from Québec have universal access to the Loan and Bursary Program of Québec's Ministry of Education. Outstanding Canadian candidates applying for a Master of Architecture should consider provincial and national scholarship programs. Tuition waivers are possible through Québec's Ministry of Education for students applying from various developing and/or French-speaking countries. A fair number of scholarships, teaching and research assistantships are offered yearly to outstanding graduate candidates.

ADMINISTRATION

Richard Pleau: Dean

Jacques White: Director, School of Architecture

Claude Demers: Director Master's Program in Architecture

André Potvin: Director Baccalaureate Program in Architecture

Geneviève Vachon: Director Master of Science in Architecture Program

Emilien Vachon, Director

UNIVERSITY AT BUFFALO, SUNY

ADDRESS

Main
University at Buffalo, SUNY
School of Architecture & Planning
3435 Main Street
Hayes Hall Rm. 112
Buffalo, NY 14214-3087
Tel.: 716.829.3483
Fax: 716.829.3256
ap-architecture@buffalo.edu
www.ap.buffalo.edu

STUDENT AND FACULTY DEMOGRAPHICS

% of Female Students	31
% of International Students	13
% of Minority Students	19
% of Out-of-State U.S. Students	8
No. Full-Time Faculty	21
No. Part-Time Faculty	23
No. Full-Time Students	523
No. Part-Time Students	5

FINANCIAL INFORMATION

Main Source of University Funding	Public
Annual Tuition & Fees (graduate, resident)	$8,334
Annual Tuition & Fees (graduate, nonresident)	$12,354
Annual Tuition & Fees (undergraduate, resident)	$6,278
Annual Tuition & Fees (undergraduate, nonresident)	$12,538
% Students Receiving Federal Financial Aid	72
% Students Receiving University Financial Aid	33
% Students Receiving Departmental Financial Aid	50
% Students Receiving Scholarships (assistantships or fellowships)	24
Average Annual Scholarship for Department	$5,300

ACADEMIC SESSIONS

Fall Semester: August to December; Application Deadline: January 15
   for priority consideration
Spring Semester: January to May

ARCHITECTURE AND RELATED DEGREE PROGRAMS

Degree	Min. Yrs. to Complete	Professional Accreditation	# of FT Students	# of PT Students	# of First-Year Students	# of Degrees Conferred	Admissions Requirements
Architecture							
BS Arch (pre-professional)	4		389	5	130	50	SAT, ACT, TOEFL, Rec. Letters, Essay
M. Arch	3.5	NAAB	66	0	20	19	Undergraduate degree, GRE, TOEFL, Portfolio, Rec. Letters, Essay
M. Arch	2	NAAB	54	0	24	26	Undergraduate Architecture degree, GRE, TOEFL, Portfolio, Rec. Letters, Essay
M. Arch + M.B.A.	3	NAAB	3	0	2	1	Undergraduate Architecture degree, GRE, TOEFL, Portfolio, Rec. Letters, Essay
M. Arch. + M.F.A.	3	NAAB	3	0	2	3	Undergraduate Architecture degree, GRE, TOEFL, Portfolio, Rec. Letters, Essay
M. Arch + M.U.P	3	NAAB	7	0	4	3	Undergraduate Architecture degree, GRE, TOEFL, Portfolio, Rec. Letters, Essay
Master of Architecture II (M.Arch.1.5 / post-professional)	1.5		2	0	1	1	Prof. Architecture degree, GRE, TOEFL, Portfolio, Rec. Letters, Essay
Environmental Design							
Bachelor of Arts in Environmental Design (urban planning & design)	4		123	5	37	26	SAT, ACT, TOEFL, Rec. Letters, Essay
Planning							
Master of Urban Planning (M.U.P.)	2	PAB	94	4	40	41	Undergraduate degree, TOEFL, Rec. Letters, Essay
M.U.P. + J.D.	4	PAB	4	0	1	0	Undergraduate degree, TOEFL, Rec. Letters, Essay

SPECIALIZATIONS

Architectural Design
Art and Design

Computer-Aided Design
Environment/Sustainability

Professional Practice
Tectonics

Theory/Criticism
Urban Planning and Design

ARCHITECTURE PROGRAM SUMMARY

University at Buffalo offers undergraduate and graduate degrees in a configuration commonly known as "4+2": four years of undergraduate study leading to a bachelor of science degree, and two years of graduate work, leading to the first professional degree, the master of architecture (M.Arch.). The university also offers a 3½-year M.Arch. for graduate students holding undergraduate or graduate degrees in a field other than architecture, and dual-degree options with the Department of Urban and Regional Planning, the School of Management, and the Department of Media Study.

UNIVERSITY SETTING

The University at Buffalo is the State University of New York's premier public center for graduate and professional education, and the state's largest and most comprehensive public university. The University at Buffalo stands in the first rank among the nation's research-intensive public universities. Students actively participate in research alongside approximately 1,600 full-time and 1,000 part-time faculty, and over 90 research centers. Over 28,000 students pursue their academic interests through more than 300 undergraduate, graduate and professional degree programs. UB Students work and study on three distinct campuses. The North Campus, South Campus, and Downtown Buffalo Campus are connected by university shuttles and Buffalo's metro system. Buffalo enjoys a city-wide park system designed by Olmsted, and a unique architectural heritage that includes built works by masters such as Wright, Sullivan, Saarinen, Richardson and Bunshaft. The University at Buffalo attracts international students from all over the world, and the university's emphasis on international education has inspired undergraduate students to study abroad at five times the national average for study abroad participation.

SCHOOL PHILOSOPHY

The School of Architecture and Planning is the only program in The State University of New York system to offer both the accredited Master of Architecture (M.Arch.) degree and the accredited Master of Urban Planning degree (M.U.P.). The school shares the university's research-oriented mission. Given this professional and disciplinary responsibility, our faculty and students participate in the production of new methods of theorizing and practicing architecture. As a public institution, we strive to instill in our graduates a concern for the public good in shaping the built—and conserving the natural—environment.

PROGRAM DESCRIPTION

The Department of Architecture is committed to the notion that architecture relies on a synthesis of knowledge and expertise gained in many areas of study from the arts and humanities to the sciences. Architecture engages its own core disciplinary practices while simultaneously integrating knowledge from many other fields. The breadth and depth of the University at Buffalo architecture curriculum prepares students to be leaders in an inherently synthetic discipline.

The Bachelor of Science in Architecture degree is a pre-professional baccalaureate degree designed to provide students with a base of concepts and skills in the field of architecture. It allows students to complete all the prerequisites to be eligible to enter a two-year ac-

credited professional Master of Architecture (M.Arch.) degree program. The undergraduate curriculum is structured around the belief that preparation for a career in architecture requires both a comprehensive liberal arts education and core coursework in the major. Students typically enter the undergraduate program as freshman and experience four years of architecture coursework including eight consecutive design studios. The pre-professional Bachelor of Science in Architecture degree requires a minimum of 128 credit hours. The department also offers an architecture minor, open to all undergraduate students, which requires 21 credit hours of architecture coursework. Transfer students without design studio experience are typically placed in the first-year studio sequence.

The Department of Architecture offers a professional Master of Architecture degree, which students work toward through one of two tracks configured for individuals with differing educational backgrounds. Students who hold a four-year, pre-professional degree in architecture from an accredited school of architecture may enter the 2-year track leading to a professional M.Arch. Students who hold non-architecture baccalaureate degrees may enter the 3.5-year program leading to a professional M.Arch. The department offers a post-professional 1.5-year M.Arch. research program. In addition, students may elect to pursue dual degree options with the Department of Urban and Regional Planning (M.Arch./MUP), the School of Management (M.Arch./MBA), and the Department of Media Study (M.Arch./MFA). Graduate students will study within one of four graduate research groups: Inclusive Design, Sustainable Urban and Natural Environments, Situated Technologies, and Material Culture.

AREAS OF FOCUS AND RESEARCH

Research activity is a fundamental component of the architecture curriculum, permitting students to take full advantage of faculty expertise and allowing faculty and students to regularly work alongside one another. Faculty have formed organized centers to conduct research. The Center for Inclusive Design and Environmental Access (IDEA Center) conducts research on issues related to universal design and environmental access. The Urban Design Project (UDP) is a service-teaching and-learning center devoted to the critical practice of urban design. The Center for Virtual Architecture (CVA) is dedicated to projects that explore the impact of digital media on architectural theory, production, representation and pedagogy.

Faculty and student collaborative research and scholarship shape the focus of the program's curriculum. Graduate students work alongside faculty in one of four graduate research groups: Inclusive Design, Sustainable Urban and Natural Environments, Situated Technologies, and Material Culture.

INCLUSIVE DESIGN is design for all. A global movement that seeks to improve the usability of environments, products, and systems for the widest range of people, inclusive design is based on the principles of social justice.

MATERIAL CULTURE projects forward from the history of material innovation in architecture, and the research group explores ways in which the culture of materials shapes our environments and contributes to our constructive sensibilities. Faculty and student research scrutinizes the transformation from idea to artifact.

SITUATED TECHNOLOGIES focuses on the design of artifacts, spaces and media that are responsive to their context. Faculty and student research investigates the possibilities offered by computational technologies for exploring new forms of social interaction with and within the built environment.

SUSTAINABLE URBAN AND NATURAL ENVIRONMENTS offers an intense exploration of the role that our discipline plays in the making of the next world. This focus requires collaborative association with allied professions and disciplines, reinforced by our close relationship with the Department of Urban and Regional Planning, and through existing joint degree programs.

SPECIAL ACTIVITIES AND PROGRAMS

Architecture students are encouraged to study abroad. The department offers international opportunities in Denmark, Germany and Belgium during the academic year. Over the summer months, graduate and undergraduate students alike may participate in global studios offered at ever-changing international locations including Costa Rica, France, Japan, Ireland, Italy and Spain.

The department hosts the Peter Reyner Banham and John and Magda McHale Fellowships each year which bring accomplished scholars and practitioners to the school to teach and conduct research. The Clarkson Chair and the Pearce Visiting Critic are endowed positions that bring distinguished architects and critics to the department annually.

The Department of Architecture offers training for graduate students considering a career in academia through funded teaching assistantships in the freshman design studios and in other courses.

FACILITIES

Historic Hayes Hall is the 62,000-square-foot home of the school's administrative offices, departmental faculty offices, research centers, Architecture and Planning Library, Visual Resources Center, Dyett Exhibition Gallery, and two digital media laboratories. Crosby Hall, with over 63,000 square feet of space, is home to the school's design studios and additional digital workshops, including the 3-D print laboratory. Digital technology is distributed throughout the studios. Parker Hall is home to the Materials and Methods Shop, a 7,000 square foot high-bay space, and one of the finest shops in any architecture school in the nation.

SCHOLARSHIPS AND FINANCIAL AID

In addition to federal, state and significant university aid available to both graduate and undergraduate students, the Department of Architecture has several scholarship programs that help support graduate education, including the Cannon Design Scholarship, the Brunkow Fellowships, and the Pella Award. The department offers tuition scholarships to qualified students based on academic merit. In addition, the department has a number of paid teaching and graduate assistantships.

ADMINISTRATION

Brian Carter, RIBA: Dean
Mehrdad Hadighi, RA: Chair
RJ Multari: Director of Advisement
Sue McDonald: Undergraduate Secretary
Shannon Phillips: Coordinator of Administration
Debi Smith: Assistant to the Chair

UNIVERSITY OF ARIZONA

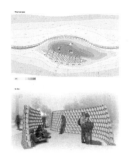

ADDRESS

Main
University of Arizona
School of Architecture
1040 N. Olive Road
P.O. Box 210075
Tucson, AZ 85721-0075
Tel.: 520.621.6752
Fax: 520.621.8700
cala.arizona.edu

STUDENT AND FACULTY DEMOGRAPHICS

% of Female Students	38
% of International Students	7
% of Minority Students	19
% of Out-of-State U.S. Students	37
No. Full-Time Faculty	19
No. Part-Time Faculty	17
No. Full-Time Students	378
No. Part-Time Students	31

FINANCIAL INFORMATION

Main Source of University Funding	Public
Annual Tuition & Fees (graduate, resident)	$6,932
Annual Tuition & Fees (graduate, nonresident)	$14,890
Annual Tuition & Fees (undergraduate, resident)	$6,142
Annual Tuition & Fees (undergraduate, nonresident)	$19,276
% Students Receiving Federal Financial Aid	
% Students Receiving University Financial Aid	
% Students Receiving Departmental Financial Aid	10
% Students Receiving Scholarships	93% graduates
(assistantships or fellowships)	29% in school
Average Annual Scholarship for Department	$950

ACADEMIC SESSIONS

Fall Semester: August to December;
  Application Deadline: May 1 (domestic)
Spring Semester: January to May;
  Application Deadline: November 1 (domestic)

ARCHITECTURE AND RELATED DEGREE PROGRAMS

Degree	Min. Yrs. to Complete	Professional Accreditation	# of FT Students	# of PT Students	# of First-Year Students	# of Degrees Conferred	Admissions Requirements
Architecture							
B. Arch	5	NAAB	348	31	170	38	3.0 GPA, 1110 SAT, 24 ACT
M. Arch—2 years	2		25	3	13	10	Undergraduate Architecture degree, Prof. Architecture degree, Portfolio, Rec. Letters, Essay
Landscape Architecture							
MLA	3	LAAB	47	1	15	13	Undergraduate degree, TOEFL, Rec. Letters (3), 3.2 GPA
Planning							
MS Urban Planning	2	PAB	38		8		Undergraduate degree, TOEFL, Rec. Letters (3), 3.2 GPA

SPECIALIZATIONS

Please see specializations under "Research"

ARCHITECTURE PROGRAM SUMMARY

The mission of the College of Architecture and Landscape Architecture (CALA) supports the institutional vision of the University of Arizona with the following goals:

- To Unite: integrating the study of Architecture and Landscape Architecture into a whole, resulting in a complete and interdisciplinary education.
- To Experiment: fostering an environment of discovery through experience and investigation in interdisciplinary laboratories, both natural and controlled.
- To Apply: educating students to be professionals in a global context through the application of knowledge.
- To Engage: reaching out and interacting beyond the university thus having a significant impact on the entire region.

The College is comprised of two professional programs focused on the development and application of the theoretical and practical knowledge necessary for the effective evolution of human settlements. The College offers an accredited five-year program leading to the professional degree, Bachelor of Architecture (B.Arch). A post-professional master's program (M.Arch) is also offered by the School of Architecture and an accredited graduate program in Landscape Architecture (MLA) is offered by the School of Landscape Architecture.

UNIVERSITY SETTING

The University of Arizona is located in the city of Tucson in southern Arizona's Sonoran Desert, an arid region of strong cultural diversity, extraordinary natural grace, and powerful ethic–aesthetic provocation. Tucson is a decentralized community with a metropolitan population of 850,000. The University of Arizona was founded in 1885, serves more than 36,000 students in 17 colleges, has 39 research and service divisions and is ranked among the top twenty research universities in the nation.

SCHOOL PHILOSOPHY

Studies at the University of Arizona are grounded on the proposition that architecture is a sensible, technical and aesthetic activity that serves the needs of shelter —the making of shelter is an imaginative cultural research that seeks to establish dwelling as a human aspiration to a graceful life. This pursuit must be inflected by the identity of the Sonoran Desert, the geography of Arizona and the culture of the Southwest— promoting an intertwined land ethic–aesthetic research binary. This practice must be observant of local traditions, tempered by material circumstances, and expressive of the ethos of time and place.

PROGRAM DESCRIPTION

Undergraduate Program

The five-year course of studies leading to the professionally accredited Bachelor of Architecture is organized in the following sequence: foundation, professional phase and capstone. The first-year foundation introduces elementary principles and technical skills that give students opportunity to test the field and prepare a portfolio for admission into the professional phase. Years two-through-four, professional phase, are aimed at developing the core of humanistic knowledge, creative ingenuity and technical craftsmanship that prepare students for professional practice. The capstone year focuses on experimentation and synthesis on topics leading to definition and development of work in

preparation for professional licensure. The architecture curriculum is an ensemble of four subjects: technologies, theory and history, communication methods and professional practices, all of which must be appropriately integrated to each level of the studio sequence. The curriculum is distributed in three pedagogical settings: studios, laboratories and classrooms. The classroom is the forum of presentation and discussion of theoretical and factual knowledge in support of sensible design. The laboratory is the playhouse of empirical experimentation, testing and demonstration of virtual and real hypothesis of design. The architectural studio is the theater of imaginative propositions of design and synthesis of empirical fact and heuristic theory.

Graduate Program

The Graduate Program advances further the proposition that the Sonora Desert is a unique natural and cultural laboratory for architectural experimentation, intertwining with greater precision the notions of land ethic (nature–grace) and aesthetic research (idea–energy.) The Graduate Program is focused on the development and refinement of methods of applied research of traditional and experimental design aimed at bioclimatic and cultural regionalism. In-house laboratories for testing and modeling energy performance include the House Energy Doctor and Visual Simulation Laboratory. Interdisciplinary collaboration with the college's Graduate School of Landscape Architecture and the Drachman Institute for Land and Regional Development expand the research resources. The prospect is further enhanced by access to the University's Arid Land Studies, the Southwest Center and top-ranked graduate programs in humanities and sciences. The School offers four emphasis areas: (1) Design & Energy Conservation, research on environmental comfort, material and construction technologies, and theory and design methods; (2) Urban Design & Infrastructure, research of patterns of settlement and urban growth, environmental quality and land ethics emblematic of arid zones; and (3) Preservation Studies, maintenance of the built and natural environments as part of a holistic conservation ethic; (4) Emerging Material Technologies.

AREAS OF FOCUS AND RESEARCH

Focus

Thematically designated Design Studios: foundation, architectural composition, ergonomics, land ethic, tectonic assembly, technical systems, urban form, research options and capstone. Integrated Technology sequence, with modular distribution of Materials & Methods, Structures, and Environmental Controls-focused on laboratory-based material experimentation and empirical demonstration. Theory & History sequence based on a heuristic disposition to act as if "we have the past in us as memory, the future as desire, in the present we must make history." Practice sequence focused on development of skills of communication, construction documents, interaction with building trades and public sector, and hands-on experience in design/build collaborative projects.

Research

Energetic agendas in the following topics: Design & Energy Conservation: experimentation and refinement of design methods, environmental comfort and material technologies appropriate for arid lands—primarily through Design/Build studios, House Energy Doctor, and Visual Simulation Laboratory. Emerging Material Technologies: advanced analysis, testing and modeling of the properties or new and traditional materials. Urban Design & Infrastructure: research of patterns of settle-

ment and urban growth integrating physiography with human needs, environmental quality and land ethics in arid zones, primarily through the CPDW, Urban Laboratory, Drachman Institute, and Arid Lands Studies. Preservation Studies: definition of holistic conservation ethics in the geographical laboratory of the Greater Southwest primarily in collaboration with The Southwest Center.

Emerging opportunities are in collaborative and interdisciplinary studio and research projects that include landscape architects and planners. Participation in these opportunities affords students to experience allied program areas of focus such as landscape ecology, sustainable tourism and community revitalization.

SPECIAL ACTIVITIES AND PROGRAMS

A thematically organized Lecture Series, light–matter, force–form, nature–grace, geography–geometry, tradition–experimentation, etc. brings a wide spectrum of artists, humanists and scientists, who are internationally prominent practitioners and educators that speak of evolving theories and practices from the vantage point of their own disciplines. Regular exhibits feature the work of internationally prominent architects and artists. Annual exhibits of student work include:

- Design Excellence Awards and Senior Capstone Projects.
- Distinguished Visitors Studio with internationally recognized practicing architects.
- The Community Planning & Design Workshop is the service outreach arm of the College.
- Structured academic exchanges and summer travel programs in Latin America (Chile and Mexico) and Europe (Denmark, Italy, Greece and Spain).
- Internship in regional professional practices.
- IMAGEN, on-line digital visual archive.
- Active student chapter of the AIAS.

FACILITIES

The College has recently completed construction of a new 32,000-sq-ft extension that includes studios, classrooms, small auditorium, visual resource collection, computer laboratory, and a 7,500-sq-ft state of the art materials laboratory for research and experimentation with metal, glass, ceramics, concrete and digital fabrication (cnc milling, stereo lithography, vacuum forming and laser cutting). The Lecture Series is held in a sophisticated 300+ capacity adjacent auditorium. The architecture library is housed with fine arts and music in the adjacent School of Music Building.

SCHOLARSHIPS AND FINANCIAL AID

Applicants are encouraged to contact the Office of Student Financial Aid, which annually administers the awarding of more than thirty million dollars in aid to over 12,000 students. Scholarships, grants and loans including Pell, NDL, GSL and work-study programs may be available. The School of Architecture also administers the award of approximately 35 scholarships to currently enrolled upper-division students. A limited number of graduate scholarships, fellowships and teaching assistantships are available to graduate students.

ADMINISTRATION

Janice Cervelli: Dean
R. Brooks Jeffery: Associate Dean
Susan K. Moody: Assistant Dean
Laura H. Hollengreen: Interim Director

UNIVERSITY OF ARKANSAS

ADDRESS

Main
University of Arkansas
School of Architecture
120 Vol Walker Hall
Fayetteville, AR 72701
Tel: 479.575.4705
Fax: 479.575.7429
architecture.uark.edu

STUDENT AND FACULTY DEMOGRAPHICS

% of Female Students	29
% of International Students	5
% of Minority Students	14
% of Out-of-State U.S. Students	30
No. Full-Time Faculty	16
No. Part-Time Faculty	7
No. Full-Time Students	292
No. Part-Time Students	23

FINANCIAL INFORMATION

Main Source of University Funding	Public
Annual Tuition & Fees (graduate, resident)	
Annual Tuition & Fees (graduate, nonresident)	
Annual Tuition & Fees (undergraduate, resident)	$8,100
Annual Tuition & Fees (undergraduate, nonresident)	$16,600
% Students Receiving Federal Financial Aid	52.9
% Students Receiving University Financial Aid	13
% Students Receiving Departmental Financial Aid	
% Students Receiving Scholarships (assistantships or fellowships)	32
Average Annual Scholarship for Department	$1,850

ACADEMIC SESSIONS

Fall Semester: August-December
Spring Semester: January-May
Summer Session: May-July

ARCHITECTURE AND RELATED DEGREE PROGRAMS

Degree	Min. Yrs. to Complete	Professional Accreditation	# of FT Students	# of PT Students	# of First-Year Students	# of Degrees Conferred	Admissions Requirements
Architecture							
B. Arch	5	NAAB	261	15	106	31	
BS Arch Studies	4		21	7	1	10	
Landscape Architecture							
B LArch	5	LAAB	68	9	28	4	
BS LArch Studies	4		3	2	1	2	

ARCHITECTURE PROGRAM SUMMARY

The Department of Architecture offers the five-year accredited Bachelor of Architecture degree and the four-year bachelor of Science in Architectural Studies. Our degrees balance the requirements, constraints, and challenges of an undergraduate professional education with the necessity for education in the humanities, the arts, and the sciences that comprise the intellectual core of a university education. Knowledge and skills gained through our educational efforts serve as the base for intellectual growth and in so doing promote the innovative, even inventive, application of specialized knowledge in defining and solving architectural problems and expanding the peripheries of practice. For students who wish to enter the architecture profession, we provide preparation for successful internship and for the increasing scope of responsibilities in practice, and we provide the impetus for life-long learning. At the center of our efforts is the necessity for understanding and knowledge in the history of architecture and our place in it, in theory and value-based philosophy, and in the range of technologies by which we implement and sustain our interventions in the built environment. With ever increasing frequency, our graduates pursue, in the work place and through graduate education, varied careers within architecture and its allied professions. We have structured our curriculum for the education of architects, with the belief that design is a necessary endeavor of a civilized society.

UNIVERSITY SETTING

The University of Arkansas is a nationally competitive, student-centered research university serving Arkansas and the world. The University of Arkansas, Fayetteville, serves as the major center of liberal and professional education and as the primary land-grant campus in the state. In addition, it is Arkansas' major source of theoretical and applied research and the provider of a wide range of public services to people throughout the state and nation. In serving its three-fold mission of teaching, research, and public service, the University strives to be recognized for excellence and continues to expand and strengthen its nationally and regionally competitive programs while maintaining a high level of competence in all programs.

SCHOOL PHILOSOPHY

The programs at the University of Arkansas School of Architecture are rooted in the best traditions of architectural education: responsibility and service to the societies and cultures to which we are inextricably connected, and the nurturing of the individual curiosity and capabilities of our students. We enthusiastically embrace the challenges of helping them in developing and refining essential skills, expanding their base of knowledge, sharpening their intellects, and polishing their sensibilities. We hope and trust that they leave us with a profound sense of confidence in themselves, and the conviction and capabilities necessary in dealing with the challenges and uncertainties they will confront in designing human habitat.

PROGRAM DESCRIPTION
Undergraduate Program

The structure and content of the architecture curriculum are conceived to provide a sound foundation in the principal skills and fundamental knowledge necessary to all students seeking the accredited degree, while retaining sufficient flexibility to allow each student to define the particular professional and personal goals to which he or she aspires. The judicious use of core, professional and free electives allows students ample opportunities for pursuing minors outside the School, electing major or minor fields of concentration within the School, or simply enjoying a diverse general education. The professional core, composed of required courses in architectural technology, history and theory, practice, and, especially, the architectural design studio, anchors the curriculum in that body of knowledge which is essential to the practice of architecture. For the overwhelming majority of our students, the design studio is the heart of the professional core and the intellectual and creative focal point of each year of the curriculum, where ideas presented in parallel avenues of study are analyzed, synthesized, and critically engaged in the production of the semester's work.

AREAS OF FOCUS AND RESEARCH
Focus

The curriculum is designed for a balance between professional studies, general studies and electives, allowing the pursuit of special interests. Our students have 60-semester hours that may, in varying degrees and different ways, be seen as electives. This includes free electives, professional electives, and, with consent and the close scrutiny of departmental academic advisors, possible self-directed design studio work in three of a student's last four semesters. This curricular structure affords opportunities for students to elect classes in other colleges, including the pursuit of established minors offered by the Fulbright College of Arts and Sciences, the College of Engineering, or the Walton College of Business, or of a concentration in a sub-disciplinary specialization within the School of Architecture.

Research

Our faculty pursue a diversity of research interests, ranging from historical scholarship and analysis to professional practice in architectural design, from theoretical inquiry and speculation to explorations of digital media, from energy management to community planning. Every faculty member has an agenda of research aimed both at producing knowledge, as well as complementing their teaching. The diverse range of investigations provides students with opportunities to engage in specialized research in line with their own interests and intended trajectories. The University of Arkansas Community Design Center offers one of our most noteworthy interdisciplinary research opportunities, affording students the chance to engage in community-scaled design solutions integrating social and environmental measures into economic development.

SPECIAL ACTIVITIES AND PROGRAMS
Leadership by Design

All students in the School of Architecture participate in the Leadership by Design Program intended to raise awareness of the unique potential design professionals have in fostering societal change through active leadership. All students in the accredited program are required, while students in the four-year degree have the opportunity, to participate in a semester-long international experience at either our Study Center located in the center of Rome or at our program housed in the Barragán Studio in Mexico City. Students also have the opportunity to engage in numerous design/build initiatives administered by our faculty including projects for local and remote institutions.

Honors Program

The Departments of Architecture and Landscape Architecture provide opportunities for students of superior academic and creative ability to enhance their professional and liberal education by participating in the School's Honors programs. Students participating in this program are simultaneously enrolled in the University's Honors College, making them eligible for merit-based scholarships and fellowships totaling more than $17 million. Visit http://honorscollege.uark.edu/ for more information.

FACILITIES

Vol Walker Hall houses the Department of Architecture together with the School's administrative offices and support staff. Originally built as the University Library, Vol Walker Hall is a substantial neo-classical revival building, housing design studios, lecture and critique spaces, a media center, exhibition spaces, a visualization lab and a shop facility. Memorial Hall, a significant collegiate gothic structure built originally as the Student Union, houses the Department of Landscape Architecture studios, classrooms, and offices. The School also maintains off-campus facilities in Fayetteville for the University of Arkansas Community Design Center, in Hot Springs for the Garvan Woodland Gardens, and in Rome and Mexico City for its international study programs.

SCHOLARSHIPS AND FINANCIAL AID

In addition to numerous merit- and need-based scholarship/fellowship programs offered at the university level, the School of Architecture awards over 80 scholarships annually, available exclusively to architecture and landscape architecture students amounting to nearly $100,000. These funds can be applied to tuition, fees, international study, and the cost of supplies. In addition to these opportunities, many students receive financial aid through state and national programs including Pell Grants, National Direct Loans, Guaranteed Students Loans, College Work-Study, and Supplemental Opportunity Educational Grants. Students participating in the Honors Program are also eligible for the merit-based scholarships and fellowships available through the Honors College. In addition, in-state tuition is available to entering freshmen scoring 25 on the ACT (1130 SAT) with a 3.5 GPA, and transfer students with a 3.0 GPA in 24 or more credit hours from TX, MS, LA, KS, MO, OK, and TN through the University's tuition waiver program.

ADMINISTRATION

Jeff Shannon, AIA: Dean
Timothy de Noble, AIA: Department Head, Architecture
Mark Boyer, ASLA: Interim Department Head, Landscape Architecture

UNIVERSITY OF BRITISH COLUMBIA

ADDRESS

Main
University of British Columbia
School of Architecture and
Landscape Architecture
#402-6333 Memorial Rd
Vancouver, BC V6T 1Z2
Canada
Tel.: 604.822.2779
Fax: 604.822.3808
soaadmit@interchange.ubc.ca
www.sala.ubc.ca

STUDENT AND FACULTY DEMOGRAPHICS

% of Female Students	45
% of International Students	25
% of Out-of-Country Students	25
No. Full-Time Faculty	24
No. Part-Time Faculty	15
No. Full-Time Students	150
No. Part-Time Students	

FINANCIAL INFORMATION

Main Source of University Funding	Public
Annual Tuition & Fees (graduate, resident)	C$4,500
Annual Tuition & Fees (graduate, nonresident)	C$10,340
Annual Tuition & Fees (undergraduate, resident)	C$5,200
Annual Tuition & Fees (undergraduate, nonresident)	C$23,000
% Students Receiving Federal Financial Aid	
% Students Receiving University Financial Aid	
% Students Receiving Departmental Financial Aid	
% Students Receiving Scholarships (assistantships or fellowships)	15
Average Annual Scholarship for Department	C$1,250

ACADEMIC SESSIONS

Fall Semester: September to December;
    Application Deadline: end of the first week in January
Spring Semester: January to April

Summer Session I: May to June
Summer Session II: July to August

ARCHITECTURE AND RELATED DEGREE PROGRAMS

Degree	Min. Yrs. to Complete	Professional Accreditation	# of FT Students	# of PT Students	# of First-Year Students	# of Degrees Conferred	Admissions Requirements
Architecture							
M. Arch	3.5	CACB	150	0	45	39	Undergraduate degree or Undergraduate Architecture degree, TOEFL, Portfolio, Rec. Letters, Essay
Master of Advanced Studies in Architecture	2		8	4	4	3	TOEFL, Portfolio, Rec. Letters, Essay
Environmental Design							
Bachelor of Environmental Design	4		52	0	27	18	Associate's Degree, TOEFL, Portfolio, Rec. Letters, Essay

SPECIALIZATIONS

Architectural Design
Building Technology/Env. Systems
Computer-Aided Design
Energy

Environment/Sustainability
Graphic Design
History
Housing

International/Regional Architecture
Landscape Design
Professional Practice
Sustainability

Tectonics
Theory/Criticism
Urban Planning and Design

ARCHITECTURE PROGRAM SUMMARY

The School of Architecture and Landscape Architecture is the only one of its kind in British Columbia. It contributes significantly to the dialogue, education, research and innovation within the architecture and landscape architecture professions and plays a positive role within both UBC and the wider community. Through its undergraduate, professional and research programs, the School aspires to produce outstanding graduates equipped to anticipate evolving realities within the realm of contemporary practice and to provide the necessary design, technical and intellectual leadership that will contribute to a built environment supportive of civil and sustainable patterns of living.

UNIVERSITY SETTING

The University of British Colubmia, Canada's third largest university, is located in Vancouver on a scenic headland overlooking Georgia Strait, Libraries, residences, and other support services, and facilities serve 30,000 students from 114 countries.

SCHOOL PHILOSOPHY

The built environment is arguably the most significant and long lasting of human accomplishments—representing and embodying its culture, aspirations and technological prowess. Architectural and landscape architectural design embrace the full range of creative, experiential, intellectual, social, scientific and technological aspects associated with the provision of human constructed environments. Architecture and landscape architecture thereby have profound direct and indirect consequences for the maintenance of human and ecological health. During a time of increasing urbanization, resource depletion and anticipated consequences of climate change, design education within these core disciplines is critical. Design education and innovative research in architecture and landscape architecture play a vital role in providing the knowledge, skills and leadership necessary to shape the future built environment.

The professions of architecture and landscape architecture share a common responsibility for creating and shaping constructed environments through the unique synthetic process of design. These professions share similar educational models and processes to professional licensure and practice within similar consulting, regulatory and legal contexts. The School of Architecture and Landscape Architecture builds on these areas of common interest and exploits logical points of intersection between the programs. Our School draws students from widely varied cultural and academic backgrounds to create a rich and dynamic context for study. Moreover, recognizing that architecture and landscape architecture must be both respectful of the uniqueness of place and responsive to international developments, it engages the advantage of being situated within a region of exceptional cultural diversity and natural amenity and also provides a context for its students to participate in studies abroad and a global discourse.

These are both exciting and challenging times as society begins to chart a path toward a more secure and sustainable future. It will require talented, skilled and committed architects and landscape architects to offer innovative cross-scale and interdisciplinary approaches and solutions to a broad range of design issues.

PROGRAM DESCRIPTION

The Architecture Program offers a dynamic milieu for engagement with the pressing issues confronting contemporary cities and regions. It does so in both its professional degree (MArch) and advanced studies (MASA) options. The professional program seeks to prepare and advance those wishing to participate critically in defining concerns and negotiating responses to the impediments and opportunities of our precipitous times. Vancouver, with its richly resourced landscape and complex cultural mix provides an instructive focus for these ambitions. This program endeavors to prepare students as informed stakeholders in the built environment via a cogent curriculum that affords both the requisite knowledge base and opportunities for direct experience in the local and global making of the world at large. The program benefits from its location in Vancouver, a Pacific Rim city that has historically attracted an ethnically diverse population from across wide, historically complicated catchments. And, while it is a port city located by a global network of cross-seas trade, it is also a city located within a web of First Nations settlements. The program supports responses to this complex and compelling locale and its contemporary matrix of issues and possibilities through research and design strategically located in communities ranging from the Downtown Eastside and Chinatown, to faculty-led research with First Nations communities in northern British Columbia, to Studies Abroad initiatives in Tokyo and Beijing.

While building upon this culturally rich and historically formed context, the program is also dedicated to exploring unprecedented future perspectives. It is deeply committed to taking a leadership role in addressing the environmental issues confronting us today and in ensuring that present-day students become future practitioners with workable responses.

AREAS OF FOCUS AND RESEARCH

The research themes and their associated faculty are: Environmental Imperatives, including

- Environmental and sustainable issues in building design
- Sustainable urban habitation

Cultural Studies, including:

- Contemporary and modern architectural history, encompassing post–colonial history and theory
- Contested landscapes and representational tools of their analysis
- The Pacific Rim and globalization
- Localized cultures of construction and housing.

Advanced Design Research explores the agency of professional activity and academic investigation

Advanced Research in Digital Applications and Emerging Technologies including:

- Fabrication technologies including digital technology and the building process
- Distributed collaborative design

SPECIAL ACTIVITIES AND PROGRAMS

A required introductory workshop for all first-year students acquaints the student with the faculty, other students and the process of working creatively as a community. A term-length Studies Abroad offered every two years gives 20 students an opportunity to study architecture in a different milieu. Organized and led by a member of the design faculty, students experience the richness and diversity, lately in Tokyo. Shorter studies abroad to places such as China, Iran, Japan, Poland, and Renaissance Italy also open opportunities for architectural experience outside Vancouver. The School enjoys exchange programs with a number of programs around the world and across Canada. The school now offers a co-operative program, design build opportunities in Vancouver and abroad, lecture series and student journals.

FACILITIES

The School supports a broad range of operating systems and software applications. Clusters of workstations are integrated into the design studio environment. Peripheral support for the system includes a laser cutter, a 3D printer, CNC milling machine and plotter, together with a variety of digital cameras, scanners and open-access printers. In addition to the Main Library, a School Reading Room with about 2,500 volumes of books, 20,000 slides and 50 periodical titles is available. The school furnishes studio space for each student either on the university campus or at the school's studio/gallery downtown. The school workshop uses a variety of materials and is a source for modeling and woodworking. Extensive audio-visual equipment is available. Seminars, lecture rooms, offices, exhibition space and student lounge is available.

SCHOLARSHIPS AND FINANCIAL AID

Graduate students may apply for UBC Graduate Fellowships, a scholarship of approximately $15,000 per annum. Several entrance scholarships ranging from $1,000–$5,000 are available. M.Arch. students are eligible for approximately 15 scholarships, ranging from $500 to $1,250. They are awarded by the faculty on the basis of merit at the end of the school year. The bulk of the need-based financial assistance for students is provided through the federal and provincial governments. For those eligible for student loans, work–study programs on campus provide supplemental financial assistance of between $700 and $3,000.

ADMINISTRATION

Ray Cole: Director, SALA
Sherry McKay: Chair, Architecture Program
Cynthia Girling: Chair, Landscape Architecture program

UNIVERSITY OF CALGARY

UNIVERSITY OF
CALGARY

ADDRESS

Main
University of Calgary
Faculty of Environmental Design
2500 University Drive, NW
Calgary, AB T2N 1N4
Canada
Tel.: 403.220.6603
Fax: 403.284.4399
arch@evds.ucalgary.ca
www.ucalgary.ca/evds

ACADEMIC SESSIONS

Fall Semester: September to December
Spring Semester: January to April

STUDENT AND FACULTY DEMOGRAPHICS

% of Female Students	44
% of International Students	2
% of Minority Students	
% of Out-of-State U.S. Students	
No. Full-Time Faculty	11
No. Part-Time Faculty	3
No. Full-Time Students	122
No. Part-Time Students	0

FINANCIAL INFORMATION

Main Source of University Funding	Public
Annual Tuition & Fees (graduate, resident)	C$6,100
Annual Tuition & Fees (graduate, nonresident)	C$11,200
Annual Tuition & Fees (undergraduate, resident)	C$2,800
Annual Tuition & Fees (undergraduate, nonresident)	C$8,800
% Students Receiving Federal Financial Aid	
% Students Receiving University Financial Aid	
% Students Receiving Departmental Financial Aid	
% Students Receiving Scholarships (assistantships or fellowships)	59
Average Annual Scholarship for Department	C$175,000

ARCHITECTURE AND RELATED DEGREE PROGRAMS

Degree	Min. Yrs. to Complete	Professional Accreditation	# of FT Students	# of PT Students	# of First-Year Students	# of Degrees Conferred	Admissions Requirements
Architecture							
M. Arch	4	CACB	122	0	42	20	Undergraduate degree, TOEFL, Portfolio, Rec. Letters
Environmental Design							
M.E.Des.	1.5						Undergraduate degree, TOEFL, Rec. Letters

SPECIALIZATIONS

Architectural Design
Building Technology/Env. Systems
Computer-Aided Design

Energy
Environment/Sustainability

History
Professional Practice

Theory/Criticism
Urban Planning and Design

UNIVERSITY SETTING

The Architecture Program is housed in the interdisciplinary graduate Faculty of Environmental Design which also includes a post-professional Master's degree in Environmental Design (MEDes). The Faculty has strong links to other faculties in the university (Communication and Culture, Engineering, Fine Arts and Management), the professions and the community. The Faculty is an integral part of a number of university design initiatives.

SCHOOL PHILOSOPHY

The Architecture Program at the University of Calgary is committed to the PRACTICE and PRACTICES of architecture. We believe that architecture is a reflective and critical discipline where theory emerges from the practice of architecture and the numerous contexts within which architecture operates. The PRACTICE of architecture emphasizes the disciplinary skills necessary to be an architect; it places priority on the execution and delivery of responsible buildings and other projects; it also acknowledges the PRACTICES, or patterns of inhabitation, that result from a built work through its use.

PROGRAM DESCRIPTION

The Master of Architecture (MArch) is a four-year program that prepares the student for practice as a registered architect in North America. The MArch degree also provides a foundation for other career opportunities in design, the construction and management of the built environment and other advanced areas of study and practice. The curriculum is accredited and provides a structured introduction for those without a previous architectural education. The first four sessions of the MArch Program focus on the building of the requisite skills and knowledge in the areas of design, communication, technology, history and theory, and practice. The remaining two sessions of course work and the Master's Degree Project reinforce and extend this foundation through advanced architectural studies and collaborative projects. It is normally expected that architecture students will complete their Master's Degree Project in two sessions, thus completing their degree in four years of study. Those admitted to the Master of Architecture Program who hold an acceptable pre-professional degree, including the University of Calgary's Minor in Architectural Studies, will be admitted to the second year.

The Minor in Architectural Studies (ARST) is designed as a pre-professional degree option for those students wishing to pursue the Master of Architecture (MArch) program at the University of Calgary, or other related graduate programs. The Minor in Architectural Studies includes courses equivalent to the architectural component of the first year of Faculty of Environmental Design's four-year Master of Architecture professional degree program. Architectural Studies may be taken as a Minor in degree programs in the Faculties of Communication and Culture (formerly General Studies), Fine Arts, Humanities, Science and Social Sciences.

For further information, consult the University of Calgary calendar, contact an Undergraduate Program Advisor, (http://www.comcul.ucalgary.ca/), or contact the Director of the MArch Program.

AREAS OF FOCUS AND RESEARCH
Focus

The Program is distinguished by its commitment to architectural practice, digital design and fabrication, sustainable design and technology, the contemporary city, socially responsible design, and the history of modern Canadian architecture. This is reflected in faculty work, student projects and research programs.

Research

Faculty research, scholarship and practice-related activities include a wide range of topics and interests relevant to the disciplines and professional areas represented in Environmental Design. Many of the architecture faculty are directly involved in award-winning forms of practice. A variety of other work carried out by our faculty includes editorial work for scholarly and professional journals, reviews, creative writing and production and curriculum development studies.

SPECIAL ACTIVITIES AND PROGRAMS

The Program offers a comprehensive program of student enrichment opportunities including study-abroad programs, field trips, guest critics, visiting instructors, lecture series, and scholarships. Students are encouraged to participate in the Faculty's study-abroad program in Barcelona. The program involves an interdisciplinary studio, an urban systems course and a field trip are taught by a group of Barcelona-based designers. The annual William Lyon Somerville Visiting Lectureship brings a distinguished visitor to the Architecture Pro-

gram to direct a week-long design charrette and give a public lecture. The Douglas Gillmor Visiting Lectureship annually brings a guest to the program to deliver a seminar course on architectural theory or history. The CAUSA lecture series brings prominent architects from Canada, the United States and Europe into the Program.

FACILITIES

The Faculty of Environmental Design provides a range of facilities including the EVDS Gallery, computer labs, photo labs, the faculty Resource Centre, and a well-equipped workshop. Lab facilities include 30 workstations, digital cameras, a digital video camera, and digital video editing suite, scanners, video I/O, digitizers, wide carriage printers, and laserwriters. The laboratory is equipped with a large collection of software for word processing, graphics, desktop publishing, and computer-aided design. The workshop includes the full range of wood, metal, and plastic fabrication tools, including a full machine shop, in addition to digital fabrication tools like a CNC machine, digital laser cutter, and ABS 3D printer. The main University of Calgary library houses the architectural book and slide collections. The main library also contains the Canadian Architectural Archives. This is a unique resource and is Canada's largest and most comprehensive collection of drawings and records of prominent twentieth-century Canadian architects.

SCHOLARSHIPS AND FINANCIAL AID

The faculty offers a number of scholarships, fellowships, bursaries and special awards, in conjunction with Graduate Research Scholarships, Graduate Teaching Assistantships, and Graduate Service Assistantships. All applicants and students registered in the Faculty should also consult the main University of Calgary calendar and Graduate Studies Calendar for other types of forms of financial assistance and application deadlines. Major scholarship programs include the Murray W. Waterman Architectural Awards, the Waugh Scholarship in Architecture and the Cohos-Evamy Partners Travel Scholarship.

ADMINISTRATION

Loraine Fowlow, MRAIC: Interim Dean
Marc Boutin, MAAA, MAIBC: Associate Dean

UNIVERSITY OF CALIFORNIA, BERKELEY

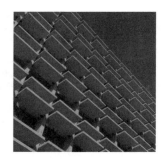

ADDRESS

Main
University of California, Berkeley
Department of Architecture
College of Environmental Design
232 Wurster Hall
Berkeley, CA 94720-1800
Tel.: 510.642.4942
Fax: 510.643.5607
arch.ced.berkeley.edu

STUDENT AND FACULTY DEMOGRAPHICS

% of Female Students	54
% of International Students	10
% of Minority Students	54
% of Out-of-State U.S. Students	13
No. Full-Time Faculty	30
No. Part-Time Faculty	25
No. Full-Time Students	750
No. Part-Time Students	0

FINANCIAL INFORMATION

Main Source of University Funding	Public
Annual Tuition & Fees (graduate, resident)	$5,112
Annual Tuition & Fees (graduate, nonresident)	$12,615
Annual Tuition & Fees (undergraduate, resident)	$4,466
Annual Tuition & Fees (undergraduate, nonresident)	$14,770
% Students Receiving Federal Financial Aid	52
% Students Receiving University Financial Aid	45
% Students Receiving Departmental Financial Aid	25
% Students Receiving Scholarships (assistantships or fellowships)	30
Average Annual Scholarship for Department	

ACADEMIC SESSIONS

Fall Semester: August to December;
    Application Deadline: UGrad Nov. 30 / Grad Dec. 30
Spring Semester: January to May; Application Deadline: N/A

ARCHITECTURE AND RELATED DEGREE PROGRAMS

Degree	Min. Yrs. to Complete	Professional Accreditation	# of FT Students	# of PT Students	# of First-Year Students	# of Degrees Conferred	Admissions Requirements
Architecture							
B.A. Architecture	4		650	0	150	188	
M. Arch	2-3	NAAB	90	0	38	35	Undergraduate degree, GRE, TOEFL, Portfolio, Rec. Letters, Essay
MS Arch	1.5		17	0	10	4	Undergraduate degree, TOEFL, Rec. Letters, Essay
M. Arch post-professional							
PhD	4		47	0	7	7	Undergraduate degree, TOEFL, Rec. Letters, Essay

SPECIALIZATIONS

Architectural Design
Computer-Aided Design

Environment/Sustainability
History

Housing
International/Regional Architecture

Theory/Criticism
Urban Planning and Design

ARCHITECTURE PROGRAM SUMMARY

The Department of Architecture at UC Berkeley has a strong tradition of fostering independent design thinking and research. Our award-winning faculty offer vigorous undergraduate and graduate educational programs, carry out leading research in constructed and virtual environments, architectural technologies and architectural humanities. The multidisciplinary interests of our faculty and graduate students form the basis of exciting new research collaborations with a variety of other disciplines including anthropology, international studies, engineering, material science, new media and urban studies.

UNIVERSITY SETTING

The University of California, Berkeley has a long history as one of America's most lively, culturally diverse, and politically adventurous academic institutions. Located across the bay from San Francisco, the Berkeley campus is divided into 14 colleges and schools with departments offering over 300 degree programs to 30,000 students, two-thirds of whom are undergraduates. A large and vital institution, Berkeley offers students a vast range of scholarly endeavor and a wide arena for personal growth.

SCHOOL PHILOSOPHY

Undergraduate Philosophy

Undergraduate study in the College of Environmental Design provides a liberal education among an active community of students, scholars, creative designers, and technologists concerned with the built environment, within the larger environment of a great university.

Graduate Philosophy

The graduate programs in architecture aim to educate architects and scholars who contribute to the practice and discipline of architecture and to the development of a technologically sophisticated and humane built environment. The professional program is intended to develop students' abilities to conceive and accurately describe appropriate built spaces at several scales, to help them learn the processes used to bring buildings into place, and provide a basis for understanding the consequences that complexes of buildings and open spaces have for inhabitants, society, and the environment.

PROGRAM DESCRIPTION

Undergraduate Program

The undergraduate program in architecture combines required courses in environmental design and architecture with opportunities for highly varied individual programs. Through its core courses, the program offers a broad introduction to the field of architecture, and through studies in the various areas it provides opportunities to prepare for specialization in the field in the areas of architectural design and representation, architectural technologies and building performance, architectural history, culture and society. In addition to offering a sound and well-rounded education, undergraduate studies can also provide pre-professional competency for entry-level employment in architecture,

the option for graduate work in architecture, or further studies in a related environmental design field. At the lower division level, students take an introductory course in environmental design, a two-course studio sequence in drawing and design, prerequisite courses in calculus and physics, and breadth area courses in natural sciences, social and behavioral sciences, historical studies, international studies, philosophy and values, and arts and literature. At the upper division level, students take a two-course architecture studio sequence, a two-course architecture history sequence, three architecture "area studies" courses and three electives within the College. Additional design and technology courses are recommended for students preparing for M Arch programs. Most students are able to take one-quarter of their program as electives.

Graduate Program

The Architecture graduate program at Berkeley offers the degrees Master of Architecture, Master of Science, and Ph.D. The Master of Architecture program is designed to provide students seeking the first professional degree with a comprehensive and challenging education leading to the practice of architecture. Graduate students have the flexibility to choose a variety of paths within a rigorous program. A required studio each semester introduces design issues through the study of a variety of building types, styles and sites. The curriculum in technology and building performance, history, society and culture, and professional practice provide the breadth and background for the individual's professional education and career goals. Students who have completed equivalent courses at other institutions may have the requirements waived to allow for more elective units. The Master of Science is an academic degree which allows students to do specialized research in the fields related to the architectural profession.

The Ph.D. is an advanced degree preparing students for research and teaching in architecture and environmental design. It is a research-oriented program, in which the student chooses specific fields of specialization, prepares sufficiently in the literature and research of those fields to pass written and oral examinations, and completes original research culminating in the written dissertation.

AREAS OF FOCUS

At both the undergraduate and graduate level, the department focuses on three broad areas of architecture: design, technology and humanities. The PhD program provides detailed focus in specific areas including: social and cultural factors in design, practice of design, design theories and methods, building environments, history of architecture and urban design, structures and construction. Additional graduate programs are available in environmental design in developing countries, environmental science and its applications, and visual studies. The department also puts special emphasis on the studio element of each of its academic programs and thus recruits active architecture professionals to work in consultation with regular faculty in leading the courses.

SPECIAL ACTIVITIES AND PROGRAMS

The department offers several unique programs and activities including study-abroad programs for undergraduate and internationally focused studios for graduate students. Recent studios have worked in India, Thailand, Mexico, Brazil and Italy. The College also offers career workshops, job fairs, and internship placements. A weekly lecture series offers students the opportunity to hear internationally acclaimed speakers who often participate in classes and seminars as part of their visit. Opportunities are also provided to visit department exhibitions, participate in a mentor program, and become involved in student chapters of professional organizations such as the AIA. Crossdisciplinary connections are established in joint graduate degree programs with the departments of City and Regional Planning, Landscape Architecture, and Structural Engineering. A post-professional master's degree is also offered in Urban Design. Department publications include *Process, Concrete,* and the refereed journals *Places and Traditional Dwellings* and *Settlements Review.*

FACILITIES

- Wurster Hall, the home of the College of Environmental Design, was designed by faculty members Joseph Esherick, Vernon DeMars and Donald Olsen and completed in 1964.
- Environmental Design Library and Archives
- Visual Resource Center
- 28,000 square-feet wood, metal and plastic-working facility
- Two computing labs: PC computers with CAD, 3D modeling and visualization software.
- CAD/CAM lab: Laser cutting, routing, and 3D modeling equipment
- Building science labs: Boundary layer wind tunnel, controlled environment chamber, sky simulator, solar test rooms, portable field measurement equipment.

SCHOLARSHIPS AND FINANCIAL AID

The department offers partial merit and need-based financial aid to graduate students through fellowships, fee grants, tuition waivers, and teaching and research assistantships. The University provides financial assistance in the form of grants, loans, and work-study to students with demonstrated financial need. Competitions, awards, and traveling fellowships are available to continuing students at all levels.

ADMINISTRATION

Sam Davis, FAIA: Interim Dean
Mary Comerio: Chair
Jill Stoner: Vice Chair and Chair of Graduate Advisors
Nezar AlSayyad: Associate Dean for International Programs
C. Greig Crysler, AIA: Associate Dean for Undergraduate Studies

UNIVERSITY OF CALIFORNIA, LOS ANGELES

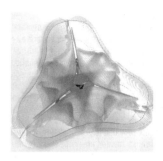

ADDRESS

Main
University of California, Los Angeles
School of the Arts and Architecture
Department of Architecture and Urban
Design
1317 Perloff Hall
Los Angeles, CA 90095-1467
Tel.: 310.825.7857
Fax: 310.825.8959
www.aud.ucla.edu

STUDENT AND FACULTY DEMOGRAPHICS

% of Female Students	44
% of International Students	24
% of Minority Students	
% of Out-of-State U.S. Students	
No. Full-Time Faculty	14
No. Part-Time Faculty	23
No. Full-Time Students	226
No. Part-Time Students	0

FINANCIAL INFORMATION

Main Source of University Funding	Public
Annual Tuition & Fees (graduate, resident)	$9,669
Annual Tuition & Fees (graduate, nonresident)	$24,675
Annual Tuition & Fees (undergraduate, resident)	$8,309
Annual Tuition & Fees (undergraduate, nonresident)	$28,917
% Students Receiving Federal Financial Aid	
% Students Receiving University Financial Aid	
% Students Receiving Departmental Financial Aid	
% Students Receiving Scholarships (assistantships or fellowships)	
Average Annual Scholarship for Department	

ACADEMIC SESSIONS

Fall Quarter/Trimester: October to December;
 Application Deadline: December 15
Winter Quarter/Trimester: January to March

Spring Quarter/Trimester: April to June
Summer Session I: June to July
Summer Session II: August to September

ARCHITECTURE AND RELATED DEGREE PROGRAMS

Degree	Min. Yrs. to Complete	Professional Accreditation	# of FT Students	# of PT Students	# of First-Year Students	# of Degrees Conferred	Admissions Requirements
Architecture							
BA in Architectural Studies	2		50		25		Portfolio, Essay
M. Arch I	3	NAAB	135	0	45		Undergraduate degree, GRE, TOEFL, Portfolio, Rec. Letters, Essay
M. Arch II	1		17	0	17	17	Prof. Architecture degree, GRE, TOEFL, Portfolio, Rec. Letters, Essay
MA	2		6		3		Undergraduate degree, GRE, TOEFL, Rec. Letters, Essay
PhD	4		18	0	4		Undergraduate degree, GRE, TOEFL, Rec. Letters, Essay

UNIVERSITY SETTING

The School of the Arts and Architecture at UCLA (UCLA Arts) is dedicated to training exceptional artists, performers, architects and scholars who are enriched by a global view of the arts and prepared to serve as cultural leaders of the 21st century. Graduate degree programs are offered in the Departments of Architecture and Urban Design, Art, Design I Media Arts, Ethnomusicology, Music, and World Arts and Cultures. The School's unique curriculum interweaves work in performance, studio and research studies, providing students with a solid creative, artistic and intellectual foundation. A world-class faculty provides a depth of expertise and achievement that supports the most ambitious vision a student can bring to the campus. To enrich their coursework students have access to outstanding art collections, exhibitions and performing arts presentations through the School's internationally acclaimed public arts institutions. One of America's leading public research universities, UCLA is also the most multicultural campus in the nation. Situated five miles from the Pacific Ocean and ten miles from downtown Los Angeles, the campus is within a short drive of mountains, beaches, lakes and deserts. The 419-acre campus is a self-contained community replete with restaurants, medical facilities, gyms, botanical and sculpture gardens, movie theaters and concert halls.

SCHOOL PHILOSOPHY

Changing global realities are causing paradigm shifts that redefine the interaction between culture, politics, economics, and the environment. These changes constantly alter the boundaries between disciplines, creating new parameters of knowledge that will define the conditions of future inquiries into architecture and urban design. At UCLA, we are deeply immersed in a research environment that anticipates change and can move from the realm of ideas to their application, from present situations to emerging new realities.

Architecture now faces fundamental issues of practice that will alter this ancient discipline. Our senior design faculty is among the most progressive in understanding and exemplifying these transformations: Thom Mayne, Greg Lynn, Neil Denari, Craig Hodgetts, Mark Mack, and Dagmar Richter. In analyzing history and theory as they impact architecture and urban design and contribute to the understanding of visual culture, we are further strengthened by the internationally recognized contributions of Sylvia Lavin, Dana Cuff and Diane Favro.

Redefining architectural education in a major research university, we emphasize interaction among the components of our program, design, technology, and critical studies (history and theory), between our departments and others in the School of the Arts and Architecture and the larger University. We are especially strong in examining the theory and impact of the computer on design, and related developments in robotics and the fabrication of building components. We regard critical studies as making a crucial contribution to the evaluation of new directions in design and issues of contemporary practice, including pressing environmental concerns. We are increasing our interest in cross-cultural studies, and exchange programs, which are central at UCLA. This year we will start offering an undergraduate major, allowing us to further expand and enrich our faculty.

Los Angeles is a prototype of the 21st-century city, embodying the cultural, social, economic, and political issues, which will be at the center of architectural and urban debates. It also represents a new edge between the West and the East, an intersection of increasing importance where diverse cultures interact, transform, and generate new developments. Los Angeles also provides an infinite resource for the study of architecture and urban design, the direction of high technology and media innovations, and as such is a prime indicator of our global future.

The Department of Architecture and Urban Design at UCLA is at the intersection of a new kind of city with an intense diversity of culture, the growing influence of Asia, and a creative milieu influenced by both high technology and entertainment media. We attract designers and thinkers from around the world who come to share their work and ideas through lectures, exhibitions, and teaching. As a tandem force, the city and the university, with their constant flows of inexhaustible energy, provide a dynamic platform for the study of architecture and urban design today.

PROGRAM DESCRIPTION

The UCLA Department of Architecture and Urban Design offers five distinct degrees: The Bachelor of Arts in Architectural Studies is a two-year major that begins in the junior year of residence. The Master of Architecture (M.Arch.I) degree is a three-year, professional program that provides a comprehensive education in architecture for those holding a non-architecture bachelor's degree or a four-year degree in Architecture. The M. Arch.I program is accredited by the NAAB. The one-year Master of Architecture (M.Arch.II) degree provides a second, advanced professional degree combining theoretical studies and practical applications in an intensive year of study. The two-year Master of Arts (M.A.) degree prepares students for research and teaching in fields related to architecture and urban design. Applicants are required to hold a bachelor's degree and should possess the experience and knowledge to allow them to do advanced research. The Ph.D. is an advanced research degree organized around the interests of the faculty, with an emphasis in critical studies and history. Distinguished faculty currently teaching at UCLA include: Hitoshi Abe (Chair), Dana Cuff, Neil Denari, Diane Favro, Craig Hodgetts, Sylvia Lavin, Robin Liggett, Greg Lynn, Mark Mack, Thom Mayne, Barton Myers, Jason Payne, Ben Refuerzo, Dagmar Richter, Heather Roberge, and Richard Weinstein.

AREAS OF FOCUS AND RESEARCH

Design: Our unsurpassed faculty in design has developed a curriculum connecting research to professional practice. The curriculum focuses on formal research and experimentation and insists that architecture and urban design respond proactively to the always-shifting contemporary world. Critical Studies explores the history, theory, and criticism of architecture and urbanism. Drawing on significant transformations in academic scholarship in recent years, the program is fundamentally interdisciplinary. Technology continues to be one of the most transformative influences in the contemporary world and UCLA gives students of architecture and urban design the opportunity to explore this constantly changing field at the highest level. The Department is not currently accepting doctoral applications in the area of Technology.

SPECIAL ACTIVITIES AND PROGRAMS

The department has an active program of lectures, exhibitions, publications and travelling studios that enhance the educational quality of the program.

FACILITIES

The Department of Architecture and Urban Design occupies its own building, Perloff Hall, at the north end of the UCLA campus. Most courses are held in the building, which contains studio spaces, electronic studios, computers, lecture halls, an exhibition gallery, classrooms, and faculty offices. Architecture students have their own drawing tables. M.A. and Ph.D. students have their own designated study area in the building. Emerging technologies for visualization and fabrication are vital to contemporary architectural practice. UCLA's Department of Architecture and Urban Design continues to set the scholastic standard for the integration of cutting-edge technologies into the overall academic curriculum.

Our Technology Center grows in equipment and expertise each year and currently provides two large-format

mills, two laser-cutters, two 3-D printers, and a large-scale vacuum formers for student use. Complementing the equipment is an expanding database of expertise on emerging technology and its application that allows new users immediate access to established techniques and methods of production. AUD students have early and continual access to this equipment and knowledge base and are vital to the continual growth of this aspect of our program. Technology is integrated into the curriculum in a variety of ways. Technology seminars and studios focus directly on applying emerging technologies to contemporary design problems using the equipment intensively throughout the quarter. Ideas and methods devised in these courses then move through the rest of the AUD atmosphere. Courses focused on history and theory also address the role and impact of these developments on practice. Ingrained within the larger culture of the department and easily accessible to students at all levels in the curriculum, emerging technology plays a central role in the work produced at UCLA. The Architecture and Urban Design Computing Facilities are devoted to advanced design, education, and research. Encompassing electronic studios, a media ready multi-purpose room (Decafè), and access to additional school-wide resources at the School of the Arts and Architecture, the Department provides a rich environment supporting professional use as well as specialized software development and design innovations. Perloff Hall is a wireless environment. The Architecture and Urban Design Infrastructure supports a networked, distributed computing environment that includes the ability for students to connect their personal systems. File and print services are available to users throughout Perloff Hall. File and print services are provided primarily by several Linux servers. These are augmented by shared disks on the network to provide over two terabytes of disk storage. Output devices range from letter size black and white and color laser printers to 36 inch wide color plotters. Flatbed and 35mm slide scanners as well as digital video capture are available for input. Workstations are equipped with CD/DVD burners for file transfer and backup. The entire Architecture and Urban Design network is connected to the UCLA campus network, which provides the Department with high-speed access to the Internet.

SCHOLARSHIPS AND FINANCIAL AID

Several avenues of financial support are available to students: (1) The university provides financial assistance in the form of grants, loans, and work-study to students who can demonstrate sufficient monetary need, while the Graduate Division sponsors competitive grants based on scholastic performance. (2) The Department offers a number of scholarships that are allocated on the basis of both financial need and academic merit. (3) Research assistantships are available under funded research projects.

ADMINISTRATION

Christopher Waterman: Dean
Hitoshi Abe: Chair
Richard S. Weinstein, RA: Vice Chair
Heather Roberge: Associate Vice Chair

UNIVERSITY OF CINCINNATI

UNIVERSITY OF
Cincinnati

ADDRESS

Main
University of Cincinnati
College of Design, Arch. Art & Planning
School of Architecture & Interior Design
P.O. Box 210016
Cincinnati, OH 45221-0016
Tel: 513.556.6426
Fax: 513.556.1230
said@uc.edu
www.daap.uc.edu

STUDENT AND FACULTY DEMOGRAPHICS

% of Female Students	37
% of International Students	4
% of Minority Students	6
% of Out-of-State U.S. Students	30
No. Full-Time Faculty	26
No. Part-Time Faculty	12
No. Full-Time Students	476
No. Part-Time Students	47

FINANCIAL INFORMATION

Main Source of University Funding	Public
Annual Tuition & Fees (graduate, resident)	$4,727
Annual Tuition & Fees (graduate, nonresident)	$9,246
Annual Tuition & Fees (undergraduate, resident)	$3,133
Annual Tuition & Fees (undergraduate, nonresident)	$7,974
% Students Receiving Federal Financial Aid	60
% Students Receiving University Financial Aid	60
% Students Receiving Departmental Financial Aid	5
% Students Receiving Scholarships (assistantships or fellowships)	10
Average Annual Scholarship for Department	$2,800

ACADEMIC SESSIONS

Fall Quarter/Trimester: September to December
Spring Quarter/Trimester: April to June

Winter Quarter/Trimester: January to March
Summer Session I: June to August

ARCHITECTURE AND RELATED DEGREE PROGRAMS

Degree	Min. Yrs. to Complete	Professional Accreditation	# of FT Students	# of PT Students	# of First-Year Students	# of Degrees Conferred	Admissions Requirements
Architecture							
BS Arch	4		303	28	39	72	ACT/SAT, HS diploma, 4 yrs HS math, 1 yr HS physics
M. Arch 1	4	NAAB	54	2	14	13	GRE, portfolio, letters of recommendation
M. Arch 2	3	NAAB	119	17	48	39	GRE, portfolio, letters of recommendation
MS Arch	2		10	2	5	4	GRE, portfolio, letters of recommendation
Interior Design/Interior Architecture							
BSID	5	CIDA	201	17	39	44	ACT/SAT, HS diploma, 4 yrs HS math, 1 yr HS physics

SPECIALIZATIONS

Architectural Design	History	Preservation	Theory/Criticism
Building Technology/Env. Systems	Interior Design	Professional Practice	

ARCHITECTURE PROGRAM SUMMARY

The School of Architecture and Interior Design at the University of Cincinnati serves over 700 students and offers four degrees: the pre-professional B.S.Arch, professional M.Arch and B.S. Interior Design, and a post-professional M.S. Arch. Cooperative education was invented at the University of Cincinnati in 1906 and has been a signature component of the architecture program since its inception in 1927. The Architecture program at UC was one of the first programs accredited by the NAAB, in 1947.

UNIVERSITY SETTING

The University of Cincinnati has developed a billion-dollar campus master plan designed by George Hargreaves that features buildings and urban landscape by Hargreaves, Frank Gehry, Thom Mayne, Michael Graves, Gwathmey Siegel, Machado and Silvetti, SOM, Leers Weinzaptl, and Bernard Tschumi, among other notable architects. Peter Eisenman's internationally acclaimed Aronoff Center for Design and Art houses the School of Architecture and Interior Design (SAID) and three other schools within the College of Design, Architecture, Art, and Planning.

SCHOOL PHILOSOPHY

The architecture program at UC prepares students for critical engagement with practice. This critical engagement presupposes sustained evaluation of the principles, traditions, and requirements of building. Our goal is to advance the profession of architecture by combining ethical judgment and technical proficiency in pursuit of excellence, whether the product of our expertise is a physical or intellectual construction. In view of constantly changing conditions for practice, our program seeks to multiply insights and abilities in every student—sensitivity to the aesthetic and social responsibilities of environmental intervention; the lifelong cultivation of a broad, synthesizing, and humanistic world view; respect for the benefits of research and innovation; deepened commitment to specific lines of inquiry; an advanced understanding of the culture of practice; readiness for licensure; design acumen; advanced graphic skills and technical vocabulary; affection for risk; and love of play.

PROGRAM DESCRIPTION

The University of Cincinnati has implemented a professional curriculum leading to the M.Arch. degree, based on the 4+ 2 model, recognizing significant changes in the conditions and requirements for effective practice. Students who enter as freshmen earn a pre-professional B.S. Arch degree in four years. Qualified UC students with a B.S.Arch degree may proceed to professional graduate study, culminating in the M.Arch.

Additionally, the School welcomes students with pre-professional and non-architectural undergraduate degrees conferred by other institutions. The program allows graduate students to bundle course work around specific career objectives beyond basic design education. Within this program, students can expand their research into the cultural significance of building and broaden the effective range and scale of conventional design intervention. The curriculum seeks to equip students to assume a larger role in the management of building economics and to prepare them to lead more phases of the building production process. We seek to prepare architects to take greater responsibility for the long-term economic and environmental consequences of construction, including the re-use and maintenance of existing buildings. We seek to promote leadership, collaboration, intellectual depth, flexibility, and teamwork, as well as to promote stronger connections between design innovation and the administrative and managerial dimensions of practice, which increasingly influence the business of architecture.

The Master of Architecture program intensifies professional education in two important ways. First, it organizes the resources of the school around individually tailored academic thesis topics that accord with emerging practices in the field. Second, it enriches graduate academic experience through the curricular integration of its longstanding co-operative education system, in which students work and learn as paid employees in over 500 participating firms in the United States and overseas.

AREAS OF FOCUS AND RESEARCH

Focus

The University of Cincinnati enjoys recognition as one of the nation's premier schools of architecture in part because of its unique program of cooperative education: beginning in the second year of studies, students work in professional firms as paid employees every other quarter, under the guidance of the University's Division of Professional Practice.

Research

Since 1988, SAID's Center for the Study of Practice has undertaken research projects on a variety of practice-related issues and topics. CSP-sponsored conferences, documentaries, and publications help disseminate ideas and information that enrich the discourse on practice and education. Faculty and students also participate in collaborative research projects managed by the Center for Electronic Restoration of Historic and Archeological Sites (CERHAS) and the Center for Design Research and Innovation (CDRI). In addition, the School's nine faculty members with Ph.D.'s maintain diverse programs of research, which include digital media, building morphology, historic conservation, con-

temporary theory and criticism, gender studies, post-occupancy evaluation and universal design, urban and interior design, building science and environmental technology, sustainability, archaeology, and African architecture. The College of DAAP promotes a rich inter-disciplinary culture, strengthened by four schools with programs in graphic, industrial, and fashion design, art, art history, art education, architecture, interior and urban design, and planning—10 undergraduate and 7 graduate programs altogether.

SPECIAL ACTIVITIES AND PROGRAMS

SAID offers regular opportunities to study abroad. Recent quarter-long programs include studios in Copenhagen, Rome, Sardinia, Paris and Switzerland. In addition, the School regularly offers students an opportunity to spend a quarter studying in the American Southwest. Students participate in the School's exchange programs in India and France and complete co-op assignments in cities throughout Ohio, the U.S., and around the world. SAID offers a certificate program in historic preservation and students pursue concurrent minors and certificates in interior design, business, and urban planning, to name a few.

FACILITIES

Peter Eisenman's Aronoff addition organizes a two-level library, a large auditorium, lecture halls, classrooms, studios, a state-of-the-art shop, an atrium, a café, an art supply store, computer graphics center and rapid prototyping center—305,000 square feet total. The completion of the Aronoff Center in 1996 unified the Schools of Design, Architecture and Interior Design, Art, and Planning under one roof for the first time in the history of the College.

SCHOLARSHIPS AND FINANCIAL AID

Most members of the entering freshman class qualify for scholarships from $2000 per year, under the University's Cincinnatus Honor Scholarship program. In addition, the School awards approximately 40 graduate assistantships to incoming M.Arch and M.S.Arch students. Additional scholarships, totaling over $100,000 each year, are awarded from private donors funds.

ADMINISTRATION

Robert Probst: Dean of the College of Design, Architecture, Art, and Planning
Michaele Pride, AIA, NOMA: Director of the School of Architecture and Interior Design
Patricia Kucker, AIA: Graduate Program Director
Ann Black, NCIDQ: Associate Director, Interior Design program coordinator
David G. Saile, RIBA: Director, Master of Science in Architecture program

UNIVERSITY OF COLORADO

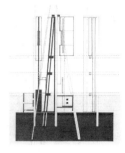
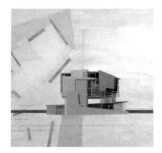

ADDRESS

Main
University of Colorado
College of Architecture and Planning
Campus Box 126
P.O. Box 173364
Denver, CO 80217-3364
Tel.: 303.556.3382
Fax: 303.556.3687
ANPDeansoffice@storm.cudenver.edu
www.cudenver.edu/Academics/
Colleges/ArchitecturePlanning/Pages.
default.aspx

STUDENT AND FACULTY DEMOGRAPHICS

% of Female Students	38
% of International Students	1
% of Minority Students	12
% of Out-of-State U.S. Students	50
No. Full-Time Faculty	30
No. Part-Time Faculty	52
No. Full-Time Students	182
No. Part-Time Students	78

FINANCIAL INFORMATION

Main Source of University Funding	Public
Annual Tuition & Fees (graduate, resident)	$5,186
Annual Tuition & Fees (graduate, nonresident)	$10,139
Annual Tuition & Fees (undergraduate, resident)	
Annual Tuition & Fees (undergraduate, nonresident)	
% Students Receiving Federal Financial Aid	
% Students Receiving University Financial Aid	90
% Students Receiving Departmental Financial Aid	10
% Students Receiving Scholarships (assistantships or fellowships)	4
Average Annual Scholarship for Department	$1,500

ACADEMIC SESSIONS

Fall Semester: August to December;
　Application Deadline: February 15

Spring Semester: January to May;
　Application Deadline: October 1
Summer Session: June to July

ARCHITECTURE AND RELATED DEGREE PROGRAMS

Degree	Min. Yrs. to Complete	Professional Accreditation	# of FT Students	# of PT Students	# of First-Year Students	# of Degrees Conferred	Admissions Requirements
Architecture							
B. Envd							
M. Arch—2 years	2	NAAB	69	23	0		B.Envd or Undegraduate Architecture Degree
M. Arch—3.5 years	3	NAAB	113	55	61	51	Non-Archit. BA
Landscape Architecture							
MLA	3	LAAB	53	10	31	23	
Planning							
Master of Urban and Regional Planning	2	PAB	42	54	41	24	Undergraduate degree, Undergraduate Architecture degree, TOEFL, Rec. Letters, Essay

SPECIALIZATIONS

Architectural Design　　　　　Environment/Sustainability　　　　Preservation

ARCHITECTURE PROGRAM SUMMARY

The University of Colorado Denver is the only institution within the state of Colorado to offer professionally accredited education in architecture. The College of Architecture and Planning offers a Bachelors of Environmental Design on the Boulder campus. The Department of Architecture offers two Master's Programs in Denver.

In the graduate program, students interact with outstanding practicing designers and planners in the Denver metro area through internships, mentorships, design juries, lectures, and engaged student professional organizations. The department has created an academic environment that is intellectually stimulating and educationally challenging and aims to educate future leaders in the discipline and profession of architecture. The Master of Architecture (MArch) program examines the interplay between architectural form and the complex cultural and technological context in which architects operate. Studies focus on integrating various design theories and practices that emphasize: (a) cross-disciplinary interdependence, (b) research orientation, and (c) real-world relevance. In this program, students collaborate with peers to produce an understanding of how connected disciplines play a role in the design and research of architectural projects. As part of this collaborative matrix, each research and design project asks a critical question that stresses environmental, economic, social, cultural, aesthetic and ethical concerns, then answers it using an appropriate method.

The College also offers a multi-disciplinary PhD Program in Design and Planning.

UNIVERSITY SETTING

The program celebrates its place in a special set of landscapes—one of the most urbanized states, healthy, "cool," metroplex Denver, as well as the mountainous beauty of Boulder. The College's graduate programs in Architecture, Landscape Architecture, Urban and Regional Planning and Urban Design are taught on the Denver campus in the heart of downtown Denver, adjacent to Lower Downtown, home to many design and planning firms. Its undergraduate programs are offered in Boulder on the original campus of the University of Colorado. Out-of-state and transfer students are accepted.

The University of Colorado Denver seeks to provide students, whatever their ages or circumstances, with opportunities to enhance their lives and careers through higher education. Emphasis is given to professional, pre-professional, and liberal arts instruction, with a strong multi-disciplinary and applied focus for the campus's research and service functions. The University is one of the most important educational resources in the Denver metropolitan area: a major urban, non-residential campus located in the heart of the city with a broad range of civic, cultural, business, professional and governmental activities in close proximity. The University is committed to research, technology, creative scholarship, and providing an institutional culture that reflects the plurality, collegiality, and integration of an increasingly diverse global workplace.

The University of Colorado at Boulder, the site of the College's undergraduate programs, is a traditional residential university campus.

SCHOOL PHILOSOPHY

The College of Architecture and Planning embraces the educational vision of INTEGRATIVE DESIGN. The College engages design and planning challenges that are significant for our society. The College will take on these challenges in partnerships among the disciplines and with our external communities.

In the College of Architecture and Planning the faculty researches, teaches and practices ways to design environments that are meaningful and beautiful. We plan, shape and interpret those environments in ways that are collaborative, responsible, sustainable, enabling, and integrative. Promoting and acknowledging diversity in subject matter, method, and orientation are essential to the College's integrative approach.

Design, research, and scholarship are the distinctive practices the faculty uses to investigate, understand, integrate and affect the complex relationships between our designed environments and their natural and cultural settings. We shape, plan and evaluate those relationships to make sure that our designs are socially and environmentally appropriate, and aesthetically significant. Our need to consistently integrate design, scholarly inquiry and research acts to unite reason and imagination, intellect and intuition, judgment and wisdom, and mind and spirit as complementary orientations affecting our work.

The architecture program's mission is to lead in the discovery, communication and application of knowledge in the discipline of architecture. The program aims to excel in the education of its students, in the research

and creative endeavors of its faculty, and in service to the community. The architecture program focuses on the design of buildings, and also on the interactions between buildings and their urban and natural settings. The program examines the interplay between architectural form and the complex cultural and technological context in which architects operate.

The Program's teaching challenges students to assert responsibility for the important role they play as a designer of buildings in urban and natural settings; understand and value the influences of history, theory, ideology, context, technology, and practice on architecture and on urban and rural landscapes; define their obligations, status, ethical behavior, and role as a member of an established design discipline and design profession; and be creative, thoughtful, and critical design leaders in the discipline and profession of architecture.

PROGRAM DESCRIPTION

This degree program is designed for students who wish to prepare for careers in architecture or architecturally related fields generally and comprehensively.

The B.Envd mainly prepares students for entry into a professional Master of Architecture (M.Arch) program. The B.Envd degree covers a number of subject areas from the social and aesthetic to the technological and ecological, and so it provides an excellent liberal education at the undergraduate level.

The MArch degree program is fully accredited by NAAB, and provides the professional degree required by most states for architectural licensure. The Master of Architecture program has two tracks, according to the type of undergraduate degree that the student holds. For students who hold a pre-professional degree, the MArch will require a minimum of four semesters of coursework and at least 60-semester hours of credit. Students who hold a bachelor's degree unrelated to architecture must complete seven semesters of coursework and at least 114-semester hours of credit. Students entering with a B.Envd or a similar pre-professional degree will have their transcripts and design portfolios evaluated to determine the exact number of semester credits that they must take.

AREAS OF FOCUS AND RESEARCH

Focus

The College has organized many of its activities around "communities of interest," which currently include:

- Emerging Practices in Design: Exploring how the digital design revolution and sustainable design practices are reshaping the professions. These include sustainable design and design/build practices as well as digital visualization and Building Information Modeling (BIM) technologies.
- Sustainable Urbanism: Exploring new ideas about creating livable cities in the midst of intense pressures for growth and fragile ecosystems.
- Healthy Environments: Exploring how to build healthier buildings, cities and landscapes.
- Cultural Heritage: Understanding, interpreting, and preserving our cultural heritage in design and planning, including historic buildings, landscapes, and intellectual and cultural ideas.

Research

Faculty have diverse research agendas, including environmental design, sustainable design, design

build, preservation and community design. Most research efforts involve outreach to the surrounding Denver community and rural areas beyond.

SPECIAL ACTIVITIES AND PROGRAMS

The Department offers a number of specialty certificates, which can be earned while pursuing the master's degree. These include the Design Build Certificate and the Historic Preservation Certificate.

The College provides a diverse range of opportunities which enrich and enhance the education of its students. Through activities and functions—including a lecture series, a visiting critic series, exhibits, publications and active student organization—the College encourages contact among students, faculty and members of the design professions. Each summer, the College offers foreign-study travel programs. The College also maintains an extensive mentorship and internship program with practitioners in the Denver metro area.

FACILITIES

College facilities include studio space for students, lecture and seminar rooms, design jury space, exhibition space, and faculty offices. The College also provides a model and furniture-making woodshop and a laser cutter lab. In addition, there is an extensive computer lab which allows focus on computeraided design (CAD), computer 2-D and 3-D imaging and analytical tools for planning. Also located in the College is a Geographic Information System (GIS) computer lab, which is open to all students. There is also a Visual Resource Center that provides access to a variety of photographic and audiovisual equipment, a portfolio photography studio room, and analog (35mm slides) and digital image collections. The Auraria Library supports the research and service requirements of all faculty and outreach mission of each of the three institutions.

On the Boulder site, beginning and advanced computer facilities, including graphic capabilities and an urban simulation lab, are available to students in the Environmental Design Building. The college also offers its students access to specialized workshop and study facilities with a state-of-the-art Wood Lab, Metal Lab, Laser Cutting machines, a 3-D Printer, two Digitizers and two 3-Axis CNC routers in the university's Center for Innovation and Creativity (CINC). The five branches of the Boulder campus library system include more than seven million books, periodicals, microforms, computer-based sources, and other research materials. Norlin Library's main branch houses an extensive art and architecture collection of special interest to architecture and planning students.

SCHOLARSHIPS AND FINANCIAL AID

Students in the College have access to a number of scholarships and other financial assistance funds. Some of these funds are provided by the institution itself, while others are provided by external sources like the American Institute of Architects Education Fund, the American Planning Association, the American Society of Landscape Architects, and the Rocky Mountain Masonry Institute.

ADMINISTRATION

Mark Gelernter: Dean, College of Arch & Planning
Yuk Lee: Associate Dean of Academic Affairs
Andy Reid: Assistant Dean
Hans R. Morgenthaler, PhD: Chair

UNIVERSITY OF DETROIT MERCY

ADDRESS

Main
University of Detroit-Mercy
School of Architecture
4001 West McNichols Road
Detroit, MI 48221-3038
Tel.: 313.993.1532
Fax: 313.993.1512
architecture.udmercy.edu

STUDENT AND FACULTY DEMOGRAPHICS

% of Female Students	39
% of International Students	7
% of Minority Students	15
% of Out-of-State U.S. Students	17
No. Full-Time Faculty	12
No. Part-Time Faculty	20
No. Full-Time Students	260
No. Part-Time Students	10

FINANCIAL INFORMATION

Main Source of University Funding	Private
Annual Tuition & Fees (graduate)	$30,600
Annual Tuition & Fees (undergraduate)	$28,000
% Students Receiving Federal Financial Aid	79
% Students Receiving University Financial Aid	86
% Students Receiving Departmental Financial Aid	
% Students Receiving Scholarships (assistantships or fellowships)	
Average Annual Scholarship for Department	$7,352

ACADEMIC SESSIONS

Fall Semester: September to December
Spring Semester: January to April
Summer Session I: April to June

Summer Session II: June to August
Summer Session III: May to August

ARCHITECTURE AND RELATED DEGREE PROGRAMS							
Degree	Min. Yrs. to Complete	Professional Accreditation	# of FT Students	# of PT Students	# of First-Year Students	# of Degrees Conferred	Admissions Requirements
Architecture							
Bachelor of Science in Architecture	4		210	10	75	35	ACT
M. Arch	1	NAAB	40	0	40	38	Undergraduate Architecture degree, Portfolio, Rec. Letters, Essay

SPECIALIZATIONS

Architectural Design

ARCHITECTURE PROGRAM SUMMARY

The University of Detroit Mercy School of Architecture offers two architectural degrees: a non-accredited four-year Bachelor of Science in Architecture degree and a one-year accredited Master of Architecture degree for students who have completed the B.Sc. Arch degree at the University of Detroit Mercy.

UNIVERSITY SETTING

The School of Architecture (SOA), as part of a Catholic university in the Jesuit and Mercy traditions, exists to provide an excellent student-centered, accredited professional architectural education in an urban context. A UDM SOA education seeks to develop architects who are sensitive designers; technically competent; exhibit the highest ethical and professional standards; are socially responsible and culturally aware; and are of service to the community and the profession. The School makes a strong commitment to a broad-based liberal arts education that prepares architects to understand the spectrum of human endeavor. The School intentionally keeps its enrollment small in order to maintain an identifiable relationship with individual students.

SCHOOL PHILOSOPHY

The SOA advocates an open dialogue about architectural issues and philosophies, but searches for deeper architectural meaning than that offered by trend, fad or style. The curriculum provides a foundation in design excellence, while addressing contemporary issues including a focus on urban revitalization. The School is actively involved in the life of the community through its design studios, including design-build studios, and through the Detroit Collaborative Design Center—an outreach arm of the School. The ability to gain real-world understanding is further enhanced through the mandatory cooperative education program and the optional international studies programs.

PROGRAM DESCRIPTION

Architecture begins with an understanding of human nature and the relationship of people to their environment. Technical skills and special knowledge are also required to translate ideas into reality; places where people live, work, worship, shop, or play. To accomplish this goal, the School of Architecture offers a five-year professional program that leads to a Master of Architecture degree. UDM lets you study architectural design beginning in your first year. Design remains a primary focus of the curriculum throughout your studies.

At UDM, the complete spectrum of human endeavor is studied. It's a small group of dedicated, creative students interacting with dynamic, professionally suc-cessful, engaged faculty members who understand the future of their profession and the needs of their students. It's a broad-based education that incorporates liberal arts, values and ethics, cutting-edge technology, mastery of sustainable design, and real world experiences in a cosmopolitan, urban setting. The Cooperative Education sequence gives students professional experience in work assignments at architectural offices of the student's choosing. The student may elect to accept a Bachelor of Science in Architecture, a non-accredited degree, at the end of the fourth year or apply to the fifth-year Master of Architecture Program. The five-year Master of Architecture program has, as its purpose, the establishment of a solid base of professional skills, as well as an appropriate background in the humanities. It is expected that this will provide the student with the perception of architecture as espoused in the school's philosophy rather than as a technical or artistic activity unrelated to man in the environment.

Candidates for the Master of Architecture degree, as part of the application process, declare an area of concentration and create a curriculum by incorporating existing graduate-level courses from the colleges of the University as concentration electives. The purpose of these concentration electives is to provide the basis for developing the specialized knowledge for the 21st century. Concentrations are also intended to build upon the strengths of the University by establishing strong cross-disciplinary ties with other academic units. The concentration will form the focus of the student's graduate study and the basis for the Master's Studio project. Examples of concentrations are: urban studies, architecture, management and marketing, imaging and representation, and the global marketplace.

AREAS OF FOCUS AND RESEARCH

Design is at the center of the curriculum. Foundation Studios concentrate on developing basic technical, analytical and critical-thinking skills. Upper-Level Studios are comprised of a "mix" of students from both third and fourth years together in investigations of complex architectural themes in more concentrated depth. Examples include community design, design-build experiences, architectural competition, historical preservation, sustainability, furniture-making, and virtual reality.

SPECIAL ACTIVITIES AND PROGRAMS

- Detroit Collaborative Design Center (DCdc)—The award winning DCdc is a full-time practice that provides design services to non-profit community organizations. DCdc provides students experiences working with clients on projects that address is-sues facing today's suburburban environments.
- Study Abroad—UDM has an exchange program with the Polytechnical University in Warsaw, Poland; a study travel program in Volterra, Italy and a student exchange program with Monterrey Technical University in Mexico.
- Cooperative Education—UDM's curriculum integrates cooperative education into its program. Students alternate terms of classroom education with terms of co-op training assignments. Many are invited back to complete additional terms of cooperative education; students are frequently offered full-time positions in these firms after graduation.
- *Dichotomy*: Journal of theory and criticism operated solely by students.
- Guest Lecture Series: Invited guest lecturers of regional, national, or international interest.
- Safety Street: AIAS sponsored Halloween alternative for community children.

FACILITIES

The University of Detroit Mercy is a private Jesuit institution of 6,000 students located on an urban campus. The School of Architecture is housed in the Warren Loranger Architecture Building. In this building the school houses studios that provide an individual work station for each student, as well as such adjunct facilities as a model shop, photography darkroom, computer graphics lab, exhibition space and seminar rooms. The university's main library, which is adjacent to the school, houses the architecture collection. This collection consists of reference materials, periodicals, slides and books. Dormitories are available on campus.

SCHOLARSHIPS AND FINANCIAL AID

Students at the School of Architecture participate in every type of financial aid available at a private university. In 2007/08, 98% of the students enrolled in architecture received financial aid totaling almost $3,000,000. This amount includes federal aid and state aid, as well as institutional scholarships in the amount of $1,500,000.

ADMINISTRATION

Stephen Vogel, FAIA: Dean
Donzetta Jones: Assistant Dean
Will Wittig: Director, Graduate Program in Architecture

UNIVERSITY OF FLORIDA

ADDRESS

Main
University of Florida
College of Design, Construction and
Planning
School of Architecture
231 ARCH, PO Box 115702
Gainesville, FL 32611-5702
Tel.: 352.392.0205
Fax: 352.392.4606
www.arch.ufl.edu

STUDENT AND FACULTY DEMOGRAPHICS

% of Female Students	32
% of International Students	9
% of Minority Students	40
% of Out-of-State U.S. Students	4
No. Full-Time Faculty	28
No. Part-Time Faculty	6
No. Full-Time Students	614
No. Part-Time Students	0

FINANCIAL INFORMATION

Main Source of University Funding	Public
Annual Tuition & Fees (graduate, resident)	$341
Annual Tuition & Fees (graduate, nonresident)	$972
Annual Tuition & Fees (undergraduate, resident)	$126
Annual Tuition & Fees (undergraduate, nonresident)	$687
% Students Receiving Federal Financial Aid	13
% Students Receiving University Financial Aid	20
% Students Receiving Departmental Financial Aid	47
% Students Receiving Scholarships (assistantships or fellowships)	47
Average Annual Scholarship for Department	$4,000

ACADEMIC SESSIONS

Fall Semester: August to December;
    Application Deadline: February 1 (Master's only)
Spring Semester: January to May

Summer Session I: May to June
Summer Session II: June to August
Summer Session III: May to August

ARCHITECTURE AND RELATED DEGREE PROGRAMS

Degree	Min. Yrs. to Complete	Professional Accreditation	# of FT Students	# of PT Students	# of First-Year Students	# of Degrees Conferred	Admissions Requirements
Architecture							
Bachelor of Design	4		500	0	150	90	Undergraduate Arch. degree, SAT, ACT
M. Arch CORE 4 year	4	NAAB	46	0	10	10	Undergraduate degree, GRE, Portfolio, Rec. Letters, Essay
M. Arch	2	NAAB	150	0	40	40	Undergraduate Arch. degree, GRE, TOEFL, Portfolio, Rec. Letters, Essay
MS in Acoustics	1		1	0	1	0	Professional Arch. degree, GRE, TOEFL, Portfolio, Rec. Letters, Essay
MS in Architectural Pedagogy	1		5	0	1	1	Undergraduate Arch. degree, Professional Arch. degree, GRE, TOEFL, Portfolio, Rec. Letters, Essay
Doctorate of Design, Construction, and Planning Program	3		10	0	4	3	Professional Arch. degree, GRE, TOEFL, Portfolio, Rec. Letters, Essay
Historic Preservation							
MS in Historic Preservation	1		8	0	4	1	Undergraduate Arch. degree, Professional Arch. degree, GRE, TOEFL, Rec. Letters, Essay

SPECIALIZATIONS

Community Design	Environment/Sustainability	Environment/Sustainability	Urban Planning and Design
Computer-Aided Design	History	Theory/Criticism	

ARCHITECTURE PROGRAM SUMMARY

The School of Architecture at the University of Florida is dedicated to providing an excellent educational experience for students intending to enter the profession of architecture. The primary mission of the School and its programs is to provide a curriculum and educational context that teaches students the means by which they can be responsive to human needs in creating the built environment. Our students must be perceptive, skilled and inventive - capable of acting in a responsible manner in today's profession, while continuing to learn throughout their lives so as to realize a visionary profession for the future. The most important facet of this educational mission is to instill in our students a strong social consciousness and a desire to be active participants in improving the quality of their communities.

UNIVERSITY SETTING

The University of Florida at Gainesville has 50,000 students, 120 departments, and numerous research centers. As an institution, it has set National standards for university system attaining the highest level of excellence. In achieving this goal, the university has actively recruited faculty and students from around the country and world. Five disciplines comprise the College of Design Construction and Planning: School of Architecture, Department of Landscape, Department of Interior Design, Department of Urban Planning and School of Building Construction. With this rich mix of specialties, ranging from design to Construction, the School of Architecture is in a unique position to lead in the development of the built environment, to initiate research projects, and to contribute to the preservation of the natural context. The College of Design Construction and Planning is housed in its own building on campus. The School of Architecture is one of the largest in the United States with over 750 students in both graduate and undergraduate programs. The architecture faculty is internationally recognized, culturally diverse and present varied approaches to architectural design. Visiting faculty and lecturers from around the world constitute an important aspect of the educational experience. Gainesville, with 250,000 in its metropolitan area, is centrally located in north Florida, one hour by car from the Atlantic Ocean and the Gulf of Mexico.

SCHOOL PHILOSOPHY

The School of Architecture recognizes design as a synthesis of thinking, analyzing and making — an iterative process that analytically engages, issues of space, historical precedent, sustainability, ecology, urbanity, landscape, built-form, and construction toward innovation. As Florida will soon support the third largest population in the US, the challenges of rapid growth within sensitive natural ecologies, fluctuating tourism, humid and hot climate, multiple urban centers, sprawling suburbs, dwindling agriculture, lack of mass transit, and extensive coastal hurricane threats requires integrative and collaborative design strategies for the future.

The School of Architecture is uniquely positioned to respond to these issues by deploying studio based design methodologies in collaboration with a new generation of experts in engineering, ecology, business, anthropology, energy, fine arts, medicine and construction. Within the University of Florida, the State's flagship research institution, a cohort of researchers and faculty dedicated to academic excellence and interdisciplinary collaboration are focused on the demands of changing culture.

PROGRAM DESCRIPTION

In the School of Architecture, teaching, research and study are intended to engage the students and faculty in advanced investigations in their discipline; with the ultimate aim of making it possible for each student to make an individual contribution to the improvement of the built environment. The architecture program is intended to foster the intellectual growth and development of students and faculty, to develop new knowledge that will materially add to the discipline of architecture and to society as a whole, to act as an integral and contributing part of the intellectual community of the University, and to encourage graduates to utilize their unique talents in the construction of places that contribute in a fundamental way to the betterment of their fellow neighbors.

The school's Master of Architecture is a professional degree allows each student the opportunity to focus coursework in one or more areas, including design, history, theory, urban design, preservation, structures, acoustis, technology and pedagogy. The student's overall college experience, including undergraduate programs and the graduate program, is intended to be a complete unit of professional education leading toward practice in architecture or related professions. Students entering the program matriculate in one of the following programs of study: B Arch base (1 year); baccalaureate with architecture major base (2 years); baccalaureate with related degree base (3 years); baccalaureate with non-related degree base (4 years).

The Master of Science in Architectural Studies degree program is a non-professional degree in architecture for those seeking to do advanced work in a specialized area of architecture. Students holding a bachelor's degree in any discipline, or a first professional degree from an accredited architecture program are eligible for enrollment in this program. The curriculum normally extends over three semesters, and each student must complete the required thesis, with their program of study being individually developed by the students with the Master of Science committee.

The Doctor of Philosophy Program recognizes a need to develop new knowledge that advances architecture through theory, technology, pedagogy and professional practice. Since 1988, College of Design, Construction and Planning doctoral faculty have led an interdisciplinary core of collaborative research, publication and teaching to improve the built environment. Doctoral students, although affiliated with a particular department, are encouraged to select a supervisory committee, seek out courses and work with faculty across the college and university to develop original and self directed dissertation topics that integrate affiliated knowledge within the design and construction disciplines.

Doctoral students are highly involved in both research and teaching through graduate assistantships, specific grant funded projects and as teaching assistants in the undergraduate curriculum. These opportunities extend through our travel and international programs in Nantucket, St. Augustine, Vicenza (northern Italy), Paris, Hong Kong, and Mexico.

Doctoral students may also participate in the College of Design, Construction and Planning Graduate Interdisciplinary Concentration and Certificate in Historic Preservation or Sustainability.

AREA OF FOCUS AND RESEARCH

In general, the curriculum engages all of the following: examination of the cultural, social, technical, economic and environmental contexts that shape buildings, analytical investigation of the history of architecture as it is present in built form and space investigation of the experience of architectural form and spaces and their resulting meanings for their occupants; knowledge and utilization of the materials, structures and technologies of construction available to the architect; and exploration of the varied and constantly evolving methods utilized in architectural design.

SPECIAL ACTIVITIES AND PROGRAMS

- Vicenza Institute for Architecture (VIA), year round studio and travel program located in the University of Florida's Teatro Berga studio in Vicenza, Italy.
- Preservation Institute: Caribbean (PI: C), a year-round design, research and documentation program located in a different city in the greater Caribbean basin each year.
- Preservation Institute: Nantucket (PI: N), a year-round design, research and documentation program located in the university's studio on Nantucket Island.
- Hong Kong summer program
- The school has an ongoing series of visiting lecturers, studio critics, exhibitions and professional seminars.
- The school organizes annual studio field trips to major cities in the region and the nation as part of the curriculum for each year of graduate and undergraduate study.
- Design Exploration Program (DEP) is a three-week summer program, introducing high school students.
- A variety of extracurricular activities are sponsored by the school, the college and student service organizations such as the AIAS, Tau Sigma Delta and Alpha Rho Chi

FACILITIES

- Library
- Wood Shop
- Computer Labs
- Acoustical Modeling Research Lab
- Architectural Preservation Lab
- Urban Studio

SCHOLARSHIPS AND FINANCIAL AID

The school has one of the nations most extensive scholarship programs for its entering graduate students. Graduate teaching assistantships are given to selected students and this involves teaching experience in the undergraduate studios and support courses. The university offers an extensive job placement program and the school places selected students in both summer and postgraduate positions. The Graduate School offers the Graduate Council Fellowships, as well as graduate fellowships for minorities, with stipends ranging to $12,000 for 11 months, to students entering for the first time. Non-Florida Tuition Waivers are available for Non-Florida students who hold fellowships or assistantships or qualify through special programs. Graduate teaching assistantships up to one-half time are available to students who have fifth-year status. Loans and Work-Study Financial Aid assistance are available to students who have demonstrated financial need.

ADMINISTRATION

Christopher Silver, PhD, AICP: Dean
Martin Gold: Interim Director
Nancy Clark: Assistant Director of Graudate Programs
John Maze: Assistant Director of
    Undergraduate Programs

UNIVERSITY OF HARTFORD

 UNIVERSITY OF HARTFORD

ADDRESS

Main
University of Hartford
College of Engineering, Technology and
Architecture
Department of Architecture
200 Bloomfield Avenue
West Hartford, CT 06117
Tel.: 860.768.4755
Fax: 860.768.5198
crosbie@hartford.edu
www.hartford.edu/architecture

STUDENT AND FACULTY DEMOGRAPHICS

% of Female Students	34
% of International Students	2
% of Minority Students	18
% of Out-of-State U.S. Students	55
No. Full-Time Faculty	6
No. Part-Time Faculty	15
No. Full-Time Students	196
No. Part-Time Students	11

FINANCIAL INFORMATION

Main Source of University Funding	Private
Annual Tuition & Fees (graduate)	$16,500
Annual Tuition & Fees (undergraduate)	$26,942
% Students Receiving Federal Financial Aid	
% Students Receiving University Financial Aid	90
% Students Receiving Departmental Financial Aid	2
% Students Receiving Scholarships (assistantships or fellowships)	
Average Annual Scholarship for Department	

ACADEMIC SESSIONS

Fall Semester: September to December;
  Application Deadline: May 1
Spring Semester: January to May

ARCHITECTURE AND RELATED DEGREE PROGRAMS

Degree	Min. Yrs. to Complete	Professional Accreditation	# of FT Students	# of PT Students	# of First-Year Students	# of Degrees Conferred	Admissions Requirements
Architecture							
BS Architectural Engineering Technology	4	ABET	186	11	75		SAT
M. Arch—2 years	2	NAAB Candidate	10	0	3	23	Undergraduate Architecture degree, TOEFL, Portfolio, Rec. Letters, Essay

SPECIALIZATIONS

Architectural Design
Community Design

Engineering

International/Regional Architecture

Urban Planning and Design

ARCHITECTURE PROGRAM SUMMARY

The Department of Architecture at the College of Engineering, Technology, and Architecture is a diverse community of practitioners, teachers, and students dedicated to educating future architectural professionals and growing the knowledge base of the profession.

UNIVERSITY SETTING

The University's spacious and scenic 320-acre wooded main campus in suburban West Hartford features housing for 3,700 students. At the heart of the campus is the Harry Jack Gray Center, housing the University's libraries, conference facilities, and art gallery. With dynamic relationships with the city of Hartford, the University of Hartford has extended its reach and renewed its emphasis on helping students, businesses and the community meet the needs of the 21st century.

SCHOOL PHILOSOPHY

The Department of Architecture is a diverse community of practitioners, teachers, and students dedicated to educating future architectural professionals and growing the knowledge base of the profession. Our commitment is to engage architecture in its civic, social, and professional realms for the ultimate benefit of the built environment and those who use it.

PROGRAM DESCRIPTION

The 130-credit undergraduate program (Bachelor of Science in Architectural Engineering Technology) has traditionally prepared students for careers in a wide assortment of careers in architecture, design, and construction. It has been estimated by the faculty that approximately one third of the graduates each year successfully enter professional graduate programs in architecture. The undergraduate program is accredited by the Technology Accreditation Commission/Accreditation Board for Engineering and Technology (TAC/ABET), one of only a handful of architecture programs in the United States with that distinction.Having been granted candidacy status by the National Architectural Accrediting Board (NAAB) effective January 1, 2003, faculty, students, and administrators have been working toward NAAB accreditation of the Master of Architecture program. The 64-credit graduate architecture program supports the mission of the University while responding to the needs of the state's architectural profession, the region, and the city. With the undergraduate program offering a pre-professional degree in architecture, the graduate professional-degree program balances theoretical, technical, professional, and creative knowledge.

AREAS OF FOCUS AND RESEARCH

The Department of Architecture views its mission as part of the University's commitment as a private institution dedicated to public purpose and influence. It shares the vision expressed in the University of Hartford motto, found on the University seal: Ad Humanitatem, "For humanity."

The Civic Realm: Located in the City of Hartford, the Department of Architecture sees the city as a "laboratory of opportunity" in the education of future architects. Urban sites are the basis of many studio projects that respond to issues of density, civic life, and the role of the urban environment in creating dynamic settings for the pursuit of public life.

The Social Realm: The Department of Architecture's focus on the Social Realm responds to the role of the architect in serving the public through leadership in design, particularly social groups that have not in the past had access to the benefits of architecture. In *Building Community,* Boyer and Mitgang lamented the fact that too often academia is viewed as a "private benefit, not a public good." Architecture is a social art, and the Department of Architecture seeks to engage the Social Realm.

The Professional Realm: The Department of Architecture's mission in the Professional Realm is part of its history. The Department believes in the value of practicing architects teaching future architects. Six of the seven part- and full-time faculty are licensed architects, as are most of the adjunct faculty. The Department continues to engage the state professional architecture society. The AIA/Connecticut chapter was an early proponent of the University's architecture program and continues as a solid supporter. The department and the campus have served as a setting for a number of professional educational events for the region's architects.

The Civic, Social, and Professional realms reinforce the mission of architectural education at the University of Hartford, and help serve the mission of the University itself. The Department views the three realms as the bedrock of the discipline and profession of architecture, reinforcing it as a social art with a civic purpose, created by professionals engaged with the community.

SPECIAL ACTIVITIES AND PROGRAMS

Study abroad opportunities are available for students who wish to further expand their global consciousness. The one-semester program, traditionally occurring during semester six of the undergraduate curriculum, has been successful in giving students outreach opportunities. Students in the Department of Architecture have chosen to study in England, Scotland, Greece, Italy, and

Australia. In Summer 07, the Department offered for the first time a course in Architectural Monuments. Professor Daniel Davis traveled to Italy with approximately nine students, spending 18 days studying the architecture of Rome, Florence, and Venice. Accessing information about the practice of architecture occurs frequently through course work but also through lectures by practicing professionals, and activities organized by the campus chapter of the American Institute of Architecture Students.

The AIAS organizes a highly successful student exhibition each spring. The event attracts more than 100 visitors to the opening reception. Architects throughout the New England region are invited to the exhibit. The AIAS chapter also sponsors fund raising efforts, such as Architecture tee-shirts and shoulder bags. Members of the AIAS chapter have traveled to various cities and architectural sites, such as Fallingwater. Over the last several years, members of AIAS have attended Northeast Quad gatherings, the most recent in 2007, when the Quad President met with the AIAS chapter at the University of Hartford. Our AIAS members attended AIAS national conference in Los Angeles, Toronto, Pittsburgh, Boston, and Chicago. Numerous students in the architecture program volunteer with the campus organization Habitat for Humanity.

FACILITIES

As the current location of the Department of Architecture, the west wing of Harry Jack Gray Center contains seven faculty/staff offices and a mail/copy/supply room on the ground floor and studios, a conference room, a computer lab, a review room, a woodshop, and storage on the lower level. It is located in the center of campus surrounded by the Mortensen Library, The Hartford School of Art, and the Integrated Science, Engineering, and Technology (ISET) complex.

SCHOLARSHIPS AND FINANCIAL AID

The University of Hartford offers need-based financial aid to eligible students to help defray their education expenses. To be considered for need-based financial aid, students must submit the Free Application for Federal Student Aid (FAFSA). The University offers scholarships which are not based on financial need. These are usually based on other factors including your academic performance, place of residence, or talent and are awarded during the admission process or through a specific school, college, or department of the University.

ADMINISTRATION

Michael J. Crosbie, AIA: Chair

UNIVERSITY OF HAWAI'I AT MANOA

ADDRESS

Main
University of Hawai'i at Manoa
School of Architecture
2410 Campus Road
Architecture Building
Honolulu, HI 96822
Tel.: 808.956.7225
Fax: 808.956.7778
arch@hawaii.edu
www.arch.hawaii.edu/site/index.php

STUDENT AND FACULTY DEMOGRAPHICS

% of Female Students	43
% of International Students	14
% of Minority Students	61
% of Out-of-State U.S. Students	5
No. Full-Time Faculty	15
No. Part-Time Faculty	60
No. Full-Time Students	240
No. Part-Time Students	40

FINANCIAL INFORMATION

Main Source of University Funding	Public
Annual Tuition & Fees (graduate, resident)	$3,948
Annual Tuition & Fees (graduate, nonresident)	$9,468
Annual Tuition & Fees (undergraduate, resident)	$2,976
Annual Tuition & Fees (undergraduate, nonresident)	$8,304
% Students Receiving Federal Financial Aid	42
% Students Receiving University Financial Aid	10
% Students Receiving Departmental Financial Aid	9
% Students Receiving Scholarships (assistantships or fellowships)	12
Average Annual Scholarship for Department	$10,000

ACADEMIC SESSIONS

Fall Semester: August to December
    Application Deadline: Priority Feb. 1; Final May 1
    Financial Aid: Mar. 1
Summer Session I: May to July

Spring Semester: January to May
    Application Deadline: Priority Sept. 1; Final Oct. 1
    Financial Aid: Sept. 1; Final Oct. 1
Summer Session II: July to August

ARCHITECTURE AND RELATED DEGREE PROGRAMS

Degree	Min. Yrs. to Complete	Professional Accreditation	# of FT Students	# of PT Students	# of First-Year Students	# of Degrees Conferred	Admissions Requirements
Architecture							
D. Arch	3–7 years	NAAB	240	40	60	10	Students without prior degree: SAT/ACT, TOEFL; Students with prior degree: TOEFL, Portfolio, Rec. Letters, Essay

SPECIALIZATIONS

Architectural Design	Energy	International Development	Sustainability
Building Information Modeling	Environment/Sustainability	International/Regional Architecture	Tectonics
Building Technology/Env. Systems	History	Preservation	Theory/Criticism
Community Design	Interior Design/Architecture	Professional Practice	Urban Planning and Design
Computer-Aided Design			

ARCHITECTURE PROGRAM SUMMARY

The School resides in a vibrant research university committed to leadership, excellence, and innovation. The School has a diverse student body of 280 Doctor of Architecture (D.Arch.) students. The School is strategically positioned between the U.S. and Asia, and is the only program offering a National Architectural Accrediting Board (NAAB) first-professional doctorate architecture degree. The School is a center for teaching, research, and community outreach in Hawaii, the Asian Pacific, and world. The School fosters intensive engagement of theory and practice.

UNIVERSITY SETTING

The University of Hawaii Manoa (UHM), is the major research campus of the University of Hawaii System, a Carnegie Foundation "RU/VH: Research Universities (very high research activity)." UHM has over 20,000 students, and comprises nine colleges and eight professional schools. Students pursue a comprehensive liberal and professional education in a multicultural urban environment. The School's program actively engages the multi-disciplinary UHM resources in developing critical and creative thinkers able to address pressing world issues.

SCHOOL PHILOSOPHY

The School of Architecture offers a global collaborative approach to improving the built and natural environment founded on intellectual inquiry, creative problem solving, and outreach with a commitment to promi-nence in innovative architectural education, design excellence, sustainability, and research with a focus on Hawaii, the Pacific, and Asia.

PROGRAM DESCRIPTION

The program allows students to expand their ability to lead positive change in the built and natural environment.

The program accepts students from high school who may complete the program in seven years. Students entering with a bachelor's degree or higher may complete the program in three to three and one-half years. Students holding a professional architecture degree or a professional architecture degree and a license to practice architecture in the United States (or equivalent) should contact the School for program information. The program includes study abroad programs, community design, research lab experience, doctorate project research, and professional studio experiences.

AREAS OF FOCUS AND RESEARCH

The School houses the Construction Process Innovations Laboratory (building materials and methods), the Heritage Center (historic preservation), the Geolabs/Hawaii Hillside Design Laboratory (hillside design), and the Environmental Control Systems Laboratory (sustainable design). The Professional Studio and international exchange provides learning and research experience in professional and academic settings. Students conduct research during their capstone two-semester Doctorate Studio Project.

SPECIAL ACTIVITIES AND PROGRAMS

The School has active chapters of the American Institute of Architecture Students (AIAS) and Tau Sigma Delta, which participate in School, UHM, and community service activities. The School offers annual travel scholarships and design and service awards. Lecture and exhibition programs offer enrichment from international architects and educators. Students participate in symposia and competitions sponsored by the School, including the biennial International Symposium on Asia-Pacific Architecture.

FACILITIES

The School is housed in a 50,000 square-foot building with 200 studio workstations, a 200-seat multimedia auditorium, lecture, seminar, and conference rooms, research labs, fabrication workshop, reading room, and a digital fabrication services facility.

SCHOLARSHIPS AND FINANCIAL AID

Student financial aid is provided by the UHM Office of Financial Aid Services. The School provides tuition waivers, travel scholarships, and Professional Studio scholarships based on academic performance and financial need.

ADMINISTRATION

Clark E. Llewellyn, AIA: Dean
David Rockwood: Associate Dean

UNIVERSITY OF HOUSTON

 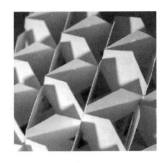 

ADDRESS

Main
University of Houston
Gerald D. Hines College of Architecture
122 College of Architecture Bldg.
Houston, TX 77204-4000
Tel.: 713.743.2400
Fax: 713.743.2358
Klechon@uh.edu
www.arch.uh.edu

STUDENT AND FACULTY DEMOGRAPHICS

% of Female Students	41
% of International Students	6
% of Minority Students	57
% of Out-of-State U.S. Students	
No. Full-Time Faculty	28
No. Part-Time Faculty	48
No. Full-Time Students	505
No. Part-Time Students	178

FINANCIAL INFORMATION

Main Source of University Funding	Public
Annual Tuition & Fees (graduate, resident)	$11,216
Annual Tuition & Fees (graduate, nonresident)	$19,646
Annual Tuition & Fees (undergraduate, resident)	$8,834
Annual Tuition & Fees (undergraduate, nonresident)	$17,826
% Students Receiving Federal Financial Aid	
% Students Receiving University Financial Aid	
% Students Receiving Departmental Financial Aid	
% Students Receiving Scholarships (assistantships or fellowships)	
Average Annual Scholarship for Department	$30,515

ACADEMIC SESSIONS

Fall Semester: August to December
Spring Semester: January to May
Summer Session I: June to July

Summer Session II: June to July
Summer Session III: June to August

ARCHITECTURE AND RELATED DEGREE PROGRAMS

Degree	Min. Yrs. to Complete	Professional Accreditation	# of FT Students	# of PT Students	# of First-Year Students	# of Degrees Conferred	Admissions Requirements
Architecture							
B. Arch	5	NAAB	428	213	151	74	SAT, ACT, TOEFL, Rec. Letters, Essay
M. Arch	3	NAAB	56	8	16	14	Undergraduate degree, Undergraduate Architecture degree, GRE, TOEFL, Portfolio, Rec. Letters, Essay
Master of Architecture and Urban Planning	4.5		13	3	4	5	Undergraduate degree, GRE, TOEFL, Portfolio, Rec. Letters, Essay
Master of Architecture and Urban Planning	3		10	0	4	3	Undergraduate Architecture degree, GRE, TOEFL, Portfolio, Rec. Letters, Essay
Environmental Design							
BS Env Design	4		3	4	0	42	
Industrial Design							
BS Industrial Design	4		51	25	22	1	Undergraduate degree, SAT, ACT, TOEFL, Portfolio, Rec. Letters
Other							
MS Space Architecture	2		3	1	2	2	Undergraduate degree, Undergraduate Architecture degree, GRE, TOEFL, Rec. Letters

SPECIALIZATIONS

Architectural Design	Energy	Preservation	Theory/Criticism
Community Design	Environment/Sustainability	Sustainability	Urban Planning and Design
Computer-Aided Design			

ARCHITECTURE PROGRAM SUMMARY

The Gerald D. Hines College of Architecture offers accredited degrees in Bachelor of Architecture and Master of Architecture. Additionally, degree offerings are B.S. Environmental Design, B.S. Industrial Design, and M.S. Space Architecture. International study opportunities are available.

UNIVERSITY SETTING

The University of Houston today is the premier urban research university in Texas and the most diverse research university in the nation. The present 557-acre central campus was settled in 1939 on a site approximately three miles from downtown Houston, and now serves more than 35,000 students in twelve academic colleges, the interdisciplinary Honors college, and a host of schools and programs offering 294 undergraduate, graduate, and professional degrees. Transfer students are accepted.

SCHOOL PHILOSOPHY

The study of architecture and industrial design at UH is focused on design as the essential activity of our disciplines. We seek applicants to our programs who possess creativity, mechanical inventiveness, aesthetic awareness, commitment, and initiative contributing to their potential to become leaders in architecture and design. We strive to produce graduates who question deeply and who are skilled in their craft, who can utilize advanced technology and advanced methods of industrialized production, who understand and respect the power of design to shape our lives, and who are equipped to use their design skills to be effective in the world.

PROGRAM DESCRIPTION

Undergraduate Program

The Bachelor of Architecture (professional) degree program is a five-year curriculum of at least 160 semester hours. The program is studio intensive, including one five-credit hour studio in each of the ten required semesters. The curriculum includes at least 100 semester hours of architecture courses, 66 of which are advanced (3000 level or higher), the university-required core courses, and 18 semester hours of elective courses. The university core curriculum is based on a conviction that all students, regardless of their areas of specialization, should have in common certain intellectual skills, an awareness of the breadth of human knowledge and cultural achievement, and the ability to integrate learning experiences so that one area of knowledge enhances and expands another. With such preparation, students will be better able to deal in an intelligent, critical, and creative way with the intellectual, moral, social, and scientific problems that confront them as individuals and as members of society.

Graduate Program

The Master of Architecture Program has three entry levels. All entry levels are studio intensive and include a substantial number of elective hours. Level I, designed for change–of–career students, is a 110 semester credit hour program including six semesters of design, a two-semester design build experience and 18 semester hours of electives. This program is eight semesters, including two summer terms. Level II, for students coming from four-year undergraduate architecture programs in the United States, and professional degree-seeking graduates of Bachelor or Master of Architecture programs in other nations, requires a total of 72 credit hours, including four semesters of design and 20 hours of elective courses. This program is normally completed in five semesters including one summer term. A summer internship is required of all students entering the Masters Degree program at Level I or Level II. Level III, for post-professional degree students seeking advanced study opportunities, requires 36 credit hours, including three semesters of design and eighteen hours of elective courses. Advanced study opportunities are available in Architectural Design, Experimental Architecture, High-rise Architecture, Historic Architecture, Study of Theory and Architecture and Urban Design.

AREAS OF FOCUS AND RESEARCH

The Workshop for Historic Architecture focuses on summer field research, designs incorporating historic building restoration, and building documentation. The Sasakawa International Center for Space Architecture produces designs for outer space and other extreme environments, and The Environmental Simulation Lab provides equipment for testing environmental performance of designs. The Graduate Program sponsors an award winning Design-Build Workshop that undertakes design and construction projects. The Computer Design Laboratory includes advanced modeling, visualization and animation capabilities, and a Visiting Critic Program brings distinguished designers and critics to the college to lecture and participate in selected design studios. Faculty appointments in the college allow time for research/creative activity. The college recognizes design as a valid form of research and scholarship and encourages studio faculty to engage in exemplary, recognized design practice. Thus, most faculty members teaching design studios in the college are practicing designers. Other current research in the college addresses the integration of building systems, habitation of space and other harsh environments, contemporary urban form, sustainability, and advanced materials.

SPECIAL ACTIVITIES AND PROGRAMS

International study programs are available, including exchange programs. The University of Houston supports foreign study with a scholarship program, and virtually every student from the college who has requested an international scholarship in the last five years has been granted one. The college offers its architecture majors dual degree opportunities, minors, and elective courses in industrial design. Each year the college offers a Summer Discovery Program to introduce high school students to the study of architecture, a Guest Lecture Series, exhibits, and a Graduating Student Design Awards program. In conjunction with the Architecture Alumni Association a Job Fair for graduating students is held in the spring. Students participate in active student organizations including the AIAS; Alpha Rho Chi Architecture Honorary Society; the UH Student Chapter of Habitat for Humanity; Veritas, a college service organization; and university student government.

FACILITIES

The college is housed in a building designed by Philip Johnson. Students have 24-hour access to the building with key cards. The first floor includes the 82,000 volume Art and Architecture Library and Rare Books Collection, a 220-seat lecture theater, administrative offices, two exhibit galleries, and the Rudge Allen Media Center. Upper floors contain design studios located in open lofts surrounding a central skylit atrium space, classrooms, offices, jury spaces, the Computer Design Laboratory, the Environmental Simulation Laboratory, the Drawing Collection, and a monitored audiovisual lab containing 130,000 slides and an extensive video collection. A newly remodeled World War II–era building, the Burdette Keeland, Jr. Design Exploration Center, with it's soaring interior space makes it ideal for students and faculty exploring design and testing materials. The building features a "green" roof, and other energy efficient technologies and strategies, and is emblematic of the college's and the university's interest in sustainable design. It houses the Graduate Design/Build Studio, the Materials Laboratory, and a Rapid Prototyping and Model Shop.

SCHOLARSHIPS AND FINANCIAL AID

The university offers a number of attractive scholarships for academically talented students, and institutional, state, and federal grants are available for need-based financial assistance. The college has several scholarship programs available to incoming students, and has added in excess of 18 new scholarships in the last three years. Scholarship awards may entitle out-of-state students to reduced tuition. Teaching assistantships are available to a limited number of qualified applicants.

ADMINISTRATION

Joe Mashburn, AIA: Dean
Lannis Kirkland, RA: Associate Dean
Trang Phan: Assistant Dean
Thomas Colbert, AIA: Director, Graduate Studies
Patrick Peters: Director, Graduate Design/Build Studio
Barry Moore, FAIA: Director, Workshop for Historic
Architecture

UNIVERSITY OF IDAHO

South

University of Idaho

College of Art and Architecture

ADDRESS

Main
Dept. of Architecture and Interior Design
University of Idaho
PO Box 442451
Moscow, ID 83844-2451
Tel.: 208.885.6781
Fax: 208.885.9428
arch@uidaho.edu
www.caa.uidaho.edu/arch

STUDENT AND FACULTY DEMOGRAPHICS

% of Female Students	36
% of International Students	4
% of Minority Students	10
% of Out-of-State U.S. Students	27
No. Full-Time Faculty	14
No. Part-Time Faculty	5
No. Full-Time Students	332
No. Part-Time Students	6

FINANCIAL INFORMATION

Main Source of University Funding	Public
Annual Tuition & Fees (graduate, resident)	$2,881
Annual Tuition & Fees (graduate, nonresident)	$7,921
Annual Tuition & Fees (undergraduate, resident)	$2,611
Annual Tuition & Fees (undergraduate, nonresident)	$7,651
% Students Receiving Federal Financial Aid	
% Students Receiving University Financial Aid	
% Students Receiving Departmental Financial Aid	
% Students Receiving Scholarships (assistantships or fellowships)	10
Average Annual Scholarship for Department	$1,500

ACADEMIC SESSIONS

Fall Semester: August to December
Summer Session I: May to June
Spring Semester: January to May

Summer Session II: June to July
Summer Session III: July to August

ARCHITECTURE AND RELATED DEGREE PROGRAMS

Degree	Min. Yrs. to Complete	Professional Accreditation	# of FT Students	# of PT Students	# of First-Year Students	# of Degrees Conferred	Admissions Requirements
Architecture							
BS Arch	4		332	5	80	40	SAT, ACT, TOEFL, Portfolio
M. Arch Seamless Program	5.5 - 6	NAAB	73	1	0	46	Undergraduate Architecture degree, TOEFL
Master of Science in Architecture	2		2	4	0	4	Undergraduate degree, TOEFL, Portfolio, Rec. Letters, Essay
Interior Design/Interior Architecture							
Bachelor of Interior Design	4		75	1	25	15	SAT, ACT, TOEFL, Portfolio

SPECIALIZATIONS

Architectural Design
Art and Design
Community Design

Energy
Environment/Sustainability

History
Interior Design/Architecture

Sustainability
Urban Planning and Design

ARCHITECTURE PROGRAM SUMMARY

The Architecture Program at the University of Idaho is part of the College of Art and Architecture which is made-up of the allied disciplines of Landscape Architecture, Interior Design, Virtual Technology and Design, and Art. The department values sustainability, social and cultural responsibility in design, and a collaborative, intergrative working and creative learning environment.

UNIVERSITY SETTING

The University of Idaho has all the benefits of a land grant university with the feel of a small residential campus. Situated in the scenic rolling hills of the Palouse in Northern Idaho, the university and its host city of Moscow, which is listed in the One Hundred Best Small Arts Towns in America, provides a memorable place to nurture an interdicsiplinary design education. Students enjoy low fees, small class sizes, internships in Boise, study-abroad opportunities, and a fully-wired campus.

SCHOOL PHILOSOPHY

The Department of Architecture and Interior Design's core value celebrates design excellence centered in the poetic merging of art and architecture. This focus is enhanced by the faculty's commitment to, and emerging leadership in, the trans-disciplinary pursuit of creative solutions to pressing contextual challenges found in a multi-dimensional built environment. We envision regenerative and inclusive environments that inspire, support, and sustain all users. Design studio is considered the heart of the professional program and is conceived as a theater of investigation, a vehicle for community outreach, and crucible for the integration of professional knowledge into the design process, covering theory, structures, materials, environmental control, history, digital technology, urban issues, and professional practice. In studio teaching we aim to sharpen the students' critical thinking skills through the systematic development of powerful representational techniques in both hand drawing and computer modeling.

PROGRAM DESCRIPTION

Combined Program

Students receive both a Bachelor of Science Arch and Master of Architecture after completing the six year program. In the first two years, students complete university core-course requirements, a foundation in visual art, mathematics, physics, English, computer applications, and beginning architectural design. Entry into the third year requires a formal application including a portfolio. The top forty-five applicants are admitted. In the third and fourth years, students take four 5-credit architecture design studios, structures, history of architecture, site planning, Urban theory, Computer Applications, and Environmental Control Systems. At the end of the fourth year students are required to apply to the College of Graduate Studies and the Department of Architecture for admission to the graduate segment of the professional program. Applications require a minimum of a 3.0 GPA and a Graduate Project Proposal. In the graduate segment students are enrolled in Professional Practice, Comprehensive Design Studio, an elective graduate studio, graduate elective seminars, and the Graduate Project Studio. Students accepted into the Boise program housed in the IURDC can be enrolled in a professional office internship for both semesters.

Graduate Program

The M.S. Arch. is a post-professional research degree program open to candidates who hold a professional architecture degree. Acceptance into the program is contingent on matching the qualified applicant's intended area of study with the expertise of the participating faculty. M.S. Arch. students work closely with their faculty mentors in one of the following areas of study: History/Theory, Wellness and Design, Non-Western Architecture, Native American Architecture and Settlements, Urban Morphology, Community Design, Urban Issues, Environmentally Responsive Design, Environment and Behavior, or Daylighting.

AREAS OF RESEARCH

Our faculty conduct research in the following areas: sustainable design, daylighting, architectural history/theory, wellness and design issues, urban morphology, computer applications, non-western architecture, Native American architecture, and community design.

SPECIAL ACTIVITIES AND PROGRAMS

The department provides the following important enrichment opportunities for students: (1) the Idaho Urban Research and Design Center (IURDC) in Boise which accepts up to 15 graduate students who may participate in office internships, community outreach projects, and graduate course work, (2) a summer Rome program open to 3rd-year, 4th-year, and graduate students. Students there are enrolled in a design studio and two seminars. Many field trips are included.

FACILITIES

Located in the heart of the university next to the new student center, the Architecture and Interior Design campus occupies five buildings which include administrative and faculty offices, studios, woodworking shop and critique rooms. The Boise Program offers studio and internship experience.

SCHOLARSHIPS AND FINANCIAL AID

The University of Idaho offers many scholarships awarded on the basis of academic record and demonstrated need. In addition, the Department of Architecture awards scholarships to 3rd–6th year students based on a portfolio review, academic record and financial need. A third of the upper-year students who applied received a scholarship. Additionally, the department offers many paid Teaching Assistantships to graduate students.

ADMINISTRATION

Mark Elison Hoversten, FASLA, AICP: Dean
Diane Armpriest: Chair
Phillip Mead: Program Coordinator

UNIVERSITY OF ILLINOIS AT CHICAGO

School of Architecture
COLLEGE OF ARCHITECTURE & THE ARTS

ADDRESS

Main
University of Illinois at Chicago
School of Architecture
M/C 030, 3100 A &B
845 West Harrison, Room 3100
Chicago, IL 60607
Tel.: 312.996.3335
Fax: 312.413.4488
arch@uic.edu
www.arch.uic.edu/index.php

STUDENT AND FACULTY DEMOGRAPHICS

% of Female Students	37
% of International Students	2
% of Minority Students	19
% of Out-of-State U.S. Students	6
No. Full-Time Faculty	22
No. Part-Time Faculty	26
No. Full-Time Students	545
No. Part-Time Students	0

FINANCIAL INFORMATION

Main Source of University Funding	Public
Annual Tuition & Fees (graduate, resident)	$13,102
Annual Tuition & Fees (graduate, nonresident)	$25,100
Annual Tuition & Fees (undergraduate, resident)	$11,546
Annual Tuition & Fees (undergraduate, nonresident)	$22,010
% Students Receiving Federal Financial Aid	56
% Students Receiving University Financial Aid	39
% Students Receiving Departmental Financial Aid	40
% Students Receiving Scholarships (assistantships or fellowships)	53
Average Annual Scholarship for Department	

ACADEMIC SESSIONS

Fall Semester: August to December
Summer Session I: May to June

Spring Semester: January to May
Summer Session II: June to August

ARCHITECTURE AND RELATED DEGREE PROGRAMS

Degree	Min. Yrs. to Complete	Professional Accreditation	# of FT Students	# of PT Students	# of First-Year Students	# of Degrees Conferred	Admissions Requirements
Architecture							
BS Arch	4		444	0	120	89	ACT
M. Arch	2	NAAB	46	0	25	27	Undergraduate Architecture degree, GRE, TOEFL, Portfolio, Rec. Letters, Essay
M. Arch	3	NAAB	55	0	19	17	Undergraduate degree, GRE, TOEFL, Portfolio, Rec. Letters, Essay
MS Arch	1					3	Prof. Architecture degree, GRE, TOEFL, Portfolio, Rec. Letters, Essay
MS Health Design	2						Prof. Architecture degree, GRE, TOEFL, Portfolio, Rec. Letters, Essay

SPECIALIZATIONS

Architectural Design

Theory/Criticism

Urban Planning and Design

UNIVERSITY SETTING

Chicago's rich architectural heritage provides a background of historical importance and contemporary innovation to the School of Architecture's programs. Our students are able to physically experience the works of some of the greatest architects in nineteenth- and twentieth-century architectural history. Chicago's large practicing architectural community serves as a profoundly important resource to our students. Many of the School's permanent and adjunct faculty practice in Chicago firms, and many of our alumni are currently practicing in Chicago, as leaders in major firms and city organizations. Another benefit of the School's Chicago location is that we are able to provide opportunities for students to gain hands-on experience through work on projects with community clients.

PROGRAM DESCRIPTION

The four-year Bachelor of Science in Architecture program provides a pre-professional education in architecture within the broader context of liberal arts courses provided by the University. The pre-professional degree provides a foundation in the discipline of architecture as preparation for either continued education in a professional degree program or for employment options in architecturally related areas. Qualified graduates from the BS in Architecture program may apply for advanced standing in a first-professional Master of Architecture degree program such as that offered at UIC or at other accredited schools of architecture. Graduates may also work in related architectural careers or apply for advanced degrees in landscape architecture, urban design and planning, law, public policy, history/theory, or business. For further information please see: www.arch.uic.edu

SPECIAL ACTIVITIES AND PROGRAMS

Study Abroad in Barcelona, Spain

The School of Architecture maintains an autonomous study-abroad program in Barcelona. Classes are taught in English by Barcelonan architects, with curricular oversight from Chicago. Coursework is coordinated with the UIC architecture curriculum, and all work in Barcelona transfers seamlessly. Classes are held in a fully-equipped studio facility that is proximate to student housing. Graduate students may participate during the fall semester. Coursework consists of a design studio, and courses in theory, drawing, and professional practice. Optional Spanish language instruction is available. Students also undertake guided travel to other locations in Europe. Undergraduate students may participate during the Spring Semester of the Third Year. The semester consists of "Design and the City" coursework, including studio, building science, and the Design and the City lecture/seminar.

Exchange Programs

Student exchange opportunities are available at a variety of international universities. UIC SoA students enroll in and attend classes at the host institution, where instruction is typically given in the native language. Similarly, students from those schools enroll directly in the UIC School of Architecture. The SoA welcomes graduate students yearly from the Delft University of Technology (the Netherlands), Hochschule der Kunst (Berlin, Germany), and the Ecole d'Architecture de Versailles (France), as well as undergraduate students from Mexican universities such as Universidad Autonoma de San Luis Potosi. SoA students may elect to attend those same universities. In addition, undergraduate students may attend Chu Hai University in Hong Kong (where instruction is in English).

SCHOLARSHIPS AND FINANCIAL AID

In addition to federal, institutional (includes undergraduates only), and departmental (includes graduates only) aid, Illinois State Aid is awarded to 32% of undergraduate students.

ADMINISTRATION

Bruno Ast, AIA: Associate Dean
Robert Somol: Director

UNIVERSITY OF ILLINOIS, URBANA-CHAMPAIGN

ADDRESS

Main
University of Illinois, Urbana-Champaign
School of Architecture
117 Temple Hoyne Buell Hall
611 Taft Drive
Champaign, IL 61820-6921
Tel.: 217.333.1330
Fax: 217.244.2900
www.arch.uiuc.edu

ACADEMIC SESSIONS

Fall Semester: August–December
Spring Semester: January–May
Summer Session: June–August

STUDENT AND FACULTY DEMOGRAPHICS

% of Female Students	41
% of International Students	12
% of Minority Students	11
% of Out-of-State U.S. Students	12
No. Full-Time Faculty	41
No. Part-Time Faculty	9
No. Full-Time Students	742
No. Part-Time Students	0

FINANCIAL INFORMATION

Main Source of University Funding	Public
Annual Tuition & Fees (graduate, resident)	See *
Annual Tuition & Fees (graduate, nonresident)	See *
Annual Tuition & Fees (undergraduate, resident)	See **
Annual Tuition & Fees (undergraduate, nonresident)	See **
% Students Receiving Federal Financial Aid	
% Students Receiving University Financial Aid	
% Students Receiving Departmental Financial Aid	50
% Students Receiving Scholarships (assistantships or fellowships)	50
Average Annual Scholarship for Department	

* www.oar.uiuc.edu/current/financial/grad_faa.html
**www.oar.uiuc.edu/current/financial/ugrad_faa.html

ARCHITECTURE AND RELATED DEGREE PROGRAMS

Degree	Min. Yrs. to Complete	Professional Accreditation	# of FT Students	# of PT Students	# of First-Year Students	# of Degrees Conferred	Admissions Requirements
Architecture							
BS Arch Studies	4		513	0	130	115	please visit www.arch.uiuc.edu
M. Arch	2	NAAB	741	0	91	72	please visit www.arch.uiuc.edu
M. Arch (Limited Standing)	4						M Arch path for applicants without BSAS degrees from undergraduate programs in NAAB accredited programs please visit www.arch.uiuc.edu
MS in Arch Studies	1		1	0	1	0	please visit www.arch.uiuc.edu
Doctor of Philosophy in Architecture	3–7		742				please visit www.arch.uiuc.edu

SPECIALIZATIONS

Architectural Design	Energy	History	Theory/Criticism
Building Technology/Env. Systems	Engineering	Preservation	Urban Planning and Design
Community Design	Environment/Sustainability	Sustainability	

ARCHITECTURE ONLINE PROGRAMS OF STUDY

Undergraduate
http://courses.uiuc.edu.cis/programs/
urbana/2008/fall/undergrad/faa/arch.html

Graduate
http://courses.uiuc.edu.cis/programs/
urbana/2008/fall/graduate/arch.html

UNIVERSITY SETTING
Founded in Urbana-Champaign in 1867, the University of Illinois is a comprehensive institution offering undergraduate, graduate, and professional degrees in more than 150 fields of study. There are approximately 31,000 undergraduate and 10,000 graduate students, with 12,000 faculty and staff members. The campus, located at the center of the adjoining cities of Urbana and Champaign, is in east-central Illinois, 130 miles from Chicago and Indianapolis, and 180 miles from St. Louis.

SCHOOL PHILOSOPHY
From its beginning in 1869, the professional program in architecture has been built on the interdependence of professional practice and architectural education. The mission of the school is to pursue architecture as a humanistic and professional discipline, which synthesizes art and science through intellectual rigor, aesthetic judgment, and technical understanding. The school achieves its mission through teaching, scholarship and applied research, and promotes a sustainable and thoughtfully designed physical environment. The school is committed to the highest ethics and ideals of the profession and culture of architecture, and to the holistic development of its students and faculty.

PROGRAM DESCRIPTION
Undergraduate Program
The School of Architecture is in the College of Fine and Applied Arts, which is also comprised of the Schools of Art and Design, and Music; the Departments of Landscape Architecture, Urban and Regional Planning, Dance, and Theater; the Krannert Art Museum; and the Krannert Center for the Performing Arts. The School of Architecture offers a four-year undergraduate pre-professional curriculum leading to the Bachelor of Science in Architectural Studies degree. It is a comprehensive program, balancing general education content, providing a broad intellectual base in the liberal arts and sciences, with professional architecture content, providing a solid intellectual base of fundamental professional knowledge in the areas of architectural history and preservation, building construction, structures, environment technology, and architectural design. Recognizing that the architectural design studio is where general and professional knowledge is applied to produce architecture, studio courses begin in the second year and occur every semester thereafter.

Graduate Program
The School of Architecture provides two tracks of study for the attainment of a Master's degree: (1) a two-year Master of Architecture (professional degree) and (2) a one-year Master of Science in Architectural Studies post-professional degree.

The Master of Architecture program is for students holding a four-year Bachelor of Science in Architectural Studies (or similar degree in architecture). One may also be admitted to the Master of Architecture program with Limited Standing if the student holds a bachelor's degree (or higher) in any field other than architecture. Students in M Arch (Limited Standing) typically take two years to complete undergraduate prerequisite courses to attain full standing in the M Arch program. The Master of Architecture degree is a professional degree accredited by the National Architectural Accreditation Board (NAAB).

The Master of Science in Architectural Studies (post-professional degree) program is for students holding a five-year Bachelor of Architecture professional degree. The MS in AS degree is not accredited by NAAB.

AREAS OF FOCUS AND RESEARCH
Focus
The faculty organize themselves into four primary areas of focus: Design, Practice and Technology, Structures, and History and Preservation. The responsibility of the Design faculty is to teach specific knowledge and abilities related to architectural design. The Practice and Technology faculty's responsibility is to teach students about building methods, construction systems, technology, and the legal aspects of the practice of architecture. The Structures faculty addresses the structural engineering content and knowledge necessary for the design of buildings. The History and Preservation faculty's responsibility is to teach students about the history of architecture and urban design, and its preservation.

Research
The Building Research Council (BRC) is the subunit of the School that facilitates research and provides continuing education courses to professional architects. Recent BRC activities cover a wide range from studies of pipe freezing in residential buildings and toxicity of mold and in building materials to technical assistance to HUD's Office of Native American Programs and their Indian Housing Block Grant program. BRC offers continuing education courses on issues such as sustainable design, accessibility, LRFD in steel structures, and water in buildings. Each year, BRC provides research opportunities to several advanced graduate students. BRC's web site is http://brc.arch.uiuc.edu.

SPECIAL ACTIVITIES AND PROGRAMS
The School offers public lectures and exhibition programs identified and organized by students and faculty.

Several national student organizations are represented: AIAS, NOMAS, APX, SAH, and the Gargoyle Honor Society. In addition, the elected Architecture Student Advisory Council (ASAC) gives counsel to the School administration. Students have access to academic and career advising through the undergraduate and graduate academic counseling system. The School Career Services Center hosts the Career EXPO each February with approximately 90 firms participating. Junior undergraduate students are offered the opportunity to participate on an exchange basis with the École d'Architecture de Versailles, France Study Abroad Program for an academic year. The School offers the discover ARCHITECTURE Program, a two-week summer introduction to architecture for high school and undergraduate students interested in architecture as a career.

FACILITIES
Three related buildings, the Architecture Building, Architecture Annex, and Temple Hoyne Buell Hall, provide studios with workspaces for every student, seminar rooms, computer labs, offices, and special labs. The Architecture Building also contains the Ricker Art and Architecture Library, the Slide Library, the Temple Buell Architecture Gallery, lecture halls, administrative offices, photo studio, model shop, and design project archives. Buell Hall contains the Director's office, the graduate program's offices, the Plym Auditorium, studio and review spaces, and faculty offices. The Architecture Annex contains studios, faculty offices, and a computer lab and shop with laser cutters and a CNC router. In the École d'Architecture in Versailles, France, a studio, lecture hall, and offices are assigned to our school to conduct our Study Abroad Program.

SCHOLARSHIPS AND FINANCIAL AID
The Annual Architecture Awards Program at the School offers over $400,000 in awards for outstanding undergraduate or graduate performance in architecture. The School provides financial aid for approximately 50 percent of its graduate students. Information about and application procedures for aid are available from the school's Office of Graduate Admissions. For undergraduate and additional graduate scholarship and loan information, please refer to university catalogues, and direct inquiries to the Student Financial Aid Office.

ADMINISTRATION
David M. Chasco, AIA: Director
Robert J. Selby, FAIA: Associate Director
    Graduate Studies
Arthur Kaha: Associate Director Undergraduate
    Studies
Michael Andrejasich, AIA, ALA: Associate Dean,
    College of Fine & Applied Arts for Undergraduate
    Admissions

UNIVERSITY OF KANSAS

ADDRESS

Main
University of Kansas
School of Architecture & Urban Planning
205 Marvin Hall
1465 Jayhawk Blvd.
Lawrence, KS 66045-2250
Tel.: 785.864.4281
Fax: 785.864.5393
archku@ku.edu
www.saup.ku.edu

STUDENT AND FACULTY DEMOGRAPHICS

% of Female Students	41
% of International Students	5
% of Minority Students	10
% of Out-of-State U.S. Students	65
No. Full-Time Faculty	24
No. Part-Time Faculty	15
No. Full-Time Students	561
No. Part-Time Students	20

FINANCIAL INFORMATION

Main Source of University Funding	Public
Annual Tuition & Fees (graduate, resident)	
Annual Tuition & Fees (graduate, nonresident)	$17,250
Annual Tuition & Fees (undergraduate, resident)	$8,676
Annual Tuition & Fees (undergraduate, nonresident)	$16,800
% Students Receiving Federal Financial Aid	40
% Students Receiving University Financial Aid	45
% Students Receiving Departmental Financial Aid	17
% Students Receiving Scholarships (assistantships or fellowships)	89
Average Annual Scholarship for Department	$1,500

ACADEMIC SESSIONS

Fall Semester: August to December;
  Application Deadline: February 1
Spring Semester: January to May;
  Application Deadline: November 1

ARCHITECTURE AND RELATED DEGREE PROGRAMS

Degree	Min. Yrs. to Complete	Professional Accreditation	# of FT Students	# of PT Students	# of First-Year Students	# of Degrees Conferred	Admissions Requirements
Architecture							
BA Arch	4		83	16	23	10	ACT
BS Arch Eng	5	ABET	165	1	42	0	ACT
M. Arch. I (5+ year)	5.5	NAAB	380	61	58	67	ACT
M. Arch. III (3+ Year)	3.5	NAAB	64	6	18	15	Undergraduate degree, Undergraduate Architecture degree, TOEFL, Portfolio, Rec. Letters, Essay
MA Arch	1.5		4	17		2	Undergraduate degree, TOEFL, Portfolio, Rec. Letters, Essay
PhD	3.5		4	0	2	0	GRE, TOEFL, Portfolio, Rec. Letters, Essay

SPECIALIZATIONS

Architectural Design	Engineering	International/Regional Architecture	Sustainability
Building Information Modeling	Housing	Professional Practice	Tectonics
Community Design			

ARCHITECTURE PROGRAM SUMMARY

The architecture program at KU is fortunate to be close to Kansas City and yet be situated at an idyllic university campus in one the top ten "smartest cities," Lawrence, Kansas. Our efforts focus on developing humane, sustainable and delightful environments in an ethical way. Architects must be creative, critical and caring. We attempt to exhibit this in all we do, whether through our award-winning Studio 804, or our award-winning research in designing healthy environments.

UNIVERSITY SETTING

The University of Kansas is a major educational and research institution with 28,000 students and 2,100 faculty members. The university includes the main campus in Lawrence, the Medical Center in Kansas City, Kansas, the Edwards Campus in Overland Park, Kansas, and educational and research facilities throughout the state. The School of Architecture and Urban Planning, located in Marvin Hall on the Lawrence campus, is one of 14 major schools or academic divisions that make up the university.

SCHOOL PHILOSOPHY

The School of Architecture and Urban Planning emphasizes critical thinking and agile responsiveness focused by a strong ethical posture in its NAAB-accredited degrees in Architecture (M.Arch.) We believe strongly that architecture as a profession has a social responsibility to be the caretaker of our built and natural environments. We view the primary responsibility of architecture as developing humane, sustainable and delightful environments in an ethical way. Architects must be creative, critical and caring. We strive in all that we do to exhibit those characteristics and to instill them in our students.

PROGRAM DESCRIPTION

The School of Architecture and Urban Planning admits freshmen to two accredited professional degree programs: the Master of Architecture and the Bachelor of Science in Architectural Engineering, which are both five-year programs. In addition, the school admits freshmen to the Bachelor of Arts in Architectural Studies, a four-year liberal arts degree program. The B.A. in Architectural Studies serves as a pre-professional degree for students who wish to complete the professionally accredited Master of Architecture Track III (3+ Year). The five-year, NAAB-accredited M.Arch. requires a minimum of 180 credits and ten semesters of study, plus a study-abroad experience. Approximately one-third of the credits are accounted for by design studios which are taken each semester. Another one-third of the degree involves technical and other architectural support classes, and a final one-third of the degree is made up of elective classes in humanities, social sciences, natural sciences and fine arts. Professional, graduate study in Architecture at Kansas leads to the Master of Architecture (M.Arch.) degree through our Track III program. Track III is a 3+ Year, 118-credit curriculum designed for students entering with a baccalaureate degree in a field outside of architecture. Students who have successfully completed coursework in a pre-architecture curriculum (i.e. a 4+2 program) may petition for advanced standing and are likely to complete the degree in two years plus a summer. All Track III students are required to complete a summer study abroad experience.

Additionally, the program offers two post-professional degrees, the Master of Arts in Architecture and the Ph.D. in Architecture. The M.A. in Architecture has two tracks, each requiring 36 credits. The Academic Track is offered on the Lawrence campus for the student who is interested in the study of architecture from an academic and scholarly perspective. The Architecture Management Track, designed for students with an undergraduate degree in Architecture or a related design discipline and some design/construction experience, focuses on Architectural Management/Practice and is offered at KU's Edwards Campus in Kansas City. The Ph.D. program is a 49-credit program offering opportunities for advanced inquiry in the areas of: Healthy and Sustainable Environments; Design and Fabrication Processes; and Social and Cultural Factors.

AREAS OF FOCUS AND RESEARCH

Focus

Students may combine elective classes with the built-in emphases that characterize our architecture degrees and focus their work in the following areas: first, in Building Technology, by completing the numerous required courses that relate to the topic and by selecting elective courses that address sustainable design, building materials, or construction methods; second, in Community-Based Urban Design, by participating in the Kansas City Urban Design Studio and by choosing elective courses from the school's Urban Planning Program.

Research

The school's faculty support a variety of research interests. The primary focus of these interests shifted from a concentration on human–environment interactions in the 1980s, to a broader range of studies in the 1990s that included historical research, landscape studies, housing research, lighting, and considerable work on urban design problems. A more current focus, particularly among our new faculty, has to do with innovative building technologies and the use of found, recycled and environmentally sensitive building materials. A secondary, but significant focus, includes research on affordable housing and adaptive reuse of commercial structures.

SPECIAL ACTIVITIES AND PROGRAMS

Students are encouraged to enroll in our off-campus programs which include summer studios in Paris, Berlin, Siena, Spannochia and Barcelona and year-long exchanges with Heriot-Watt University in Edinburgh, Scotland, and with the Universities of Stuttgart and Dortmund in Germany. Fifth-year B.Arch. students can enroll in the Kansas City Urban Design Studio and finish their degree while working in a firm and participating in a high-visibility community design project in Kansas City. Fifth year undergraduate students may have the opportunity to participate in the School's award-winning design-build studio (see Studio804.com). The school also participates in a number of inter-university programs including the Talent Identification Program each summer with Duke University (for junior-high students). Numerous student organizations such as AIAS, Alpha Rho Chi and ASHRAE add to the cultural vitality of the school and special services.

FACILITIES

Marvin Hall, winner of two AIA design awards, is located on Jayhawk Boulevard, the main thoroughfare on the Lawrence campus. Housed within Marvin Hall are the Hatch Resource Center and Slide Library, the school's computing center, a wood and metal shop, three 24-hour computer labs, a photographic lab, over 20 digital and non-digital studios, a gallery, classrooms, conference rooms and faculty offices. In adjacent buildings, the school has additional studios, two illumination labs, an acoustics lab, a structures lab, an environmental systems lab, and a construction management computer lab.

SCHOLARSHIPS AND FINANCIAL AID

The University Scholarship Center awards thousands of scholarships each year, and many students within the school receive renewable awards. The School of Architecture and Urban Design also awards more than 100 scholarships each year and a limited number of these awards are reserved for entering first-year students. In addition, the school's Ewart Fund supports scholarships for third-year students selected for our exchange programs.

ADMINISTRATION

John C. Gaunt, FAIA: Dean
Michael Swann: Associate Dean
Keith Diaz Moore, PhD, AIA: Architecture Program Chair

UNIVERSITY OF KENTUCKY

ADDRESS

Main
University of Kentucky
College of Architecture
117 Pence Hall
Lexington, KY 40506-0041
Tel.: 859.257.3030
Fax: 859.323.1990
www.uky.edu/Design

STUDENT AND FACULTY DEMOGRAPHICS

% of Female Students	60
% of International Students	2
% of Minority Students	4
% of Out-of-State U.S. Students	23
No. Full-Time Faculty	20
No. Part-Time Faculty	12
No. Full-Time Students	492
No. Part-Time Students	46

FINANCIAL INFORMATION

Main Source of University Funding	Public
Annual Tuition & Fees (graduate, resident)	
Annual Tuition & Fees (graduate, nonresident)	
Annual Tuition & Fees (undergraduate, resident)	
Annual Tuition & Fees (undergraduate, nonresident)	
% Students Receiving Federal Financial Aid	48
% Students Receiving University Financial Aid	28
% Students Receiving Departmental Financial Aid	15
% Students Receiving Scholarships (assistantships or fellowships)	
Average Annual Scholarship for Department	$1,500

ARCHITECTURE AND RELATED DEGREE PROGRAMS

Degree	Min. Yrs. to Complete	Professional Accreditation	# of FT Students	# of PT Students	# of First-Year Students	# of Degrees Conferred	Admissions Requirements
Architecture							
B. Arch	5	NAAB	310	13	65	59	
BA Arch	4		0	0	0	0	

UNIVERSITY SETTING

The University of Kentucky, founded in 1865 as the state's only comprehensive land-grant institution, is committed to exellence in teaching, research, and service. There are approximately 18,000 undergraduate and 6,000 graduate and professional students. All fifty states and 100 foreign countries are represented in the student body. The University is actively engaged with the Lexington-Fayette Urban County Government to develop a vibrant "college town" relationship between the university and the city.

SCHOOL PHILOSOPHY

The UK College of Design (formerly the College of Architecture) was established in January 2003 to create a cohesive culture among the design disciplines on campus. Design professions continue to become increasingly integrated—with architects, interior designers, and historic preservationists working together in close collaboration. The College of Design offers space for this integration early on, at an academic level, creating a stimulating environment for the exchange of ideas and perspectives and for the free exploration of interdisciplinary connections between various practices of design.

PROGRAM DESCRIPTION

Architecture is an act of design, which creates space and structure for human activity and establishes a poetic dialogue between the built domain and its inhabitants. Architecture serves as a durable contextual symbol of the lives of a people, their spirit, their aspirations, and their history. The objective of the School of Architecture is to encourage students to develop the creative exploration, professional skill, and social awareness that an architect must possess if his or her architecture is to enhance contemporary life and serve as an enduring and valid expression of our culture and time.

The UK School of Architecture offers the only architecture program in the state of Kentucky accredited by the National Architecture Accreditation Board (NAAB). The curriculum leads to a professional degree in architecture, which allows the graduating student to pursue professional registration. The professional curriculum offered by the School of Architecture is comprised of two consecutively acquired degrees: a four-year Bachelor of Arts in architecture degree and a two-year Master of Architecture degree. There is an opportunity for students with a NAAB-accredited Bachelor of Architecture degree to receive admission with advanced standing to the Masters of Architecture program.

The undergraduate curriculum is structured around an intense, design-oriented approach to architecture

education. The architecture studio is the foundation of the program. Studios provide a social and curricular framework for the architecture student. In studio, design problems range from developing highly abstract ideas into concrete forms to providing architectural solutions for specific problems arising from detailed building programs and defined sites. Representational skills such as drawing, model making, and computer modeling are practiced rigorously as essential skills for design. A secure personal studio workplace is available at all times for all students. In addition to design studio, students study technical aspects of building technology including building materials and structural systems; the history, theory, and criticism of architecture; and the ethical and professional principles of successful architecture practice.

At the graduate level, students pursue more complex design problems with a greater degree of independent scholarship and research. Students at the graduate level choose specialized professional concentrations for deeper study and exploration, which eventually serve as a framework for a final Master's project. Professional concentrations include building design and technology; town design; digital visualization; history, theory, and criticism; and historic preservation.

AREAS OF FOCUS AND RESEARCH

Focus

The Architecture program at the University of Kentucky has achieved a national reputation for excellence through the commitment of its faculty and the spirit, talent, and work of its students. The School of Architecture continues to focus on design at the highest level. These aspirations find applications on several scales including "real-world" design projects with direct community impact, a nationally recognized furniture design program, cutting-edge digital design collaborations, and prize-winning written research in architecture history and criticism. Urban Design, Sustainable Cities, and Smart Growth are also areas in which faculty and students have made significant contributions locally and globally.

Research

The University of Kentucky is actively pursuing status as a "top-20" research institution, with new programs facilitating both graduate and undergraduate research initiatives. The College of Design operates design centers in Lexington and Louisville, which engage in projects that benefit the region and raise the public profile of design in Kentucky. These projects range from urban design and affordable housing initiatives to community engagement and preservation advocacy. In 2003, the College's Department of Historic Preservation

published the first edition of its scholarly journal, *Kentucky Places & Spaces*. The new graduate program in Architecture will also offer new opportunities to expand and define contemporary architecture research.

SPECIAL ACTIVITIES AND PROGRAMS

The UK School of Architecture believes that travel is an integral part of architecture education. Each year first-year students take a major field trip to destinations as diverse as Havana, Cuba; Barcelona, Spain; and Beijing, China. Additionally, travel semesters abroad have been conducted in Venice, Italy; Berlin, Germany; Chile; Boston; Paris; India; and Japan. The School of Architecture also hosts an annual Summer Workshop for high school students interested in pursuing architecture education. These popular, two-week sessions introduce participants to the culture and practice of architectural design. Each semester the College of Design hosts a prestigious lecture series with such notable guest speakers as Robert Venturi, Michael Rotondi, Deborah Berke, Adam Tihany, Michael Bierut, Kurt Andersen, Will Bruder, and Michael Graves. The College also hosts exhibitions at its two satellite design centers in Lexington and Louisville.

FACILITIES

The College of Design is currently situated in three buildings—Pence Hall, Miller Hall, and the Funkhouser Building—with design centers in downtown Lexington and downtown Louisville and a satellite studio in Venice, Italy. Students have access to the entire University of Kentucky Library System, and the Architecture Library is located in Pence Hall. A slide library and media center, a CAD computer lab, and a fully equipped design workshop are also resources available to architecture students.

SCHOLARSHIPS AND FINANCIAL AID

University Merit Scholarships, work-study, and basic student grants and loans are available through the University of Kentucky office of Financial Aid. Additionally, the College of Design awards students nearly $100,000 a year in scholarship support. These awards are based on merit and achievement and take into consideration demonstrated financial need. Additionally, UK Architecture students have been highly successful in receiving competitive, non-College, scholarship awards.

ADMINISTRATION

Michael A. Speaks: Dean
David Biagi: Director

UNIVERSITY OF LOUISIANA AT LAFAYETTE

ADDRESS

Main
University of Louisiana at Lafayette
School of Architecture & Design
P.O. Box 42811
Lafayette, LA 70504-2811
Tel.: 337.482.6225
Fax: 337.482.1128
soad.louisiana.edu

STUDENT AND FACULTY DEMOGRAPHICS

% of Female Students	22
% of International Students	15
% of Minority Students	29
% of Out-of-State U.S. Students	
No. Full-Time Faculty	18
No. Part-Time Faculty	1
No. Full-Time Students	428
No. Part-Time Students	45

FINANCIAL INFORMATION

Main Source of University Funding	Public
Annual Tuition & Fees (graduate, resident)	$3,579
Annual Tuition & Fees (graduate, nonresident)	$9,759
Annual Tuition & Fees (undergraduate, resident)	$3,573
Annual Tuition & Fees (undergraduate, nonresident)	$9,753
% Students Receiving Federal Financial Aid	
% Students Receiving University Financial Aid	
% Students Receiving Departmental Financial Aid	
% Students Receiving Scholarships (assistantships or fellowships)	
Average Annual Scholarship for Department	

ACADEMIC SESSIONS

Fall Semester: August to December
Spring Semester: January to May
Summer Session I: June to July

ARCHITECTURE AND RELATED DEGREE PROGRAMS

Degree	Min. Yrs. to Complete	Professional Accreditation	# of FT Students	# of PT Students	# of First-Year Students	# of Degrees Conferred	Admissions Requirements
Architecture							
B.S. Architectural Studies	4		248	29	86	22	ACT
M. Arch	1.5	NAAB	28	1	20	7	Undergraduate Architecture degree, GRE, Portfolio, Rec. Letters, Essay
Interior Design/Interior Architecture							
B. of Interior Design	4	CIDA/FIDER NASAD	104	8	36	16	ACT
Industrial Design							
B. of Industrial Design	4	NASAD	85	2	20	10	ACT
Other							
B.S. Fashion Design	4						ACT

SPECIALIZATIONS

Architectural Design	Environment/Sustainability	Preservation	Theory/Criticism
Art and Design	Interior Design/Architecture	Sustainability	Urban Planning and Design
Community Design	International/Regional Architecture	Tectonics	

ARCHITECTURE PROGRAM SUMMARY

The School of Architecture and Design considers that a primary component of its educational mission be an ethic that is both poetical and critical in order to help students envision new scenarios of possibilities for our design professions. Therefore, our primary focus is the education of designers who are capable of being proactive participants in the process of identifying, reflecting upon, and making relevant choices regarding contemporary issues. Every studio in the curriculum offers each of our students the opportunity to take a position on such issues. All faculty foster processes out of which the student can design responses that are significant because they frame meaningful and timely concerns.

UNIVERSITY SETTING

The University of Louisiana at Lafayette is a Doctoral Research Intensive public institution offering bachelor's, master's, and doctoral degrees. The current enrollment is 16,345. The University is dedicated to achieving excellence in undergraduate and graduate education, in research, and in service. Acadiana is a unique region offering many cultural opportunities to students. Collaboration amongst the arts is provided by the location of the School of Architecture and Design within the College of the Arts. Transfer students are accepted per University guidelines.

SCHOOL PHILOSOPHY

The educational sequence is an exploration of architecture through inquiries that pertain to architecture and the physical environment, social and cultural environment, technological environment, and professional environment. The structure of the program is four-year preprofessional Bachelor's degree and a Masters of Architecture degree. Pedagogically this is framed as the foundation sequence, the professional development sequence, and specialized study in the graduate sequence. The foundation is a set of pivotal experiences that begin in the first year initiating design processes and explorations. The professional development phase demonstrates a complete integration of all aspects and concerns involved in building design, internship, and the practice of architecture. Graduate studies develop research abilities and professional areas of interest.

PROGRAM DESCRIPTION

The fundamental teaching mission of undergraduate studies is "to awaken, nurture, and challenge the capacities of each student." Students are engaged in the disciplined pursuit of knowledge, developing the essential tools of critical, analytical thought, effective self-expression, and the exploration of the record of human experience. The liberal studies core ensures an introduction to the studies of humanities, social sciences, natural sciences and the arts. Building upon this core enables the architecture program to articulate ideas about architecture, which strengthen our students' work and our discipline's relationship to the University and communities around us. The foundation sequence initiates an interdisciplinary heuristic student center learning process for architecture, fashion design, interior design and industrial design students. The second year uses the integration of history, materials, the environment and digital design technology, into the design process. Third-year students investigate the relation of cultural issues and social concerns and the relationship to built form. Third year marks the transition to the professional development sequence with an annual competition. Fourth year emphasizes the comprehensive development of architecture and the responsibility of the designer-developed community.

The graduate curriculum marks the advanced study of architecture culminating in the student's self-directed thesis project. The Master of Architecture provides opportunities for scholarly inquiry and research culminating in the Master's project or thesis. The Master of Architecture degree is a first-professional degree and meets the degree requirement for licensure in architecture. The Bachelor of Science in Architectural Studies and portfolio review is required for admissions. Application for admissions is initiated through the University's Graduate School. Transfer students must meet all appropriate accreditation and program requirements prior to admission to the Master of Architecture program.

AREAS OF FOCUS AND RESEARCH

The University actively supports the advancement of knowledge through research. Faculty in the School of Architecture and Design work with faculty from across the University in the University's Center for Culture and Eco-Tourism, a designated Center of Excellence by the State of Louisiana. The faculty engages the issues of the built environment focusing on planning, community development, and housing through research sponsored by the Community Design Workshop. The Building Institute provides a hands-on understanding of building construction and is dedicated to developing relationships with the community, profession, and industry. Faculty focus on preservation through research sponsored by the Historic American Building Survey. Faculty actively engage in research of design education, architectural theory, architectural technology, digital technology, development, historic preservation, and architectural practice.

SPECIAL ACTIVITIES AND PROGRAMS

The School of Architecture and Design fosters a variety of experiences necessary for a university education through providing students special opportunities. Urban study or study abroad exposes students to urban conditions and cultural landscapes through domestic and international travel. Students are able to attend the University's France program centered in Paris, Italy program centered in Florence, or the Mexico program centered in Mexico City. In addition to international travel, each studio year has established annual trips to study the architecture and the built environment. The School of Architecture and Design has an annual lecture series that culminates each spring in Design Week. At the conclusion of each academic year, the School of Architecture and Design hosts its annual Awards Ceremony and Senior Exhibition opening where faculty recognize the achievements of their students' academic and studio design work. Students are actively involved in student chapters of the American Institute of Architecture Students, the Tau Sigma Delta Society and the Student Government Association.

FACILITIES

The center of the School of Architecture and Design is located in Fletcher Hall. The Community Design Workshop is located off-campus in downtown Lafayette, providing additional studio space for courses. Fletcher Hall studios are networked and students have access to the College's Visual Resource Center for advanced computer needs. To support the school's hands-on design philosophy, there is a supervised wood workshop, metal and forging workshop, and CAD/CAM lab. The University supports several distance-learning classrooms.

SCHOLARSHIPS AND FINANCIAL AID

The School of Architecture and Design offers scholarships for academic and design achievements at the second-, third- and fourth-year levels. To facilitate student travel to approved study programs, the school has several travel scholarships available. In addition to these, the University offers both scholarship and financial aid programs. For information on these programs, contact the University's Financial Aid Office for state and federal aid programs. Information on scholarships is available through the University's Scholarship office.

ADMINISTRATION

H. Gordon Brooks II, FAIA: Dean
Robert W. McKinney, AIA: Director

UNIVERSITY OF MANITOBA

ADDRESS

Main
University of Manitoba
Department of Architecture
201 Russell Building
Winnipeg, MB R3T 2N2
Canada
Tel.: 204.474.6578
Fax: 204.474.7532
macdona@cc.umanitoba.ca
umanitoba.ca/faculties/architecture

STUDENT AND FACULTY DEMOGRAPHICS

% of Female Students	58
% of International Students	8
% of Minority Students	20
% of Out-of-State U.S. Students	11
No. Full-Time Faculty	11
No. Part-Time Faculty	11
No. Full-Time Students	140
No. Part-Time Students	0

FINANCIAL INFORMATION

Main Source of University Funding	Public
Annual Tuition & Fees (graduate, resident)	
Annual Tuition & Fees (graduate, nonresident)	
Annual Tuition & Fees (undergraduate, resident)	
Annual Tuition & Fees (undergraduate, nonresident)	
% Students Receiving Federal Financial Aid	
% Students Receiving University Financial Aid	
% Students Receiving Departmental Financial Aid	17
% Students Receiving Scholarships (assistantships or fellowships)	23
Average Annual Scholarship for Department	$42,850

ACADEMIC SESSIONS

Fall Semester: September to December; Application Deadline: February 1
Spring Semester: January to April

ARCHITECTURE AND RELATED DEGREE PROGRAMS

Degree	Min. Yrs. to Complete	Professional Accreditation	# of FT Students	# of PT Students	# of First-Year Students	# of Degrees Conferred	Admissions Requirements
Architecture							
B.E.D	4		240	60	100	73	TOEFL
Master of Architecture	2	CACB	54	0	23	43	Undergraduate Architecture degree, Prof. Architecture degree, TOEFL, Portfolio, Rec. Letters, Essay
Pre-Masters 1 & 2	2		9	1	10		Undergraduate degree, TOEFL, Portfolio, Rec. Letters, Essay

SPECIALIZATIONS

Architectural Design
Art and Design
Building Information Modeling
Building Technology/Env. Systems
Community Design

Computer-Aided Design
Environment/Sustainability
History
Interior Design/Architecture
International Development

Landscape Design
Photography
Preservation
Professional Practice
Sustainability

Sustainability
Tectonics
Theory/Criticism
Urban Planning and Design

ARCHITECTURE PROGRAM SUMMARY

To help students establish an intense and critical working method we structure our program around a diverse range of studios that are mostly driven by the research fascinations of the professors. Students are encouraged to take possession of the subject areas and develop their own basis for research. Where possible we make connections between the supporting courses and the studio. Acknowledging the way architecture gathers diverse practical and theoretical content we try not to be consumed by single issues, so while there are people undertaking groundbreaking work in the area of sustainability, for instance, their work tends to be framed by wider concerns.

UNIVERSITY SETTING

Such descriptions are often filled with statements saying things like Winnipeg is a city in the centre of the continent with a population of 700,000 and all the associated vibrant cultural events such a size of city supports. While this is all true, Winnipeg's charms are much more subtle and often strange. As a consequence it attracts a community of creative and often eccentric people who construct a cultural life that is not only rather special but also distinct from the increasingly homogonous cultural formulas found in most western cities.

SCHOOL PHILOSOPHY

The Faculty is a consortium of five program of studies of Environmental Design, Interior Design, Architecture, City Planning and Landscape Architecture all interrelated and interdependent. The program is premised on the notion that the design professions share a common corpus of knowledge which forms the basis for the curriculum of the first two years of the program.

The architecture department supports a diverse range of studio concerns for students to choose from (rather than having a school position). Each places great emphasis on students developing methods of research appropriate to their concerns and then finding an architectural resolution of this work. A lot of emphasis is placed on learning through discovery and exploration (even if such discoveries have been made before) as a profound and engaging way of making an education.

PROGRAM DESCRIPTION

Undergraduate Program

At undergraduate level, Environmental design students study two foundation years common to all disciplines (Architecture, Interior Design, Landscape and City Planning) before electing into the department of their choice for the final two years. Students with previous degrees in other subject areas can take the Pre-Master's route that runs in parallel to the final two years of the Environmental Design Architecture option to prepare for entry into the Master's Program. The design studio is at the core of both programs, with appropriate course work related to studio projects. The studios are diverse research-based entities that last for the academic year that encourage students to develop an intense and critical relationship to the subject.

Graduate Program

The Master's program encourages well-supported individual research in the design studios with parallel enquiry into history, theory and technology through a rich seminar series.

AREAS OF FOCUS AND RESEARCH

The department supports a diverse range of research that in turn feeds the teaching program. As a consequence teaching themes and focus are under constant review. The current research programs at the school include Fabric Formed Concrete (in the CAST laboratory), Architecture and Psychoanalysis, various studies into fabrication techniques, Intelligent Architectures Drawing Indeterminate architecture etc.

SPECIAL ACTIVITIES AND PROGRAMS

The Pre-Master's program offers preparation for the two-year graduate program. Students with a four-year undergraduate degree in the field of design or a B.E.D. degree are eligible for admission to the Master's program. Students with three-year undergraduate degrees in allied fields of study are admitted to the two-year Pre-Master's Qualifying program. Our curriculum includes courses in design and design theory, history, architectural criticism, structural design, building science, and computer-aided design.

FACILITIES

The resources of the Faculty of Architecture include an extensive architecture and fine arts library, a sophisticated state-of-the-art computer-aided design laboratory, fully equipped workshops, photographic labs, a major building materials and resources center. The CAST (Centre for Architectural Structures and Technology) laboratory has extensive fabrication and testing facilities. We work in collaboration with a number of industries in the city.

SCHOLARSHIPS AND FINANCIAL AID

To request a copy of the University of Manitoba's "Awards Bulletin," write to: Financial Aid and Awards Office, University of Manitoba, Winnipeg, MB Canada R3T 2N2; Tel.: 204/474-9531.

ADMINISTRATION

David Witty, RAIC, FCIP: Dean
Nat Chard: Head

UNIVERSITY OF MARYLAND

ARCHITECTURE
PLANNING &
PRESERVATION

ADDRESS

Main
University of Maryland
School of Architecture, Planning and
Preservation
College Park, MD 20742-1411
Tel.: 301.405.8000
Fax: 301.314.9583
arcinfo@umd.edu
www.arch.umd.edu

ACADEMIC SESSIONS

Fall Semester: August to December;
  Application Deadline: UG: December 1 GR: January 2

STUDENT AND FACULTY DEMOGRAPHICS

% of Female Students	47
% of International Students	14
% of Minority Students	12
% of Out-of-State U.S. Students	35
No. Full-Time Faculty	21
No. Part-Time Faculty	8
No. Full-Time Students	300
No. Part-Time Students	4

FINANCIAL INFORMATION

Main Source of University Funding	Public
Annual Tuition & Fees (graduate, resident)	$13,889
Annual Tuition & Fees (graduate, nonresident)	$28,709
Annual Tuition & Fees (undergraduate, resident)	$7,968
Annual Tuition & Fees (undergraduate, nonresident)	$22,207
% Students Receiving Federal Financial Aid	45
% Students Receiving University Financial Aid	30
% Students Receiving Departmental Financial Aid	6
% Students Receiving Scholarships (assistantships or fellowships)	45
Average Annual Scholarship for Department	$3,000

Spring Semester: January to May

ARCHITECTURE AND RELATED DEGREE PROGRAMS

Degree	Min. Yrs. to Complete	Professional Accreditation	# of FT Students	# of PT Students	# of First-Year Students	# of Degrees Conferred	Admissions Requirements
Architecture							
BS Arch	4		225	5	60	52	SAT, ACT
M. Arch—2 years	2	NAAB	31	1	15	15	Undergraduate Architecture degree, GRE, TOEFL, Portfolio, Rec. Letters, Essay
M. Arch—3.5 years	3.5	NAAB	45	1	12	13	Undergraduate degree, GRE, TOEFL, Portfolio, Rec. Letters, Essay
MS Arch—2 years	1		0	0	0	0	Undergraduate Architecture degree, GRE, TOEFL, Portfolio, Rec. Letters, Essay
Historic Preservation							
M HISP	2		25	2	9	0	Undergraduate degree, GRE, TOEFL, Rec. Letters, Essay
Planning							
MCP	2		35	16	25	15	Undergraduate degree, GRE, TOEFL, Portfolio, Rec. Letters, Essay
Urban Design							
Urban and Regional Planning and Design	3		15	3	6	3	GRE, TOEFL, Rec. Letters, Essay
Other							
M Real Estate Dev	1		12	50	35		Undergraduate degree, GRE, TOEFL, Rec. Letters, Essay
M Arch/M HISP		NAAB	0	0	0	0	
M Arch/MCP		NAAB	0	0	0	0	

SPECIALIZATIONS

Architectural Design	History	International/Regional Architecture	Theory/Criticism
Community Design	Housing	Preservation	Urban Planning and Design
Environment/Sustainability			

ARCHITECTURE PROGRAM SUMMARY

The School of Architecture, Planning and Preservation is an intimate academic environment committed to developing future leaders in four interdisciplinary fields with a strong foundation in history and the practical integration of technology and design. The School offers undergraduate and graduate degrees in Architecture, and graduate degrees and certifications in Urban Studies and Planning, Historic Preservation and Real Estate Development as well as Ph.D. in Urban and Regional Planning and Design.

UNIVERSITY SETTING

The University of Maryland is located in the Baltimore–Washington, DC corridor. With more than 200 buildings on 1,300 acres, the campus has an enrollment of more than 35,000 undergraduate students, over 7,000 graduate students and a 4,000-member faculty. The Architecture Program within the School of Architecture, Planning, and Preservation is small and intimate with only 300 students. For exceptional undergraduate students, the University Honors Program and College Park Scholars Program offer a focused and personalized course of study. Transfer students are welcome and encouraged.

SCHOOL PHILOSOPHY

The educational philosophy of the school is shaped by the dynamic nature of the city and the need for intelligent and sensitive professionals. By emphasizing the full scope of what is involved in environmental design and architectural decision making, the school seeks to develop architects who are able to deal with the complex and changing needs of society. To serve the educational objectives of individuals seeking to prepare for the varied roles afforded in the architectural profession, as well as the related fields of urban planning and architectural research, consulting, and teaching, the school offers several graduate degree programs.

PROGRAM DESCRIPTION

Undergraduate Program

The Bachelor of Science in Architecture degree is designed to provide students with an intensive liberal educational background in preparation for professional studies at the graduate level. Since architecture is both art and applied science, the undergraduate curriculum has been designed to expose students to the fine arts, history, the humanities, the social sciences, and the sciences. Because the initial years at the University of Maryland permit a broad selection of courses, students are able to tailor their education to best meet their needs and interests. The first two years of the program are primarily general university studies but include an introduction to the built environment, history of architecture, and drawing courses. The third- and fourth-year curricula have been designed to provide a solid foundation for architectural education. The architecture studio is the locus for the integration of knowledge. Introductory architecture studios expose students to the elements and principles of architectural design. Throughout the curriculum knowledge imparted through courses in architectural history, theory, technology, urban studies, site analysis, and drawing are integrated and tested in the architecture studios. The emphasis of the program is on developing and maintaining a reasonable balance among the theoretical, practical, technical, and aesthetic aspects of architecture.

Graduate Programs

Accredited by the NAAB, the **Master of Architecture** offers a rich and demanding mix of design studio, history and theory, and technology. The teaching-learning philosophy in design studio synthesizes aesthetic, historical, practical and technical issues, with an emphasis on urban design, site specificity, and architectural design development. Advanced studios focus on topical issues including: housing, urban design, international and regional architecture, and architectural competitions. The thesis is the culmination of graduate studies.

The **Master of Community Planning** is the professional degree accredited by AICP, ACSP, and APA. The 48-credit program includes a core curriculum emphasizing an understanding of the political, institutional and social context in which planners develop and implement programs.

The 45-credit **Master of Historic Preservation** is an interdisciplinary program that emphasizes policy, planning, and management issues as they shape the historic built environment. Collaboration with faculty from other academic units on campus ensures a broad curriculum as well as extensive opportunities for focused individualized study.

The 33-credit **Master of Real Estate Development** is an integrated, interdisciplinary and balanced approach to real estate development education. The program consists of seven required courses covering development: law, finance, planning, design, construction, negotiation, and property management, three electives, and a thesis/project/capstone course.

A 39-credit program, the **Ph.D. in Urban and Regional Planning and Design** prepares students to teach at the University level in departments of urban planning, architecture, and/or historic preservation, as well as qualify graduates to conduct research and participate in high-level decision-making in the public, private, and nonprofit sectors.

AREAS OF FOCUS AND RESEARCH

The School of Architecture, Planning, and Preservation's focus is the education and training of those who will participate in the professions that directly impact our living environment. The focus of the Architecture program is on urban design, site specificity, and architectural design development. Policy, planning, and management issues and the opportunity for individualized study are the focus of the programs in Urban Studies and Planning, Historic Preservation and Real Estate Development.

SPECIAL ACTIVITIES AND PROGRAMS

Every summer students and faculty participate in study programs located in England, France, Israel, Italy, Northern Africa, Russia, and Turkey. In each of these programs students gain an understanding of architecture and urbanism of foreign cultures through an intensive program of drawing, analysis, and historical studies. Students travel in the company of the School's own faculty who expertly guide students on visits to both historic and contemporary monuments of architecture and urbanism.

Urban studies studio and field instruction seminars are held in Baltimore, and classes have done workshop projects for a wide range of Baltimore groups. Other opportunities available to students include the visiting critics program; exhibitions; lecture series; Student Government Association, AIAS, and Emerging Green Builders Chapter; Beaux Arts Ball and annual Career Fair. The Architecture Program also conducts Discovering Architecture, a summer program designed for high school students.

FACILITIES

The School is housed in a modern air-conditioned building that provides design work-stations for each student, a large auditorium, seminar and classroom facilities and the Kibel Gallery. A well-equipped woodworking and model shop are also provided. A full range of computer facilities, including a laser cutter, IBM, Macintosh, and Silicon Graphics computers are available with a wide variety of programs including computer aided design and mapping support. The Architecture Library (which includes the entire library of the National Trust for Historic Preservation) and Visual Resource Collection provide comprehensive research opportunities with rare books, special collections, and slides and photographs on architecture, architectural technology, planning and preservation.

SCHOLARSHIPS AND FINANCIAL AID

Financial assistance is available to students in the form of graduate assistantships, limited graduate school fellowships, work-study grants, scholarships and loans. The School offers the Herbert Rycroft, Leonard Dressel, Laurence Sangston, Alumni Chapter, and other endowed scholarships for architecture majors. Urban Studies students are eligible for the U.S. Department of Housing and Urban Development Community Development Work Study Grants, the Patricia Roberts Harris Public Service Fellowships, and the LeFrak Fellowship.

ADMINISTRATION

Garth Rockcastle, FAIA: Dean
John Maudlin-Jeronimo, FAIA: Associate Dean
Qing Shen: Associate Dean
Madlen Simon, AIA: Director

UNIVERSITY OF MASSACHUSETTS, AMHERST

ADDRESS

Main
University of Massachusetts, Amherst
Architecture + Design Program
457 Fine Arts Center
151 Presidents Drive, OFC1
Amherst, MA 01003
Tel.: 413.577.1575
Fax: 413.545.3929
architecture@art.umass.edu
www.umass.edu/architecture

STUDENT AND FACULTY DEMOGRAPHICS

% of Female Students	67
% of International Students	21
% of Minority Students	32
% of Out-of-State U.S. Students	40
No. Full-Time Faculty	7
No. Part-Time Faculty	11
No. Full-Time Students	180
No. Part-Time Students	0

FINANCIAL INFORMATION

Main Source of University Funding	Public
Annual Tuition & Fees (graduate, resident)	$9,921
Annual Tuition & Fees (graduate, nonresident)	$20,499
Annual Tuition & Fees (undergraduate, resident)	$9,921
Annual Tuition & Fees (undergraduate, nonresident)	$20,499
% Students Receiving Federal Financial Aid	40
% Students Receiving University Financial Aid	30
% Students Receiving Departmental Financial Aid	20
% Students Receiving Scholarships (assistantships or fellowships)	60
Average Annual Scholarship for Department	$500

ACADEMIC SESSIONS

Fall Semester: September to December
Spring Semester: January to May
Summer Session I: June to August

ARCHITECTURE AND RELATED DEGREE PROGRAMS

Degree	Min. Yrs. to Complete	Professional Accreditation	# of FT Students	# of PT Students	# of First-Year Students	# of Degrees Conferred	Admissions Requirements
Architecture							
BFA Design	4		123		40	32	SAT, ACT, Portfolio, Rec. Letters, Essay
M. Arch	2	NAAB	22	0	11	6	Undergraduate Architecture degree, GRE, TOEFL, Portfolio, Rec. Letters, Essay
M. Arch	3	NAAB	23	0	7	5	Undergraduate degree, GRE, TOEFL, Portfolio, Rec. Letters, Essay
Interior Design/Interior Architecture							
Master of Science in Design	2		8	0	6	2	Undergraduate Architecture degree, GRE, TOEFL

SPECIALIZATIONS

Architectural Design	Community Design	Housing	Theory/Criticism
Art and Design	Engineering	International/Regional Architecture	Urban Planning and Design
Building Information Modeling	Environment/Sustainability	Landscape Design	
Building Technology/Env. Systems	History	Sustainability	

ARCHITECTURE PROGRAM SUMMARY

The University of Massachusetts Amherst is the first public institution in New England to offer a professional architecture degree after its recent accreditation by the National Architecture Accrediting Board. Offered through the Architecture+Design program in the Department of Art, the Master of Architecture is available in 2- and 3-year tracks. The program offers an undergraduate BFA Design, the Master of Architecture degree, and a graduate, post-professional Master of Science.

UNIVERSITY SETTING

One of today's leading centers of public higher education in the Northeast, the University of Massachusetts Amherst was established in 1863 under the original Land Grant Act. In recent decades it has achieved a growing reputation for excellence in an increasing number of disciplines, for the breadth of its academic offerings, and for the expansion of its historic roles in education, research, and outreach. A large number of faculty, especially in the physical sciences and engineering, actively engage in sponsored activities. Research expenditures in the past year totaled more than $100 million. An increase in applications has made enrollment more selective. Within its 10 schools and colleges the University offers bachelor's degrees in 90 areas, master's degrees in 68, and the doctorate in 49. Ninety-four percent of the approximately 1,063 full-time faculty hold the highest degree in their fields. There are approximately 24,000 students, made up of nearly 18,000 undergraduates and 6,000 graduates, including part time. The University prides itself on the diversity of its student body, and is committed to the principles of affirmative action, civility, equal opportunity, and the free exchange of ideas. Located in the historic Pioneer Valley of Western Massachusetts, the 1,450-acre campus provides a rich cultural environment in a rural setting. The University is one of the founding members of the Five College cooperative program, offering reciprocal student access among the University, and Amherst, Hampshire, Mount Holyoke and Smith colleges. The University of Massachusetts Amherst is the flagship campus of the Commonwealth's university system. There are three other undergraduate campuses, at Boston, Dartmouth and Lowell. The University's Worcester Medical School includes the medical school and associated teaching hospital.

SCHOOL PHILOSOPHY

UMass Architecture+Design provides an accessible, intellectually rigorous design education that firmly grounds students in the art and science of the built environment The interdisciplinary, collaborative program embraces spirited, socially progressive, and environmentally responsive design. As New England's first and only public architecture program, the faculty and students use the region as a laboratory for integrated teaching, research, and outreach.

PROGRAM DESCRIPTION

The Architecture+Design program is committed to interdisciplinary collaboration, research and public outreach. By forging new links with the many university departments that are engaged in issues of the built environment, the graduate architecture program has developed an innovative curriculum with cross-disciplinary educational and research opportunities. Graduate students select a "concentration" at the end of their first year of study in order to develop a focused expertise. Graduate concentrations are derived from five "Areas of Knowledge," which consist of thematic groupings of select courses offered throughout the University and Five Colleges. Each graduate student is guided in assembling a coherent Concentration Study Plan which is reinforced in the Research Seminar and culminates in the Master's Project.

AREAS OF FOCUS AND RESEARCH

Each student is guided in assembling a coherent concentration study plan:

Areas of Knowledge

AGENCY INHABITATION Anthropology & Cultural Studies, Assistive Technology, Economics, Gender Studies, History, Hotel/Restaurant Management, Mechanical Engineering, Performance Arts, Physics of Sound, Planning, Psychology, Sociology

LEGACY Archeology, Art/Architecture History, History, Legal Studies, Public History, Politics, Religion

MATERIAL Visual Arts, Construction, Building Materials and Wood Technology, Material Science, Structural Engineering, Resource Economics

SUSTAINABILILTY Anthropology and Cultural Studies, Building Materials & Wood Technology, Environmental History, Environmental Engineering, Environmental Science, Geosciences, Landscape Architecture, Legal Studies, Resource Economics

TERRAIN Landscape Architecture, Environmental Engineering, Environmental Science, Geosciences, Urban and Regional Planning

SPECIAL ACTIVITIES AND PROGRAMS

UMass is part of the Five Colleges—the country's oldest and most effective consortium of colleges. The group includes Smith, Amherst, Mt. Holyoke, and Hampshire Colleges, in addition to the university. The four colleges have initiated architectural programs within the context of liberal arts education. The program in studio architecture at Smith College is the longest-running program in architecture for women in the country. The Five Colleges have developed a unique interdisciplinary Architectural Studies program that capitalizes on each college's unique approach to liberal and professional education.

UMass Amherst already has several strong programs in fields closely associated with architecture. The Department of Landscape Architecture and Regional Planning, for instance, offers eight degree programs, ranging from an undergraduate program in Environmental Design to a dual Master's degree in Landscape Architecture (MLA) and Regional Planning (MRP). The Building Materials and Wood Technology program has strong emphasis on innovative construction technology in the building industry. The Department of Engineering offers a professional practice graduate degree geared toward professions like architectural engineering. It is also the base for the building–science based Center for Energy Efficiency and Renewable Energy. The Art History program offers the only publicly funded M.A. in New England, and the History Department has established a historic preservation concentration in their Public History program. UMass is also home to an innovative interdisciplinary Environmental Sciences program.

FACILITIES

The Architecture+Design Program is primarily housed in the cutting edge UMass Fine Arts Center, designed by Kevin Roche, a winner of both the Pritzker Prize and the AIA Gold Medal. The facility houses all faculty and administrative offices, design studios, small seminar rooms, and a computer lab. Support functions (gallery, woodshop) and lecture halls are housed in other buildings on campus.

SCHOLARSHIPS AND FINANCIAL AID

The Master of Architecture and Master of Science in Design degree programs offer to selected qualified students teaching and research assistance that carries a semester stipend and a waiver of tuition, the Curriculum Fee, and most of the Health Fee in accordance with University guidelines.

ADMINISTRATION

Stephen Schreiber, FAIA: Director

UNIVERSITY OF MEMPHIS

THE UNIVERSITY OF
MEMPHIS.

ADDRESS

Main
University of Memphis
College of Communication and Fine Arts
Department of Architecture
404 Jones Hall
Memphis, TN 38152
Tel.: 901.678.2724
Fax: 901.678.1755
architecture.memphis.edu
architecture@memphis.edu

STUDENT AND FACULTY DEMOGRAPHICS

% of Female Students	64
% of International Students	5
% of Minority Students	25
% of Out-of-State U.S. Students	10
No. Full-Time Faculty	10
No. Part-Time Faculty	8
No. Full-Time Students	180
No. Part-Time Students	

FINANCIAL INFORMATION

Main Source of University Funding	Public
Annual Tuition & Fees (graduate, resident)	$3,939
Annual Tuition & Fees (graduate, nonresident)	$9,732
Annual Tuition & Fees (undergraduate, resident)	$3,244
Annual Tuition & Fees (undergraduate, nonresident)	$9,037
% Students Receiving Federal Financial Aid	
% Students Receiving University Financial Aid	
% Students Receiving Departmental Financial Aid	
% Students Receiving Scholarships (assistantships or fellowships)	10
Average Annual Scholarship for Department	$2,500

ACADEMIC SESSIONS

Fall Semester: August to December
Spring Semester: January to May

Summer Session I: June to July
Summer Session II: July to August

ARCHITECTURE AND RELATED DEGREE PROGRAMS

Degree	Yrs. to Complete	Professional Accreditation	# of FT Students	# of PT Students	# of First-Year Students	# of Degrees Conferred	Admissions Requirements
Architecture							
BFA in Architecture	4		99	0	38	10	ACT, Portfolio, Essay
M. Arch	2	NAAB Candidate	6	0	6	0	4-year arch degree, Minimum GPA = 3, Portfolio, Rec. Letters, Essay
Interior Design							
BFA	4	CIDA/FIDER	74	0	18	8	ACT, Portfolio, Essay

SPECIALIZATIONS

Architectural Design
Community Design

Environment/Sustainability
Interior Design/Architecture

Sustainability

Urban Planning and Design

ARCHITECTURE PROGRAM SUMMARY

The Department of Architecture consists of the Architecture Program and the Interior Design Program. It is administratively housed within the College of Communication and Fine Arts which also includes the Department of Art, the Department of Communication, the Department of Journalism, and the Department of Theatre and Dance as well as the Rudi E. Scheidt School of Music. The College also houses the Art Museum of the University of Memphis and the Institute of Egyptian Art and Archeology.

UNIVERSITY SETTING

The University of Memphis is a learner-centered metropolitan research university providing high quality educational experiences while pursuing new knowledge through research, artistic expression, and interdisciplinary and engaged scholarship. Founded in 1912, The University of Memphis is one of three comprehensive doctoral-extensive institutions of higher learning in Tennessee and the flagship institution of the Tennessee Board of Regents system. Situated in a beautiful park-like setting in the largest city in the state, the University has an enrollment of approximately 21,000 students and awards more than 3,000 degrees annually. The University of Memphis has 24 Chairs of Excellence, more than any other Tennessee university, and five state-approved Centers of Excellence. The University is centrally located in the city of Memphis, approximately twenty minutes from Downtown.

SCHOOL PHILOSOPHY

The mission of the Department of Architecture at the University of Memphis is to prepare graduates to enter the professional practice of architecture and interior design, and to serve the Memphis and mid-South region through research, engaged scholarship, interdisciplinary collaboration, and creative expression that contributes to sustainable, healthy, stable communities and enhances the quality of life for all citizens. The Department offers a rigorous, high-quality educational experience through a low student to faculty ratio (class sizes average less than fifteen students), opportunities to become involved in wide-ranging community-based practice and research in a variety of areas, and a student-driven studio culture of cooperation and collaboration. The Department provides research opportunities for faculty and students with emphasis on "hands on" multi-disciplinary projects through which students gain valuable professional experience while providing services to the citizens of the region.

PROGRAM DESCRIPTION

At the University of Memphis, the study of architecture encompasses both the art and science of design. The program of study is structured with a primary objective: to engage students in the processes and professional standards of design and technology necessary for shaping the built environment. Toward this, the program places the student at the center of discovery-based studies, and requires each student to assume responsible participation in their education.

Through a series of professional core and elective courses, students (1) become competent in a range of intellectual, spatial, technical, and interpersonal skills; (2) understand the historical, socio-cultural, and environmental context of architecture; (3) are able to solve architectural design problems, including the integration of technical systems and health and safety requirements; and (4) comprehend the roles and responsibilities of the architect in society. The culturally diverse Memphis and mid-South region serves as an urban and non-urban issues laboratory.

Graduate

The professional Master of Architecture is a 60 credit-hour degree based on the 4+2 model. Students already holding an appropriate pre-professional degree may seek admittance into the M.Arch degree program. The post-professional Master of Architecture degree is for individuals already holding a professional degree in architecture who are interested in pursuing opportunities for research, teaching, and independent studies. The focus of the M.Arch degree program is "city building" which brings together architecture, urban design, planning, and real estate development.

Undergraduate

The BFA in Architecture is a four year, 128 credit- hour, pre-professional degree. The first year consists of foundations studios and courses while the upper three years make up the professional program including six design studios, a building technology and structural sequence, a professional technical sequence, a computer applications sequence, and a history and theory sequence. Each of these design studios is "thematic" at the undergraduate level (Cultural/Social, Regionalism, Environmental/Sustainability, Structural, Urban Issues, Capstone).

All undergraduate students must complete the Incoming Evaluation in order to enroll in first year architecture and interior design courses. At the completion of the third semester, all students must submit a Candidacy Review Portfolio and be approved for admission into the upper level courses.

AREAS OF FOCUS AND RESEARCH

The faculty of the Department of Architecture represents a diversity of professional and academic backgrounds and interests, reflected not only in its teaching, but also in research and creative activities. It is a faculty united in the attempt to maintain the highest standards in both classroom and studio work. The faculty strives to include undergraduate and graduate students in their professional practice and research activities, particularly community-based applied research and engaged scholarship. Faculty interests include architectural design, interior design, urban design, building structural and mechanical systems, historic preservation, sustainable design, city planning, history and theory of architecture, and design foundations. Through multi- and inter-disciplinary partnerships students are offered a wide-range of educational and practical experiences.

SPECIAL ACTIVITIES AND PROGRAMS

The Memphis region serves as a laboratory for research and practice and undergraduate and graduate students have the opportunity to work with faculty on their research projects. The Department of Architecture regularly partners with community and non-profit organizations and works closely with faculty and students in the School of Urban Affairs and Public Policy including the City + Regional Planning and Urban Anthropology programs in hands-on, community-based activities. Advanced elective design studios and seminars are available in a wide range of topics including architecture and urbanism, sustainable design, urban design, city building, furniture design and making, and study abroad, among others.

The Department hosts lectures and special activities designed to expand the educational opportunities for students and the general public. The Department and AIA Memphis regularly partner on these activities and also co-host a special summer camp each year targeted towards high school students.

Four registered student organizations are active within the Department. These are the American Institute of Architecture Students (AIAS), Alpha Rho Chi (APX), the Construction Specifications Institute Student Affiliate (CSI-S), and the International Interior Design Association Campus Center (IIDA). These organizations sponsor various events throughout the academic year including workshops, special lectures, and site visits to architecture and design offices and built and under construction projects. They offer an opportunity to meet other students and practicing professionals through participation in both educational and recreational activities.

In addition to a robust honors program, the Department offers a special student-driven peer-mentor program in which beginning students and upper-level students meet with one another. Whether in a formal setting or an informal late night conversation, the students learn from each other and build upon their experiences to enhance their success in the studio. The Student Mentors offer advice on classes, techniques, model-making supplies, books, and a variety of other subjects. The small class size and student to faculty ration adds to the quality of the educational experience.

FACILITIES

The Department of Architecture is located in Jones Hall which is situated in the center of the main campus, a short walk from the university library. Instructional space dedicated to architecture and interior design students includes fully equipped design studios, classrooms, two CAD and Visualization labs, presentation spaces, a lighting laboratory, and special purpose rooms. The department also operates an imaging center and a gallery space. All students enrolled in a design studio course have 24-hour access to their dedicated space within the appropriate studio. A small faculty library is available for students to use in their research and students also have access to the Visual Resource Center. Jones Hall, as well as the entire campus, has a wireless network.

The Architecture + Design Houses, two apartment-style residences located on campus in the Carpenter Complex, are restricted to architecture and interior design students. These units are part of the University of Memphis Living Learning Community program and each house has private bedrooms, a large kitchen, a wireless network, and a fully equipped studio space on the ground floor.

SCHOLARSHIPS AND FINANCIAL AID

Several academic and need-based scholarships are made available through the Department of Architecture and the College of Communication and Fine Arts. In addition, the University offers academic and other scholarships at various levels in a number of different categories. The Department enjoys a positive relationship with AIA Memphis and the local professional community and internships and part-time positions are available to upper-level undergraduate students and graduate students. Research and other assistantships are also available to qualified students. Several prizes and special awards are also available to students. Both the Department and the University have a strong Honors Program which offers a number of special opportunities and incentives.

ADMINISTRATION

Michael Hagge: Chair, Department of Architecture
Sherry Bryan: Director, Architecture Program
Brent DeLatte: Coordinator, Interior Design Program

UNIVERSITY OF MIAMI

SCHOOL OF ARCHITECTURE

ADDRESS

Main
University of Miami
School of Architecture
P.O. Box 249178
Coral Gables, FL 33146-5010
Tel.: 305.284.5000
Fax: 305.284.5245
epz@miami.edu
www.arc.miami.edu

STUDENT AND FACULTY DEMOGRAPHICS

% of Female Students	45
% of International Students	11
% of Minority Students	52
% of Out-of-State U.S. Students	52
No. Full-Time Faculty	29
No. Part-Time Faculty	47
No. Full-Time Students	363
No. Part-Time Students	3

FINANCIAL INFORMATION

Main Source of University Funding
Annual Tuition & Fees (graduate, resident)
Annual Tuition & Fees (graduate, nonresident)
Annual Tuition & Fees (undergraduate, resident)
Annual Tuition & Fees (undergraduate, nonresident)
% Students Receiving Federal Financial Aid
% Students Receiving University Financial Aid
% Students Receiving Departmental Financial Aid
% Students Receiving Scholarships (assistantships or fellowships)
Average Annual Scholarship for Department

ACADEMIC SESSIONS

Fall Semester: August to December;
Spring Semester: January to May

Summer Session I: June to July
Summer Session II: July to August

ARCHITECTURE AND RELATED DEGREE PROGRAMS

Degree	Yrs. to Complete	Professional Accreditation	# of FT Students	# of PT Students	# of First-Year Students	# of Degrees Conferred	Admissions Requirements
Architecture							
B. Arch	5	NAAB	306	3	75	57	
M. Arch—2 years	1	NAAB	13	0	13	16	
M. Arch—3.5 years	2	NAAB	44	0	0	17	

SPECIALIZATIONS

Community Design
Computer-Aided Design

History

Preservation

Urban Planning and Design

UNIVERSITY SETTING

George Merrick, the visionary founder of Coral Gables, one of America's most notable garden-cities, inspired the founding of the School in Architecture in the late 1920's when he assembled the first planners and designers of Coral Gables and encouraged their association with the newly-formed University of Miami, a private, independent, non-sectarian institution. That initial and close association of architects, planners, landscape architects and artists, working within the context of experimental towns and cities, remains a hallmark of the school today. Small classes, individual mentorship, and internationally recognized faculty, dedicated to both teaching and advancing the profession, characterize the School of Architecture. Numerous opportunities for research, particularly in the relationship of architecture to the environment and urban context, promote collegial associations among faculty and students and attract numerous visiting architects and scholars from around the world.

The cosmopolitan nature of Miami provides a unique resource for the school in both the study and application of contemporary design issues. As the emerging continental capital of the Caribbean and Latin America, Miami offers international opportunities unique in the United States. The resources of a large research university also provide a broad range of cross-disciplinary opportunities. Selected study programs, honors programs, and the Residential College system, in which undergraduate students live in a college with faculty masters and associates, reinforce the school's effort to build a personal, attentive and responsive environment which nurtures and develops each student's unique abilities and contributions. Beyond the academic forum, the School of Architecture, uses its extensive professional contacts and alumni network, in a career placement to assist students with summer and post-graduate internships and employment.

SCHOOL PHILOSOPHY

School of Architecture programs are based upon the belief that architecture is a civic art, placing the architect squarely at the vital core of society, central to an active citizenry. This view of architectural education encourages each student to develop the capacity to participate in the public role of architecture and to respond creatively to the inevitable changes that characterize modern life. Themes of urbanism, tradition and innovation in architecture intertwined with the knowledge of related disciplines establish a context for analysis and synthesis in the seeking of solutions for the enhancement of the physical environment.

PROGRAM DESCRIPTION

The five-year Bachelor of Architecture program is organized into two major components. The Core Years 1, 2 and 3, focus on fundamental education in architecture and the liberal arts and sciences. The first three years of studio are team taught; projects are coordinated with knowledge developed through accompanying coursework outside of studio, in the arts, sciences, mathematics, literature, history and the social sciences. The Senior Years 4 and 5 offer opportunities for directed study in individually selected areas and advanced professional studies that correspond to studio pursuits. The uniqueness of the school's location fosters extensive investigation and demonstration of ideas in the living laboratory of the evolving city. The opportunity for active engagement in a forum the size of Miami significantly contributes to a framework for the interaction of theory and practice. The school also recognizes the multiple and evolving forces that shape the nature of professional activity. Intellectual exploration serves as a model for a method of understanding and participating in the world. Professional participation focuses that model on a specific enterprise and discipline. The changing demands of the profession reinforce the faculty's determination to provide a foundation of principles and methods, in order to best prepare graduates to meet future professional and societal challenges.

The School offers both professional and post-professional graduate degree programs. The **professional Master of Architecture** is designed for college graduates desiring a first professional degree in architecture. It consists of two tracks. The 3.5-year program serves students holding undergraduate degrees in non-design fields. The Advanced Standing Track program is for students holding a previous non-professional degree in architecture or a closely related field. Both tracks fulfill the requirements for professional licensing.

The **post-professional Master of Architecture in Suburb and Town Design** program focuses on the guiding principles for the design of communities. The one-calendar-year curriculum includes special opportunities to work directly with municipalities, civic and neighborhood groups, and other governmental agencies and prepares students to be effective designers and advocates for both private and public development and public sector redevelopment enterprises. The Master of Architecture Research program allows students to tailor a program of advanced study in a variety of topics, including, design computing. A specific program of study, reflecting the proposed professional objectives, is established of each student. An advisory committee of the faculty of the School supervises each student program that culminates in a comprehensive project a thesis.

SPECIAL ACTIVITIES AND PROGRAMS

During the academic year, students can participate in a number of programs and activities. The Rome program provides the opportunity for upper level and graduate students to spend a semester studying architecture in Rome. Travel study tours are offered throughout the year to a variety of destinations in the Caribbean, South American, Europe and Asia. The Center for Urban and Community Design and the Knight Program in Community Building offer students the opportunity to participate in research and service to community through urban design. Upper level students participate as teaching assistants in the summer program offerings to high school students. The AIAS, Tau Sigma Delta National Honor Society, and the Student Council each offer a number of special activities including the Annual Symposium and Black & the White balls.

FACILITIES

The School of Architecture is organized around a courtyard and green along Lake Osceola on the Coral Gables campus. Two major buildings form the primary studio spaces with large open studios for the first and second years. Smaller office-like studios, adjacent to faculty offices, ensure close collaboration among senior and graduate students. Studios are open 24 hours a day, seven days a week. The Computer Laboratory is a major center for design and research. The Architecture Library is located within the school housing reference works, reserve material, drawings, and maps. The school's slide collection and library house major collections in world and regional architecture, landscape and new urbanism. The school also operates a wood and model shop, which provides a range of opportunities for fabrication and assembly.

SCHOLARSHIPS AND FINANCIAL AID

The University of Miami attracts students with recognized academic achievement, by offering a substantial financial assistance program that consists of scholarships and grants based on merit and need, administered by the University, as well as, by federal and state agencies. Each year, approximately 60% of the incoming freshmen receive merit scholarships which range form $5,200 to $15,600. More than half of the incoming graduate students receive scholarships and assistantships. More than 75% of all recipients are offered financial aid packages corresponding with full demonstrated need.

ADMINISTRATION

Elizabeth Plater-Zyberk, FAIA: Dean
Denis Hector, RA: Associate Dean
Teofilo Victoria: Director, Graduate Studies

UNIVERSITY OF MICHIGAN

ADDRESS

Main
University of Michigan
A. Alfred Taubam College of Arch. &
Urban Planning
2000 Bonisteel Blvd
Ann Arbor, MI 48109-2069
Tel.: 734.764.1300
Fax: 734.763.2322
arch@umich.edu
arch.umich.edu

STUDENT AND FACULTY DEMOGRAPHICS

% of Female Students	46
% of International Students	12
% of Minority Students	22
% of Out-of-State U.S. Students	35
No. Full-Time Faculty	42
No. Part-Time Faculty	8
No. Full-Time Students	409
No. Part-Time Students	12

FINANCIAL INFORMATION

Main Source of University Funding	Public
Annual Tuition & Fees (graduate, resident)	$20,214
Annual Tuition & Fees (graduate, nonresident)	$31,250
Annual Tuition & Fees (undergraduate, resident)	$12,250
Annual Tuition & Fees (undergraduate, nonresident)	$35,202
% Students Receiving Federal Financial Aid	63
% Students Receiving University Financial Aid	20
% Students Receiving Departmental Financial Aid	27
% Students Receiving Scholarships (assistantships or fellowships)	26
Average Annual Scholarship for Department	$10,892

ACADEMIC SESSIONS

Fall Semester: September to December;
Spring Semester: January to April
Summer Session I: July to August

ARCHITECTURE AND RELATED DEGREE PROGRAMS

Degree	Min. Yrs. to Complete	Professional Accreditation	# of FT Students	# of PT Students	# of First-Year Students	# of Degrees Conferred	Admissions Requirements
Architecture							
BS Arch	4		205	9	123	86	SAT, ACT, TOEFL, Portfolio, Rec. Letters, Essay
M. Arch—2 years	2	NAAB	98	1	50	45	Undergraduate Architecture degree, GRE, TOEFL, Portfolio, Rec. Letters, Essay
M. Arch—3 years	3	NAAB	106	2	40	27	Undergraduate degree, Prof. Architecture degree, GRE, TOEFL, Portfolio, Rec. Letters, Essay
Master of Science	1		8	0	8	4	Undergraduate degree, GRE, TOEFL, Portfolio, Rec. Letters, Essay
Doctoral Program in Architecture	5		50	0	5	5	Undergraduate degree, Undergraduate Architecture degree, GRE, TOEFL, Portfolio, Rec. Letters, Essay

SPECIALIZATIONS

Architectural Design
Art & Design
History

Community Design
Computer-Aided Design

History
International/Regional Architecture

Theory/Criticism
Urban Planning and Design

ARCHITECTURE PROGRAM SUMMARY

Architecture's agency is dependent on the depth and breadth of its engagement with contemporary culture. Critical cultural immersion provides the basis for meaningful cultural production and is the foundation for the study of architecture at the University of Michigan. Taubman College of Architecture + Urban Planning is an internationally renowned, culturally diverse and intellectually dynamic community of students, scholars and teacher practitioners.

Located in Ann Arbor, a small yet culturally vibrant city, the Architecture Program has powerful connections to Detroit, the Great Lakes and global partners. Our deepest connection, however, is to Detroit—a working city, a raw and an undone city. It is also a locus of diverse, vital ethnic neighborhoods, technical innovation and artistic production with an edge. It provides an exciting challenge to our faculty and students and inspires creative work in provocative and inventive ways.

UNIVERSITY SETTING

One of the country's premier public universities, the University of Michigan was founded in 1817. Each year, approximately 40,000 students enroll in top-ranked academic programs ranging from the arts and humanities to medicine, engineering, law and business administration. With its world-renowned faculty and researchers, 19 libraries, numerous centers for specialized study and research, and continuous schedule of conferences and academic forums, Michigan offers a rich intellectual environment that nurtures creativity and interdisciplinary exchange.

SCHOOL PHILOSOPHY

Architecture is both an art and a science. As a profession, it calls for creativity and imagination. But it also demands precision and requires skills in engineering, mathematics, drawing and planning, as well as an abiding interest in people and the ways they live. At Taubman College of Architecture + Urban Planning, we have long held the belief that it is the responsibility of architects to unite the art and science of building. That tradition began in 1870 with the eminent Chicago architect William LeBaron Jenney, the first person to teach architecture at the University of Michigan.

PROGRAM DESCRIPTION

Taubman College offers a non-professional Bachelor of Science degree. The Bachelor of Science provides an opportunity for developing skills, knowledge and perceptions in areas related to the built environment. During the first two years (freshman/sophomore), students pursue studies in the liberal arts either at Michigan or another accredited university or community college. At the beginning of the third (junior) year, they enroll in Taubman College of Architecture + Urban Planning for required core courses in architecture. Upon graduation, they receive the Bachelor of Science, a nonprofessional degree. At this point, many students choose to continue

their graduate studies in architecture or a related field in design or construction. Others work for a year or two in preparation for future graduate study. Undergraduate applications are due February 1st, a portfolio of visual work is due March 10th.

The Master of Architecture degree is a professional program that complements a broad undergraduate education with two years of intensive training. Students are admitted to the program after earning a Bachelor of Science degree in architecture. During their two years of graduate work, they complete 60 hours of course work leading to a professional degree. The program meets all standards set by the National Architectural Accrediting Board.

The 3G Program, designed for students with baccalaureate degrees in non-architectural fields, enables them to earn a Master of Architecture degree in three or three-and-a-half years. Dual Master Degrees, which require three years of graduate study, are offered in conjunction with several other units of the University including the Michigan Business School, the College of Engineering and Taubman College's Programs in Urban and Regional Planning and Urban Design. It is also possible for graduate students in architecture to initiate dual degrees with other disciplines. Recently, these have included social work, art and design. The application deadline for both Graduate programs is January 15th.

AREAS OF FOCUS AND RESEARCH

The Architecture Program at Michigan offers a broad range of specializations. Faculty are actively involved in design practice and in research in environmental technology, lightweight structures and materials, urban design, environmental behavior, history and theory. Dual Degrees are also offered at the graduate level, which connect architecture, business, engineering and urban planning. The Master of Science degree provides post-professional education in research and advanced specialization in architecture. It is a non-professional degree typically completed in two-and-a half terms and is designed for architecture graduates wishing to specialize, mid-career professionals seeking to broaden their skills, and is also appropriate for some students preparing to enter a Doctoral Program. The doctoral program in Architecture at Taubman College contributes to a comprehensive understanding of the knowledge base of architecture. It formulates curriculum around concepts and methods of related disciplines to offer a comprehensive model of architectural research.

SPECIAL ACTIVITIES AND PROGRAMS

International studios are an essential part of the college's course offerings, granting students the prospect of visiting other countries while gaining access to facilities, groups and individuals that might otherwise be closed to them. The college has an innovative internship program. Each year, students are able to work in architectural offices throughout the United States and

worldwide. Annual college lectures attract international speakers and honor Eliel Saarinen, a former professor at the College; the American designers Charles + Ray Eames; and distinguished alumni including Raoul Wallenberg, Guido A. Binda and John Dinkeloo. Taubman College has excellent galleries and a program of international exhibitions. DIMENSIONS, an annual publication edited and designed by students, and a collection of significant lectures presented at the College are published annually.

FACILITIES

Taubman College provides a range of facilities: generous studio space including a dedicated workspace for every student, galleries, classrooms, well-equipped laboratories, a 150-seat lecture hall, conference and seminar rooms, faculty and administrative offices and fabrication workshops arranged around a central courtyard. The design studio, three-fourths of an acre in area, is the largest open studio in the country. The building conforms to all barrier-free design regulations. Computer access is widely available and distributed throughout the building.

Students have access to a host of educational facilities and cultural amenities at the University of Michigan, including a university library system of international repute; the Duderstadt Center, a 250,000 square-foot learning center that gives students and faculty access to extensive libraries and advanced technology-based tools for synthesis, creativity and production; hundreds of computers and the latest software; well-equipped workshops and design research laboratories; the North Campus Pierpont Commons and Recreation Center, offering a full range of social and recreational facilities and the University Museum of Art, with an outstanding collection and international touring exhibitions.

SCHOLARSHIPS AND FINANCIAL AID

In the 2007 academic year, undergraduate students received approximately $2,309,023 in financial assistance through the University of Michigan. This included $602,732 in need-based grants, $354,811 in merit-based scholarships, $28,905 in work-study awards, and $1,322,575 in federal loan assistance. The College awarded graduate students about $352,233 in need-based grants, $1,332,191 in merit-based scholarships, and 61 graduate student instructor positions. Federal programs provided an additional $3,029,842 in loans and $478,923 in work-study funds.

ADMINISTRATION

Monica Ponce de Leon: Dean
Jean Wineman: Associate Dean for Research,
    Chair Doctoral Program
Roy Strickland: Director / Urban Design Program
Tom J. Buresh, AIA: Chair

UNIVERSITY OF MINNESOTA

ADDRESS

Main
University of Minnesota
College of Design
101 Rapson Hall, 89 Church St. SE
Minneapolis, MN 55455
Tel.: 612.624.7866
Fax: 612.625.7525
arch.cdes.umn.edu

STUDENT AND FACULTY DEMOGRAPHICS

% of Female Students	41
% of International Students	2
% of Minority Students	10
% of Out-of-State U.S. Students	30
No. Full-Time Faculty	18
No. Part-Time Faculty	48
No. Full-Time Students	451
No. Part-Time Students	20

FINANCIAL INFORMATION

Main Source of University Funding	Public
Annual Tuition & Fees (graduate, resident)	$7,880
Annual Tuition & Fees (graduate, nonresident)	$13,090
Annual Tuition & Fees (undergraduate, resident)	$3,975
Annual Tuition & Fees (undergraduate, nonresident)	$9,790
% Students Receiving Federal Financial Aid	
% Students Receiving University Financial Aid	
% Students Receiving Departmental Financial Aid	50
% Students Receiving Scholarships (assistantships or fellowships)	50
Average Annual Scholarship for Department	

ACADEMIC SESSIONS

Fall Semester: September to December
Summer Session I: June to July

Spring Semester: January to May
Summer Session II: July to August

ARCHITECTURE AND RELATED DEGREE PROGRAMS

Degree	Min. Yrs. to Complete	Professional Accreditation	# of FT Students	# of PT Students	# of First-Year Students	# of Degrees Conferred	Admissions Requirements
Architecture							
B.A. Architecture	4		68	0	4		SAT, ACT
B.S. Architecture	4		132	0	13		SAT, ACT
Bachelor of Design in Architecture	4		165		120		SAT, ACT
M.S. in Architecture-Sustainable Design	2		12	22			Undergraduate degree, GRE, TOEFL, Portfolio, Rec. Letters
M. Arch	3	NAAB	154	0	50	60	Undergraduate degree, GRE, TOEFL, Portfolio, Rec. Letters, Essay
Historic Preservation							
M.S. Heritage Preservation & Conservation	2						Undergraduate degree, GRE, TOEFL, Rec. Letters, Essay

SPECIALIZATIONS

Architectural Design
Building Information Modeling

Environment/Sustainability
History

Sustainablility

Theory/Criticism

UNIVERSITY SETTING

The University of Minnesota is one of the most comprehensive public universities in the United States. It is both a land-grant university, with a strong tradition of education and public service, and Minnesota's primary research university, with faculty of national and international reputation. Located in the heart of the Twin Cities of Minneapolis & Saint Paul, the University enjoys a vibrant, world-class arts environment that includes institutions as the Walker Art Center, The Guthrie Theater and many others.

SCHOOL PHILOSOPHY

Architecture has a responsibility to serve society. The profession's ethical obligations form an arc that encompasses a respect for our inheritance from the past, a commitment to improve the quality of life in the present, and a dedication to producing a sustainable environment for the future.

PROGRAM DESCRIPTION

The accredited professional program in Architecture is offered at the graduate level (M. Arch.) and has developed an innovative curriculum committed to preparing graduate students for the changes taking place in professional practice. Our balanced approach links theory with technology and the ideas of culture with ethical and sustainable practice.

AREAS OF FOCUS AND RESEARCH

The College of Design sponsors and houses 6 research centers: Center for Sustainable Building Research; Metropolitan Design Center, Design Institute; Center for World Heritage Studies; Digital Design Consortium and the Center for Rural design.

SPECIAL ACTIVITIES AND PROGRAMS

We offer a comprehensive array of study abroad options including both full–semester and between-term programs. In 2007–08, we offered 10 programs in locations including Berlin, Istanbul, India, Mexico and the U.S. Gulf Coast.

FACILITIES

The School of Architecture is housed in two connected buildings—a 1950's Miesian Box renovated by Vincent James Associates linked to the copper-clad 50,000 square-foot addition designed by Steven Holl Architects. The new design doubled the library's size, providing special collection and rare manuscripts room and expanded reading and stack space for the 38,000 volume collection. Other expanded resource and support areas include the visual resource collection that archives 100,000 slides, expanded workshop for wood and metal fabrication linked to an exterior building yard, a materials resource collection archiving building case studies.

SCHOLARSHIPS AND FINANCIAL AID

Students in the professional/graduate program have access to departmental fellowships, teaching assistantships, and research assistantships, that significantly reduce the cost of tuition. Additionally, graduate students may seek university-wide fellowships and awards. Typically 50–60% of architecture graduate professional degree students receive some kind of financial assistance from the School.

ADMINISTRATION

Thomas Fisher: Dean
Stephen Weeks, AIA: Director of Graduate Studies
Renée Cheng, AIA: Head, Design Director

UNIVERSITY OF NEBRASKA–LINCOLN

  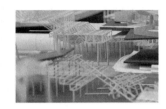

ADDRESS

Main
University of Nebraska-Lincoln
College of Architecture
232 Architecture Hall West
Lincoln, NE 68588-0107
Tel.: 402.472.9233
Fax: 402.472.3806
archweb.unl.edu
architecture2@unl.edu

STUDENT AND FACULTY DEMOGRAPHICS

% of Female Students	34
% of International Students	2
% of Minority Students	10
% of Out-of-State U.S. Students	30
No. Full-Time Faculty	17/30
No. Part-Time Faculty	9
No. Full-Time Students	339/537
No. Part-Time Students	13/16

FINANCIAL INFORMATION

Main Source of University Funding	Public
Annual Tuition & Fees (graduate, resident)	
Annual Tuition & Fees (graduate, nonresident)	
Annual Tuition & Fees (undergraduate, resident)	
Annual Tuition & Fees (undergraduate, nonresident)	
% Students Receiving Federal Financial Aid	
% Students Receiving University Financial Aid	
% Students Receiving Departmental Financial Aid	
% Students Receiving Scholarships (assistantships or fellowships)	
Average Annual Scholarship for Department	

ACADEMIC SESSIONS

Fall Semester: August to May; Application Deadline: March 15

ARCHITECTURE AND RELATED DEGREE PROGRAMS

Degree	Min. Yrs. to Complete	Professional Accreditation	# of FT Students	# of PT Students	# of First-Year Students	# of Degrees Conferred	Admissions Requirements
Architecture							
Bachelor of Science in Design	4		308	13	110	45	Undergraduate Architecture degree, ACT
M. Arch	2	NAAB	70	3	35	34	Undergraduate Architecture degree, TOEFL, Portfolio, Rec. Letters, Essay
M. Arch	3+	NAAB	6	1	4	2	Undergraduate degree, Rec. Letters, Essay
Master of Science in Architecture	2		1	2	1	0	Undergraduate Architecture degree, GRE, TOEFL, Rec. Letters, Essay
PhD			4	3			Undergraduate Architecture degree, GRE, TOEFL, Rec. Letters, Essay
Landscape Architecture							
Bachelor of Landscape Architecture	5		26	1	9	0	SAT, ACT
Interior Design/Interior Architecture							
Bachelor of Science in Design	4	CIDA/FIDER	128	12	39	24	SAT, ACT
Master of Science in Interior Design	2		1	5			Undergraduate Architecture degree, GRE, TOEFL, Portfolio, Rec. Letters, Essay
Planning							
Master of Community and Regional Planning	2	PAB	8	15	10	6	Undergraduate degree, GRE, TOEFL, Rec. Letters, Essay

UNIVERSITY SETTING

Nebraska's College of Architecture enjoys an excellent reputation. The college offers small, high-quality classes and studios in an outstanding educational facility. Enrollment is controlled on a space-available basis, with an emphasis on quality rather than quantity. Not all coursework is in the classroom. Working in concert, the architecture, interior design, and planning programs offer a wide range of field projects throughout the state, combining experiential education with research and community service. A student body numbering approximately 500 and composed not only of Nebraska residents, but also students from Latin America, Europe, Africa, the Middle East, and Asia, provides a stimulating cultural mix. At least four of the larger architectural firms in the US are located in nearby Omaha. These firms design work worldwide and take an active interest in the school and the employment of its graduating students.

The city of Lincoln, as well as the university, provide numerous cultural activities that bring outstanding performers, artists and personalities of national and international repute to the area. The Hyde Chair of Excellence allows the college to attract visiting faculty of national and international distinction. Through this endowment, renowned scholars and practitioners are invited to spend a semester or more in residence at the college, teaching and working with architecture, interior design, and planning students in lectures, seminars, studios, and in an informal mentor role. Faculty interests and specializations range from design-construction delivery, energy-conscious and historic preservation to environment and behavior. Practicing architects serve as adjunct faculty, and this helps to maintain a strong tie between the department and the professional community.

SCHOOL PHILOSOPHY

Undergraduate Philosophy

It is the goal of the department to provide the maximum opportunity for undergraduates to develop their interest and fundamental education in the design professions. This foundation should enable the undergraduate to select a specific design discipline to pursue as a professional. Students are expected to become visually literate and skilled in solving problems by the time they complete their undergraduate work. Such skills will then be applicable in the professional architecture degree program, as well as in alternative design fields that a student may choose to pursue.

Graduate Philosophy

The final two years of the professional program are oriented toward empowering the student to define who they want to be as an architect. Believing an Architect is no longer a singular personality, the graduate program has no singular focus, but instead strives to allow student and faculty to pursue their individual vision within the ever-growing diversity of the field. Ultimately it is the program's goal to develop the leadership qualities of its students so they may direct the profession to meet the needs of the future as well as the present.

PROGRAM DESCRIPTION

The **undergraduate degree program** is a four-year course of study consisting of two years of pre-architecture and two years of professional study. Every attempt is made, through a strong student advisory program, to keep the student's options for career alternatives open throughout the Bachelor of Science in Design (BSD) program. Students often will complete several years of the program and learn that their interests and talents may lead more to other design disciplines than to architecture. The BSD program is considered excellent preparation for those fields, and students have found most credits to be transferable. The emphasis of the BSD curriculum is on the development of problem-solving abilities. The context is "designs for humankind" and the concentration is on the development of the essential graphic, analytical, and intellectual skills necessary to solve and communicate design; both the curriculum and the experiential studies serve to sensitize students to environmental, tectonic, and humanitarian concerns. The first two years of the program, the pre-architecture phase, may be taken in the College of Architecture on either the Lincoln or Omaha campus. The objective of the pre-architecture program is to develop a diversified and mature student with good basic design and graphics skills.

Following successful completion of the prearchitecture phase, qualified students may apply to the Department of Architecture for admission to the professional program. The professional curriculum is organized to provide a solid foundation in architectural studies. The third two-year segment of the six-year professional curriculum, leading to the Master of Architecture degree, is flexible focusing on the individual development of the student into a design professional. The curriculum is essentially directed toward the study of building design, but with many interdisciplinary opportunities integrated into the curriculum with other units both within the College and the University.

A professional internship program, providing academic credit for professional field experience, is available to the students. International study is available at both the undergraduate and graduate level. Students may choose between Dublin, Ireland; Hannover, Germany; Clermont-Ferrand, France; Bejing, China; among other places at the undergraduate level and London, England and Tianjin, China at the graduate level. Dual degree programs are available to students in Business Administration, Community and Regional Planning, Civil Engineering, and Construction Management. Students who have a professional degree in architecture may consider a PhD program in the College of Architecture and College of Education and Human Sciences.

AREAS OF FOCUS AND RESEARCH

Sustainable Design
Digital Design
Public Health

SPECIAL ACTIVITIES AND PROGRAMS

- The Nebraska Community Improvement Program (cosponsored by the College of Architecture and the state Department of Economic Development)
- Specially funded projects
- Summer make-up and special courses
- Job placement assistance
- Professional internship program for advanced architecture and planning students
- Foreign studies program in London, England; Dublin, Ireland; Bejing and Tianjin, China; Clermont-Ferrand, France and Hannover, Germany
- Participating organization in the Center for Great Plains Studies, UNL
- Annual visits by prominent lecturers and studio critics (Hyde Lecture Series)
- Student Advisory Board
- Professional student organizations
- Tau Sigma Delta Honorary Society
- Alpha Rho Chi professional fraternity
- Field trips
- Charettes
- Summer High School Workshop

FACILITIES

The College of Architecture provides the most remarkable educational facilities offered anywhere in the Midwest. College facilities offer an exhibit gallery, two computer labs, digital fabrication facilities, materials shop, and Media Center Complex. All seminar and classroom facilities have multimedia capability and and studios have both hard wire and wireless capability. The college also houses a 52,000-volume architecture library, a slide library with a 200,000 online digital-image collection, student organization office.

SCHOLARSHIPS AND FINANCIAL AID

The University and the College combined distribute $683,368 in scholarships each year. The Architecture Program Student Affairs Committee distributes more than $110,175 annually to approximately 96 students in the third-to-sixth year of the architecture program. The university Office of Scholarships and Financial Aid offers support with National Merit Scholarships, Regents Scholarships, Pell Grants, National Direct Student Loans, College Work-Study Programs, and Guaranteed Student Loans. The College of Architecture also has a student loan fund to help students in emergencies. These interest-free loans are available to students on a short-term basis.

ADMINISTRATION

R. Wayne Drummond, FAIA: Dean
Mark A. Hoistad, AIA: Associate Dean and Director,
    Architecture Program

UNIVERSITY OF NEVADA, LAS VEGAS

ADDRESS

Main
University of Nevada, Las Vegas
School of Architecture
4505 Maryland Pkwy, Box 454018
Las Vegas, NV 89154-4018
Tel.: 702.895.3031
Fax: 702.895.1119
www.architecture.unlv.edu
architecture@nevada.edu

STUDENT AND FACULTY DEMOGRAPHICS

% of Female Students	46
% of International Students	4
% of Minority Students	30
% of Out-of-State U.S. Students	
No. Full-Time Faculty	11
No. Part-Time Faculty	34
No. Full-Time Students	352
No. Part-Time Students	147

FINANCIAL INFORMATION

Main Source of University Funding	Public
Annual Tuition & Fees (graduate, resident)	$198.00 per credit
Annual Tuition & Fees (graduate, nonresident)	$198.00 per credit
Annual Tuition & Fees (undergraduate, resident)	$129.50 per credit
Annual Tuition & Fees (undergraduate, nonresident)	$129.50 per credit
% Students Receiving Federal Financial Aid	73
% Students Receiving University Financial Aid	
% Students Receiving Departmental Financial Aid	
% Students Receiving Scholarships (assistantships or fellowships)	
Average Annual Scholarship for Department	

ACADEMIC SESSIONS

(Fall) approx. last week in August through the second week in December

(Spring) approx. second week in January through the second week in May

ARCHITECTURE AND RELATED DEGREE PROGRAMS							
Degree	Min. Yrs. to Complete	Professional Accreditation	# of FT Students	# of PT Students	# of First-Year Students	# of Degrees Conferred	Admissions Requirements
Architecture							
BS Arch	4		397	147		25	
M. Arch	2	NAAB	33	4		12	
Landscape Architecture							
BLA	4	LAAB	50	0		12	
Interior Design/Interior Architecture							
B.S. Int. Design	4	CIDA/FIDER	50	0		10	
Planning							
BSURP	4		0	0		0	

ARCHITECTURE PROGRAM SUMMARY

The School of Architecture offers interdisciplinary professional programs structured to inspire and educate future leaders in the design professions; future leaders with design creativity, social responsibility, historical perspective, technical competence, and global awareness. Collectively, the students, faculty, and staff constitute a creative and dynamic community that is committed to the improving the quality of life through integrative sustainable design. The School advocates competitive excellence through its programs in architecture, interior architecture and design, and landscape architecture and planning. The mission of the School is guided by its core values:

- Innovative education that fosters intellectual and creative discovery
- Research, creative activity, technical mastery and scholarship to inform and enhance learning
- Pursuit of excellence in a diverse and inclusive collegial environment
- Maintenance of a socially responsible, culturally engaging, and technology-sophisticated environment that is supportive of the acquisition of knowledge

UNIVERSITY SETTING

The UNLV School of Architecture is a component of a "Premier Urban University," located in the center of Las Vegas, the fastest growing metropolitan area of the United States, near the world-renowned Las Vegas Strip. The school uses its unique location to focus architectural study upon resort/entertainment design, desert sustainability, and speculative development.

The school enjoys good working relations with the Las Vegas professional design community and draws upon that community for adjunct faculty. The active local construction climate provides opportunities for students to learn first-hand about design and construction. Most upper-level and graduate UNLV students work in design or design-related firms.

PROGRAM DESCRIPTION

Undergraduate Program

The undergraduate program in Architecture leads to the pre-professional degree of Bachelor of Science in Architecture. The program is designed to provide a broad, but rigorous design studio-based educational experience that is a pre-requisite to graduate studies in architecture and subsequently fundamental to the professional practice of providing architectural services. In this context the students' creative and innovative design activities are guided by an understanding of the complexity of factors relating to human interaction with the designed and natural environments and an awareness of the fact that architectural design decisions have consequences that impact global habitability, cultural evolution, environmental change, and the sustainability of human societies.

To effectively address challenges of the 21st century architects collaborate with various design professionals on complex design and planning issues related to the built environment where the interconnections of science, art and technology are self-evident. The program's curriculum reflects this interdisciplinary and inter-professional realm and transcends traditional disciplinary boundaries by drawing from related curricula. Design studio and technology courses systematically incorporate concern for the social, economic, political and physical components of design-research

problem-solving processes.

The pre-professional degree of Bachelor of Science in Architecture is desirable for those wishing a foundation in the field of architecture, as preparation for either continued education in a professional degree program or for employment in architecturally related areas. Graduates are employed in related fields such as digital arts, urban development, real estate, and construction. Public agencies, nonprofit organizations, private firms and service providers also offer employment opportunities. Generally it is an excellent preparation for roles in society that benefit from an understanding of and exposure to architectural design.

Graduate Program

The graduate program in architecture leads to the Master of Architecture professional degree. The program's diverse, creative, and scholarly activities are focused on innovation and the synthesis of new ideas in sustainable desert climate architecture in which the applications and propagation of new knowledge are demonstrated in solar and energy efficient building design that responds to environmental, historic, and socio-cultural contexts. Educational experiences in the program are enriched and broadened by the close interaction among the students already grounded in the liberal arts and the school's faculty that is comprised of international studio critics and theorists prominent across the breadth of the discipline of architecture. The metropolitan context of Las Vegas, one of the most vibrant modern cities in the world, complements these unique learning experiences by affording students not only extraordinary opportunities to experience cutting-edge architecture in the making, but also unparalleled opportunities to actively participate in this experience by practicing in the profession that shapes this metropolis.

A commitment to design excellence that requires not only creative conceptualization of environmental form, but also inspiration derived from diverse bodies of knowledge is fundamental to the program's philosophy. Instruction and research activities therefore are organized around design processes guided by theoretical and practical understanding of factors bearing on socially and environmentally responsible professional practice. The school's state-of-the-art technology support provides for various forms of communication inherent in such practices and affords students new ways to access knowledge, model buildings, and represent ideas.

The requirements for the Master of Architecture degree — in terms of length of residency, number of credits, and specific courses — vary according to a candidate's academic background.

Students entering with an undergraduate or graduate degree in a discipline other than architecture undertake a three-year course of study in the Master of Architecture 3 Plus Program consisting of both undergraduate and graduate level preparatory coursework as specified by the program faculty. Upon completion of the preparatory courses, an additional 48 graduate credit hours are to be completed to satisfy the degree requirements.

Students holding a Bachelor of Science in Architecture degree or its equivalent in curriculum content to the UNLV undergraduate program may receive advanced standing of up to one year and begin their studies in the Master of Architecture 4 Plus 2 Program. The completion of 48 graduate credit hours is required to satisfy the degree requirements.

Graduates of the program are prepared to anticipate and adapt to new ways of practice in the profession as the demands on the architecture profession grow increasingly complex. They continue to successfully assume leadership roles in shaping the built environment in response to challenges posed by contemporary society. Their career directions are diverse and multifaceted and among others include architectural journalism, architectural history, corporate architecture, building construction, construction management, facilities management, graphic design, industrial design, municipal architecture, real estate, and urban planning.

AREAS OF FOCUS AND RESEARCH

The Natural Energies Advanced Technologies (NEAT) Laboratory is a research unit of the School of Architecture pursuing environmentally and culturally responsible design through the use of appropriate technologies.

The NEAT Lab promotes research that integrates natural phenomena and local resources and traditions into the design and operation of buildings; education in the basic interrelationships that exist among humans, buildings, and the environment; and outreach through actual projects that enhance the quality of life by way of using appropriate technologies. The lab is directed by Alfredo Fernandez-Gonzalez.

SPECIAL ACTIVITIES AND PROGRAMS

The UNLV School of Architecture holds conferences, symposia, and charrettes on emerging design technologies, resort and entertainment architecture, desert development, and urban issues each year. The school also sponsors a chapter of the American Institute of Architecture Students, a student chapter of the American Society of Interior Designers, and a student chapter of the American Society of Landscape Architects. The school has several opportunities for international study including a Rome, Italy Program led by Dr. Janet White and an installation-based design elective that travels to Adelaide, Australia led by Glenn NP Nowak. A professional internship program is also supported by the school.

FACILITIES

The 76,000 square-foot UNLV Paul B. Sogg Architecture Building contains over 20,000 square feet of loft-type studio space, a 14,000 square-foot library, classrooms, laboratories, and shops. There are three computer labs, a graphics lab, a CAD lab, and the 3-D Westwood Animation Lab. Other facilities include a model shop with laser cutting, a building materials lab, and a building systems simulation lab.

SCHOLARSHIPS AND FINANCIAL AID

UNLV grants scholarships to both in-state and out-of-state students based upon need and scholarly achievement. Scholarships and financial aid are administered by the Student Financial Aid offi ce. The school administers a number of graduate assistantships and a large number of work-study opportunities for undergraduate students. In addition, the school and local professional community award scholarships and design awards each year based upon scholarly and professional achievement during the academic year.

ADMINISTRATION

Attila Lawrence: Interim Director

UNIVERSITY OF NEW MEXICO

ADDRESS

Main
University of New Mexico
School of Architecture & Planning
2401 Central Avenue NE
MSC04 2530
Albuquerque, NM 87131-0001
Tel.: 505.277.2903
Fax: 505.277.0076
sneedha1@unm.edu
saap.unm.edu

STUDENT AND FACULTY DEMOGRAPHICS

% of Female Students	40
% of International Students	4
% of Minority Students	40
% of Out-of-State U.S. Students	7
No. Full-Time Faculty	17
No. Part-Time Faculty	17
No. Full-Time Students	200
No. Part-Time Students	35

FINANCIAL INFORMATION

Main Source of University Funding	Public
Annual Tuition & Fees (graduate, resident)	$6,146
Annual Tuition & Fees (graduate, nonresident)	$16,986
Annual Tuition & Fees (undergraduate, resident)	$6,157
Annual Tuition & Fees (undergraduate, nonresident)	$16,608
% Students Receiving Federal Financial Aid	80
% Students Receiving University Financial Aid	
% Students Receiving Departmental Financial Aid	
% Students Receiving Scholarships (assistantships or fellowships)	18
Average Annual Scholarship for Department	varies

ACADEMIC SESSIONS

Fall Semester: August to December, Application Deadline: February 1 Grad, May 15 UGrad
Summer Session I: June to July
Summer Session II: July to August

ARCHITECTURE AND RELATED DEGREE PROGRAMS

Degree	Min. Yrs. to Complete	Professional Accreditation	# of FT Students	# of PT Students	# of First-Year Students	# of Degrees Conferred	Admissions Requirements
Architecture							
Bachelor of Arts in Architecture	4		125	6	47	35	Portfolio, Letter of Intent, Specific Courses
M. Arch	2	NAAB	36	12	15	8	Undergraduate Architecture degree, Portfolio, Rec. Letters, Letter of Intent, TOEFL for International Applicants
M. Arch	3.5	NAAB	39	17	10	15	Undergraduate degree, Portfolio, Rec. Letters, Letter of Intent
M. Arch post-professional	1.5						Professional Architecture degree

SPECIALIZATIONS

Community Design
Environment/Sustainability

Preservation
Professional Practice

Theory/Criticism

Urban Planning and Design

ARCHITECTURE PROGRAM SUMMARY

We seek to graduate students who have developed excellent design, critical thinking, and communication skills; students who are ethical and compassionate scholars and practitioners invested in the deep exploration of ideas. Our students gain a global perspective and understand regional and local cultures as rich contexts for design. The Architecture Program is engaged with our local, regional, professional, scholarly, and global communities in environmentally responsible and culturally vibrant ways.

UNIVERSITY SETTING

The School is located on historic Route 66 in a metropolitan region of roughly 1.5 million people with a vital arts, culture, and design community. The deep and complex histories and environments of the Rio Grande Valley, the desert Southwest, and the Mexico-U.S. border provide a rich context for study, work, and play. The region is progressive in its critical discourse on the future of architecture and urbanism. Within this powerful topographic, cultural, and natural context, the school is deeply involved in the challenges of a 21st-century city. Through practice, research, and teaching, our faculty and students lead the discussion about architecture in an influential and unique region.

SCHOOL PHILOSOPHY

The mission of the Architecture Program is to critically investigate the architectural systems and social forces that define sustainable built environments, both locally and globally, while honoring cultural identities through teaching, reasearch, and practice.

PROGRAM DESCRIPTION

The **Bachelor of Arts in Architecture** comprises the first four years of our accredited Master of Architecture professional degree program. It also provides excellent preparation for a diverse range of career opportunities. The undergraduate program provides firm grounding in the essential ideas, principles, theories, and technolo-gies that underlie the built environment. The design studio sequence, the core of the program, is where all elements of the design process come together in exercises that build increasing skill and sophistication in the student designer. The program balances liberal arts, architecture and the related disciplines, while integrating content of technical, practical, and theoretical courses into studio work.

The School of Architecture and Planning offers three graduate degree programs in architecture:

- Master of Architecture (2 years)—A fully accredited studio-based professional program for students with pre-professional undergraduate degrees
- Master of Architecture (3.5 years)—A fully accredited studio-based professional program for students with undergraduate degrees in non-architectural fields
- Master of Architecture (1.5 years)—A specialized research program for students with professional architecture undergraduate degrees

The graduate programs are oriented to professional preparation through advanced and specialized coursework. The programs are organized around required courses in architectural and urban design, architectural history, theory and criticism, technology, community design, and professional practice. Electives in architecture and related fields are available in a curriculum that is rigorous and challenging.

AREAS OF FOCUS, RESEARCH AND ENGAGED SCHOLARSHIP

Multi-disciplinary opportunities for research and engaged context-based scholarship are fostered by the Design and Planning Assistance Center, collaboration with the state Main Street program, and faculty research agendas. Current faculty scholarship includes issues of sustainability, fabrication and construction, education and school design, cultural landscapes, digital media, and urban design. The School offers graduate certificate programs in Town Design and in Historic Preservation and Regionalism. Students may take courses from the certificate programs' offerings or apply to add these certificate programs to their degrees. The School also offers degree programs in Landscape Architecture, and in Community and Regional Planning.

SPECIAL ACTIVITIES AND PROGRAMS

Critical to the educational experience, numerous opportunities are provided for students to engage in traditional and non-traditional education programs in the summer. These include international travel and exchange programs; off-campus workshops and field studies; and internships in professional offices.

FACILITIES

Adjunct Professor Antoine Predock's winning entry in the competition to design a new architecture and planning school for the University of New Mexico is "quietly didactic." The building is a case study in certain fundamental elements of architecture; the relationship between plan and section, the way light can enter and give shape to a space, and methods of accommodating a structure to its site.

SCHOLARSHIPS AND FINANCIAL AID

The university offers a complete array of financial aid programs ranging from federally funded student loans to special university scholarships. The school itself offers about thirteen stipends for graduate and teaching assistants, each ranging from $1,600 to $3,500, plus some tuition waivers. Work-study jobs are also available. A number of merit awards are offered annually by the School, professional community, the local AIA chapters and other Associations. Students are also eligible for National AIA awards and scholarships.

ADMINISTRATION

Roger Schluntz, FAIA: Dean
Gabriella Gutierrez, AIA: Associate Dean
Geraldine Forbes Isais, AIA, AWA: Director
Mark C. Childs: Associate Director

UNIVERSITY OF NORTH CAROLINA AT CHARLOTTE

ADDRESS

Main
University of North Carolina at Charlotte
School of Architecture
9201 University City Blvd.
Charlotte, NC 28223-0001
Tel.: 704.687-2336
Fax: 704.687-2002
www.soa.uncc.edu

STUDENT AND FACULTY DEMOGRAPHICS

% of Female Students	45
% of International Students	2
% of Minority Students	13
% of Out-of-State U.S. Students	25
No. Full-Time Faculty	27
No. Part-Time Faculty	6
No. Full-Time Students	310
No. Part-Time Students	33

FINANCIAL INFORMATION

Main Source of University Funding	Public
Annual Tuition & Fees (graduate, resident)	$4,698
Annual Tuition & Fees (graduate, nonresident)	$14,905
Annual Tuition & Fees (undergraduate, resident)	$4,295
Annual Tuition & Fees (undergraduate, nonresident)	$14,707
% Students Receiving Federal Financial Aid	48
% Students Receiving University Financial Aid	25
% Students Receiving Departmental Financial Aid	0
% Students Receiving Scholarships (assistantships or fellowships)	10
Average Annual Scholarship for Department	$1,500

ACADEMIC SESSIONS

Fall Semester: August to December; Application Deadline: January 31
Spring Semester: January to May

Summer Session I: May to June
Summer Session II: July to August

ARCHITECTURE AND RELATED DEGREE PROGRAMS

Degree	Min. Yrs. to Complete	Professional Accreditation	# of FT Students	# of PT Students	# of First-Year Students	# of Degrees Conferred	Admissions Requirements
Architecture							
B. Arch	1	NAAB	16	2	18	17	BA from NAAB-accredited institution
BA Arch	4		191	39	55	45	Separate application, portfolio, essay, interview
M. Arch—2 years	2	NAAB	3	2	3	4	Undergraduate Architecture degree, TOEFL
M. Arch—3.5 years	3.5	NAAB	17	8	13	6	BA degree, GRE, TOEFL

SPECIALIZATIONS

Architectural Design
Building Information Modeling
Building Technology/Env. Systems
Community Design

Computer-Aided Design
Energy
Environment/Sustainability

History
International/Regional Architecture
Professional Practice

Sustainability
Theory/Criticism
Urban Planning and Design

ARCHITECTURE PROGRAM SUMMARY

The School of Architecture (SoA) provides an architectural education to both undergraduate and graduate students that balances an understanding of architecture & community, material traditions of architecture, creative leadership, visual literacy, and liberal education.

UNIVERSITY SETTING

The School of Architecture (SoA) is a partner in the College of Arts + Architecture at UNC Charlotte, one of the fastest-developing of the 16 constituent institutions of the University of North Carolina system. The College of Arts + Architecture includes the School of Architecture and the departments of Art & Art History, Theatre, Dance, and Music. The School's alliance with these arts units provides a diversity of multidisciplinary educational, research, and experimental opportunities for both faculty and students. Charlotte is a fast-growing urban area with a lively urban culture that includes center-city housing, business, retail, major public facilities, and expanding mass transportation options. The region has a strong architectural community committed to the School and its students. In turn, the School has a reputation for its consistent and vital involvement in the community.

SCHOOL PHILOSOPHY

We are PROFESSIONALS. We prepare our students to serve society as active and knowledgeable practitioners. The mission of the SoA is to PROVOKE CHANGE and GROWTH. One of our highest mandates is to explore not only the physical but also the environmental, social, and cultural issues of architecture and urban design. We prepare our students to be COMMITTED TO LIFELONG LEADERSHIP. We provide an intellectual, innovative, and ethical education in architecture and urban design through excellence in teaching, creative architectural practice, scholarly research, and meaningful community activism. Success in the SoA requires PASSION and GRIT. Our programs are time-intensive and intellectually demanding. A strong architectural education demands the development of a well-rounded, well-informed individual who meets the challenge of integrating a strong liberal arts education with a rigorous professional education. Students must master five areas of competence to effectively realize their intellectual, architectural and leadership potential:

- **Critical thinking:** the ability to construct relationships between areas of knowledge drawn from theory and diverse cultures;
- **Design:** innovative and reflective concepts coupled with synthesis, development, and refinement of architectural form, space and materiality;
- **Building:** expertise at developing, integrating, and implementing architectural technologies both conceptually and in practice;
- **Visual literacy:** representational skill to communicate design intent and execution through a wide range of media, both analogue and digital;
- **Professionalism:** development of innovative and ethical business practices as well as active leadership in the profession and the larger community.

Students are admitted who we believe will thrive in the dynamic, diverse, intense and exploratory environment created in the School. Our goal is to equip students to succeed in a multitude of career paths connected to the built environment. A student-to-faculty ratio of 12:1 creates an intimate and respectful atmosphere in which students can learn and mature. Each student is recognized and treated as an individual with specific talents and interests. All receive professional advising each semester.

PROGRAM DESCRIPTION

The School provides undergraduate and graduate degree programs, interdisciplinary programs in community planning, dual-degree graduate programs and international education options.

Bachelor of Arts in Architecture & Bachelor of Architecture Programs

All undergraduate students complete a three-year **Core Program** of courses to provide a solid understanding of fundamental issues, knowledge, and skills in architectural design and theory through a series of coordinated studios and seminars, a four-semester sequence of architectural history, and two semesters of building science.

The **Advanced Program** (4th and 5th years) extends and applies core knowledge in theory, building science, building analysis, and comprehensive building design. Students may choose between two academic tracks: a four-year, 128-credit-hour **Bachelor of Arts in Architecture** program (not a professionally accredited degree) or the five-year, 158-credit-hour **Bachelor of Architecture** program (a professionally accredited de-

gree program). Students who complete all course requirements through the BA degree and maintain a 3.0 GPA are automatically admitted to the **Bachelor of Architecture program**.

Master of Architecture Programs

The MArch I program is a three-year + two–summer session curriculum designed for incoming students who have earned their undergraduate degree in a discipline other than architecture. The MArch II program is a two-year curriculum designed for incoming students with an undergraduate architecture degree from an NAAB-accredited institution. The MArch I Program is structured around four primary components: a first year which establishes fundamental design skills, architectural history and theory, and building systems; a second year focused on building technology, comprehensive building design, and urban issues; a summer study experience; and a third year dedicated to individual student architectural thesis investigations. The MArch II Program is individually tailored through the advising process to complement the previous educational background of incoming students and to serve their individual professional and research goals.

AREAS OF FOCUS AND RESEARCH

Three primary issues will direct the future of both architectural education and practice: efficient design, sustainable urbanism, and digital media. In response, the School has three active research centers:

- Design + Society Research Center (est.1999) focused on work within our community and region;
- Digital Design Center (est. 2005) includes a full range of advanced computer teaching and digital fabrication facilities (and works with the Charlotte Visualization Center in the College of Computing and Infomatics);
- Center for Integrated Building Design Research (est. 2006) includes the Daylight and Energy Performance Laboratory which has been active since 1988.

SPECIAL ACTIVITIES AND PROGRAMS

Annually, School of Architecture faculty, students and local professionals organize an extensive and diverse series of lectures and symposia. Students create a true "learning community" with their peers through participation in student organizations, field study trips, and group projects. Student organizations include the American Institute of Architecture Students, Tau Sigma Delta Honor Society, Freedom by Design, the National Organization of Minority Architects, U.S. Green Building Council, and Construction Specifications Institute. Students are respected as active partners in establishing and reaching the School's educational philosophy and structure. Often students and faculty work side-by-side on SoA educational and cultural events as well as research projects and other activities. Some of the School's special activities and programs are listed below.

- Visiting Architects' Studio: On a regular basis an upper-level studio is directed by one or more nationally significant visiting architects.
- Visiting Lecture Program
- Field Study Week: Each semester has a designated period when travel is encouraged to expose students to significant works of art and architecture,

major urban environments, and a variety of cultural experiences.

- Study Abroad Program: The SoA participates in study abroad partnerships including exchange programs in London and the Netherlands. In addition, SoA faculty offer six hours of seminar credit each summer in Rome, London, China, etc.
- Summer Architectural Traveling Scholarship: Each spring, an outstanding upper-year student is awarded a scholarship for a self-organized summer architectural study.
- criticalMASS: Each year the graduate students of the SoA organize a regional symposium for graduate students in their thesis year. This event offers students from a variety of institutions the opportunity to have their thesis project juried by internationally recognized practitioners and educators.
- Keynote critics/speakers include Rafael Moneo, Chris Sharples, Glenn Murcutt, Brian MacKay Lyons, Rick Joy, Larry Scarpa, and Mark and Peter Anderson.
- Summer High School Program: Each summer high school students participate in a week-long program that introduces them to architecture and architectural education.

FACILITIES

The School of Architecture inhabits an 88,000-square-foot building designed specifically for the architecture program by architects Ferebee Walters and Gwathmey-Siegal. In addition to classroom and studio space, the building houses a large auditorium, a branch library, a digital image library, a lighting lab, a digital fabrication lab, a full woodshop and metal shop, computer labs, and a photography lab. The close proximity of studios, crit rooms, classrooms, offices, gallery, and library encourage interaction between faculty and students. Each student has an individual studio space with natural light, views to the exterior, and an associated outdoor space. All studios are networked, and the public spaces of the building are equipped with wireless communication. The School also runs the Design and Society Research Center in Charlotte's center city. This location supports the goals of this center which are focused on innovative scholarship exploring the role of design within our collective cultural, social, and physical landscapes.

SCHOLARSHIPS AND FINANCIAL AID

UNC Charlotte's Financial Aid Office has a comprehensive financial assistance program consisting of scholarships, fellowships, work-study funds, and loans. In addition, the School of Architecture awards both graduate and undergraduate Teaching Assistant and research Assistant funding, a series of merit-based and need-based scholarships, and undergraduate, fifth-year, and graduate fellowships.

ADMINISTRATION

Ken Lambla, AIA: Dean
Lee Gray: Associate Dean
Kelly Carlson-Reddig: Associate Director

UNIVERSITY OF NOTRE DAME

ADDRESS

Main
University of Notre Dame
School of Architecture
110 Bond Hall
Notre Dame, IN 46556
Tel.: 574.631.6137
Fax: 574.631.8486
arch@nd.edu
www.architecture.nd.edu

STUDENT AND FACULTY DEMOGRAPHICS

% of Female Students	51
% of International Students	7
% of Minority Students	14
% of Out-of-State U.S. Students	87
No. Full-Time Faculty	19
No. Part-Time Faculty	6
No. Full-Time Students	246
No. Part-Time Students	0

FINANCIAL INFORMATION

Main Source of University Funding	Private
Annual Tuition & Fees (graduate)	$34,980
Annual Tuition & Fees (undergraduate)	$34,980
% Students Receiving Federal Financial Aid	62
% Students Receiving University Financial Aid	72
% Students Receiving Departmental Financial Aid	10
% Students Receiving Scholarships (assistantships or fellowships)	9
Average Annual Scholarship for Department - Undergraduate	$1,278
Average Annual Scholarship for Department - Graduate	$15,000

ACADEMIC SESSIONS

Fall Semester: August to December

Spring Semester: January to May

ARCHITECTURE AND RELATED DEGREE PROGRAMS

Degree	Min. Yrs. to Complete	Professional Accreditation	# of FT Students	# of PT Students	# of First-Year Students	# of Degrees Conferred	Admissions Requirements
Architecture							
B. Arch	5	NAAB	202	0	60	53	
M. Arch—2 years	2	NAAB	5	0	3	2	Undergraduate Architecture degree, GRE, TOEFL, Portfolio, Rec. Letters, Essay
M.ADU	2		8	0	4	4	Undergraduate Architecture degree, GRE, TOEFL, Portfolio, Rec. Letters, Essay
Master of Architecture	3	NAAB	27	0	9	3	Undergraduate degree, GRE, TOEFL, Portfolio, Rec. Letters, Essay

SPECIALIZATIONS

Architectural Design
Building Technology/Env. Systems
Community Design
Computer-Aided Design

Environment/Sustainability
History
International/Regional Architecture
Preservation

Professional Practice
Sacred Spaces
Sustainability

Tectonics
Theory/Criticism
Urban Planning and Design

ARCHITECTURE PROGRAM SUMMARY

The University of Notre Dame School of Architecture offers a five-year undergraduate program leading to the BArch degree in addition to two-year and three-year graduate programs leading to the MArch degree. The School has a focus on classical and traditional architecture and urbanism.

UNIVERSITY SETTING

The University of Notre Dame, founded in 1842, is an independent, national Catholic university located in Notre Dame, Indiana, approximately 90 miles east of Chicago. Admission to the University is highly competitive, with five applicants for each freshman class position. Sixty-nine percent of incoming freshmen were in the top five percent of their high school graduating classes. The University is organized into four colleges — Arts and Letters, Science, Engineering, and the Mendoza College of Business—the School of Architecture, the Law School, the Graduate School, six major research institutes, more than 40 centers and special programs, and the University library system. The Graduate School, established in 1918, encompasses 46 master's and 23 doctoral degree programs in and among 35 University departments and institutes. With 1,250 acres containing two lakes, Notre Dame is well known for its beautifully renovated 128-year-old Main Building with its famed Golden Dome, one of the most widely known university landmarks in the world.

SCHOOL PHILOSOPHY

From the smallest details to the most profound ideals, the School of Architecture strives to educate leaders who will build a future at once more functional, beautiful and humane. Architecture does more than give us the structures where we live; it gives structure to our lives. In the design of our cities and towns, our neighborhoods, our homes and offices and parks and places of worship, architecture should reflect our highest aspirations. Using that as our blueprint, the School of Architecture emphasizes traditional and classical design, the timeless principles that transcend trends and fads. We are part of a continuum from the past to the future, honoring a grand legacy and carrying it forward with cutting-edge ideas and technology that preserve both the built and natural environments. These principles apply from the smallest towns to the biggest cities, establishing civic identity and facilitating an efficient and satisfying way of life, built to a human scale. Great architecture is at once local in scale, global in scope, and eternal in aspiration—not a fashionable footprint that tramples the past and threatens the future.

PROGRAM DESCRIPTION
Undergraduate Program

Undergraduate students at the University of Notre Dame's School of Architecture immerse themselves in the principles of traditional and classical architecture and its application in the modern world. That means learning more than the basics of design and construction. It means developing an understanding of society itself and how the buildings where people live, work and worship facilitate a sense of community. To that end, Notre Dame has developed an extensive five-year program to prepare students to become licensed architects and engaged citizens committed to the greater good of cities large and small. First-year students receive a challenging introduction to architecture and drawing skills in addition to the university's universal first-year requirements. In the second year, permanence, long-term function, accessibility and beauty of buildings are examined from social and environmental viewpoints. Students also begin studio work and study Italian in preparation for their third year in Rome. In the third

year, as part of the Rome Studies Program, students see first-hand how enduring structures blend with the modern, how the interconnected network of streets and squares contribute to the communal life of one of the world's greatest cities. During the fourth year principles studied in Rome are applied to the American city and its architecture with an emphasis on regional characteristics. Individual thesis projects dominate the final year as students apply knowledge and skills gained over the previous four years to a topic of their choice, many of which are published and win national and international competitions.

Graduate Program

The graduate curriculum examines and extends the discourses of classical architecture and traditional European and American urbanism. The School of Architecture currently offers three (3) paths of graduate study that each lead to one of two (2) graduate degrees. Path A is a four-semester course of study leading to the Master of Architectural Design and Urbanism (M.ADU) post-professional degree. Path B is a four-semester course of study leading to a 2-year Master of Architecture (M. Arch) N.A.A.B.-accredited professional degree. Path C is a six-semester course of study leading to a 3-year Master of Architecture (M.Arch) N.A.A.B.-accredited professional degree. All students in all paths begin with foundational courses, spend a semester as part of the Rome Studies Program, complete a one-year concentration in either Classical Architecture or Urban Design, and end with a one-semester terminal project.

AREAS OF FOCUS AND RESEARCH
Focus

Graduate and undergraduate programs, as well as much of the faculty's research, focus on the relationship between contemporary practice, architecture and the city, and the inheritance of tradition. Classical typologies and classical ways of thinking characterize approaches to the relationships between things, such as the constituent elements of a building, one to another, and the relationship of a building to its broader urban or natural setting.

Research

Research conducted by the faculty over the past decade ranges broadly. Ongoing projects resulting in published books written by faculty have involved the following: a history of ancient Roman architecture; a history of the Modern Movement in architecture in Europe; a historical and environmental study of an island in the Greek Aegean archipelago; a survey of works worldwide among contemporary classical and traditional architects; an exploration of the cultural concept of nature and its relationship to the built environment; a history of neo-classicism in nineteenth-century Athens, Greece; the architecture of Chicago's North Michigan Avenue, and a study of the use of the computer to reproduce drawings from classical architectural treatises.

With an $85,000 grant, the School has purchased a Lecia 3-D laser scanner beneficial for capturing interiors of buildings and monuments, such as the Taj Mahal which faculty and students filmed in summer 2008. In partnership with CyArk, a non-profit organization that collects the most accurate 3-D models of cultural heritage sites, the School plans to use the scanner to document endangered historic buildings. They also intend to perform an X-Ray Fluorescence (XRF) analysis to the building using a mobile XRF machine to map the distribution of pollution.

This School has also started the Center for Building Communities (CBC), to address architectural and urban design needs around the country using modular building technology. Modular construction methods allow neighborhoods to be transformed within one-third to one-half the time of conventional construction.

SPECIAL ACTIVITIES AND PROGRAMS

All undergraduate students spend a full academic year, and graduate students spend a semester at the School's Rome Studies Program. Founded in 1969, the Rome Studies Program is the only year-long foreign studies program among American university architecture schools that is required for all its students. The most unique aspect of the program is the four yearly field trips taken to different regions of Italy, plus all of the major ancient Greek cities, Segesta, Selinus, Akragas, and Syracuse.

The undergraduate program also includes three optional concentrations: Furniture Design, Preservation and Restoration, and Architectural Practice and Enterprise.

Recent foreign studies summer programs have taken place in Cuba, China, Japan and Italy. In addition, the School conducts a summer "Career Discovery Program" for high school students who wish to explore architecture before they go to college.

An active chapter of the American Institute of Architecture Students (AIAS-ND), Students for New Urbanism (SNU-ND) and Student Association for Women in Architecture (SAWA) enliven the School's educational and social environment. In addition, the AIAS-ND sponsors an annual career fair.

The School also annually presents the $200,000 Richard H. Driehaus Prize to a living architect whose work embodies the principles of traditional and classical architecture and urbanism in contemporary society. In conjunction with the Driehaus Prize, the School also gives the $50,000 Henry Hope Reed Award to an individual working outside the practice of architecture who has supported the cultivation of the traditional city, its architecture and art through writing, planning or promotion.

FACILITIES

The School of Architecture is housed on the home campus in Bond hall, formerly the campus library, which underwent a $12 million dollar renovation several years ago to accommodate up-to-date studios, computing facilities, classrooms, exhibition and display spaces, a woodworking shop, and an extensive architecture library collection which includes a rare books library to house special collections. In Rome, the School owns a building in the city's centro storico, near the Piazza Navona. The Rome facility was also renovated recently, and accommodates studios, classrooms, library and offices of the School of Architecture's Rome Studies Program. The School maintains a Downtown Urban Design Studio in the city of South Bend.

SCHOLARSHIPS AND FINANCIAL AID

Graduate Program scholarships and stipends come from the earnings of an endowment of the School of Architecture amounting to about $2.5 million dollars. Undergraduate students receive scholarships, prizes and awards from specific donations to the School and from the University's scholarship and financial aid programs. In recent years, approximately 61% of all undergraduate students in architecture receive scholarship and financial aid in a variety of types and amounts, dependent upon need and academic accomplishments.

ADMINISTRATION

Michael N. Lykoudis, RA: Dean
John W. Stamper, PhD, AIA: Associate Dean, Director of Undergraduate Studies
Fr. Richard S. Bullene: Assistant Dean
Philip Bess: Director of Graduate Studies
Steven Semes: Director of Rome Studies Program
Jennifer Parker: Architectural Librarian

UNIVERSITY OF OKLAHOMA

ADDRESS

Main
University of Oklahoma
College of Architecture
830 Van Vleet Oval
Gould Hall, Rm 162
Norman, OK 73019-0265
Tel.: 405.325.3990
Fax: 405.325.0108
arch@ou.edu
arch.ou.edu

STUDENT AND FACULTY DEMOGRAPHICS

% of Female Students	37
% of International Students	5
% of Minority Students	23
% of Out-of-State U.S. Students	33
No. Full-Time Faculty	40
No. Part-Time Faculty	4
No. Full-Time Students	617
No. Part-Time Students	71

FINANCIAL INFORMATION

Main Source of University Funding	Public
Annual Tuition & Fees (graduate, resident)	$6,650
Annual Tuition & Fees (graduate, nonresident)	$16,483
Annual Tuition & Fees (undergraduate, resident)	$7,423
Annual Tuition & Fees (undergraduate, nonresident)	$17,404
% Students Receiving Federal Financial Aid	
% Students Receiving University Financial Aid	83
% Students Receiving Departmental Financial Aid	
% Students Receiving Scholarships (assistantships or fellowships)	27
Average Annual Scholarship for Department	$9,000

ACADEMIC SESSIONS

Fall Semester: August to December; Application Deadline: April 1
Spring Semester: January to May; Application Deadline: November 1

ARCHITECTURE AND RELATED DEGREE PROGRAMS

Degree	Min. Yrs. to Complete	Professional Accreditation	# of FT Students	# of PT Students	# of First-Year Students	# of Degrees Conferred	Admissions Requirements
Architecture							
B. Arch	5	NAAB	237	42	104	38	SAT, ACT
Bachelor of Science in Environmental Design	4		20		6		SAT, ACT
M. Arch—1 year	1		6	12	0	3	Prof. Architecture degree, Portfolio, Rec. Letters, Essay
M. Arch—2 years	2	NAAB	8	2	9	6	Undergraduate Architecture degree, Portfolio, Rec. Letters, Essay
Master of Science in Architectural Urban Studies	2		0	15	7	4	Undergraduate degree, GRE, Rec. Letters
Landscape Architecture							
MLA	2		15		8	5	Undergraduate degree, Rec. Letters, Essay
Interior Design/Interior Architecture							
B. Arts—ID	4	CIDA/FIDER	80	10	45	20	SAT, ACT
Planning							
MRCP	2	PAB	20		10		Undergraduate degree, TOEFL, Rec. Letters, Essay
Planning							
B.S. Construction Science	4	ACCE	189	20	69	28	SAT, ACT
M.S. Construction Administration	2		20			9	Undergraduate Degree

SPECIALIZATIONS

Architectural Design	Computer-Aided Design	Interior Design/Architecture	Sustainability
Building Information Modeling	Engineering	International/Regional Architecture	Theory/Criticism
Building Technology/Env. Systems	Environment/Sustainability	Landscape Design	Urban Planning and Design
Community Design	History	Professional Practice	

ARCHITECTURE PROGRAM SUMMARY

The University of Oklahoma's Division of Architecture is dedicated to a comprehensive approach to architectural education which will instill in students a knowledge of and concern for the responsibilities of architecture and the related disciplines; train students to enter the profession and function effectively within multi-disciplinary teams; prepare students for lifelong learning; and develop students' ability to engage the forces of change. The Division is committed to advancing the profession through research, scholarship, and creative activity.

UNIVERSITY SETTING

The University of Oklahoma is a major PhD-granting university rated "Research I" by Carnegie. The University serves 28,000 students at the Norman campus. Graduate programs are also offered at the University of Oklahoma–Tulsa campus. The College of Architecture contains five divisions offering undergraduate professional degrees in Architecture, Interior Design, and Construction Science, as well as graduate degrees in Architecture, Construction Management, Regional and City Planning and Landscape Architecture. The College accepts transfer students from all related disciplines.

SCHOOL PHILOSOPHY

The College seeks to develop professionals that are well-prepared for careers in its interrelated disciplines. Architecture is viewed as both an applied discipline as well as a cultural study. Interaction toward solving environmental issues is encouraged between disciplines. Community involvement is encouraged and practiced, such as the annual design-build project, urban design studies with nearby communities, and special topics projects. The College is dedicated to producing highly competent professional leaders that are also community centered.

PROGRAM DESCRIPTION

The undergraduate program in Architecture is a 10-semester, 160-credit first-professional degree program accredited by NAAB. The studio is the central pedagogical tool in which all other learned skills are focused. The program curriculum is grouped into design, structural, environmental, and urban studies. All architecture students also take the university-mandated general education courses.

Graduate programs in Architecture include the M. Arch I, a post-professional 32-credit degree program centered on research, sustainability, or urban studies. Also offered is the M. Arch II for students holding an undergraduate degree in Environmental Design or other four-year related degree. This program is based on 64 credits of graduate work and leads to an NAAB-accredited first-professional degree. The College also offers a unique Master of Science graduate program based on urban design, which is located at the University of Oklahoma–Tulsa campus.

AREAS OF FOCUS AND RESEARCH

Focus

The College's areas of focus are centered on the organization of its disciplines. Thus, community-centered programs that engage both Architecture and Planning students together with Landscape Architecture are prolific. Students frequently explore the interrelation of Architecture and Construction Science, and/or Architecture and Interior Design through community building efforts.

Research

Research is encouraged and supported at the graduate level. Upper-division students may participate in sponsored projects engaging issues of sustainability, environmental aspects of buildings, energy conservation, and other areas. Research Assistantships for graduate students are available through these projects.

SPECIAL ACTIVITIES AND PROGRAMS

We offer a series of travel, professional practice, and hands-on learning experiences to our students. A special design-build program is often offered to third- and fourth-year undergraduate students. In this program, students design and construct a project relevant to the community. A Preceptorship Program in the fourth year of study permits students to earn college credits while working in a professional office. The College maintains an active career counseling and academic advisement office. An annual Job Fair brings many professional employers to campus for advanced student interviews. The Bruce Goff Professorship Program brings distinguished professionals throughout the academic year to lecture and work with students in studio. Additionally, the College offers a number of opportunities for students to study architecture and design abroad. Recent courses taught abroad have included visits to such locations as Istanbul, Beijing, Vienna, and London. The College annually awards approximately 35 scholarships to outstanding students. These are made possible by alumni and professionals through the College Development Officer.

FACILITIES

The College of Architecture is located in Gould Hall, which is currently undergoing $33 million dollars worth of renovations. These comprehensive renovations are expected to take around two years to complete, and will result in a state-of-the art facility with expanded gallery and educational spaces, improved computer and visualization labs, and new furniture and finishes for the building's interiors, among other improvements. After the renovations are complete, Gould Hall will house all five Divisions of the College of Architecture for the first time since the inception of the College. While Gould Hall is undergoing these comprehensive renovations, the College of Architecture has re-located to Main Street, in downtown Norman. The Main Street facilities allow over 19,000 square feet of classroom, studio, lab, library, and administrative space. The Architecture Branch Library, also temporarily located in Main Street, contains over 20,000 volumes, including bound periodicals. The College's main computer lab houses a variety of computers with high-end capabilities. Output devices in the main lab include laser printers, photo-quality thermal dye sublimation printers and large format color inkjet plotters. In addition, the computer network serves over 100 computers located throughout the building. The College has an immaculate, diversified model shop. Tailored to meet the needs of our students, the shop holds equipment and tools for working with plastics, sheet metal, and wood and is staffed by expert builders.

SCHOLARSHIPS AND FINANCIAL AID

Need-based financial assistance is available through the University Financial Aid office. The College annually awards approximately 35 scholarships to students on the basis of merit. Approximately 10 College scholarships are awarded annually based on need. These are made possible by alumni and professionals through the College Development Officer.

ADMINISTRATION

Charles W. Graham, AIA: Dean
James Patterson, AIA: Associate Dean
Nick L. Harm, AIA: Director

UNIVERSITY OF OREGON

Urban Grid

ADDRESS

Main
University of Oregon
Department of Architecture
1206 University of Oregon
Eugene, OR 97403-1206
Tel.: 541.346.3656
Fax: 541.346.3626
archinfo@aaa.uoregon.edu
architecture.uoregon.edu

STUDENT AND FACULTY DEMOGRAPHICS

% of Female Students	56
% of International Students	6
% of Minority Students	14
% of Out-of-State U.S. Students	61
No. Full-Time Faculty	32
No. Part-Time Faculty	45
No. Full-Time Students	663
No. Part-Time Students	

FINANCIAL INFORMATION

Main Source of University Funding	Public
Annual Tuition & Fees (graduate, resident)	$11,577
Annual Tuition & Fees (graduate, nonresident)	$16,341
Annual Tuition & Fees (undergraduate, resident)	$6,321
Annual Tuition & Fees (undergraduate, nonresident)	$19,530
% Students Receiving Federal Financial Aid	
% Students Receiving University Financial Aid	
% Students Receiving Departmental Financial Aid	
% Students Receiving Scholarships (assistantships or fellowships)	
Average Annual Scholarship for Department	

ACADEMIC SESSIONS

Fall Quarter/Trimester: September to December;
   Application Deadline: Contact the Department

Winter Quarter/Trimester: January to March
Spring Quarter/Trimester: April to June
Summer Session I: June to August

ARCHITECTURE AND RELATED DEGREE PROGRAMS

Degree	Min. Yrs. to Complete	Professional Accreditation	# of FT Students	# of PT Students	# of First-Year Students	# of Degrees Conferred	Admissions Requirements
Architecture							
B. Arch	5	NAAB	340	0	81	73	SAT, TOEFL, Portfolio, Rec. Letters, Essay
M. Arch	3	NAAB	139		47		Undergraduate degree, GRE, TOEFL, Portfolio, Rec. Letters, Essay
M. Arch	2	NAAB	60		46		Undergraduate Architecture degree, GRE, Portfolio, Rec. Letters, Essay
M. Arch	1		5		3		Prof. Architecture degree, TOEFL, Portfolio
Interior Design/Architecture							
B. Iarch	5	CIDA/FIDER	75		17	15	SAT, TOEFL, Portfolio, Rec. Letters, Essay
M. Iarch	3	CIDA/FIDER	10		6	7	Undergraduate degree, GRE, TOEFL, Portfolio, Rec. Letters, Essay
M. Iarch	2	CIDA/FIDER			0	2	Portfolio
M. Iarch	1		1				GRE, TOEFL, Portfolio

SPECIALIZATIONS

Architectural Design	Energy	Interior Design/Architecture	Sustainability
Building Technology/Env. Systems	Environment/Sustainability	Landscape Design	Urban Planning and Design
Computer-Aided Design	Housing	Preservation	

ARCHITECTURE PROGRAM SUMMARY

The University of Oregon Department of Architecture offers accredited undergraduate and graduate professional degrees and research-oriented post-professional degrees in architecture and interior architecture with an emphasis on interdisciplinary collaboration and ecological design. Students are actively engaged in curriculum development, extracurricular programs, and community service. Graduates are broadly educated designers who attain leadership positions in the professions of architecture, interior design and allied fields.

UNIVERSITY SETTING

The University of Oregon (UO) is the flagship institution of the Oregon University System and the only Oregon member of the prestigious Association of American Universities. As a comprehensive research university with responsibility for leadership in the arts and sciences and in the professions of architecture and allied arts, business, law, journalism, music, dance, and education with academic support systems including libraries, interdisciplinary programs and research centers the UO provides a rich context for the study of architecture.

The main campus, recognized nationally for its proactive stance on environmental issues, is located in the city of Eugene, at the southern end of the beautiful Willamette River valley of Oregon. With a reputation for being one of the top 10 livable college towns and the greenest city in the country, Eugene is an ideal host community for an architecture program with a longstanding commitment to sustainability and community engagement. The UO in Portland is the home to the department's Portland Program where architecture students can study in the center of downtown Portland, one of the world's most progressive urban centers and an international model for environmentally and socially conscious urban development.

The value placed upon interdisciplinary linkages in academic life is reflected in the structure of the curriculum as well as in the relationship of the department to the school and to the university. Building on the liberal arts mission of the university, the School of Architecture and Allied Arts (A&AA) has from its founding emphasized the humanistic traditions of architecture. Undergraduate students enrolled in architecture programs have access to a robust menu of general education courses and opportunities to minor in other disciplines. Graduate students with special interests in interdisciplinary studies have access to graduate studies and faculty throughout the university.

Academic units within A&AA include the departments of Architecture; Art; Art History; Planning, Public Policy and Management and Landscape Architecture as well as programs in Historic Preservation, Interior Architecture, Product Design, Digital Arts and Arts Administration. The department's place within the school affords architecture students with extensive contact with other design fields. Undergraduate minors and concurrent enrollment in master's degrees in art history, interior architecture, historic preservation and landscape architecture are common, and collaborations among faculty members across the school's programs provide students with access to team taught courses and jointly sponsored lectures and extracurricular activities.

SCHOOL PHILOSOPHY
A&AA is dedicated to advancing the understanding and quality of visual culture and the built, natural, and social environments through excellent and distinctive teaching, research, and creative endeavors. Grounded in a unique multi-disciplinary structure, A&AA is a diverse, collegial learning community of faculty, students and staff. We seek to enhance the lives of individuals and communities through endeavors that stem from intellectual curiosity, critical thinking, and broad inquiry, rooted in the inter-relatedness of theory, history, and practice. In support of this mission, A&AA affirms the following values: Excellence, Open Discourse, Inclusiveness, Cooperation, Inter-Disciplinary Experience and Responsibility.

The Department of Architecture is dedicated to recognizing designers' accountability for the impact of their actions on environmental, social, and cultural systems. Students, faculty and staff participate in a tradition where studio teaching serves as the primary means of integrating all design issues—e.g., social and behavioral, environmental, contextual, technological, theoretical, economic, political, and professional, that together result in meaningful design achievements. The programs in architecture and interior architecture emphasize collaboration and a noncompetitive but rigorous learning environment. Studio work is evaluated using individualized discussion and written assessments rather than letter grades, and a supportive studio culture is encouraged through facilitated peer teaching and teamwork. Intellectual inquiry is the basis for design exploration and the department promotes design excellence without dictating a specific design aesthetic or ideology. The department is nationally recognized for the achievements of its faculty and students in innovation and environmental sustainability research including the design of buildings, interiors, and communities. Student organizations assume leadership roles in curriculum development, extracurricular programs, and community service. Graduates are broadly educated designers who attain leadership positions in the professions of architecture, interior design and allied fields.

PROGRAM DESCRIPTION
The curriculum of the department's architecture and interior architecture programs requires the development of detailed professional skills and sound professional judgment. Accordingly, the undergraduate program includes a strong liberal education. Students develop a broad base of knowledge that will enable them to become contributing members of society whose insights are not limited by their professional education. Graduate students are selected for admission on the basis of their previous academic preparation and their potential contribution to the professional program. The primary objective within the professional component of the program is the development of integrative design skills. Every member of the tenure-related faculty teaches both design studio and subject courses. This is one of the unique and most important traditions of the department. Because all faculty members, no matter what subject areas they teach, also teach design studios, not only are design studios more comprehensive, but also subject-area courses stress the implications of the specific topic as an integrative aspect of the design process.

The NAAB-accredited degrees (B. Arch., M. Arch. II, M. Arch. III) require ten quarter-term studio courses. The sequential completion of these studios and the associated subject courses defines the length of the graduate programs. In the undergraduate program the studios are distributed two per year over the full five-year period. This structure gives students time to mature as designers as well as opportunities throughout the five years to pursue required liberal studies outside the department. Architectural subject courses include a required core curriculum and advanced electives. The core curriculum is organized in interactive cycles that grow in their complexity as students develop the capacity to apply the course topics in the design studio. The first year provides a general introduction including foundation knowledge, concepts, skills and methods fundamental to further study. In subsequent years courses instill competence with knowledge, concepts, skills, and methods that are representative of a particular subject area and prepare students for advanced study. The CIDA-accredited degrees (B.Iarc, M.Iarc II, M. Iarc III) have a similar structure.

In addition to providing an education that supports the future professional registration of its graduates, the department seeks to develop well-rounded critical thinkers prepared to attain leadership positions in architecture, interior design and related fields. Both the curriculum and the assessment of student performance in the design studio are organized according to the following educational contexts: architectural design, human behavior and social factors, the environment, aesthetics and spatial composition, building technology, media and communication, architectural history.

AREAS OF FOCUS AND RESEARCH
The research interests of the architecture and interior architecture faculty provide students who wish to specialize in a particular subject area with access to advanced coursework, independent study, or involvement in research. Grant-supported and department-supported graduate research fellowships are also available. The following concentrations reflect current areas of faculty research:

Architectural Education
Computer-aided Design
Design Process and Theory
Energy-conscious Design
Environment and Behavior
Housing Design
Interdisciplinary Design
Interior Components and Furniture
Lighting Design
Proxemic Design and Ergonomics

Structures and Construction
Urban Architecture and Urban Design
Vernacular Architecture, Landscape, Settlement, and Site Design

Students with interests that align closely with faculty research in other departments and programs within the school can study with faculty members in the departments of art history, landscape architecture, art, planning, public policy and management and the historic preservation, arts administration and product design programs.

SPECIAL ACTIVITIES AND PROGRAMS
The Portland Program: With approximately 100 graduate and advanced undergraduate students, the Department of Architecture's Portland Program is an extension of the department's degree-granting programs in Eugene. Qualified M. Arch. II students can be admitted directly to Portland but most of the students in Portland begin their studies in Eugene. Study in Portland is voluntary and the duration of study ranges from one quarter (usually in the summer) to two years (usually graduate students with no general education or introductory coursework requirements). Students choose the Portland Program in order to focus their studies on urban architecture. The program also serves students who prefer Portland's location for its urban life, employment opportunities and connections to Portland's much larger, nationally acclaimed community of practicing architects. For many of these students, Portland provides an effective transition from school to internship. It also allows students from the Portland area to study closer to their home base.

Graduate Certificate Programs: Graduates students in the department of architecture have the option of expanding their degree program to include one or more of the following graduate certificates: The Technical Teaching Certificate Program prepares architecture students to teach building technology subjects in schools of architecture and professional settings. The Ecological Design Certificate Program prepares students enrolled in environmental studies disciplines for engagement in green design processes. The Museum Studies Certificate Program prepares students from architecture, arts & administration.

FACILITIES
On the Eugene campus, Lawrence Hall and adjacent Pacific Hall house all facilities of the Department except for the furniture design studio, the woodshop, and construction technology labs which are housed in the nearby Millrace complex. Facilities include the A&AA Library, studios, classrooms, lecture halls, review rooms, photographic labs, the Materials Resource Center, computer graphics laboratories, Willcox Hearth and the Krause Gallery. The Portland Program is situated in a building in the heart of downtown Portland owned by the University and includes a gallery, review and class rooms, studios, offices, a model shop, library, spray booth and computing lab.

SCHOLARSHIPS AND FINANCIAL AID
Undergraduate and graduate students have access to several regularly recurring departmental scholarships, most of which are awarded on the basis of need and scholastic achievement. Awards generally cover in-state tuition costs for one to three terms. Students may also apply for a number of grants/loans on a university-wide basis. In addition, there are numerous opportunities for graduate students as Graduate Teaching Fellows (GTF) which pay tuition costs, as well as a stipend.

ADMINISTRATION
Frances Bronet: Dean
Christine O. Theodoropoulos, AIA, PE: Department Head
Glenda Utsey: Associate Department Head

UNIVERSITY OF PENNSYLVANIA

ADDRESS

Main
University of Pennsylvania
Department of Architecture
207 Meyerson Hall
210 South 34th Street
Philadelphia, PA 19104-6311
Tel.: 215.898.5728
Fax: 215.573.2192
arch@design.upenn.edu
design.upenn.edu/new/arch

STUDENT AND FACULTY DEMOGRAPHICS

% of Female Students	44
% of International Students	64
% of Minority Students	12
% of Out-of-State U.S. Students	
No. Full-Time Faculty	18
No. Part-Time Faculty	55
No. Full-Time Students	300
No. Part-Time Students	20

FINANCIAL INFORMATION

Main Source of University Funding	Private
Annual Tuition & Fees (graduate)	$37,144
Annual Tuition & Fees (undergraduate)	$37,525
% Students Receiving Federal Financial Aid	50
% Students Receiving University Financial Aid	70
% Students Receiving Departmental Financial Aid	70
% Students Receiving Scholarships (assistantships or fellowships)	5
Average Annual Scholarship for Department	$4,500

ACADEMIC SESSIONS

ARCHITECTURE AND RELATED DEGREE PROGRAMS							
Degree	**Min. Yrs. to Complete**	**Professional Accreditation**	**# of FT Students**	**# of PT Students**	**# of First-Year Students**	**# of Degrees Conferred**	**Admissions Requirements**
Architecture							
BA	4		36	0	24	24	SAT, Essay
BA Intensive	4		12	0	12	12	SAT, Essay, Application in Junior Year
M. Arch I	3	NAAB	180	0	60	60	Undergraduate Degree, GRE, TOEFL, Portfolio, Rec. letters, Essay
M. Arch I AP	2	NAAB	24	0	12	12	Undergraduate Degree, GRE, TOEFL, Portfolio, Rec. letters, Essay
M. Arch II	1		24	0	24	24	Undergraduate Degree, GRE, TOEFL, Portfolio, Rec. letters, Essay
MS	1.5		4		4	4	Undergraduate Degree, GRE, TOEFL, Portfolio, Rec. letters, Essay
PhD	5		24	6	2	4	Undergraduate Degree, GRE, TOEFL, Portfolio, Rec. letters, Essay
Other							
M. Arch-MLA	4	NAAB/ASLA	16	0	4	4	Undergraduate Degree, GRE, TOEFL, Portfolio, Rec. letters, Essay
M. Arch-MCP	4	NAAB/PAB	2	0	1	1	Undergraduate Degree, GRE, TOEFL, Portfolio, Rec. letters, Essay
M. Arch-MS.HSPV	4	NAAB	2	0	1	1	Undergraduate Degree, GRE, TOEFL, Portfolio, Rec. letters, Essay
M. Arch-MBA (Wharton)	4	NAAB/AACSB	2	0	1	1	Undergraduate Degree, GRE, TOEFL, Portfolio, Rec. letters, Essay

SCHOOL PHILOSOPHY

Undergraduate Philosophy The mission of the undergraduate program is to develop basic skills, knowledge, and methods of inquiry in the discipline of architecture within the context of a studiobased liberal arts education. The program provides for the study of acrhitecture on three levels of engagement: a Minor; a Major with a concentration in either Design or History, Theory, and Critisism; and Intensive Major qualifying an undergraduate student in the Design concentration for advanced standing in the Master of Architecture professional degree program. The Major in Architecture is a studio-based liberal arts program offering two tracks or concentrations in the study of architecture. The Design Concentration includes a three-year sequence of design studios combined with courses in art history and architectural theory. The History, Theory, and Criticism Concentration includes a two-year sequence of design studios and courses in art history, architectural theory, and related subjects. Students declare the Major in Architecture upon completion of ARCH 202, taken during the sophmore year. Admission into the Concentration in Design is dependent on a student earning a minimum 3.0 grade point average in ARCH 201 and 202. Upon graduation, students are awarded a four-year, non-professional degree: a Bachelor of Arts with a Major in Architecture. Graduate Philosophy.

PROGRAM DESCRIPTION

The program provides for the study of architecture on three levels of engagement: a Minor; a Major with a concentration in either Design or History, Theory, and Criticism; and an Intensive Major qualifying an undergraduate student in the Design concentration for advanced standing in the Master of Architecture professional degree program. The Major in Architecture is a studio-based liberal arts program offering two tracks or concentrations in the study of architecture. The Design Concentration includes a three-year sequence of design studios combined with courses in art history and architectural theory. The History, Theory, and Criticism Concentration includes a two-year sequence of design studios and courses in art history combined with additional coursework in art history, architectural theo-

ry, and related subjects. Students declare the Major in Architecture upon completion of ARCH 202, taken during the sophomore year. Admission into the Concentration in Design is dependent on a student earning a minimum 3.0 grade point average in ARCH 201 and 202. Upon graduation, students are awarded a four-year, non-professional degree: a Bachelor of Arts with a Major in Architecture. Architecture was the first formal course of study in what was to become the Graduate School of Fine Arts. From its founding in 1890, the department has emphasized the link between theoretical speculation, professional practice, and artistic expression, offering in its first catalogue "a full theoretical, practical, and artistic course of study." A full spectrum of education in the discipline of architecture is currently offered in four degree programs: Doctor of Philosophy, Ph.D.; Master of Science, M.S.; Master of Architecture, M.Arch.; and Bachelor of Arts, B.A.

AREAS OF FOCUS AND RESEARCH

Focus

Students may concentrate their studies in theory, technology, or digital design. Certificates are offered in urban design, historic preservation, and real estate design and development. Students may participate in Architecture in the Schools, a K-12 educational program in liaison with the Philadelphia public schools.

Research

In addition to traditional academic research in the history and theory of architecture, research is conducted in digital media and computer simulation.

SPECIAL ACTIVITIES AND PROGRAMS

Many opportunities for study abroad are available to our graduate students. For those enrolled in the three-year professional degree program, the fall semester of the third-year can be spent at the Architectural Association in London, as well as schools in Venice, France, the Netherlands and Germany. Summer study programs are currently offered in Paris and Japan. The Department of Architecture invites prominent and emerging architects from around the world to take part in a school-wide lecture series offered throughout the academic year.

- Dual-Degree Programs
- Certificate Programs
- Annual Career Day: Over fifty of the country's leading architectural firms make an annual visit to campus to review and recruit Penn's architectural students for positions in their practices.

FACILITIES

All graduate architecture students work in a dedicated studio space with each work station wired to a network. In addition to a long list of software available to all students in the computing lab, the GSFA Computing Center is equipped with several plotters. The Architectural Conservation Laboratory, Digital Media Lab, Fabrication Lab, and several galleries are found in Meyerson Hall, the building of the Graduate School of Fine Arts. Meyerson Hall is located in the heart of campus. The Fisher Fine Arts Library of the GSFA is housed in the original 19th-century Landmark Building designed by Frank Furness - recently renovated by the firm of Venturi Scott Brown.

SCHOLARSHIPS AND FINANCIAL AID

Students who are US citizens and demonstrate need are given the opportunity to meet all their expenses through a comprehensive financial aid package composed of partial scholarship, loans, and work options. Foreign students who demonstrate need, though not eligible for federal loans, may also receive partial scholarship. Minority scholarships are granted to eligible students throughout the length of their program. A limited number of teaching assistantships are given, primarily to third-year students. Merit-based aid is awarded to students through competitions held during the spring.

ADMINISTRATION

William W. Braham: Interim Chair
Annette Fierro: Associate Chair
Richard Wesley: Chair, Undergraduate Program
David Leatherbarrow: Chair, Graduate Group
Winka Dubbeldam: Director, M.Arch II
    Post-Professional Program

UNIVERSITY OF SOUTHERN CALIFORNIA

ADDRESS

Main
University of Southern California
School of Architecture
University Park
Watt Hall - Room 204
Los Angeles, CA 90089-0291
Tel.: 213.740.2723
Fax: 213.740.8884
uscarch@usc.edu
arch.usc.edu

STUDENT AND FACULTY DEMOGRAPHICS

% of Female Students	50
% of International Students	11
% of Minority Students	21
% of Out-of-State U.S. Students	40
No. Full-Time Faculty	26
No. Part-Time Faculty	65
No. Full-Time Students	695
No. Part-Time Students	

FINANCIAL INFORMATION

Main Source of University Funding	Public
Annual Tuition & Fees (graduate, resident)	$37,634
Annual Tuition & Fees (graduate, nonresident)	$37,634
Annual Tuition & Fees (undergraduate, resident)	$37,634
Annual Tuition & Fees (undergraduate, nonresident)	$37,634
% Students Receiving Federal Financial Aid	60
% Students Receiving University Financial Aid	60
% Students Receiving Departmental Financial Aid	
% Students Receiving Scholarships (assistantships or fellowships)	
Average Annual Scholarship for Department	$556,462

ACADEMIC SESSIONS

Fall Semester: August to December
    Application Deadline: Dec. 1 Freshmen, Jan. 15 Graduate

Spring Semester: January to May

ARCHITECTURE AND RELATED DEGREE PROGRAMS

Degree	Min. Yrs. to Complete	Professional Accreditation	# of FT Students	# of PT Students	# of First-Year Students	# of Degrees Conferred	Admissions Requirements
Architecture							
B. Arch	5	NAAB	537	0	130	113	SAT, ACT, TOEFL, Portfolio, Rec. Letters, Essay
Bachelor of Science in Architecture	4		20	0	0	10	SAT, ACT, TOEFL, Portfolio, Rec. Letters, Essay
M. Arch +2	2	NAAB	61	0	46	18	Undergraduate Architecture degree, GRE, TOEFL, Portfolio, Rec. Letters, Essay
Master of Architecture Post-Professional	1.5		28	0	19	4	Prof. Architecture degree, GRE, TOEFL, Portfolio, Rec. Letters, Essay
PhD in Architecture	3		3	0	3	0	Undergraduate degree, GRE, TOEFL, Rec. Letters, Essay
Landscape Architecture							
Bachelor of Landscape Architecture	4		0	0	0	0	SAT, ACT, TOEFL, Portfolio, Rec. Letters, Essay
Master of Landscape Architecture	1.5		12	0	5	0	Undergraduate Architecture degree, GRE, TOEFL, Portfolio, Rec. Letters, Essay
Master of Landscape Architecture	2		6	0	6	0	Undergraduate Architecture degree, GRE, TOEFL, Portfolio, Rec. Letters, Essay
Historic Preservation							
Master of Historic Preservation	2		11	8	9	7	Undergraduate degree, GRE, TOEFL, Portfolio, Rec. Letters, Essay
Other							
Master of Building Science	2		20	0	12	17	Undergraduate degree, GRE, TOEFL, Rec. Letters, Essay

SPECIALIZATIONS

Architectural Design	Energy	International/Regional Architecture	Sustainability
Building Information Modeling	Environment/Sustainability	Landscape Design	Tectonics
Building Technology/Env. Systems	History	Preservation	Theory/Criticism
Community Design	Housing	Professional Practice	Urban Planning and Design
Computer-Aided Design	International Development		

ARCHITECTURE PROGRAM SUMMARY

The USC School of Architecture is located in the heart of Los Angeles, a singular laboratory in which to study and understand urban conditions and their architectural implications. With the recent appointment of Dean Qingyun Ma the School extends its global reach into new territories, launching new initiatives in cross-cultural and cross-disciplinary discourses, strengthening ties in the community and around the world. Established in 1919, the USC School of Architecture was the first of its kind in southern California. Educational offerings include architecture, landscape architecture, building science and historic preservation. Among its notable graduates are Conrad Buff III, Donald H. Hensman, Pierre Koenig, and two Pritzker Prize Laureates: Frank O. Gehry (1989) and Thom Mayne (2005).

UNIVERSITY SETTING

The University of Southern California, the ninth-largest private research university in the United States, is located in the heart of Los Angeles, only minutes away from the central business district. The university enrolls approximately 28,000 students, yet the School of Architecture enjoys the intimacy of a student body of 592 students. Founded in 1919, it is the only private school of architecture in the western United States associated with a major research university.

SCHOOL PHILOSOPHY

The fundamental premises of the school include: recognition of the interdependence of theory and practice; understanding the basis of architecture as a profound response to the human condition and human experience; and respect for the disciplines of visual form and technology as the means for realization of the objectives of the design process. The academic mission of the school is stated in four principal dimensions:

- To train professionals within the context of a humanistic academic tradition
- To advance knowledge about the theory and practice of architecture
- To address social and cultural issues
- To be a stimulating environment for learning.

PROGRAM DESCRIPTION

Undergraduate Program

The Bachelor of Architecture curriculum provides the foundation of understanding on which to build advanced studies and professional practice. Continuous through the entire 10 semesters of the program is the design studio in which projects are engaged as a means for developing the skills, knowledge, understanding, and judgment to create appropriate and exemplary designs. Foundation Program: Years one through three introduce students to the discipline of architecture: its subjects, its ideas, its methods, and the skills required for its practice. Full-time faculty members are prominent in the foundation program, providing leadership and experience to beginning students. The foundation program culminates in the second semester of the third year with a studio project that assists students in sum-marizing what they have learned and in making the transition toward the more independent studies of the advanced program.

Advanced Program

Three semesters of Topic Studios and Fifth-Year Comprehensive Project provide the opportunity to explore individual interests and strengths in a variety of types and sizes of projects under the guidance of individual faculty critics. Based upon a theoretical premise for design exploration, the Fifth-Year Comprehensive Project serves as the capstone of the degree, employing the skills and knowledge gained in previous courses. The School offers interrelated graduate programs in architecture, landscape architecture, building science, and historic preservation, as well as dual-degree programs with the School of Policy, Planning and Development. These programs are designed for students who hold either preprofessional or professional degrees in the appropriate fields.

Graduate Program

The Master of Architecture is offered in two programs: the +2 professional program for students with pre-professional degrees, and the March program for students who hold a professional degree such as the Bachelor of Architecture or its equivalent. The Master of Building Science, a 48-unit degree program, is intended for students who already possess a first degree in architecture or engineering. The typical length of the program is two years, centering on each student's thesis and supported by research seminars and electives from architecture, engineering, and other related fields. The Master of Landscape Architecture is designed to significantly augment the professional capabilities of students who already possess a first degree in landscape architecture. The typical length of time required to complete the 48-unit program is two years. The School also offers a 48-unit Master of Historic Preservation Program whose objective is to familiarize students with the philosophies and practices of the historic preservation movement.

AREAS OF FOCUS AND RESEARCH

Focus

The USC School of Architecture is a professional school with a curriculum that focuses on architectural design and its important connections to urban design and building technology. Design studios often select projects that take advantage of the rich Los Angeles architectural context. The School has an off-campus facility with two design studios that address community issues. A close relationship with Los Angeles Unified School District supports students to work on the design of educational facilities. The School is a member of USC's Art Initiative and Urban Initiative, allowing students from Architecture the opportunity to work on projects with students from the Arts and the Social Sciences.

Research

All faculty conduct research in the form of scholarly investigation and writing or through professional practice. Grants from various private and public sources fund architecture faculty in numerous projects including: • Earthquake forces and building structures • Urban design • Historic preservation and conservation • Educational facilities planning and design • Sustainable design • Frank Lloyd Wright textile concrete block Many faculty conduct interdisciplinary research with faculty from other units on campus. Professional practice by full-time and adjunct faculty has resulted in numerous design awards and publications for building and urban design projects throughout the world. Students from all programs assist faculty in research and professional practice.

SPECIAL ACTIVITIES AND PROGRAMS

Three school-run, one semester abroad programs are available in Italy, France, and Asia for undergraduates and one for graduate students in China. • An extensive internship program with leading Los Angeles firms provides professional practice opportunities to students. • Three endowed visiting design positions bring internationally renowned lecturers, critics, and exhibitions. • The School offers a minor in architecture and landscape architecture, and graduate certificates in historic preservation, building science, landscape architecture and urbanism. • Four endowed international traveling fellowships are awarded yearly. • The School's Scholar-in-Residence Fellowship allow students to live in the famous Greene and Greene designed Gamble House. • Design studios often conduct projects involving two historic structures that are owned by the School; the Gamble House and the Frank Lloyd Wright designed Freeman House. • The summer Exploration of Architecture program exposes high school students to the discipline of architecture. • Annual Career Fairs bring approximately 100 architects each semester to interview students for professional practice positions.

FACILITIES

The School is located in Harris and Watt Halls on the University Park campus. The Helen Topping Library houses the most extensive collection of architecture books and periodicals in Southern California. The Helen Lindhurst and the Verle Annis Architecture Galleries are devoted solely to architecture. Test equipment simulating sun, wind, and earthquake conditions are available for students. In addition to having web access from each desk, students have access to specialized computer labs and a digital output center.

SCHOLARSHIPS AND FINANCIAL AID

The university provides a need-based financial aid package to all undergraduates admitted to the School of Architecture. Approximately 60% of USC undergraduates receive some form of need-based financial aid. The USC Architectural Guild raises over $300,000 per year for special student support.

ADMINISTRATION

Qingyun Ma: Dean
Amy Murphy: Vice Dean

UNIVERSITY OF SOUTH FLORIDA

ADDRESS

Main
University of South Florida
School of Architecture &
Community Design
4202 E. Fowler Ave. HMS 301
Tampa, FL 33620
Tel.: 813.974.4031
Fax: 813.974.2557
www.arch.usf.edu

STUDENT AND FACULTY DEMOGRAPHICS

% of Female Students	39
% of International Students	3
% of Minority Students	42
% of Out-of-State U.S. Students	0
No. Full-Time Faculty	8
No. Part-Time Faculty	12
No. Full-Time Students	173
No. Part-Time Students	9

FINANCIAL INFORMATION

Main Source of University Funding	Public
Annual Tuition & Fees (graduate, resident)	$7,100
Annual Tuition & Fees (graduate, nonresident)	$21,000
Annual Tuition & Fees (undergraduate, resident)	
Annual Tuition & Fees (undergraduate, nonresident)	
% Students Receiving Federal Financial Aid	
% Students Receiving University Financial Aid	
% Students Receiving Departmental Financial Aid	20
% Students Receiving Scholarships (assistantships or fellowships)	11
Average Annual Scholarship for Department	$1,200

ACADEMIC SESSIONS

Fall Semester: August to December; Application Deadline: February
Spring Semester: January to May
Summer Session I: May to July
Summer Session II: May to June

ARCHITECTURE AND RELATED DEGREE PROGRAMS

Degree	Min. Yrs. to Complete	Professional Accreditation	# of FT Students	# of PT Students	# of First-Year Students	# of Degrees Conferred	Admissions Requirements
Architecture							
M. Arch	1		5	1	4	2	
M. Arch	2	NAAB	10	8	10	8	
M. Arch	3	NAAB	15	9	15	17	
M. Arch	5	NAAB	12	12	15	0	

SPECIALIZATIONS

Architectural Design   Community Design   Environment/Sustainability   Urban Planning and Design

SCHOOL PHILOSOPHY

The School of Architecture and Community Design emphasizes architecture and community design proficiency, technical competency, and applied research that constitute thorough preparation for practice into the 21st century. The School seeks to create environments in which students and faculty can:

- Experience and appreciate the poetry of architecture
- Study the myriad forms of community and human habitat
- Understand how past designs can inform future possibilities
- Master the technologies necessary to create a sound, ecological world
- Develop a vision of what such a world might be
- Assume leadership roles in helping achieve this vision

The School also aims to increase the general understanding of environmental design through undergraduate education programs, public events and exhibitions, and dialogue about emerging issues. And it develops and transmits new knowledge through advanced certificate programs and continuing education programs. The School of Architecture and Community Design emphasizes architecture and community design proficiency, technical competency, and applied research that constitute thorough preparation for practice into the 21st century.

PROGRAM DESCRIPTION

The comprehensive and rigorous curriculum prepares graduates for a full range of professional activities. The Master of Architecture is fully accredited by the National Architectural Accrediting Board. The course of study emphasizes urban architecture and related topics to take advantage of its diverse metropolitan setting in Florida's Tampa Bay. A sequence of design studios and an individually defined master's project provides the integrating element in a curriculum offering a broad mix of history, theory, technology, and professional practice, along with an array of elective courses.

Master of Architecture-post bachelors degree

1.5 Year Program. For students with a five-year professional degree in architecture. 30-credit hour track (minimum)

2 Year Program. For students with a four-year pre-professional degree in architecture. 52-credit hour track (minimum)

3+ Year Program. For students with a degree in a non-architectural field. 105-credit hour track (maximum)

Master of Architecture-no bachelor's degree
5+ Year Program

This accelerated program allows students to earn a Master of Architecture in five years of full-time study.

The first two years (67 credit hours) consist of general education and prerequisite courses.

The remaining 105 credit hours are the same as the 3+ Master of Architecture. Students are classified as undergraduate students for the first 120 credit hours, and as graduate students for the remaining hours. No bachelor's degree is awarded. Pre-professional Architecture Studies for Undergraduate Students in the USF Bachelor of Arts degree in Liberal Studies (Architecture tracks) begin taking graduate architecture classes as part of the undergraduate courses of study. (Tracks are available for honors students). The program allows undergraduate students who successfully complete required architecture courses to enter the Master of Architecture program with advanced standing.

AREAS OF FOCUS AND RESEARCH
Research

The Florida Center for Community Design and Research is a non-profit public service institute of the School of Architecture and Community Design. It was founded in 1986 to assist the citizens of Florida in the creation of more livable and sustainable communities through applied community design, multi-disciplinary research, and public education. The Florida Center provides clients with access to academic expertise, cutting-edge technology, and highly-qualified graduate student internships. Using interdisciplinary teams, the staff works with clients to ensure high quality work, transfer of technology and expertise, and enhanced graduate education.

Certificate in Community Design and Development

This graduate certificate curriculum offers an opportunity for specialized, post-professional degree studies in the emerging paradigms of theory, practice and technology of sustainable urban communities' design and development.

SPECIAL ACTIVITIES AND PROGRAMS
Lectures/Exhibits

Throughout the year, nationally and internationally known architects, planners, landscape architects, and others participate in the School's lecture series. The School also exhibits outstanding work of students, alumni/ae, and professionals at galleries at USF and elsewhere in Tampa.

Charrettes

Each fall semester students in design studios participate in a weekend design charrette. Teams of students develop solutions to urban design problems in the region.

Field Trips

Each year students in the fall term Core Design I. Students in upper-level design studios take field trips to such cities as New York, Boston, Seattle and Chicago in the spring.

Student Groups

Students at USF have access to a wide range of activities within the School of Architecture and Community Design and elsewhere in the university and community. At the school, one may join the American Institute of Architecture Students (AIAS) and the Architecture College Council. Students participate in a wide range of school governance committees and task forces.

Study-Abroad

The School sponsors annual study-abroad programs in Italy, Japan, China, other locations.

FACILITIES

The School of Architecture and Community Design is located on the main campus of the University of South Florida in Tampa. The School is adjacent to new graduate and married-student housing, a full-service all-suites hotel, and facilities of the Colleges of Engineering and College Visual and Performing Arts. Each student in the professional programs is provided with space for his or her studies while taking studio courses. The School has a computer laboratory equipped with Windows computers, a wood shop, and a small resource room has important reference and professional books. Students may check out equipment such as slide projectors, digital and video cameras for studio and class projects. The holdings for the School of Architecture and Community Design are in the main USF library.

SCHOLARSHIPS AND FINANCIAL AID

A wide range of merit- and need-based awards and scholarships are available through the school, university, and professional organizations. These include:

- Floy Damon award
- Masonry Contractors scholarship
- Faculty/staff sponsored summer travel grants
- AIA Tampa Bay chapter award
- Milo Smith scholarships
- Florida Foundation for Architecture
- H. Dean Rowe, FAIA, scholarship
- Alpha Rho Chi bronze medal
- FA/AIA bronze medal
- AIA/AAF Henry Adams medal
- Eduardo Garcia Award
- University graduate fellowships
- Graduate Assistantships

ADMINISTRATION

Ron Jones: Dean
Barton Lee: Interim Director

UNIVERSITY OF TENNESSEE–KNOXVILLE

ADDRESS

Main
University of Tennessee–Knoxville
College of Architecture & Design
1715 Volunteer Boulevard, Rm 224
Knoxville, TN 37996-2400
Tel.: 865/974-5265
Fax: 865/974-0656
www.arch.utk.edu

STUDENT AND FACULTY DEMOGRAPHICS

% of Female Students	40
% of International Students	3
% of Minority Students	10
% of Out-of-State U.S. Students	30
No. Full-Time Faculty	22
No. Part-Time Faculty	8
No. Full-Time Students	371
No. Part-Time Students	17

FINANCIAL INFORMATION

Main Source of University Funding	Public
Annual Tuition & Fees (graduate, resident)	$6,720
Annual Tuition & Fees (graduate, nonresident)	$18,962
Annual Tuition & Fees (undergraduate, resident)	$5,972
Annual Tuition & Fees (undergraduate, nonresident)	$18,174
% Students Receiving Federal Financial Aid	46
% Students Receiving University Financial Aid	40
% Students Receiving Departmental Financial Aid	16
% Students Receiving Scholarships (assistantships or fellowships)	30
Average Annual Scholarship for Department	$1,300

ACADEMIC SESSIONS

Fall Semester: August to December; Application Deadline: Undergraduate: November 1;
   Graduate: February 1

Spring Semester: January to May
Summer Session I: June to July; Summer Session II: July to August

ARCHITECTURE AND RELATED DEGREE PROGRAMS

Degree	Min. Yrs. to Complete	Professional Accreditation	# of FT Students	# of PT Students	# of First-Year Students	# of Degrees Conferred	Admissions Requirements
Architecture							
B. Arch	5	NAAB	332	15	78	50	SAT, ACT, TOEFL, Portfolio
M. Arch - 2 years	2	NAAB	11	0	9	5	Undergraduate Architecture degree, GRE, TOEFL, Portfolio, Rec. Letters, Essay
M. Arch - 3.5 years	3.5	NAAB	30	2	13	5	Undergraduate degree, GRE, TOEFL, Portfolio, Rec. Letters, Essay
M. Arch II post-professional	1.5						Prof. Architecture degree, GRE, TOEFL, Portfolio, Rec. Letters, Essay
Landscape Architecture							
M.A. LA	1.5						Undergraduate degree, GRE, TOEFL, Portfolio, Rec. Letters, Essay
M.S. LA	1.5						Undergraduate degree, GRE, TOEFL, Portfolio, Rec. Letters, Essay
MLA - 2 years	2	LAAB (2011)					Landscape Architecture/ Design Degree, GRE, TOEFL, Portfolio, Rec. Letters, Essay
MLA - 3.5 years	3.5	LAAB (2011)					Undergraduate degree, GRE, TOEFL, Portfolio, Rec. Letters, Essay
MLA II post-professional	1.5						Prof. Landscape Arch. Degree, GRE, TOEFL, Portfolio, Rec. Letters, Essay
Interior Design/Interior Architecture							
B.S. Interior Design	4	CIDA/FIDER	81	2	23	19	SAT, ACT, TOEFL, Portfolio

SPECIALIZATIONS

Architectural Design	Environment/Sustainability	Landscape Design	Theory/Criticism
Building Technology/Env. Systems	History	Sustainability	Urban Planning and Design
Community Design	Housing		

ARCHITECTURE PROGRAM SUMMARY

With a mission to educate future design professionals, the School of Architecture within the College of Architecture and Design is committed to the development of individuals with creative imagination, intellectual curiosity and technical knowledge. We educate students in design disciplines who can form independent judgments grounded in the broader contexts of intellectual traditions. We strive to provide an academic environment of respect and empowerment for our students.

UNIVERSITY SETTING

As both a flagship and land-grant institution, the University of Tennessee at Knoxville is a 550-acre campus that serves the state and nation with a broad spectrum of academic programs, public service, and the research/creative activity of its faculty. Eleven colleges enroll 20,400 undergraduates and 6,000 graduates. It is a Category I research institution, with the caliber of faculty and resources that the designation would imply. The library system is a particular strength, as is the wide variety of student support services. Knoxville is a medium-sized city in an area blessed with natural beauty and a desirable climate.

SCHOOL PHILOSOPHY

Architecture involves the study and transformation of the built environment, from the scale of furniture to the scale of the city. The goal of an architectural education is to develop a rigorous thought process that is simultaneously analytical and creative. Creative thinkers must address all aspects of the built environment, in its cultural, social, and ethical context. Undergraduate and graduate design education is based on a passionate commitment to the teaching mission.

PROGRAM DESCRIPTION

Undergraduate Program

Students begin design studio courses in their first year of study, so they receive immediate exposure to a creative and rigorous thought process in visual thinking. While the design studio is at the core of the professional program, students also take architectural history and technology courses, including computer applications. Approximately 30% of the curriculum is devoted to the humanities and electives, so students have an opportunity to explore areas of personal interest. Many students have been able to pursue minors in other subjects such as language or business. Others have laid the groundwork for pursuing additional academic degrees. Students in their fourth year of study may elect to spend one semester off campus in one of three programs organized by the college, or at any number of other international programs. At the advanced level, elective studios are offered in special topics such as advanced structures, urban design, sustainability, housing, and real estate development.

Graduate Program

The Graduate Program in Architecture offers both a professional and a post-professional graduate degree. These degrees are distinguished by the length of study required and by the nature of each degree's thesis. The M. Arch 3.5-year program is a professional degree program designed to accommodate students who come from a variety of academic backgrounds and interests. This includes students who have had little or no previous formal study in architecture. The M. Arch 2-year program (4+2) accommodates students who have received an undergraduate architectural education but have not completed the requirements for a professional degree. The M. Arch II program is a post-professional design or research degree designed for students holding an accredited professional degree in architecture, who seek to develop an area of specialization. Most

graduate-level classes are small with the student/teacher ratio in design studios approximately 12:1. The core values of the Graduate Program in Architecture are based on a design-centered curriculum that promotes personal development, ethical imperatives, critical thinking, and ecologically sustainable practices. These values are expressed in an education that challenges students to expand their awareness, to become leaders, to master the discipline, and to engage real-world problems in their cultural and social contexts with the responsibility of stewardship for the built and natural environment. The program is committed to preparing our students for leadership roles not only within the profession, but also within the broader communities they join and influence. The College recently added an intercollegiate Landscape Architecture Program to its Graduate Studies. This program offers graduate students in Architecture opportunity to substantively explore the integration of designed and naturally occurring landscapes with the built realm.

AREAS OF FOCUS AND RESEARCH

The School of Architecture offers a design-focused curriculum, with particular strengths in technology, sustainability, urban design, digital applications in design, and community design initiatives. In a spectrum of philosophical interpretations ranging from the poetic to the pragmatic, the faculty share a strong appreciation for the technology of building, believing that technical and structural considerations are a major source of architectural ideas, spatial character, expression and meaning. While respecting the core goals of design education, the school has developed a model computer-aided design program that provides all students confidence in their information technology skills. Within a research university, the College of Architecture and Design demonstrates a broad interpretation of research, scholarship, and creative activity. Design is viewed as a form of "applied research," which can be of direct benefit to communities within Tennessee. Faculty design work and creative activity have received national and international recognition. The faculty has research areas related to environmental issues and sustainability, specialized environments and materials, climate, visualization and representation, color theory, urban design, landscape architecture, medieval architecture, contemporary theory, light-weight structures, Japanese architecture, and historic preservation.

SPECIAL ACTIVITIES AND PROGRAMS

The School of Architecture is committed to providing a variety of meaningful learning opportunities beyond the classroom itself. Lectures, films, exhibits, and student organizations are all important components of a lively academic environment. Some of the most notable activities and programs are listed below.

- The Robert B. Church III Memorial Lecture Series, which exposes students to nationally and internationally prominent architects, designers, historians and theorists
- Well-developed study abroad programs, in Krakow, Poland, Weimar, Germany, Copenhagen, Denmark, Helsinki, Finland, as well as study tour courses offered during summer and mini-terms, which give students international and intercultural architecture experience
- A well-established job interview program occurring annually in the spring semester, which matches graduating students with prospective employers
- AIA Mid-term Review, an annual exhibition of student work where students have the opportunity to discuss their projects with practicing architects
- The Nashville Civic Design Center, a nonprofit organization whose mission is to improve the

quality of Nashville's built environment, provides the opportunity for students to partake in actual projects and design studies that affect the growth and development of Nashville
- The Downtown Design Studio, off-campus studio space where design studies of local conditions are conducted and public forums about civic and urban issues are held
- The Burlington Studio, an off-campus facility where students work with local communities to design and build affordable housing units
- An array of active student organizations including the Dean's Student Advisory Council, American Institute of Architecture Students, Construction Specification Institute, Tau Sigma Delta, and National Organization of Minority Architecture Students are available to students
- The Annual All-college Spring Thing (TAAST), a week-long event organized by students that features lectures, workshops, design competitions, a kick-ball tournament, and the Beaux Arts Ball
- *current*, the school's journal of student work, which is organized and co-designed by students.

FACILITIES

The award-winning Art + Architecture Building, completed in 1981, provides one of the finest facilities in the country for architecture and design students. According to the National Architecture Accreditation Board, the building is a landmark facility for the campus and sets a standard for other schools of architecture. The building is home to architecture, interior design, landscape architecture, and art students who occupy extensive studio space surrounding an open Commons space, filled with natural light.

The 400'-long Commons space visually unifies the different functions of the building. Open stairs and hallways promote interaction of students and faculty. This space contains a student cafe, auditoriums, small supply store and an open atrium area. Changing art and architecture exhibits are installed in the Ewing Gallery, the Exhibition Space, the Commons and the Sculpture Garden.

The building is home to excellent educational and instructional technology resources including 24- hour computer labs, the Materials Resource Lab, the Woodshop, the Image Center, the 3-D Digital Fabrication Center, and the Visual Resource Library. All design studios have computer network ports for the students' laptop computers, which are required.

SCHOLARSHIPS AND FINANCIAL AID

The School of Architecture is fortunate to have many loyal alumni and members of the professional community who have funded a variety of scholarships, fellowships, internships, and student prizes. Qualified students are matched with available awards by the school's scholarship committee based mostly on academic performance or financial need. In addition to scholarships, students are also eligible for paid assistantships with faculty who are working on special design and research projects. Graduate teaching assistantships are available for qualified graduate students. Students can apply for external university scholarships as well.

ADMINISTRATION

John M. McRae, FAIA: Dean
Barbara Klinkhammer, RA: Associate Dean, Interim Chair Interior Design
Mark Schimmenti, FAAR, RA: Director, School of Architecture
Mark DeKay, RA: Director Graduate Studies
Tracy W. Moir-McClean, RA: Interim Chair, Landscape Architecture

UNIVERSITY OF TEXAS AT ARLINGTON

ADDRESS

Main
University of Texas at Arlington
School of Architecture
Box 19108
601 W. Nedderman Drive
Arlington, TX 76019
Tel.: 817.272.2801
Fax: 817.272.5098
www.uta.edu/architecture

STUDENT AND FACULTY DEMOGRAPHICS

% of Female Students	40
% of International Students	5
% of Minority Students	47
% of Out-of-State U.S. Students	1
No. Full-Time Faculty	26
No. Part-Time Faculty	15
No. Full-Time Students	821
No. Part-Time Students	338

FINANCIAL INFORMATION

Main Source of University Funding	Public
Annual Tuition & Fees (graduate, resident)	$3,349
Annual Tuition & Fees (graduate, nonresident)	$5,878
Annual Tuition & Fees (undergraduate, resident)	$3,962
Annual Tuition & Fees (undergraduate, nonresident)	$7,334
% Students Receiving Federal Financial Aid	58
% Students Receiving University Financial Aid	58
% Students Receiving Departmental Financial Aid	
% Students Receiving Scholarships (assistantships or fellowships)	15
Average Annual Scholarship for Department	

ACADEMIC SESSIONS

Fall: Late August—mid-December
Spring: Mid January—mid-May
Summer: Early June—mid-August

ARCHITECTURE AND RELATED DEGREE PROGRAMS

Degree	Min. Yrs. to Complete	Professional Accreditation	# of FT Students	# of PT Students	# of First-Year Students	# of Degrees Conferred	Admissions Requirements
Architecture							
BS Arch	4		553	250	252	85	Refer to University website
M. Arch—2 years	2	NAAB	97	21	66	42	Refer to University website
M. Arch—3 years	3.5	NAAB	60	11	27		Refer to University website
Landscape Architecture							
M. Landscape Arch	3.5	CELA	54	3		16	Refer to University website
Interior Design							
BS Interior Design	4	CIDA	111	56	84	20	Refer to University website

ARCHITECTURE PROGRAM SUMMARY

The School of Architecture at the University of Texas at Arlington offers professionally accredited degrees in Architecture (4 yr BS. Arch +2 yr M. Arch and 3.5 year M. Arch), Interior Design (BS. Interior Design) and Landscape Architecture (M. Landscape Arch).

UNIVERSITY SETTING

The university is located in Arlington, mid-way between Dallas and Fort Worth, at the heart of a metropolitan area of nearly 6,000,000. Dallas/Fort Worth is one of the major regional centers in the United States with every cultural, professional, entertainment, and business opportunity nearby. Dallas/Fort Worth International Airport, 20 minutes from the school, provides easy direct access to national and overseas destinations. For the design student the area is especially rewarding. Excellent examples of the built work of many of the leading contemporary architects maybe seen and studied firsthand, including Louis Kahn, Renzo Piano, Tadao Ando, OMA, and Norman Foster. Hundreds of professional offices of all types and scales provide access to architectural practice through networking and full- or part-time employment. In addition, the Kimbell Art Museum, the Fort Worth Museum of Modern Art by Tadao Ando, the Nasher Sculpture Gardens by Renzo Plano and numerous galleries regularly bring design and the visual arts to the public.

SCHOOL PHILOSOPHY

Undergraduate Philosophy

Architecture for the undergraduate at UT-Arlington is a major course of study within a liberal education. It is the first part (4 years) of a 6-year sequence leading to the professional M Arch degree. Architecture belongs in the context of a liberal education, much as it did in the Renaissance. Architecture can be seen as both the "vehicle" and the "object" of this education. As "vehicle," architecture provides a ready avenue to the larger domain of ideas, history, and the human condition. As "object," architecture calls upon and tests our knowledge in unavoidable ways—it focuses our attitudes and abilities in order to produce tangible, concrete things. This capacity to alternately widen and narrow our vision is one of the great virtues of the field and is a source of its effectiveness as course of study. Within a broad and varied curriculum, design as a discipline is emphasized. Students are encouraged to give rich visual and formal substance to both theoretical and pragmatic ideas.

Graduate Philosophy

Architecture at the graduate level at UT-Arlington prepares for leadership positions in the profession. Building on undergraduate studies—in architecture or other subjects—the graduate program educates for the demands of a sophisticated and changing field. The program's philosophy rests on four basic premises:

- Architecture is, above all, a discipline.
- Architecture is both a culture and a profession.
- Architectural design is at the essential core of the field.

- Architecture's most fertile ideas and pressing responsibilities concern themselves with the urban condition.

What follows is an approach that accepts a diversity of sources, issues, and constraints and seeks to refract them through design. Ideas—structural and visual—acquire form, pattern, and character. The process of making and of craft is seen to be integral to design and hence, to architecture, whether as a drawing, a model, an argument, or a full-scale construction. Finally, graduate education develops a critical capacity toward one's work and the context of that work: the profession and society.

PROGRAM DESCRIPTION

The 4-year BS in Architecture degree is organized in two 2-year segments: Basic Studies and Major Studies. Liberal arts, sciences, and introductory architecture courses and design studios are the focus of the Basic Studies curriculum. The student is provided a sequence of settings in which knowledge, skill, and confidence is developed in a cumulative way. Following Basic Studies, architectural studios and courses in history, theory, and technology—along with more advanced offerings from the liberal arts and sciences—form the Major Studies curriculum. At the Major Studies level, the student progresses to more professional concerns and their appropriate responses; these years form the concentration of ideas and capabilities necessary to pursue graduate work, should the student desire to do so. The graduate program at UT-Arlington offers three distinct avenues earning the M Arch degree, each serving students with differing undergraduate backgrounds. These are called Path A, Path B, and Path C and require a minimum of 3.5, 2, and 1 years. The 3.5-year program, Path A, is for students holding a degree outside architecture. An intensive and integrated professional curriculum has been specifically developed for those with degrees in liberal arts, science, business, or other professions. A four-term intensive core of graduate courses precedes the later advanced portion of the curriculum in which there are choices among studio options and elective courses. The 2-year program, Path B, is for students holding the BS or BA degree with a major in architecture. Having begun their professional education as undergraduates, these students may choose among advanced studio options and elective courses and seminars. The 1-year program, Path C, is for students already holding a recognized professional degree in architecture such as the B Arch. These students choose among advanced studio options and elective courses and seminars. A thesis, either written or a comprehensive design study, is available for those wishing to pursue it. Advanced independent studio work may also be undertaken with a sponsoring faculty member.

RELATED PROGRAMS

The School of Architecture also offers professionally accredited programs in Interior Design (at the undergraduate level) and Landscape Architecture (as graduate study). All three disciplines are highly inte-

grated, share philosophy and faculty and some coursework.

SPECIAL ACTIVITIES AND PROGRAMS

Visiting critics in many advanced graduate studios: Teaching half-term studio segments (8 weeks), visitors come from leading academic and professional ranks in the United States and abroad. Studios, seminars and symposia in topics related to the practice of architecture involve major Dallas/Fort Worth architectural firms, and provide access to the most current ideas in the profession.

Foreign Study Options: The School provides multiple opportunities for overseas study from short two-week intersession courses, to summer long options and several semester exchanges. Summer options include Rome: Summer session in May and June is based in Rome with travels to Florence, the Veneto, and Ticino. Finland Summer Program, based in Helsinki. Central America Program, based in Guatemala in collaboration with the Universidad Francisco Marroquin.

The School recently initiated a community design/build program active in low-income communities in the region. The annual lecture series is augmented by other special events organized by AIAS and the student council, including a well attended annual Career Fair that draws participating firms from a multi-state region.

FACILITIES

The School of Architecture offers extensive, very well equipped facilities for study and research. Completed in 1984, the Architecture Building houses—in addition to studios, classrooms, and offices—a large exhibition gallery, several digital media laboratories, a large fabrication shop equipped with both traditional and digital tools for model making, prototyping and furniture building. The School maintains a digital image database of the history of architecture, and a branch library serving architecture and fine arts containing 40,000 books and 190 periodical subscriptions. The university's collection of nearly 1 million volumes is supplemented by the students' access to the University of Texas System Library containing 12 million volumes.

SCHOLARSHIPS AND FINANCIAL AID

In addition to university loans and grants, the school offers a number of graduate assistantships to qualified students for teaching or research. Competitive scholarships may entitle nonresident students to resident tuition rates. Also, part-time employment opportunities are relatively abundant in the Dallas/Fort Worth area.

ADMINISTRATION

Donald Gatzke: Dean
David Jones: Associate Dean, Graduate Advisor
Bijan Youssefzadeh: Director, Architecture Program
Pat Taylor: Director of Landscape Architecture
Rebecca Boles: Director, Interior Design

UNIVERSITY OF TEXAS AT AUSTIN

ADDRESS

Main
University of Texas at Austin
School of Architecture
Goldsmith Hall 2.308
1 University Station, B7500
Austin, TX 78712-0222
Tel.: 512.471.1922
Fax: 512.471.0716
cleary@mail.utexas.edu
soa.utexas.edu

ACADEMIC SESSIONS

Fall Semester: August to December
Spring Semester: January to May

STUDENT AND FACULTY DEMOGRAPHICS

% of Female Students	49
% of International Students	12
% of Minority Students	11
% of Out-of-State U.S. Students	38
No. Full-Time Faculty	45
No. Part-Time Faculty	12
No. Full-Time Students	605
No. Part-Time Students	49

FINANCIAL INFORMATION

Main Source of University Funding	Public
Annual Tuition & Fees (graduate, resident)	$3,500
Annual Tuition & Fees (graduate, nonresident)	$9,100
Annual Tuition & Fees (undergraduate, resident)	$3,945
Annual Tuition & Fees (undergraduate, nonresident)	$12,624
% Students Receiving Federal Financial Aid	1
% Students Receiving University Financial Aid	1
% Students Receiving Departmental Financial Aid	22
% Students Receiving Scholarships (assistantships or fellowships)	15
Average Annual Scholarship for Department	$4,500

ARCHITECTURE AND RELATED DEGREE PROGRAMS

Degree	Min. Yrs. to Complete	Professional Accreditation	# of FT Students	# of PT Students	# of First-Year Students	# of Degrees Conferred	Admissions Requirements
Architecture							
B. Arch	5	NAAB	238	0	64	50	SAT, ACT, TOEFL, Essay
BS Arch Studies	4		11	0	0	13	SAT, ACT, TOEFL, Essay
M. Arch First Professional 3.5 years	2.5	NAAB	154	7	49	33	Undergraduate degree, GRE, TOEFL, Portfolio, Rec. Letters, Essay
M. Arch Post-Professional 2 years	1.5		14	0	5	10	Prof. Architecture degree, GRE, TOEFL, Portfolio, Rec. Letters, Essay
MA Architectural History	1.5		3	1	2	3	Undergraduate degree, GRE, TOEFL, Rec. Letters, Essay
MS Architectural Studies	1.5		0	0	0	0	Undergraduate degree, GRE, TOEFL, Rec. Letters, Essay
MS Sustainable Design	2		5	3	2	4	Undergraduate degree, GRE, TOEFL, Rec. Letters, Essay
PhD Architecture	4		9	0	4	1	Undergraduate degree, GRE, TOEFL, Rec. Letters, Essay
Landscape Architecture							
MLA Landscape Architecture	2.5	LAAB	33	4	14	11	Undergraduate degree, GRE, TOEFL, Portfolio, Rec. Letters, Essay
Interior Design/Interior Architecture							
B.S. Interior Design	4	CIDA/FIDER	49	0	17	9	SAT, ACT, TOEFL, Essay
Historic Preservation							
MS Historic Preservation	2		13	4	3	4	Undergraduate degree, GRE, TOEFL, Rec. Letters, Essay

Planning							
MS Community and Regional Planning	2.5	PAB	63	24	35	29	Rec. Letters
PhD Community and Regional Planning	4.5	PAB	10	6	2	3	Rec. Letters
Urban Design							
MS Urban Design	2		3	0	2	1	Undergraduate degree, GRE, TOEFL, Portfolio, Rec. Letters, Essay

UNIVERSITY SETTING
One of the smallest of the 16 schools and colleges of U.T. Austin that enrolls 50,170 students, the school benefits from its small-school atmosphere in the center of the vast resources of a major university. The school employs up to 51 graduate students per semester as teaching assistants. The faculty is a diverse group of backgrounds emphasizing a pluralistic approach to the discipline of architecture. Austin, the state capital, enjoys the Central Texas location along the beautiful Highland Lakes on the Colorado River as it descends from the Texas Hill Country to meet the grassy expanses of the Gulf Plains. Austin's abundant undulant vegetation, its parks and trails along the many waterways and its temperate subtropical climate support a population of about 1.6 million people. Within a 200-mile range are San Antonio, Dallas/Fort Worth, Houston, Galveston, and Mexico.

SCHOOL PHILOSOPHY
The School of Architecture offers a broad range of degree options to address the individual aspirations and needs of each candidate who comes here to study. Each degree option has a relatively small number of participants and has a strong identity of its own. Together, they produce a whole that benefits significantly from the diversity of its parts.

PROGRAM DESCRIPTION
Our undergraduate programs allow students to discover architecture in the context of a broad liberal arts education and encourage a view of architecture as a diverse discipline with many different career paths. The school offers a traditional five-year Bachelor of Architecture program requiring ten sequential design studios, other professional courses, and the Basic Education Requirements. Students follow a highly structured curriculum for the first three years and, after a satisfactory qualifying review, enter the fourth year. In fourth- and fifth-year design, students select studios focusing on various aspects of architecture including interdisciplinary studios with interior design, landscape architecture, historic preservation, and urban design or programs such as the Professional Residency Program and study-abroad programs. Intensive dual degree programs combine the Bachelor of Architecture with the Bachelor of Science in Architectural Engineering, requiring six years of study, or with the Liberal Arts Honors Program (B.A. Plan II), requiring five years of study including summers. The school also offers a four-year Bachelor of Science Interior Design program requiring eight sequential design studios, other professional courses, and the Basic Education Requirements. Students follow a highly structured curriculum for the first three years and, after a satisfactory qualifying review, enter the fourth year. A four-year program leading to the Bachelor of Science in Architectural Studies, including a possible Architecture History Track, is offered for students who elect a non-professional or pre-professional undergraduate degree.

The first-professional degree program leading to the Master of Architecture may be completed in three and a half years of concentrated study by students entering with degrees in disciplines unrelated to architecture. For students entering with pre-professional degrees in architectural studies, the required hours of professional coursework are prescribed on the basis of the student's previous work. Students complete a rigorous four-semester curriculum in design and other professional subjects and, after a satisfactory qualifying review, enter advanced design studios, which are taken with advanced undergraduates. Students may earn a Certificate of Specialization in Historic Preservation, Urban Design, or Sustainable Design by completing the relevant sequence of courses. For students holding professional degrees in architecture, the Master of Architecture is a post-professional degree offering several opportunities for advanced study including Design and Theory, Historic Preservation, Sustainable Design, and Urban Design. The Master of Science in Architectural Studies degree program consists of advanced academic work in areas allied with architectural design, historic preservation, design with climate, architectural history, urban design, theory, and interdisciplinary studies. This degree program is tailored to applicants who wish to pursue research and advanced academic study in these fields for a nonprofessional degree. It is available to students with or without a professional degree in architecture.

AREAS OF FOCUS AND RESEARCH
Sustainable design, urban design, historic preservation, architectural history, transportation planning, environmental planning.

SPECIAL ACTIVITIES AND PROGRAMS
Additional opportunities include study-abroad programs, studios with a significant travel component, and internship programs. Recent international programs and studios have occurred in Brazil, Chile, China, England, India, Italy, Mexico, The Netherlands, and across Europe. The Professional Residency Program allows successful architecture students at the advanced level to engage in a six- or seven-month internship in many of the most prominent national and international architectural firms. The Community and Regional Planning Professional Internship Program allows second-year planning students to work and receive academic credit in professional planning offices or agencies. In addition, Career Services schedules on-campus interview sessions, including Career EXPO and CAREER WEEK, and offers seminars pertinent to professional life throughout the year. For those considering a career in architecture, the Summer Academy is an intensive studio program designed to prepare students for admission to an architectural degree program and encourage a personal exploration into design solutions grounded in notions of experience and perception.

In addition to the lecture series, symposia and exhibitions, school publications include a biennial Platform magazine, a bi-weekly electronic newsletter, the student-run publication of design work titled ISSUE and the annual CENTER: A Journal for Architecture and Design.

FACILITIES
The Architecture Library, the Architectural Drawings Collection, and the Center for American Architecture and Design in Battle Hall; the Materials Lab, the Conservation Lab, the Design with Climate Lab, and a Lighting Lab in West Mall Building; Information Technologies (IT), the Visual Resources Collection, the Career Services Center, the Student Lounge, and the Photo Union (darkroom) in Sutton Hall; and the Digital Fabrication and Design Lab in Goldsmith Hall.

SCHOLARSHIPS AND FINANCIAL AID
A variety of scholarship funds established by individuals, foundations, and the university are available to incoming students. These awards are based on criteria ranging from scholastic performance to financial need. Students are encouraged to apply to the Office of Student Financial Services (http://www.utexas.edu/student/finaid/) several months prior to anticipated enrollment. Teaching assistantships, research assistantships, and specific financial assistance for study-abroad programs in the School of Architecture are also available, although, in general, these are reserved for students already participating in one of the school's graduate programs. Research opportunities are available through the Center for Sustainable Development, the Dallas Urban Lab, and the Lady Bird Johnson Wildflower Center. Current and recent topics of applied research sponsored by governmental and private institutions include architectural history, urban design, park planning and design, land-use and growth management, economic development, transportation, environmental planning, sustainability, and green building design. The School of Architecture has an active minority recruitment program.

ADMINISTRATION
Frederick Steiner, PhD, FASLA: Dean
Kevin Alter: Associate Dean, Graduate Programs
Nichole Wiedemann: Associate Dean, Undergraduate Programs
Kent Butler, PhD: Associate Dean for Research and Operations

UNIVERSITY OF TEXAS AT SAN ANTONIO

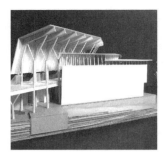

ADDRESS

Main
University of Texas At San Antonio
College of Architecture
501 W. Durango Blvd.
San Antonio, TX 78207
Tel.: 210.458.3010
Fax: 210.458.3016
gayle.nicoll@utsa.edu
www.utsa.edu/architecture

STUDENT AND FACULTY DEMOGRAPHICS

% of Female Students	42.7
% of International Students	4.7
% of Minority Students	66.3
% of Out-of-State U.S. Students	2.1
No. Full-Time Faculty	35
No. Part-Time Faculty	9
No. Full-Time Students	846
No. Part-Time Students	236

FINANCIAL INFORMATION

Main Source of University Funding	Public
Annual Tuition & Fees (graduate, resident)	$6,857
Annual Tuition & Fees (graduate, nonresident)	$21,772
Annual Tuition & Fees (undergraduate, resident)	$5,686
Annual Tuition & Fees (undergraduate, nonresident)	$12,359
% Students Receiving Federal Financial Aid	64
% Students Receiving University Financial Aid	24.3
% Students Receiving Departmental Financial Aid	12
% Students Receiving Scholarships (assistantships or fellowships)	10.9
Average Annual Scholarship for Department	$500

ARCHITECTURE AND RELATED DEGREE PROGRAMS

Degree	Min. Yrs. to Complete	Professional Accreditation	# of FT Students	# of PT Students	# of First-Year Students	# of Degrees Conferred	Admissions Requirements
Architecture							
BS Arch	4		348	86	165	38	
M. Arch	2	NAAB	11	8	7	3	
Interior Design/Interior Architecture							
B.S. Int. Design	4	CIDA/FIDER	85	34	55	12	

UNIVERSITY SETTING

Located in South Texas, San Antonio is a cultural gateway into the American Southwest.With a population of 1,328,984 as of the 2007 U.S. Census estimate, San Antonio is the second-largest city in the state of Texas, the seventh largest city in the United States, and the fourth fastest growing large city in the nation. With its major tourist attractions such as the Alamo, the River Walk, and HemisFair Park (home to the Institute of Texan Cultures and the Tower of Americas), and the various special events stationed around the city throughout the year, San Antonio provides an exceptional opportunity to experience the history, racial diversity, and multiple cultures that only this city can provide.

The College of Architecture at UTSA, located within the downtown area of San Antonio, is a laboratory for the exploration of design in relationship to issues of place, culture, regionalism, historic preservation, professional practice, sustainable design, the urban environment, international community planning, and architecture of the southwest and Mexico. Because of its status as a historic urban center, the architecture and layout of San Antonio is traditionally urban. The program's size, location, and open curriculum provide a unique atmosphere opportunity for students to study with our highly varied faculty.

SCHOOL PHILOSOPHY

Within its rich environment, the architecture program seeks to develop a synergistic relationship between the setting and the contemporary context of rapid technological change. Our graduates enter the realm of architecture in an age of wireless communications, globalization, and increasingly complex professional networks. The architecture program focuses on the threshold between the particulars of an historic setting and the universal ideas as exemplified by contemporary theory. We are committed to a holistic education which encompasses the mastery of a body of knowledge and a set of skills, as well as the honoring of a social contract to advance basic human values.

PROGRAM DESCRIPTION

Undergraduate Programs

The College of Architecture offers degrees in three major areas: Bachelor of Science in Architecture, Construction Science and Management, and Interior Design.

B.S. in Architecture

This is a four-year pre-professional degree made up of design studios and course work, and provides students with the opportunity to continue studies in a professional graduate program, a Master of Architecture (M. Arch.). Completion of the B.S. in Architecture degree allows the graduate to pursue limited architectural practice but does not fully prepare the graduate for architectural licensure.

B.S. in Construction Science and Management

Designed to meet the accreditation requirements of the American Council for Construction Education (ACCE), this program combines courses in construction science, architecture and business to educate managers for the construction industry. The College of Architecture not only strives to maintain a close partnership with the construction industry to provide quality graduates who will be in great demand, but also offers students the opportunity to continue their studies in a graduate program.

B.S. in Interior Design

Accredited by the American Council for Interior Design Accreditation (CIDA, formerly FIDER), the Bachelor of Science (B.S.) in Interior Design is a four-year professional degree centered on a collaborative studio-based curriculum grounded in architectural design.

Graduate Programs

The Master of Architecture degree program (M. Arch) offered by the Department of Architecture at UTSA is NAAB-accredited and committed to providing students with a rich education for entry into the architecture profession. Graduate students are given the opportunity to pursue a Master's degree in Architecture (M.Arch.) or a Master of Science in Architecture (M.S. Arch.).

The Master of Architecture degree is offered in two forms: the **M.Arch. 2 Program**, for students who have earned architectural degrees; and the **M.Arch. 3 Program**, for students with undergraduate degrees in fields other than architecture.

The **M.Arch. 2 program** is designed for students who have earned architectural degrees (such as a B.A., B.S., or B.E.D.) and consists of studies focused on developing the next generation of critical practitioners. This studio-based professional program is normally two years (52 credits) in length and is completed via an independently-derived, research-informed design project.

The **M.Arch. 3 program**, formerly known as Career Change Program, is designed for students with undergraduate degrees in fields other than architecture. This professional program includes one year of preparatory studies (39 credits) beginning in the summer, in preparation for the following two years (48 credits) of the Master of Architecture (M.Arch 2) program sequence.

These preparatory studies are required, as a condition of admission, to be completed in full. We encourage students from all disciplines to consider this program as a means for entering the profession of architecture.

The **Master of Science in Architecture (M.S. Arch.) program** is a non-studio research program that prepares students for careers in research, teaching, consulting, and further graduate study. Areas of research include historic preservation, urban and regional planning, architectural history, sustainability in architecture, and health and wellness. The program stresses critical writing and research methods in architecture.

AREAS OF FOCUS AND RESEARCH

The College of Architecture offers a wide range of traditional academic and community-based research including published scholarly research in architectural theory and history, community and regional design endeavors, design/build initiatives, and current topics such as sustainability and health. The faculty engages in and investigates a wide variety of topics appropriate to architectural knowledge and practice that expands the depth of the curriculum offerings. Traditional academic research and critical design practice are considered equal means of investigation into such areas as: architectural and interior design; architectural theory; historic preservation; urban and community planning; environmental analysis and policy; medieval and modern architectural history; southern American and Mexican architectural history; digital media and process; sustainable design; cultural geography; and environmental and human health.

SPECIAL ACTIVITIES AND PROGRAMS

Study Abroad

The College of Architecture offers four study-abroad programs within the spring semester and summer sessions each year: Tuscany, Italy; Barclelona, Spain; Chihuahua, Mexico; and Mexico City, Mexico. Currently the College is in the process of launching the East Asia Initiative, a new study-abroad program intended to study and experience places such as Japan. These programs substitute for regular coursework and electives.

Graduate Certificates

Degree-seeking, special graduate or non-degree seeking students from any discipline at UTSA are allowed to complete the following certificate programs: Historic Preservation, which is a process of design for continuity and the management of change within an existing historic context; and Urban and Regional Planning which provides students with an introductory understanding of the historical, social, international, and physical context of comprehensive land planning and sustainable urbanism.

Design-Build

Design-build focuses on combining the design and construction in order to train students to understand the full mechanism of architecture and the building industry, and is increasingly taking a bigger part in our curriculum as Architecture, Interior Design, and Con-

struction Science and Management are the backbone of design-build programs. The College's location in the heart of San Antonio offers a rich opportunity to work and learn in a collaborative environment.

Community Engagement

The College of Architecture, in a joint effort with the San Antonio Chapter of the American Institute of Architects (AIA), is working to develop and conduct collaborative efforts to focus on urban issues of city in the satellite space in the city.

Lecture Series

In a joint effort with the AIA San Antonio Chapter, the College sponsors a Design Lecture Series featuring leading national and international design and construction professionals. Other special activities and programs include: visiting critics and guest lecturers, public gallery exhibitions, practicum/internship (for credit) program, community design-build studios, sponsored field trips, AIAS and IIDA groups.

FACILITIES

The College of Architecture programs are housed in various UTSA Downtown Campus facilities. This placement allows the students to draw on community resources and opportunities, including the Institute of Texas Cultures, architecture and design firms, community organizations such as the San Antonio Conservation Society and the living laboratory of the city itself. The Downtown Campus is also utilized for a design lecture series and other public events. The support facilities include a library with over 20,000 titles in architecture and related areas, a multimedia center with over 100,000 slides, computer laboratory, materials library, historic preservation laboratory, galleries and a shop.

SCHOLARSHIPS AND FINANCIAL AID

The UTSA Office of Student Financial Aid and Enrollment Services administers programs to help students finance their education. Students may apply for financial assistance through scholarship, grant, work-study and loan programs. The office will consider all prospective students who complete the application process for grants and loans. Additionally, the College also awards a number of graduate assistantships and research assistantships, and competitive graduate and undergraduate scholarships on the basis of financial need, academic achievement and professional potential. These include scholarships administered through American Institute of Architects (AIA) and Texas Society of Architects (TSA) programs.

ADMINISTRATION

Robert Baron: Interim Dean
Taeg Nishimoto: Associate Dean
Dr. Gayle Nicoll: Department of Architecture Chair
Susan Lanford: Interior Design Program Coordinator
James R. Lewis: Construction Science and Management Program Coordinator

UNIVERSITY OF TORONTO

Daniels

ADDRESS

Main
University Of Toronto
John H. Daniels Faculty of Architecture,
Landscape, and Design
230 College Street
Toronto, ON M5T 1R2
Canada
Tel.: 416.978.5038
Fax: 416.971.2094
enquiry@daniels.utoronto.ca
www.daniels.utoronto.ca

ACADEMIC SESSIONS

Fall Semester: September to December; Application Deadline: January 14
Winter Quarter/Trimester: January to May

Graduate Admissions
Yvonne Hilder, Coordinator
Graduate Admissions
Recruitment, Admissions & Financial Aid
John H. Daniels Faculty of Architecture,
Landscape, and Design
University of Toronto
230 College Street
Toronto, ON M5T 1R2 Canada
Tel: 416 978 4340
Fax: 416 971 2094
yvonne.hilder@daniels.utoronto.ca

STUDENT AND FACULTY DEMOGRAPHICS

% of Female Students	45
% of Interational Students	10
% of Minority Students	
% of Out-of-State U.S. Students	
No. Full-Time Faculty	16
No. Part-Time Faculty	71
No. Full-Time Students	311
No. Part-Time Students	9

FINANCIAL INFORMATION

Main Source of University Funding	Public
Annual Tuition & Fees (graduate, resident)	C$6,956
Annual Tuition & Fees (graduate, nonresident)	C$19,845
Annual Tuition & Fees (undergraduate, resident)	
Annual Tuition & Fees (undergraduate, nonresident)	
% Students Receiving Federal Financial Aid	
% Students Receiving University Financial Aid	
% Students Receiving Departmental Financial Aid	
% Students Receiving Scholarships (assistantships or fellowships)	60
Average Annual Scholarship for Department	C$5,700

ARCHITECTURE AND RELATED DEGREE PROGRAMS

Degree	Min. Yrs. to Complete	Professional Accreditation	# of FT Students	# of PT Students	# of First-Year Students	# of Degrees Conferred	Admissions Requirements
Architecture							
Bachelor of Arts in Architectural Studies	4		224				TOEFL
Master of Architecture (M.Arch)	3.5	CACB	241	9	83	56	Undergraduate degree, TOEFL, Portfolio, Rec. Letters, Essay
Landscape Architecture							
Master of Landscape Architecture (MLA)	3		55		22	16	Undergraduate degree, TOEFL, Portfolio, Rec. Letters, Essay
Urban Design							
Master of Urban Design (MUD)	2		15		7	7	TOEFL, Portfolio, Rec. Letters, Essay

SPECIALIZATIONS

Architectural Design	Energy	Housing	Professional Practice
Art and Design	Engineering	Interior Design/Architecture	Sustainability
Building Technology/Env. Systems	Environment/Sustainability	International/Regional Architecture	Tectonics
Community Design	Graphic Design	Landscape Design	Theory/Criticism
Computer-Aided Design	History	Preservation	Urban Planning and Design

ARCHITECTURE PROGRAM SUMMARY

The John H. Daniels Faculty of Architecture, Landscape, and Design offers rigorous programs for the emerging architect, landscape architect, or urban designer. The Faculty offers intensive study focusing on the vibrant multi-ethnic, multicultural world metropolis of Toronto. It complements this local focus with teaching by faculty from Canada and elsewhere, with a wide range of enrichment programs, and with a distinguished visitor each year occupying the Frank Gehry International Visiting Chair in Architectural Design.

UNIVERSITY SETTING

Founded in 1827, the University of Toronto is Canada's largest and most distinguished university. With a long tradition of excellence, it is consistently ranked Canada's top research-intensive university. A Department of Architecture was established at the University of Toronto in 1890, making ours the first architecture program in Canada and one of the earliest on the continent. The John H. Daniels Faculty of Architecture, Landscape, and Design is located at the campus' southwest corner, surrounded by urban vitality-lively streets, diverse neighbourhoods, and great cultural institutions. As the largest city in Canada and one of the most dynamic in North America, Toronto is a thriving metropolis, providing exceptional resources for the aspiring architect, landscape architect, or urban designer to study the early 21st-century human condition. Diversity of race, religion, and lifestyle help define and set Toronto apart from other world cities.

SCHOOL PHILOSOPHY

The fields of architecture, landscape architecture, and urban design are characterized today by exceptional pressure for change. Globalization and the convergence of new media, materials, and building technologies have led to radical change in economic, technical, and aesthetic formations in the design fields. The John H. Daniels Faculty of Architecture, Landscape, and Design has a global orientation in its teaching and research while simultaneously believing in the importance of sensitively addressing local forces. In this context, the John H. Daniels Faculty of Architecture, Landscape, and Design strives to harness the potential of Toronto's distinctive multi-ethnic and multicultural society. The greater Toronto region serves as a dynamic laboratory for critical studies and the imaginative exploration of design alternatives that will be of consequence internationally. Students not only have the city to use as a resource, but also have access to Toronto's large professional design community, many of whom teach at the school. The John H. Daniels Faculty of Architecture, Landscape, and Design focus on interdisciplinary training and research will test your limits and challenge you to rethink design for the 21st century. For 118 years, graduates of our school have spread across Canada and the world as innovators and leaders in design.

PROGRAM DESCRIPTION

The John H. Daniels Faculty of Architecture, Landscape, and Design offers a BA Architectural Studies program in collaboration with the Faculty of Arts and Science. The non-professional Architectural Studies program provides major degree options for students wishing to study architecture as part of a liberal arts education. The program serves as an introduction to the discipline of architecture, focusing on current issues and emerging practices considered from critical, theoretical, and historical perspectives. Project-based courses in design and visual communication provide opportunities to learn practical, formal, and analytical skills, and are augmented by advanced courses in allied design arts, such as furniture, graphic and set design. The Architectural Studies program (BA) has concentrations in Architectural Design, and in History, Theory, Criticism.

Our 3.5-year professional Master of Architecture degree program is for individuals who have completed a bachelor's degree in any discipline with a final-year average of at least mid-B. Preference is given to individuals who have completed a balanced undergraduate education that includes study in the arts, sciences, and humanities and who demonstrate leadership potential in the field. The Master of Architecture is a rigorous and comprehensive program, preparing graduates for the full range of professional activities in architecture. It provides a thorough base of knowledge in history, theory, technology, ecology, society, and professional practice, while developing skills in design through a sequence of design courses. The core program is extensive, and students use their electives to develop an area of special skill and knowledge through independent research that culminates in a design thesis. The program aims to develop critical, creative, and independent thinking and research that responds to current design issues and societal change.

The Faculty also offers an accredited (by CSLA) three-year professional Master of Landscape Architecture program (for students with a bachelor's degree in any discipline) and a two-year post-professional Master of Urban Design program (for students with a professional degree in architecture or landscape architecture).

AREAS OF FOCUS AND RESEARCH

First and foremost, the Faculty focuses on design. A number of prominent Toronto architects in the city of Toronto are members of the faculty, and many of the faculty members have received recognition in recent international competitions.

For example, Professors Petricone, Shnier, Sampson, and Blackwell were winners in the 2007 Toronto Urban Design Awards program; Professor Sampson's professional firm won the 2007 "Firm of the Year Award" of the Royal Architectural Institute of Canada; Professors el-Khoury, Fong and Levit were finalists in the 2007 competition for an International Museum of Contemporary Art and Architectural Planning in Shenzhen, China; and Professors Alissa and Peter North won second prize in the 2007 Envisioning Gateway competition for a design for a national park in New York State.

Of increasing prominence in many of our studios are issues of sustainability in architecture.

Notable recent areas of research by faculty members have included landscape urbanism; built-form studies for urban growth centres in Ontario; environmental retrofitting of facades of buildings from the 1950s and '60s; digital fabrication and computer visualization. Other scholarly productions have included publications on a number of aspects of modernism from the 18th century to the present.

SPECIAL ACTIVITIES AND PROGRAMS

The Global Architecture (GA) program offers graduate students the opportunity to study abroad within a design- and research-oriented summer program. Courses are taught by John H. Daniels Faculty of Architecture, Landscape, and Design faculty members, as well as leading architects and faculty from abroad. GA identifies and studies areas in flux, where the relations between local conditions and global modernizing strategies need to be negotiated. In each venue, the program seeks to identify the distinctive features of the architectural and urban culture of the place and how these features are formed and transformed by design, planning, and historical forces. GA programs have been held in Havana, Barcelona, the Netherlands, and China.

The Professional Experience Program (PEP) provides graduate students with the opportunity to select from a list of firms practicing in architecture and landscape architecture, apply for work placement, and gain professional experience in their field of study. The PEP Award provides students with access to challenging and exciting work experience in award-winning, internationally acclaimed offices, and the PEP Job Bulletin connects a wide variety of international and local offices with students seeking job opportunities.

The Collaborative Program in Knowledge Media Design provides a specialization for graduate students from a variety of academic backgrounds to engage in the design, prototyping, evaluation, and use of media intended to support and enhance communication, learning, and the creation of knowledge. John H. Daniels Faculty of Architecture, Landscape, and Design evening public lecture series runs from September to April.

FACILITIES

Facilities include 24-hour-access studios equipped with individual work spaces and a wireless Local Area Network (LAN), lecture and seminar rooms, the Shore + Moffat Library, The Eric T. Arthur Gallery, the Larry Wayne Richards Project Gallery, the Centre for Landscape Research, a prototyping laboratory, a photography/audiovisual studio, a woodworking shop with a laser cutter, and the student-run Café 059. Our facilities include labs equipped with CAD-ready computers and peripherals, connected by a high-speed network. The University of Toronto's excellent facilities include the Athletic Centre three blocks north and Robarts Library, the third-ranked research library in North America. The John H. Daniels Faculty of Architecture, Landscape, and Design is located within easy access to public transport and the resources of the city, provincial government, and metropolitan agencies.

SCHOLARSHIPS AND FINANCIAL AID

The John H. Daniels Faculty of Architecture, Landscape, and Design graduate students are eligible for financial support from a number of sources, including the John H. Daniels Faculty of Architecture, Landscape, and Design admissions fellowships, University of Toronto Fellowships, Ontario Graduate Scholarships, teaching assistantships, and work study positions. All applicants are automatically considered for University-based financial aid and need make no special application. The generous Howarth-Wright Graduate Fellowship supports one student in independent study at Taliesin West in Arizona.

ADMINISTRATION

George Baird: Dean
Charles Waldheim: Associate Dean/Director,
   Master of Landscape Architecture/ Coordinator of
   Graduate Studies
Komala Prabhakar: Assistant Dean,
   (Administration)/Registrar
Pina Petricone: Director, Master of Architecture
Robert Levit: Director, Master of Urban Design
Tom Bessai: Director, BA Architectural Studies
Shane Williamson: Director, Computing Operations
Larry Wayne Richards: Coordinator, The Eric Arthur
   Gallery/Co-Coordinator, Professional Experience
   Program
John Danahy: Coordinator of Research/Co-Director,
   Centre for Landscape Research
Irene Puchalski: Librarian

UNIVERSITY OF UTAH

ADDRESS

Main
University of Utah
College of Architecture and Planning
375 S. 1530 E Room 235
Salt Lake City, UT 84112-9154
Tel.: 801.581.8254
Fax: 801.581.8217
www.arch.utah.edu

STUDENT AND FACULTY DEMOGRAPHICS

% of Female Students	30
% of International Students	4
% of Minority Students	11
% of Out-of-State U.S. Students	16
No. Full-Time Faculty	15
No. Part-Time Faculty	27
No. Full-Time Students	312
No. Part-Time Students	64

FINANCIAL INFORMATION

Main Source of University Funding	Public
Annual Tuition & Fees (graduate, resident)	$7,500
Annual Tuition & Fees (graduate, nonresident)	$20,500
Annual Tuition & Fees (undergraduate, resident)	$4,500
Annual Tuition & Fees (undergraduate, nonresident)	$16,500
% Students Receiving Federal Financial Aid	40
% Students Receiving University Financial Aid	5
% Students Receiving Departmental Financial Aid	30
% Students Receiving Scholarships (assistantships or fellowships)	30
Average Annual Scholarship for Department	

ACADEMIC SESSIONS

Fall Semester: August to December;
  Application Deadline: January (Grad) or March (Undergrad)
Spring Semester: January to May;
  Application Deadline: Fall Admission Only

Summer Session I: May to June
  Application Deadline: Fall Admission Only
Summer Session II: June to August;
  Application Deadline: Fall Admission Only

ARCHITECTURE AND RELATED DEGREE PROGRAMS

Degree	Min. Yrs. to Complete	Professional Accreditation	# of FT Students	# of PT Students	# of First-Year Students	# of Degrees Conferred	Admissions Requirements
Architecture							
BS Arch	4		94	0	45	46	
M. Arch 3 +	3	NAAB	45		15	15	Undergraduate degree, TOEFL, Portfolio, Rec. Letters
M. Arch	2	NAAB	90		45	45	Undergraduate Architecture degree, TOEFL, Portfolio, Rec. Letters
Master of Science in Architecture	1		2		1	1	Prof. Architecture degree, TOEFL, Portfolio, Rec. Letters
Historic Preservation							
Certificate in Historic Preservation	1			5	2	1	Undergraduate degree, TOEFL, Portfolio, Rec. Letters
Planning							
Bachelor of Urban Planning	4						
Master of Urban and Metropolitan Planning	2		50		25	15	TOEFL, Rec. Letters

SPECIALIZATIONS

Architectural Design	Energy	International/Regional Architecture	Tectonics
Building Information Modeling	Environment/Sustainability	Preservation	Theory/Criticism
Building Technology/Env. Systems	History	Sustainability	Urban Planning and Design
Computer-Aided Design			

ARCHITECTURE PROGRAM SUMMARY

The University of Utah offers the best of both worlds, a large research one institution and a small school with plenty of contact between students and faculty. The undergraduate program is the place where students build a basic knowledge of the many sides of architecture. The graduate program allows students to choose their path through the program allowing them to specialize in their own interests in architecture. The program offers many unique features including a design build program on the Navajo Nation, an academic exchange with an architectural school in Argentina, and many travel experiences throughout the world. Furthermore, the University of Utah is located in an incredibly beautiful part of the country which allows for many outdoor activities including skiing, snow boarding, cross country skiing, hiking, mountain biking and exploring of the natural beauty of the Rocky Mountain West.

UNIVERSITY SETTING

The University of Utah is a major research university (26,000 students) centrally located within the dynamic and growing city of Salt Lake. Salt Lake rests in a beautiful and fragile ecology of alpine mountains and deserts, offering challenging building conditions and a wide variety of recreational opportunities. The intimate size of the professional program in architecture (approximately 180 students) creates informal and personal working relationships within the context of a highly active and diverse university community. Students holding a four-year pre-professional degree are encouraged to apply to the highly regarded two-year Master of Architecture program.

SCHOOL PHILOSOPHY

The architecture program fosters individual development and creativity within an intimate-scale school environment. The faculty and students support an ethical agenda, in which architecture is seen as defined by a humanistic response to the systems of the urban setting, the historical and cultural vernacular (ordinary buildings and places), and the natural (beautiful/delicate/dangerous) environment. Students are challenged to view architecture in an interdisciplinary context, where answers to complex problems may be found outside the traditional discipline.

PROGRAM DESCRIPTION

The undergraduate experience is divided into two, two-year programs of study. The first two years focus around general education, exploring a variety of subject areas and methodologies of critical inquiry. At the same time, students take courses that are directed toward a strong foundation in the technical, graphic and design areas of architecture. Following admission to the major, the junior and senior years are a highly focused study of architecture. As a design-centered curriculum, the coursework undergirds and amplifies consistent studio exploration with strong digital work, history and theory, as well as the technologies and methods of making buildings. Students with an undergraduate pre-professional degree in architecture from Utah or elsewhere may apply to enter the two-year graduate professional degree program. Recognizing the maturity and background of the graduate student, the program emphasizes choice and flexibility allowing each student to tailor a program that reflects their particular interests and intentions. Students do this by selecting courses from a variety of offerings in each of several areas of study: Design studio, communications, structures, technology, history, theory, professional practice and elective work. A final master's project represents the culmination of the program. It is a comprehensive synthesis of all the program's content and is the student's best opportunity to explore design philosophy. Students with a baccalaureate degree in a subject other than architecture may apply to enter the "three-plus" graduate program, which begins with an intensive 1.5-year course of study before the standard graduate degree program.

AREAS OF FOCUS AND RESEARCH

Focus

The University of Utah is well known as a pioneer in digital media, and our students and faculty have developed a natural strength in this area. However, traditional modes of expression such as drawing, modeling and other graphic communication are also strengths of the program. Digital technology and traditional visualization is integrated into all areas of the curriculum and school facilities; it is the foundation of several major research initiatives and is a focus of post-professional graduate work. The second focus of the school is the study of ordinary and historical environments and their relationship to the natural environment. The school offers a wide range of history courses from Scandinavian to Japanese architecture, with a particular focus on architecture and urban form of the American west.

Research

The school maintains an active research agenda in two broad areas: visualization and vernacular/historical studies. Research is underway in the interpretation of the drawings and sketches of well-known architects, the use of traditional models, and innovative use of computer visualization to examine historical sites. A program of computer graphic and visualization research is sponsored by the Kajima Corporation of Tokyo, Japan. Architecture faculty are working with interdisciplinary teams to explore digital representation of complex data sets. In vernacular studies, the Western Regional Architecture Program allows students and faculty to study the built landscape of the American West through research and publication. Other faculty study urban vernacular morphology.

SPECIAL ACTIVITIES AND PROGRAMS

The Utah program offers students a variety of special opportunities to enrich the basic curriculum. A Design/Build program takes students into the community to construct projects of their own design. This program is known as the Design/Build Bluff program and is located just off the Navajo Nation in the four courners region of the state. Special opportunity exists for foreign study in South America through a strong exchange program with Universidad Nacional del Litoral in Santa Fe, Argentina. Long-standing relationships also exist for study in Japan, as well as with European universities. An active distinguished speakers series and exhibition program is featured each year. Writing in architecture is celebrated through the Louis Symposium, which annually publishes an essay by a major architectural theorist together with student responses. A joint M.Arch./M.B.A. program is offered. A variety of student activities are sponsored by an extremely active chapter of the American Institute of Architecture Students.

FACILITIES

The Architecture Building, located in proximity to the Department of Art and the Utah Museum of Fine Arts, is an excellent facility. All studios are fully networked with students maintaining their own platforms and the school providing all peripherals. Labs with high-end platforms and special equipment, a shop equipped for wood and metal work, an excellent exhibition hall, a reference and slide/video library and reading room, as well as lecture, seminar, office and administrative spaces are all conveniently located.

SCHOLARSHIPS AND FINANCIAL AID

Financial assistance is available to advanced undergraduate and all graduate students through the School of Architecture in the form of scholarships, teaching assistantships and research assistantships. Over 50% of graduate students receive some form of assistance from the school. Many scholarships are provided by local architectural offices, who maintain an excellent relationship with the program and frequently hire its graduates. The Roger Bailey Traveling Fellowship for foreign travel is awarded each year.

ADMINISTRATION

Brenda C. Scheer, AIA, AICP: Dean
Peter B. Atherton: Associate Dean
Patrick J. Tripeny, RA: Director, School of Architecture

UNIVERSITY of VIRGINIA

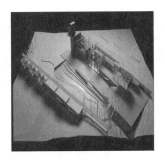  

ADDRESS

Main
University of Virginia
School of Architecture
Campbell Hall
PO Box 400122
Charlottesville, VA 22904-4122
Tel.: 434.924.1493
Fax: 434.982.2678
www.arch.virginia.edu

STUDENT AND FACULTY DEMOGRAPHICS

% of Female Students	54
% of International Students	10
% of Minority Students	18
% of Out-of-State U.S. Students	51
No. Full-Time Faculty	22
No. Part-Time Faculty	10
No. Full-Time Students	362
No. Part-Time Students	0

FINANCIAL INFORMATION

Main Source of University Funding	Public
Annual Tuition & Fees (graduate, resident)	
Annual Tuition & Fees (graduate, nonresident)	
Annual Tuition & Fees (undergraduate, resident)	
Annual Tuition & Fees (undergraduate, nonresident)	
% Students Receiving Federal Financial Aid	40
% Students Receiving University Financial Aid	
% Students Receiving Departmental Financial Aid	
% Students Receiving Scholarships (assistantships or fellowships)	
Average Annual Scholarship for Department	

ARCHITECTURE AND RELATED DEGREE PROGRAMS

Degree	Min. Yrs. to Complete	Professional Accreditation	# of FT Students	# of PT Students	# of First-Year Students	# of Degrees Conferred	Admissions Requirements
Architecture							
BS Arch	4		306	0	87	59	
M. Arch	3	NAAB	28	0	10	5	
M. Arch	2	NAAB	25	0	13	10	
M. Arch post-professional	1		3	0	2	3	Professional Architecture degree

SPECIALIZATIONS

Community Design
Computer-Aided Design

Environment/Sustainability

History

Preservation

UNIVERSITY SETTING

The University of Virginia is distinctive among institutions of higher education. Founded by Thomas Jefferson in 1819, the University sustains the ideal of developing leaders, through education, who are well prepared to help shape the future of the nation. It is consistently ranked as one of the strongest public universities in the country. The University is renewing its commitment to the Fine and Performing Arts with current plans for a new arts precinct.

SCHOOL PHILOSOPHY

Design is the central mode of inquiry in architecture. Graduate and undergraduate students investigate vital issues that shape our built environment, representing their ideas through design. Design interprets the past and projects an ethical future for urban and rural landscapes. Students are immersed in a studio culture that values the artful making of inventive physical and digital representations of cities, buildings and landscapes. Students have the advantage of a close affiliation with Landscape Architecture, Architectural History and Planning. We endeavor to provide students with the skills needed to assume leadership roles in architecture and other disciplines that engage the physical environment.

PROGRAM DESCRIPTION

The Bachelor of Science in Architecture Program is a rigorous pre-professional curriculum with a strong liberal arts component. The prime objective of the first three years is to provide a framework for the study of contemporary culture through observation, analysis, and design of the built environment. This exploration uses design as a mode of critical inquiry from the scale of the city to the scale of the hand while maintaining its focus on the value of this effort to the community and the land, both immediate and extended. The curriculum is based on the foundation of a liberal arts education formed broadly during the first two years of study, while subjects directly related to making architecture are pursued in the third year. Students entering the Program in Architecture follow one curriculum for their first three years. Starting in their second year, the strategic choices of electives, minors and concentrations will prepare the student to pursue a variety of disciplines and careers at the graduate level. The Master of Architecture curriculum emphasizes strong foundation studies in design with support courses in architectural history, theory, building, and technology. To gain a broader understanding of the relationships within and parallel to the field of architecture, students take courses in Architectural History, Landscape Architecture, and Urban and Environmental Planning. The Department is committed to the development of architectural pedagogy and upper-level graduate students are encouraged, through an optional teaching elective, to expand their knowledge by serving as teaching assistants to undergraduate design, theory or technology courses. The Master of Architecture Program attracts a diverse range of students with undergraduate degrees in liberal arts as well as architecture. After an introductory summer session, students with liberal arts degrees typically complete their courses in six semesters, while those with pre-professional degrees frequently gain advanced standing. A two-semester Master of Architecture Post-Professional Degree Program, directly tailored to the interests of each student, is available for those with an undergraduate professional degree in architecture. Students who wish to obtain the Master of Architecture degree should have at least a 3.0 cumulative grade point average with a 3.5 average in design studios. Admission to the Master of Architecture programs is extremely competitive.

AREAS OF FOCUS AND RESEARCH
Research

Our faculty members pursue research in urban design, building technology, sustainability, computer graphics and architectural and urban theory. A limited number of research assistantships are available.

SPECIAL ACTIVITIES AND PROGRAMS

At the graduate level, a certificate program is offered in Historic Preservation, and a concentration is available in Sustainable Design. Dual master's degree opportunities with Landscape Architecture, Planning and Architectural History are increasingly popular. Undergraduate students may pursue minors and concentrations in a variety of areas, including Urban Studies. The majority of students at both the undergraduate and graduate levels take advantage of the numerous study-abroad opportunities.

FACILITIES

The Architecture programs are based in Campbell Hall, a short walk from Jefferson's Lawn. The Fiske Kimball Fine Arts Library, also located in Campbell Hall, is one of the finest architectural research libraries in the nation. Students have access to a woodshop, photography darkroom and computer labs. New additions to the east and south of Campbell Hall will be opening in summer 2008, providing further exhibition and studio space, technology labs, seminar spaces, and faculty offices. The Fine Arts Cafe specializes in dishes produced from locally grown, organic, and fair trade ingredients.

SCHOLARSHIPS AND FINANCIAL AID

Financial support is available to graduate students through scholarships, loans and the federal work-study program. The school-funded partial tuition scholarships are awarded based on merit and need. Undergraduates receive need-based scholarships and loans through the University's Office of Financial Aid.

ADMINISTRATION

Karen Van Lengen: Dean
Craig Barton, AIA: Chair, Department of Architecture & Landscape Architecture

UNIVERSITY OF WASHINGTON

ADDRESS

Main
University of Washington
Department of Architecture
208 Gould Hall
Box 355720
Seattle, WA 98195-5720
Tel.: 206.543.4180
Fax: 206.616.4992
bainfo@u.washington.edu (ugrad)
archinfo@u.washington.edu (grad)
depts.washington.edu/archdept

STUDENT AND FACULTY DEMOGRAPHICS

% of Female Students	48
% of International Students	8
% of Minority Students	19
% of Out-of-State U.S. Students	31
No. Full-Time Faculty	26
No. Part-Time Faculty	11
No. Full-Time Students	211
No. Part-Time Students	11

FINANCIAL INFORMATION

Main Source of University Funding	Public
Annual Tuition & Fees (graduate, resident)	$10,419
Annual Tuition & Fees (graduate, nonresident)	$22,464
Annual Tuition & Fees (undergraduate, resident)	$6,385
Annual Tuition & Fees (undergraduate, nonresident)	$22,131
% Students Receiving Federal Financial Aid	53
% Students Receiving University Financial Aid	43
% Students Receiving Departmental Financial Aid	28
% Students Receiving Scholarships (assistantships or fellowships)	32
Average Annual Scholarship for Department	$7,100

ACADEMIC SESSIONS

Fall Quarter: September to December
Application Deadline: January 15

Winter Quarter: January to March
Spring Quarter: March to June

ARCHITECTURE AND RELATED DEGREE PROGRAMS (2007 - 2008)

Degree	Min. Yrs. to Complete	Professional Accreditation	# of FT Students	# of PT Students	# of First-Year Students	# of Degrees Conferred	Admissions Requirements
Architecture							
BA in Arch Studies	4		98		49	43	
M. Arch—1+ year	1		2	0		2	
M. Arch— 2+ year	2.25	NAAB	49	2	19	21	
M. Arch—3+ year	3.25	NAAB	59	6	25	19	
MS Arch	2		3	3		4	
PhD in the Built Environment	3		23	0	4	2	
Other							
Arch/CM Dual Degree	5		14		N/A	2	

SPECIALIZATIONS

Architectural Design
Art and Design
Building Information Modeling
Building Technology/Env. Systems
Community Design

Computer-Aided Design
Energy
Engineering
Environment/Sustainability
History

Housing
International/Regional Architecture
Landscape Design
Photography
Preservation

Professional Practice
Sustainability
Tectonics
Theory/Criticism
Urban Planning and Design

ARCHITECTURE PROGRAM SUMMARY

The faculty, staff, and students of the Department of Architecture value excellence in research and teaching, the traditions of architecture within the context of social and technological change, the continuing legacy of craft in the making of architecture, an activist and community-based design process, and ethical action used to address human and environmental concerns. The department provides leadership in contemporary issues of design to the college, the university, and the region through innovative research and teaching and interdisciplinary collaboration.

UNIVERSITY SETTING

The University of Washington is the oldest state-assisted institution of higher learning on the Pacific Coast. Located between Lake Washington and Lake Union, the Seattle campus and environs form a distinctive enclave within a city that is one of the most picturesque in the nation. The campus is within minutes of downtown Seattle, which is the central business district and cultural hub for a growing metropolis of approximately 3 million people. The UW has earned an international reputation for its research and graduate programs. Since 1969, the university has ranked among the top five institutions in the nation in receipt of federal awards. Since 1974, it has been the number one public university in America in receiving federal support for research and training.

There are over 4,000 teaching and research positions at the University of Washington and a total faculty and staff of 27,600. Student enrollment at the university's main campus in Seattle is over 39,000, of which about one fourth are graduate and professional students. The freshman class entering in 2007 had an average high school grade point of 3.69, with an average SAT score, math and verbal combined, of 1231.

The Seattle campus is made up of seventeen major schools and colleges. The University of Washington Libraries system is one of the largest research libraries in North America, with one of the most innovative and well-integrated electronic campus information networks in the world. Members of the university's teaching and research faculty are known nationally and internationally. The University of Washington is one of the major seats of learning and research in the western United States.

SCHOOL PHILOSOPHY

The core value of the department is design—a fundamentally integrative activity that incorporates ethical, cultural, and ecological values with emerging technologies and advanced areas of research. We believe in a culture of creative research and teaching where design is a vehicle for research, and research is a vehicle for design. We value our presence in a multidisciplinary college within a public research university, and critically engage our city as a physical, cultural and ecological system. We also recognize the importance of diversity broadly construed to include the range of our research and teaching interests as well as the composition of our faculty and student body.

The Department of Architecture is a community of educators, scholars, and professional architects. We advance the discipline and practice of architecture by educating architects who practice in a manner responsive and responsible to society, culture and the environment. We advance architectural knowledge through research, scholarship, and critical practice, and use this knowledge to benefit local, regional, national and global communities.

PROGRAM DESCRIPTION

The Department of Architecture is the largest of four departments in the College of Architecture and Urban Planning—Architecture, Landscape Architecture, Urban Planning, and Construction Management—with ap-

proximately 200 students, and more than 30 permanent faculty. The department offers a B.A. in Architectural Studies, an accredited M.Arch. for 2+ and 3+ year students, a 1+ year post-professional M.Arch., an M.S. in Architecture, and certificates in Design Firm Management and Leadership, Design Computing, and Lighting Design. The department also contributes to interdisciplinary certificate programs in Historic Preservation, and Urban Design as well as a college-wide Ph.D. in the Built Environment.

The B.A. in Architectural Studies program prepares students for graduate work in architecture and for a wide variety of opportunities in other fields. It is comprised of two, two-year sequences. The first includes preparatory architectural coursework and courses devoted to satisfying general education requirements. In the first two years students build their critical thinking and communication skills, gain broad exposure to other disciplines, and build an academic foundation essential to successful study in architecture. There is a competitive admissions process for the second two-year sequence. At this level, coursework provides a firm foundation in the historical, theoretical, technological, and environmental forces that influence architectural design.

The accredited M.Arch. degree program educates students already grounded in the liberal arts to become registered, licensed architects who assume enlightened, responsible, and imaginative roles in society. Design studio projects in the M.Arch. program are often set within urban areas or natural settings in the Puget Sound region and aim to foster and respond to its distinctive sense of place. In addition, many studios focus on issues surrounding the making of architecture—tectonics, design/build, wood and metal craft—this reflects a strong craft heritage in the region. Studios also frequently include a significant community service component, reflecting the department's commitment to the people of the city and the region. The requirements of the M.Arch. vary depending upon the candidate's academic and professional background.

The M.S. in Architecture offers an advanced degree with research concentrations in Design Computing or History and Theory. Students in Design Computing work in the Design Machine Group (DMG), a collaborative research studio environment aimed at developing ideas that will shape the future of design and information technology. Students in History and Theory develop a research concentration in the architectural, cultural, and political forces that have shaped the continuing discourse of modernity in architecture.

AREAS OF FOCUS AND RESEARCH

The UW Department of Architecture places particular emphasis on design, especially in the context of Seattle and the Pacific Northwest. The regional heritage of craft, finely-detailed design, and an appreciation for the natural setting and the roles architecture plays in it have all contributed to the broad regional ethos of the department. The department also benefits from a strong relationship with the Seattle architectural profession, with a number of leading professionals as permanent faculty, many others who teach on a part-time basis, as well as an active professional advisory group. In addition to its strong regional connections, the department faculty contribute to national and international issues relating to sustainability, modernity, and globalization.

The University of Washington is one of the leading research institutions in the United States. Architecture faculty are involved in research in design computing, design and education, building science (lighting, acoustics), design/ build, cultural studies, architectural history, urban design, and other areas. Department faculty lead the Design Machine Group (DMG) and the Center for Environment, Education and Design Studies (CEEDS),

and the Integrated Design Lab (IDL). The College of Architecture & Urban Planning supports significant research in planning, landscape, and construction as well.

SPECIAL ACTIVITIES AND PROGRAMS

The Department of Architecture hosts a wide range of activities that enhance its degree programs. Specialized design studios each year connect students to local and international communities, and give them opportunities to develop highly specialized skills. Groups like CEEDS and AIAS connect people in the department with other academic, cultural and professional worlds. Each year, department publications, *Column 5* and *Skin*, disseminate faculty and student scholarship and design work. Regular exhibitions and lectures infuse new design ideas and visions into the department.

The Department of Architecture offers many opportunities for international study. Each fall the department offers full-time study, including design studio, coursework, and field study, at the University of Washington Rome Center located in the Palazzo Pio, in the city's historic center. The department also offers a regular summer program in Scandinavia. Other programs include summer study in Switzerland, full-time study in India, as well as design/build studios with the Yakama Nation in central Washington. Students can also take part in exchanges with universities in Scandinavia (through the Valle Scholarship Program and the Scan/Design fellowship program); Kobe, Japan; and Liverpool, England. Architecture students can also take advantage of the many international study programs offered by departments in the College of Architecture and Urban Planning, as well as exchanges offered by the University of Washington's Office of International Education.

FACILITIES

The Department of Architecture at the University of Washington occupies two major buildings on the UW campus, Gould Hall and Architecture Hall. The department also provides studio and thesis space in the Gould Hall Annex and the Community Design Building, just west of Gould Hall. The college is centered primarily in Gould Hall, where a large central skylit atrium and coffee shop serves as a gathering place for the college community. Gould Hall also houses shared college facilities including the Architecture and Urban Planning library, digital commons, wood and metal shop, photography laboratory, visual resources collection, classrooms, and the dean's office, as well as spaces for the Departments of Urban Design & Planning and Landscape Architecture. Architecture Hall was designed in 1907 by Howard & Galloway of San Francisco and is one of the last remaining buildings from the Alaska Yukon Pacific Exposition of 1909. It was extensively remodeled in 2006–2007 and now houses the Department of Construction Management, Department of Architecture studios, exhibition spaces, faculty offices, university classrooms, computer facilities, and a coffee shop.

SCHOLARSHIPS AND FINANCIAL AID

The department awards a limited number of scholarships and assistantships each spring quarter for the following academic year. Most awards are based on financial need. Although they are normally available only to students currently enrolled in the graduate program in architecture at the time of the awards, the department has been able to use some scholarships in the recruitment of students applying to the M. Arch degree program.

ADMINISTRATION

Daniel S. Friedman, PhD, FAIA: Dean
David E. Miller, FAIA: Chair
Alex Anderson, PhD: Associate Chair

UNIVERSITY OF WATERLOO

ADDRESS

Main
University of Waterloo
School of Architecture
7 Melville Street South
Cambridge, ON N1S 2H4
Canada
Tel.: 519.888.4567
Fax: 519.622.3525
www.architecture.uwaterloo.ca
info@architecture.uwaterloo.ca

STUDENT AND FACULTY DEMOGRAPHICS

% of Female Students	
% of International Students	
% of Minority Students	
% of Out-of-State U.S. Students	
No. Full-Time Faculty	17
No. Part-Time Faculty	14
No. Full-Time Students	240
No. Part-Time Students	

FINANCIAL INFORMATION

Main Source of University Funding	Public
Annual Tuition & Fees (graduate)	
Annual Tuition & Fees (graduate, nonresident)	
Annual Tuition & Fees (undergraduate, resident)	
Annual Tuition & Fees (undergraduate, nonresident)	
% Students Receiving Federal Financial Aid	
% Students Receiving University Financial Aid	
% Students Receiving Departmental Financial Aid	
% Students Receiving Scholarships (assistantships or fellowships)	
Average Annual Scholarship for Department	

ACADEMIC SESSIONS

Fall Quarter/Trimester: September to December
Winter Quarter/Trimester: January to April

Spring Quarter/Trimester: May to August

ARCHITECTURE AND RELATED DEGREE PROGRAMS							
Degree	Min. Yrs. to Complete	Professional Accreditation	# of FT Students	# of PT Students	# of First-Year Students	# of Degrees Conferred	Admissions Requirements
Architecture							
M. Arch		CACB					

UNIVERSITY SETTING

Founded in 1957, Waterloo has come to be recognized as one of the best and most innovative post-secondary institutions in Canada. While its reputation rests on its pioneering of the cooperative form of education and the application of computers in university teaching and research, it is a comprehensive university with six faculties. Situated on a verdant 1,000-acre campus on the north side of the twin cities of Kitchener/Waterloo, the university has grown to be the eighth largest in Canada with an enrollment of 16,000 full- and 8,000 part-time students. The area is becoming well known for high-quality design; the region is also gaining a reputation for environmental-and ecosystem-based land use planning. The twin cities have a combined population of 250,000 and are located 100 kilometers west of Toronto. Easily accessible by bus, train, and automobile, Toronto is the focus of much of the design work in the school, the source of part-time instructors and critics, and the site of practice for a great many graduates. Waterloo, however, is not a metropolitan school; students' lives are focused on the academic program and the design studio. At the same time, the school aims to create opportunities in a world far wider than that represented by the glow of the metropolis on the horizon.

SCHOOL PHILOSOPHY

The Waterloo School of Architecture is a professional school dedicated to providing the best possible preparation for a career in architecture. But any simple axiality implied by this statement must quickly be qualified, for while the school is profoundly linked to practice by its aims and by virtue of the co-op program, it is also firmly committed to the proposition that architecture is a cultural praxis, and thus, that in the education of the architect, there must be continuous components of humanistic study, critical discourse, environmental theory, and open and speculative design activity. Crucial as well is wide experience in both traditional and contemporary techniques of visualization. Waterloo would contend that these tools are the most useful in confronting the realities of diminished opportunity in traditional practice and in bringing the skills of the architect to bear in a world much in need of design, but virtually innocent of its value.

PROGRAM DESCRIPTION

The School of Architecture at Waterloo is an outstanding nationally and internationally respected design school. It attracts top students and is dedicated to educating the best young architects in the world.

The School is located in a splendid historic building - the former Riverside Silk Mill - located in the heart of the old Galt neighbourhood of Cambridge. Situated along the banks of the Grand River, the former industrial building provides wonderful spaces for design studios, labs, and classrooms. It also includes a superb design library, exhibition galleries, public auditorium, and cafe.

As part of the historic downtown core of Galt, set within the larger City of Cambridge, the location is extremely attractive for a School of Architecture. The urban landscape in the surrounding community is one of the most beautiful in Ontario. There is a marvellous stock of heritage buildings nearby and the Grand River is a powerful presence, a designated Heritage River and the principal element in a diverse system of natural spaces within the City of Cambridge.

Students are immersed in the urban setting by living in the community surrounding the School. Architecture students often find that the structured nature of residence doesn't suit their schedule in the program and that they prefer the flexibility of living off campus. Students have access to recreational facilities in Cambridge as well as to services on the main UW campus. The Off-Campus Housing office at UW can provide a list of rental accommodations in Cambridge.

Working with colleagues in related professions, our professors and students will make the UW School of Architecture in Cambridge a dynamic centre of research and teaching in construction, development, built heritage, "green" architecture, visualization, prototyping, and computer assisted design.

For several years, the School of Architecture was limited in studio and classroom space. A Cambridge-based group of business owners and friends of the School of Architecture approached the University with the idea of providing a new home for the School. The Cambridge Consortium, as the group became known, spearheaded the School's fundraising drive to cover a portion of the $27 million cost of creating the new School. The University now has a regional presence and a wonderful building in which to teach Architecture, and the City of Cambridge benefits from having a university campus with 400 students, staff, and faculty in the downtown core of Galt.

The Professional Degree offered by the School of Architecture at the University of Waterloo is a two degree program. All students must first complete their 4 year Pre-Professional Bachelor of Architectural Studies, Honours Cooperative Degree. This degree includes 5 mandatory 4 month terms of cooperative work experi-ence, accompanied by 4 work reports and one optional work term. All students participate in Coop Education. As of 2007 at least 50% of our students are employed outside of Canada, many working in London, New York and Miami. The balance of employment is typically in the larger Canadian cities, with students working predominantly in Toronto, Montreal, Calgary, Edmonton and Vancouver. The Co-operative Education & Career Services department at UW assists students in finding employment. Co-op income helps many students to reduce their overall cost of education.

The Honours BAS degree is followed by a nominal one year Master of Architecture Degree, which constitutes the professional finish to our fully accredited program. The focus of our masters degree is the completion of a substantial thesis.

The passing average for the Honours BAS Degree is 70%. The entry average to the Master of Architecture Degree is 75%. We normally accept 70 students into the first year of our undergraduate program. The two degree program is designed with the intention and capacity to allow all of our qualified graduating BAS students priority admission into our Master of Architecture degree program. Students with undergraduate pre-professional four year degrees from other insititutions wishing to apply to our Master of Architecture program will be required to make a special application for consideration, and if accepted, complete a Qualifying Year of study prior to admission to the MArch.

The BAS + MArch Degree that is offered by the School of Architecture at the University of Waterloo was awarded a 6 year term of Professional Accreditation by the Canadian Architectural Certification Board as of November 2005.

SCHOLARSHIPS AND FINANCIAL AID

Some teaching and research assistantships are available to graduate students in the Master of Architecture program. Some University of Waterloo Graduate Scholarships are also available to qualified students. These scholarships are assigned by the School. Students may also apply for University of Waterloo Graduate Bursaries, after their first semester, if they can demonstrate financial need.

ADMINISTRATION

Rick Haldenby, FRAIC: Director

UNIVERSITY OF WISCONSIN–MILWAUKEE

ADDRESS

Main
University of Wisconsin–Milwaukee
School of Architecture & Urban Planning
Department of Architecture
P.O. Box 413
Milwaukee, WI 53201
Tel.: 414.229.4014
Fax: 414.229.6976
www.uwm.edu/SARUP

STUDENT AND FACULTY DEMOGRAPHICS

% of Female Students	31
% of International Students	2
% of Minority Students	9
% of Out-of-State U.S. Students	14
No. Full-Time Faculty	33
No. Part-Time Faculty	17
No. Full-Time Students	854
No. Part-Time Students	63

FINANCIAL INFORMATION

Main Source of University Funding	Public
Annual Tuition & Fees (graduate, resident)	$9,604
Annual Tuition & Fees (graduate, nonresident)	$23,630
Annual Tuition & Fees (undergraduate, resident)	$7,309
Annual Tuition & Fees (undergraduate, nonresident)	$17,037
% Students Receiving Federal Financial Aid	8
% Students Receiving University Financial Aid	5
% Students Receiving Departmental Financial Aid	15
% Students Receiving Scholarships (assistantships or fellowships)	22
Average Annual Scholarship for Department	$23,000

ACADEMIC SESSIONS

Fall Semester: September to December; Application Deadline: BS: Jan 1. M.Arch. Jan. 15; M.U.P.: Mar.1
Spring Semester: January to May; Application Deadline: BS: Nov. 1; M.U.P.: Oct. 1

ARCHITECTURE AND RELATED DEGREE PROGRAMS							
Degree	**Min. Yrs. to Complete**	**Professional Accreditation**	**# of FT Students**	**# of PT Students**	**# of First-Year Students**	**# of Degrees Conferred**	**Admissions Requirements**
Architecture							
Bachelor of Science, Architectural Studies	4		684	29	211	102	SAT, ACT, Essay
M. Arch	2	NAAB	64	14	32	25	Undergraduate Architecture degree, GRE,TOEFL, Portfolio, Rec. Letters, Essay
M. Arch	3.5	NAAB	53	2	19	7	Undergraduate degree, GRE, TOEFL, Portfolio, Rec. Letters, Essay
PhD in Architecture	4		7	8	3	5	Undergraduate degree, Undergraduate Architecture degree, Prof. Architecture degree, GRE, TOEFL, Portfolio, Rec. Letters, Essay
Planning							
Master of Urban Planning	2	PAB	35	8	22	15	Undergraduate degree, GRE, TOEFL, Rec. Letters, Essay
Other							
Master of Architecture and Urban Planning	4.5	NAAB	5	0	1	0	Undergraduate degree, GRE, TOEFL, Portfolio, Rec. Letters, Essay
Master of Architecture and Urban Planning	3	NAAB	6	2	1	2	Undergraduate Architecture degree, GRE, TOEFL, Portfolio, Rec. Letters, Essay

SPECIALIZATIONS

Architectural Design	Energy	Preservation	Building Technology/Environmental Systems
Environment/Sustainability	Professional Practice	Community Design	History
Tectonics	Computer-Aided Design	Housing	Theory/Criticism
International Development	International/Regional Architecture	Urban Planning and Design	Building Information Modeling
Sustainability			

ARCHITECTURE PROGRAM SUMMARY

The School of Architecture and Urban Planning advances design and planning of the built and natural environment, focusing on the creation of value and the conservation of resources. Faculty in the departments of Architecture and Urban Planning prepare students for professional careers by actively engaging our academic, professional, and urban communities and by an integrative approach to architectural and urban theory and practice.

UNIVERSITY SETTING

A major research university with a student population of nearly 30,000, UWM has been designated by the University of Wisconsin System as its campus with an urban mission and it has designated the School of Architecture and Urban Planning a Center of Excellence. Milwaukee's cityscape, strong in historical and modern architecture, has proved itself to be an excellent learning laboratory for students of architecture and urban planning. Only blocks from Lake Michigan, the campus has convenient access to downtown and lively historic neighborhoods. Milwaukee is a city rich in cultural diversity and natural beauty.

SCHOOL PHILOSOPHY

The educational philosophy of the school is shaped by the dynamic nature of the city and the need for intelligent and sensitive professionals. By emphasizing the full scope of what is involved in environmental design and architectural decision making, the school seeks to develop architects who are able to deal with the complex and changing needs of society. To serve the educational objectives of individuals seeking to prepare for the varied roles afforded in the architectural profession, as well as the related fields of urban planning and architectural research, consulting, and teaching, the school offers several graduate degree programs.

PROGRAM DESCRIPTION

Undergraduate Program

The four-year undergraduate program leads to a non-professional degree, the **Bachelor of Science in Architectural Studies**. This degree prepares students for graduate study in an accredited professional degree program, for graduate work in related fields, or for a career in fields associated with the architectural profession. Admission to the architectural studies major is not considered until the junior year, after a student has completed undergraduate liberal arts study including fundamental courses in architectural design, technology, history, and theory and has satisfied university-wide General Education Requirements. Freshmen or sophomores initially enroll in the department as pre-architecture majors. The 48-credit architectural studies major includes a core program of design studios dealing with various scales of the physical environment and resolving problems of programming, design, and implementation as well as lecture courses treating basic is-

sues related to architectural composition and theory, construction technology, environmental controls, and human behavior.

Graduate Program

The **Master of Architecture** degree program is structured to allow students to pursue an educational program that best meets their individual career objectives while achieving a high level of professional competence. Organized around a distribution requirement in the areas of theory, technologies, and professional practice, the program integrates these subject areas in the design studio. Students with an undergraduate degree in architecture or architectural studies from an accredited architecture program may enroll in the 2-year, 60-credit M.Arch. Program. Undergraduates with degrees in other disciplines enroll in the 3.5-year, 101-credit M.Arch. Program. The **Master of Urban Planning** degree program offers a skills-oriented curriculum preparing students for roles in either the public or private sector. Beyond the the study of planning theory and methods, the program explores such substantive areas as finance, housing, land use, transportation, and urban ecology. Students may also enroll in a joint **Master of Architecture and Urban Planning** degree. The **PhD in Architecture** program offers advanced research into the interrelation of the built environment with human behavior, as well as social, cultural, and ecological conditions

AREAS OF FOCUS AND RESEARCH

Areas of Focus

Particular program strengths include building design, ecological design, historic preservation, environment-behavior studies, and urban design and development. Students have a variety of opportunities in advanced design studios for specialized study. For example, projects in Latin America, historic preservation, "green" and sustainable design, design/build, specialized housing, urban design, involvement with community planning and design, as well as projects that focus on theoretical and artistic issues. The Distinguished Visiting Professor, Marcus Prize, and Urban Edge Prize studios provide opportunities to work with influential practicing architects from the United States and abroad. Practicing architects who are faculty members or visiting instructors play an important role in teaching design studios. In addition, the M.Arch/MUP Joint Program allows students to pursue graduate degrees in architecture and urban planning simultaneously.

Research

The Center for Architecture and Urban Planning Research promotes, facilitates and coordinates the wide variety of funded research, community service and instructional projects that occur in the school, and coordinates collaborative programs with other UWM entities. The school has focused its expertise in various research institutes including the Institute for Aging and the Environment, the Historic Preservation Institute, the Frank Lloyd Wright Initiative, and the Center for Advanced Spatial Information Research. Faculty research

is wide-ranging: many projects cluster around themes such as Geographic Information Systems, urban transportation issues, urban sprawl, neighborhood revitalization, Smart Growth; Aging and Environment, in general, and Design for Dementia, in particular; Historic Preservation Projects; Building Information Modeling; Housing Technology; Environmental Quality; Community Empowerment; Visualization and Multimedia Studies.

SPECIAL ACTIVITIES AND PROGRAMS

Graduate Open Houses (fall and spring)• Architecture Summer Camp for high school students • Academic credit opportunities for independent study and directed research • Visiting design critic studios • Foreign studies programs • Joint M.Arch/MUP program • Lecture series • AIAS, APA Students, and Habitat for Humanity chapters • Student employment opportunities on campus through workstudy and off-campus through firms and public agencies • Publication series • Student design and research competition • Invited school in annual Chicago AIA student design competition • Special events, including sandcastle competition, graphics day, masonry day, careers day, etc. • Student/alumni mentoring program • Continuing education program

FACILITIES

• Graphics laboratory with photographic studio and darkroom • Resource Center containing reference materials, major professional journals, and slide collection • Computer laboratory with graphics, programming and word processing capabilities • Geographic Information Systems • Student lounge • Research and project rooms • Dedicated computers for thesis and doctoral students • High-tech classrooms • 50 node wireless network • In-studio computer work stations • Student-operated supply and book store • Woodworking Shop for wood, metal, and plastics and Rapid Prototyping Workshop • Center for Architecture and Urban Planning Research • Student Advising Office

SCHOLARSHIPS AND FINANCIAL AID

Although most forms of undergraduate financial assistance are based on demonstrated need and administered by the UWM Financial Aid Department, a number of awards based on academic and design merit are available to advanced students and are administered by the Department of Architecture. Other types of financial assistance include graduate school fellowships, AIA awards, Wisconsin Architects Foundation Scholarships and stipends supported by the local profession and construction industry. The department also awards teaching and project assistantships to qualified graduate students.

ADMINISTRATION

Robert Greenstreet: Dean
Linda Krause: Associate Dean
Gil Snyder: Associate Dean
Nancy Frank: Department Chair, Urban Planning

VIRGINIA POLYTECHNIC INSTITUTE & STATE UNIVERSITY

ADDRESS

Main
Virginia Tech
School of Architecture + Design
201 Cowgill Hall (0205)
Blacksburg, VA 24061-0205
www.archdesign.vt.edu

STUDENT AND FACULTY DEMOGRAPHICS

% of Female Students	42
% of International Students	6
% of Minority Students	8
% of Out-of-State U.S. Students	41
No. Full-Time Faculty	42
No. Part-Time Faculty	14
No. Full-Time Students	694
No. Part-Time Students	19

FINANCIAL INFORMATION

Main Source of University Funding	Public
Annual Tuition & Fees (graduate, resident)	$9,735
Annual Tuition & Fees (graduate, nonresident)	$16,866
Annual Tuition & Fees (undergraduate, resident)	$8,198
Annual Tuition & Fees (undergraduate, nonresident)	$20,825
% Students Receiving University Financial Aid	
% Students Receiving Departmental Financial Aid	
% Students Receiving Scholarships (assistantships or fellowships)	
Average Annual Scholarship for Department	

ACADEMIC SESSIONS

Fall Semester: August to December; Application Deadline: January 15;
February 15 (UndergraduateTransfer)
Spring Semester: January to May

Summer Session I: May to June
Summer Session II: July to August

ARCHITECTURE AND RELATED DEGREE PROGRAMS

Degree	Min. Yrs. to Complete	Professional Accreditation	# of FT Students	# of PT Students	# of First-Year Students	# of Degrees Conferred	Admissions Requirements
Architecture							
B. Arch	5	NAAB	544	10	86	97	SAT, TOEFL, Rec. Letters
M. Arch 1	1.5		6	1	4	2	GRE, TOEFL, Portfolio, Rec. Letters, Essay
M. Arch 2	2	NAAB	50	3	23	10	Undergraduate Architecture degree, GRE, TOEFL, Portfolio, Rec. Letters, Essay
M. Arch 3	3.5	NAAB	63	2	23	9	Undergraduate degree, GRE, TOEFL, Rec. Letters, Essay
MS Arch	2		11	0	3	2	Undergraduate degree, GRE, TOEFL, Portfolio, Rec. Letters, Essay
PhD Architecture	2		20	3	4	2	Undergraduate Architecture degree, GRE, TOEFL, Portfolio, Rec. Letters, Essay

SPECIALIZATIONS

Architectural Design
Art and Design
Building Information Modeling
Building Technology/Env. Systems
Community Design

Computer-Aided Design
Energy
Environment/Sustainability
Graphic Design
History

Housing
Interior Design/Architecture
International/Regional Architecture
Landscape Design
Photography

Professional Practice
Tectonics
Theory/Criticism
Urban Planning and Design

PROGRAM SUMMARY

Architecture enriches our lives by offering us environments that are sensibly compelling, thought provoking, and capable of lifting our spirits. In addition to being beautiful, architecture is, by ancient definition, functional and durable. Like art, architecture is permeated by dualities. It is stable and transitory, measureable and immeasurable, and capable of both being touched and touching us. Like science, architecture involves systematic study. Its methods are iterative, experimental, and rely on intense observation. By intertwining the poetic and practical, architecture is uniquely poised to address the challenges of contemporary life and build the culture of the 21st century.

UNIVERSITY SETTING

The university is located in Blacksburg, a vibrant community of 40,000 situated in the mountains of southwestern Virginia, near the Blue Ridge Parkway and the Jefferson National Forest. Founded in 1872 as a land-grant college named Virginia Agricultural and Mechanical College, Virginia Tech is now a comprehensive research university of national and international prominence. As Virginia's largest university with over 25,600 students and a commitment to excellence in teaching, research, and public service, it is an institution poised to become a model land-grant university of the twenty-first century. The 2,600-acre main campus includes more than 100 buildings, a 1,700-acre agricultural research farm, a state-of-the-art conference center, and an airport. Adjacent to the university is the Virginia Tech Corporate Research Center [CRC] a subsidiary of the Virginia Tech Foundation.

SCHOOL PHILOSOPHY

The mission of the School of Architecture + Design is to create a setting for the pursuit of theoretical, practical, and productive knowledge, embracing the duality of the education of an individual and the practice of a profession. The School takes a decidedly Modern position toward design and simultaneously seeks to understand the structure of historical development and culture. The School has a long-standing commitment to international and urban studies through the Washington Alexandria Center, the Study Abroad Program, and the University's Center for European Studies and Architecture. The objective of the School of Architecture + Design is to produce graduates who will be leaders in their chosen professions and in the communities in which they live. The School seeks to provide a forum that cultivates vigorous dialogue and debate, enriching the interrelations between education and practice.

PROGRAM DESCRIPTION

Bachelor of Architecture

The undergraduate Architecture curriculum is structured as two programs, or stages, of study, the Foundation Program and the Professional Program. All architecture, industrial design, interior design and landscape architecture majors study together for the first year.

Master of Architecture

The M.Arch. 1 option results in a post-professional degree, while the M.Arch. 2 and 3 options result in the conferring of a first professional degree, fully accredited by the National Architectural Accrediting Board. The one-year Master of Architecture from Virginia Tech is a post-professional degree and does not constitute an accredited first professional degree in architecture. International applicants who hold architecture degrees from schools outside the U.S. and who aspire to professional licensure in the U.S. are normally advised to apply to the M.Arch.2 program.

Master of Science

The Master of Science in Architecture Program has been initiated in relation to the need for new and specialized knowledge in design to respond to the changing scope of professional practice.

Ph.D. in Architecture and Design Research

Doctoral studies in architecture and design are for those students who desire to pursue careers in the research fields of advanced professional and academic practice and teaching.

AREAS OF FOCUS AND RESEARCH

The educational focus of the School of Architecture + Design is on guiding students to discover their own beliefs and values through their work, in relation to their chosen profession and other design and planning disciplines.

SPECIAL ACTIVITIES AND PROGRAMS

In addition to an array of on-campus activities, the School of Architecture + Design offers a number of off-campus opportunities. These include the European study-abroad travel and residency programs, our Washington–Alexandria Architecture Center, the Chicago Studio, and an Xtern Program. Students also have the opportunity to work side by side with faculty members on a variety design/build and sponsored research projects.

FACILITIES

In addition to the main campus, in Blacksburg, the School of Architecture + Design has teaching and research centers in a major metropolitan area (the Washington–Alexandria Center) and a small European town (The Center for European Studies and Architecture in Riva San Vitale, in the Canton of Ticino, Switzerland).

On campus, the School has over 150,000 square feet of physical space. Each of the School's main facilities—Cowgill, Burchard, and it's new spaces in Burruss Hall are either less than 10 years old or have undergone significant renovation. Our shops—wood, metal, plastics—are extensive and well equipped, our computing facilities and digital fabrication tools embody state of the art technologies, and our darkrooms, ceramics, print, silk-screen, and plaster workshops offer a rich array of representation and fabrication opportunities for our students. All of the School's facilities are connected via a wireless network. Located approx. 1 mile from Cowgill Hall at the University's Plantation Road Research District is the Research and Demonstration Facility. The main purpose of this facility is to link the academic, research, and outreach efforts of the School. It contains an interior high bay space for full-size prototyping, an auditorium, studio space, office areas, and testing facilities.

SCHOLARSHIPS AND FINANCIAL AID

Virginia Tech administers a comprehensive financial aid program awarding support to qualified undergraduate and graduate students in the form of merit-based scholarships provided by corporations and foundations, grants, loans, and work-study employment. Financial assistance available to graduate students also includes fellowships, tuition remission scholarships, and teaching and research assistantships awarded by academic programs.

ADMINISTRATION

A. Jack Davis, FAIA: Dean
Robert P. Schubert: CAUS Associate Dean of Research
Scott Poole, AIA: Director of Architecture
Kathryn Albright: Assistant Director, Chair,
  Foundation Program
Jaan Holt: Center Director, Washington-Alexandria Center
Michael Ermann, LEED AP: Chair, Architecture 2-3
Greg Tew: Chair, Interior Design
Steve Thompson: Chair, Graduate Program
  in Architecture
Terry Surjan: Chair, Architecture 4+
Ron Kemnitzer, FIDSA: Chair, Industrial Design
Brian Katen, ASLA: Chair, Landscape Architecture

WASHINGTON STATE UNIVERSITY

ADDRESS

Main
Washington State University
School of Architecture & Construction
    Management
P.O. Box 642220
Pullman, WA 99164-2220
Tel.: 509.335.5539
Fax: 509.335.6132
www.arch.wsu.edu

STUDENT AND FACULTY DEMOGRAPHICS

% of Female Students	35
% of International Students	15
% of Minority Students	5
% of Out-of-State U.S. Students	3
No. Full-Time Faculty	24
No. Part-Time Faculty	4
No. Full-Time Students	550
No. Part-Time Students	

FINANCIAL INFORMATION

Main Source of University Funding	Public
Annual Tuition & Fees (graduate)	$8,068
Annual Tuition & Fees (undergraduate, resident)	$6,720
Annual Tuition & Fees (undergraduate, nonresident)	$17,756
% Students Receiving Federal Financial Aid	
% Students Receiving University Financial Aid	
% Students Receiving Departmental Financial Aid	50
% Students Receiving Scholarships (assistantships or fellowships)	
Average Annual Scholarship for Department	$1,000

ACADEMIC SESSIONS

Fall Semester: August to December
Spring Semester: January to May

ARCHITECTURE AND RELATED DEGREE PROGRAMS

Degree	Min. Yrs. to Complete	Professional Accreditation	# of FT Students	# of PT Students	# of First-Year Students	# of Degrees Conferred	Admissions Requirements
Architecture							
Bachelor of Science in Architecture	4		350		200	55	Accredited high school degree and admission to WSU
M. Arch	5.5	NAAB	350		200	55	Undergraduate degree, Undergraduate Architecture degree, Prof. Architecture degree, TOEFL, Portfolio, Rec. Letters, Essay
Master of Science in Architecture	2		6				Undergraduate degree, Undergraduate Architecture degree, GRE, TOEFL, Portfolio, Rec. Letters, Essay
Construction Management/Technology							
Bachelor of Science Construction Management	4	ACCE	250		120	50	

SPECIALIZATIONS

Architectural Design	Computer-Aided Design	Housing	Tectonics
Art and Design	Energy	International Development	Theory/Criticism
Building Technology/Env. Systems	Environment/Sustainability	Landscape Design	Urban Planning and Design
Community Design	History	Sustainablility	

ARCHITECTURE PROGRAM SUMMARY

One of the most compelling reasons to receive a degree in architecture is that perhaps more than any other profession there is the opportunity to make a significant contribution to the quality of our collective environment and human life. The quality of our buildings, spaces, landscapes and construction methods play a critical role in how people feel, behave, interact and communicate. It is this first principle that underscores the collective goals of the faculty and curriculum in the School.

Within this context, the School is dedicated to providing exceptional professional education in architecture focusing upon the quality of our built environment. Our programs are structured to provide students with diversity in terms of educational experience while maintaining rigorous standards of performance required for success in the profession as well as academic accreditation. A significant benefit of attending WSU is that students have direct access to dedicated and extraordinary faculty. The faculty in the School is composed of individuals with a breadth and scope of experience that spans many countries and cultures. Through their research and contributions to the profession, the faculty has achieved national and international recognition and continues to be influential in the development and progress of the profession. It is through the faculty and curriculum that students in the School are exposed to global, regional and local forces which structure and determine the built environment. The curriculum is organized in a manner that encourages understanding in the areas of philosophy, theory and history as well as technical areas such as structures, materials and environmental systems. As such, students will receive a focused and comprehensive education, which is why the School is so well known for providing remarkable graduates and leaders.

UNIVERSITY SETTING

Washington State University is located in the community of Pullman, Washington, and has a population 21,500 (17,000 of whom are students). Pullman, located in the Palouse area, is 75 miles south of the city of Spokane. As a major land-grant institution, WSU is a comprehensive university that offers a wide range of academic choices encompassing over 60 degree-granting programs. The School of Architecture and Construction Management is housed within the College of Engineering and Architecture. The School has a diverse student body and accepts both new freshman and transfer students. The Construction Management program is housed within the School and provides opportunities for cross-disciplinary studies.

SCHOOL PHILOSOPHY

The School of Architecture and Construction Management is dedicated to the education of future architects who are intellectually aware and who critically understand social, political and global conditions that have an impact on the profession of architecture. It is the intent of the School to graduate future professionals who are committed to excellence in the built environment through the incorporation of intellectual, analyti-

cal and artful aspects of the architectural profession. Within this context, students and faculty seek to investigate issues within diverse contexts in order to creatively advance the built environment. A rigorous sequence of 11 semesters of design studios encompasses issues of environment, technology and culture, preparing students for architectural design and professional practice. Design studios are complemented with courses in technology, theory and environment, providing a comprehensive educational experience.

PROGRAM DESCRIPTION

The accredited professional education program is structured in a 1-3-1 format. Students are screened for admission into the professional program at the start of second year. Admission procedures take into account GPA in architecture and GER courses. Transfer students commonly apply at the second- and third-year levels. The vehicle for learning is focused around the design studio core. Studios are sequenced around a first year of graphic communication and visual design, three middle years of thematic studios and a fifth year of courses and independent studio work. The thematic studios are organized around three themes of environment/context, culture/theory and technology, as well as a sequence of special topics. Each theme is developed in the second, third and fourth years, with projects in each year advancing in complexity. The primary role of the faculty is one of managing learning opportunities, asking questions and encouraging students to be inquisitive. The responsibility of the student is to be an active, motivated participant, constantly searching. Learning is seen as a dynamic participatory process that provides enrichment for both the students and the faculty.

There is no limitation on students entering the first year of architecture, however there is a screening process at the end of first year based on scholastic standing. This process leads to certification at the beginning of the second year. Transfer students are given equal consideration at these screening points.

First Year (Pre-Architecture): Screening for admission into second-year courses is based on the student's GPA in all architecture program requirements including GER's. To be considered, the student must have successfully completed at least 26 semester credit hours of requirements.

Second Year: Sixty students are selected to proceed into the second-year architectural design and construction courses. During this year, students complete most of the WSU General Education Requirements, including calculus and physics, and start the architectural history sequence.

Third and Fourth Years: Complete the requirements for the four year non-accredited Bachelor of Science in Architecture. The professional accredited program is the Master of Architecture. All students must submit required application materials by stipulated dates in order to be eligible for admission. The school also offers a non-accredited Master of Science in Architecture degree at the WSU Spokane campus.

AREAS OF FOCUS AND RESEARCH

Research Faculty and students are engaged in research resulting in contributions to the profession and environment. Faculty research is diverse and comprehensive and includes energy conservation, building materials and development, theory and philosophy, construction and forensic engineering. Faculty utilize their courses as well as professional organizations, publications and books to disseminate results of their research areas. Students are encouraged to be actively engaged in faculty research topics.

SPECIAL ACTIVITIES AND PROGRAMS

The school has an active off-campus program. All undergraduates at the third and fourth year participate in domestic study tours in the fall semester. Undergraduates may also participate in semester long programs in the spring of the fourth year. Graduate students participate in international study tours each spring. The school has very active student memberships in AIAS and Builders Without Borders (BWB). The lecture series includes both international scholars and practicing architects as well as local and regional architects. The school is part of the College Institute for Sustainability. The Institute integrates architecture, construction management, civil engineering and the WSU wood materials lab. The Institute provides opportunities for students and faculty to work on selected research regarding sustainability and the built environment.

The School also offers graduate Master of Architecture education a the WSU Spokane campus where students may focus on issues of community development and design, health and environment, as well as sustainability.

FACILITIES

Historic and contemporary masonry-type buildings in conjunction with rolling hills comprise the main landscape of the campus. The School has been located in Carpenter Hall since the program was initiated in 1913. This historic landmark was renovated in 1992 and houses modern facilities such as studios, lecture halls, computer labs and the architecture library. The School also has a comprehensive slide library accessible for student use. The building, studios and computer labs are accessible to students 24 hours a day.

Facilities in Spokane encompass two buildings located adjacent to the urban core. Students in Spokane work in new and renovated buildings and have direct access to professionals in the area.

SCHOLARSHIPS AND FINANCIAL AID

The school has active scholarships for undergraduate students beginning in the second year. Undergraduate scholarships awarded in 2008 from the School were $30,000. This does not include university scholarships. Graduate-level scholarships and teaching assistantships were $40,000.

ADMINISTRATION

Candis Claiborn: Dean
Gregory A. Kessler, AIA: Professor and Director

WASHINGTON UNIVERSITY IN ST. LOUIS

ADDRESS

Main
Washington University in St. Louis
Sam Fox School of Design & Visual Arts
Architecture Programs
Campus Box 1079
One Brookings Drive
St. Louis, MO 63130-4899
Tel.: 314.935.6200
Fax: 314.935.7656
www.arch.wustl.edu

STUDENT AND FACULTY DEMOGRAPHICS

% of Female Students	49
% of International Students	9
% of Minority Students	17
% of Out-of-State U.S. Students	
No. Full-Time Faculty	17
No. Part-Time Faculty	25
No. Full-Time Students	380
No. Part-Time Students	1

FINANCIAL INFORMATION

Main Source of University Funding	Private
Annual Tuition & Fees (graduate)	$34,500
Annual Tuition & Fees (undergraduate)	$34,500
% Students Receiving Federal Financial Aid	85
% Students Receiving University Financial Aid	77
% Students Receiving Departmental Financial Aid	90
% Students Receiving Scholarships (assistantships or fellowships)	85
Average Annual Scholarship for Department	$11,541

ACADEMIC SESSIONS

Fall Semester: August to December; Application Deadline: February 1 (graduate)
Spring Semester: January to May

ARCHITECTURE AND RELATED DEGREE PROGRAMS

Degree	Min. Yrs. to Complete	Professional Accreditation	# of FT Students	# of PT Students	# of First-Year Students	# of Degrees Conferred	Admissions Requirements
Architecture							
BA	4		184	0	46	35	ACT, TOEFL, Rec. Letters, Essay
BS Arch	4		20	0		6	ACT, TOEFL, Rec. Letters, Essay
M. Arch1	1		1	0	1		Prof. Architecture degree, GRE, Portfolio, Rec. Letters, Essay
M. Arch2	2	NAAB	51	0	20	13	Undergraduate Architecture degree, GRE, TOEFL, Portfolio, Rec. Letters, Essay
M. Arch3	3	NAAB	120	0	41	21	Undergraduate degree, GRE, TOEFL, Portfolio, Rec. Letters, Essay
Urban Design							
MUD	1		6		6	3	Prof. Architecture degree, GRE, TOEFL, Portfolio, Rec. Letters, Essay

SPECIALIZATIONS

Architectural Design
Art and Design
Building Technology/Env. Systems

Community Design
Environment/Sustainability
History

International/Regional Architecture
Sustainablility
Tectonics

Theory/Criticism
Urban Planning and Design

ARCHITECTURE PROGRAM SUMMARY

The graduate and undergraduate programs in architecture at Washington University in St. Louis are committed to cultivation of the designer's identity through programs intended to educate expressive, skillful, socially responsible individuals ready to address the physical, economic and social challenges of design.

UNIVERSITY SETTING

Washington University in St. Louis, founded in 1853, is a private, independent, comprehensive university of national and international stature. (*U.S. News and World Report* ranks the University 12th.) Academic excellence and collaboration predominate across the University's teaching units. With 7,500 undergraduates and 6,000 graduate/professional students, the University's faculty and resources are characteristic of a much larger institution.

The Sam Fox School of Design & Visual Arts is comprised of the Graduate School of Architecture & Urban Design, the College of Architecture, the Graduate School of Art, the College of Art, and the Mildred Lane Kemper Art Museum. The School provides enhanced opportunities for interdisciplinary study; encourages the application of emerging information technologies to scholarly and creative work; and fosters the integration of visual literacy as a component in today's liberal arts education for all university students.

Metropolitan St. Louis provides a rich, varied architectural heritage and a unique urban and landscape design laboratory; these qualities are balanced by intensive initiatives in international education.

SCHOOL PHILOSOPHY

The School's programs cultivate the designer's identity as a leader: as both an expressive individual and a socially responsible citizen. Our commitment to the ethical practice of architecture spans disciplines and emphasizes the physicality of design. The School's identity resonates with the diverse realities of its multiple locations: St. Louis, which possesses a rich architectural heritage and complex urbanity, and international semesters in Florence, Barcelona, Buenos Aires, and Helsinki, all cities of vibrant architectural cultures.

PROGRAM DESCRIPTION

M.Arch and MUD degrees in the Graduate School of Architecture & Urban Design are attained through a variety of degree options and terms of study. The Master of Architecture program leads to a NAAB-accredited first professional degree and is open to those who already hold baccalaureate degrees. Depending on an applicant's prior experience and academic qualifications, an M.Arch degree may be completed in 4, 5 or 7 semesters. The Master of Urban Design program, a one-year post-professional program, focuses on contemporary urban issues through architectural, landscape, and planning perspectives. The post-professional M.Arch program offers opportunities for advanced design work and research to those who already hold NAAB-accredited professional degrees. Beyond the focus on St. Louis and North America, international semesters expand the physical reach of all graduate programs.

Four-year pre-professional undergraduate degree programs lead to either a Bachelor of Science in Architecture degree or a Bachelor of Arts degree with a major in architecture. These degrees are founded on the humanities, with an intensifying focus on architectural studies. An undergraduate architectural education offers preparation for professional education, employ-ment options in related areas, or accomplishment in any field valuing innovative, synthetic thought and work. First- and second-year students enroll in humanities coursework as well as introductory design and architecture studio courses in the Sam Fox School. The intensive junior year consists of architectural design studios, supported by architectural history and building technologies. Satisfactory completion of the 300-level coursework qualifies a student for the Bachelor of Arts degree with a major in architecture with flexible curricular options in the senior year. Senior students pursuing advanced architectural studies receive the Bachelor of Science degree.

AREAS OF FOCUS AND RESEARCH

Architectural design focuses the curriculum. Other specific areas include: urban design, building technology/environmental systems, community design, environment/sustainability, architectural history, international and regional architecture, theory/criticism, and art and design.

Research efforts occur across building technologies, sustainable design, modern architectural history, urban design, design pedagogy, materials studies and digital media. Funded research is supported by the university, by the Sam Fox School, and within specific programs, by national and international organizations. The Sam Fox School's Design Research Studio and the Kemper Art Museum focus interdisciplinary and collaborative research efforts and support grant writing/funding strategies.

SPECIAL ACTIVITIES AND PROGRAMS

Dual degree programs combine M.Arch or MUD curricula with Master of Business Administration, Master of Social Work and Master of Construction Management degrees. Graduate international semesters of full-time study, located in Barcelona, Buenos Aires and Helsinki, are an integral part of the professional curriculum. Undergraduate programs abroad include a senior semester in Copenhagen, a junior semester in Florence, or the Architectural Study Abroad Program summer in Europe.

Master classes in environmental design provide intensive sessions with design professionals engaging students in current sustainable design techniques. The Sam Fox Lecture Series offers an array of architects, landscape architects, urbanists and artists of national and international reputation. Substantial assistance with career planning and placement is available for all students as well as an annual Career Fair of potential employers.

The Kemper Art Museum within the Sam Fox School campus, known for its extensive collection of 20th/21st-century art, provides challenging and thought-provoking exhibits of interest on a local, national and international scale. Steinberg Gallery exhibitions focus on topics of architectural interest. Collaborative workshops in the Sam Fox School encourage students in all disciplines to expand their knowledge while working together. Collaborations with the St. Louis AIA pursue community and city projects. The Architecture Discovery Program offers a two-week summer experience for high school students. The Graduate School sponsors the Steedman Traveling Fellowship, a $30,000 international design competition for recent graduates of accredited architecture programs.

FACILITIES

The Sam Fox School complex at the east end of the university's Danforth Campus includes Givens Hall, Steinberg Hall, Bixby Hall, Walker Hall and the Kemper Art Museum building. Dedicated in 2006, the Kemper Art Museum building and Walker Hall, designed by Pritzker Prize architect and former faculty member Fumihiko Maki, house a renowned collection of art, as well as the Kranzberg Art and Architecture Library, the Whitaker Learning Lab (digital facilities), and expanded studio space.

Givens Hall houses design studios as well as a main lecture room, review spaces and classrooms. Additional studio, review, classroom, and computer areas are also in adjacent Steinberg Hall, which includes Steinberg Auditorium, Steinberg Gallery, darkroom facilities and the Steinberg café. Extensive fabrication workshops are used for model building, full-scale detail construction, and furniture design and fabrication. Givens Hall's digital fabrication lab houses three laser cutters, a CNC milling machine and a 3-D printer.

The Sam Fox School complex is joined as both a network and as a wireless community. A laptop computing emphasis facilitates digital media-based education. The Whitaker Learning Lab provides output equipment available to all students as well as classroom space for high-end digital teaching.

The Kranzberg Library's collection includes more than 105,000 volumes in all formats. Its valuable collection, depth and electronic access make it a leading library of its kind in the Midwest. The collection annually acquires approximately 2,000 new books, periodicals, videotapes, DVDs and CD-ROMs.

SCHOLARSHIPS AND FINANCIAL AID

The Sam Fox School invests in its students by providing significant financial assistance. Approximately 60% of undergraduates and over 90% of graduate students receive need-based financial aid, most often consisting of a combination of scholarship and loan assistance. A variety of student loans (long-term payments) and part-time employment are available. An application for financial aid has no effect on admissions decisions. Generally speaking, aid is provided to as many admitted applicants as possible rather than concentrating large awards to fewer students.

A typical financial assistance award may include a combination of scholarships, federal grants, student loans, and a part-time employment opportunity. Individual components will vary with each student's unique circumstances. Financial packages may equal or exceed the cost of tuition. For undergraduate applicants, Washington University has instituted a program that seeks to eliminate need-based loans as part of its undergraduate financial assistance awards to students from low- to middle-income families. Students receiving financial assistance come from a broad range of economic backgrounds; exceptional candidates for admission can apply for academic scholarships regardless of need.

ADMINISTRATION

Carmon Colangelo: Dean, Sam Fox School
Peter MacKeith: Associate Dean, Sam Fox School
Bruce Lindsey: Dean, Architecture
Kathryn Dean: Director, Graduate Programs
Iain Fraser: Director, Undergraduate Programs
John Hoal: Chair, Urban Design Program

WENTWORTH INSTITUTE OF TECHNOLOGY

ADDRESS

Main
Wentworth Institute of Technology
Department of Architecture
550 Huntington Avenue
Boston, MA 02115
Tel.: 617.989.4450
Fax: 617.989.4591
www.wit.edu/arch

STUDENT AND FACULTY DEMOGRAPHICS

% of Female Students	30
% of International Students	3
% of Minority Students	10
% of Out-of-State U.S. Students	36
No. Full-Time Faculty	23
No. Part-Time Faculty	30
No. Full-Time Students	750
No. Part-Time Students	15

FINANCIAL INFORMATION

Main Source of University Funding	Private
Annual Tuition & Fees (graduate)	
Annual Tuition & Fees (undergraduate)	$20,150
% Students Receiving Federal Financial Aid	80
% Students Receiving University Financial Aid	83
% Students Receiving Departmental Financial Aid	
% Students Receiving Scholarships (assistantships or fellowships)	
Average Annual Scholarship for Department	$4,680

ACADEMIC SESSIONS

Fall Semester: September to December
Spring Semester: January to April

Application Deadline: see website: www.wit.edu
Summer Session I: May to August

ARCHITECTURE AND RELATED DEGREE PROGRAMS

Degree	Min. Yrs. to Complete	Professional Accreditation	# of FT Students	# of PT Students	# of First-Year Students	# of Degrees Conferred	Admissions Requirements
Architecture							
BS Arch	4		700	15	290		SAT, ACT, TOEFL, Rec. Letters, Essay
M. Arch*	1	NAAB	50	0	50	48	Undergraduate Architecture degree, GRE, Portfolio, Rec. Letters, Essay

*Approved by NAAB and MBHE; pending NEASC final approval

SPECIALIZATIONS

Architectural Design   Building Technology/Env. Systems   Community Design   Tectonics

ARCHITECTURE PROGRAM SUMMARY
Architectural education at Wentworth integrates knowledge of building technology with understanding of theory and design. Amidst a multiplicity of approaches to architecture, Wentworth embraces the traditional role of the practitioner: to design and construct buildings that contribute to society and enrich people's lives. We offer two degree programs:
- The 4-year, pre-professional BS in Architecture provides students with a broad understanding of architecture.

- The 1-year first professional degree (MArch*) prepares students for registration and professional practice.

UNIVERSITY SETTING
Wentworth is an independent college offering undergraduate degrees in fifteen majors in the design and engineering technology disciplines. Architecture is a prominent program at Wentworth, with over 800 students enrolled in its degree programs.

Wentworth's 35-acre residential campus is situated in the Fenway district of Boston, near the Museum of Fine Arts, Symphony Hall and other cultural landmarks. The Institute has close ties with five nearby colleges through the Colleges of the Fenway consortium, allowing students access to classes and events at neighboring schools. Students' academic experience is enhanced by access to the rich cultural and architectural heritage of Boston, as well as the city's diverse scholarly and professional community.

SCHOOL PHILOSOPHY

The Architecture Department at Wentworth is deeply rooted in the Institute's tradition of building and technological innovation, and these core values are woven throughout the design program. The architecture program cultivates a well-grounded approach to design, providing students with the skills and insight to make positive contributions to our built environment. The department places particular emphasis on the tangible, material nature of architecture and the technologies that inform design thinking. The curriculum encompasses both the art and the science of architecture, examining the theory, history, culture, and technology of the built environment. Wentworth students gain a broad perspective on the profession, which is essential to informed contemporary practice. They also acquire a detailed knowledge of design and building systems, strong analytical and communication skills, and the ability to work with clients, community groups, and professionals from many disciplines. The program includes two semesters of cooperative work experience, offering a valuable introduction to professional practice. Many students participate in the program's full-semester study abroad program, which provides an opportunity to live and work in another culture while experiencing that culture's historical and contemporary architecture and urbanism.

A well-integrated sequence of studios and coursework, complemented by two semesters of cooperative work experience, presents students with a comprehensive view of the profession and prepares graduates for a broad range of career opportunities. Most importantly, the program provides graduates with the skills and perspective to pursue challenging, rewarding, and responsible careers in architecture.

PROGRAM DESCRIPTION

Architecture at Wentworth is an exciting and rigorous course of study, grounded in design creativity and technological innovation. The curriculum integrates laptop computers and advanced digital skills, professional co-op work placements, study-abroad and community-based service learning opportunities. Wentworth offers a 4-year Bachelor of Science in Architecture followed by a 1-year Master of Architecture* degree. All entering freshmen are admitted to the BS degree program. During the sophomore year, students apply to one of three academic concentrations in architecture that offer a point of focus within a shared curricular structure— Design + Research, Design + Technology or Design + Culture (see Areas of Focus). Upon successful completion of the BS curriculum, students may apply to the 1-year MArch* degree program (*pending NEASC approval).

In the first two years, students receive a broad introduction to architecture, including history, theory, technology and practice. They also acquire the tools necessary for developing and communicating their visions, including manual and digital representational techniques as well as research and writing skills. In the third and fourth years, studio topics become more complex, requiring the synthesis of fundamental design tenets and the incorporation of a growing body of techni-

cal expertise. The final year provides an intensely focused program, offering each student the opportunity to fully develop and defend original research in the form of a design thesis. The studio environment is at the core of architectural education. Wentworth students work intensively and collaboratively in this setting, testing new ways of thinking and exploring conceptual methods and emerging technologies.

AREAS OF FOCUS AND RESEARCH

The 4-year BS in Architecture provides a broad, NAAB-based architectural education for all students. Within this framework, students focus their educational interests by choosing one of the following concentrations at the end of the sophomore year.

Design + Research is an intellectually rigorous curriculum grounded in the formal, historical and compositional aspects of the built environment. Students explore design theories and methods, while maintaining a strong connection to architecture's material nature.

Design + Technology provides an in-depth knowledge of the nature of building systems and the architectural processes that inform the built environment. Rooted in the Institute's tradition of building and technological innovation, this concentration examines the art, culture and technology of making buildings.

Design + Culture focuses on the existing physical and cultural fabric in the design of communities, as well as the role of research in promoting imaginative design thinking. Students gain the skills and insight to make positive contributions to communities and their social, cultural and built environments.

Wentworth Architecture faculty pursue a broad range of research interests including: new media applications in architectural education, the role of theory in contemporary practice, the implications of new design/build models, new possibilities of green architecture, innovative urban design to empower community development, and adaptive reuse and conservation as methods within cultural landscape studies. Urbanism is a research interest shared by many faculty who pursue the study of cities both locally and internationally, including work in Asia, Latin America, the Middle East, and Europe. Students may work with faculty as research assistants or as participants in special field school programs. Wentworth faculty frequently incorporate their research explorations in the classroom and studio, adding to the richness and vibrancy of student experience.

SPECIAL ACTIVITIES AND PROGRAMS

Experiences outside the traditional classroom build upon Wentworth's educational strengths. Program curriculum includes two terms of cooperative work placement, promoting student learning in a professional setting. This experience offers a valuable introduction to practice, and typically fulfills requirements for portions of the Intern Development Program (IDP), a key step toward professional licensure.

The architecture department works with Wentworth's Center for Community Learning Partnerships to enrich students' experience by applying their professional training in a community service context. Service learning opportunities are available through work-study, co-op placements and alternative spring break

programs. The studio curriculum includes a semester dedicated to community design, in which students work directly with local community residents and planners to develop urban proposals that have helped guide and inform the growth of these communities. Students and faculty have also worked in conjunction with organizations in New Orleans, contributing through design studio research and hands-on construction during trips to the city.

Architecture student clubs include the American Institute of Architecture Students (AIAS), Associated Builders and Contractors, and the Society of Women Engineers. The AIAS sponsors special events and field trips, and served as co-host for Forum 2006, the national conference of AIAS.

The department runs a full-semester study abroad program, based in Berlin and affiliated with the Technische Fachhochschule Berlin. This program is an extension of the regular curriculum, fully integrated with students' academic requirements. Additional travel elective options currently include focused study trips to Scandinavia and Italy. The department has agreements for exchange programs with universities in Venezuela and China for academic and cooperative work placements.

FACILITIES

The Department of Architecture is centrally located on campus, adjacent to other design and construction-related programs at the Institute. This proximity encourages interaction with related fields of study. Shared teaching facilities, meeting spaces and exhibit areas foster community and interchange among the design disciplines. Dedicated design studio space provides open, naturally lit workspaces supported by review rooms, printing services and a student resource center. The department maintains its own model shop and shares construction laboratories with the allied design departments. Wentworth's campus-wide computer technology office supports the department's laptop program and student printing needs. The Alumni Library supports the department with an extensive print and digital collection, supplemented by materials available through the consortium of Fenway college libraries.

SCHOLARSHIPS AND FINANCIAL AID

Approximately 80% of Wentworth students receive financial aid. The average aid package totals more than $4,600 and financial need is not considered in the admissions process. Wentworth scholarships are offered on a financial need basis as determined by the FAFSA. Arioch Scholarships and President's Scholarships are awarded in recognition of outstanding academic achievement and participation in extracurricular activities. Wentworth also participates in Federal Pell grants, specific State grants and the Federal Work-Study program. Work-Study students may work either in placements on campus or through the Office of Community Relations.

ADMINISTRATION

Glenn E. Wiggins: Department Head
Ann Borst, AIA: Associate Department Head
John Stephen Ellis, AIA: Associate Department Head

WOODBURY UNIVERSITY

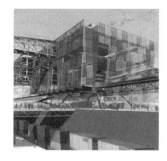

ADDRESS

Los Angeles
Woodbury University
School of Architecture
7500 Glenoaks Blvd
PO Box 7846
Burbank, CA 91510-7846
vic.liptak@woodbury.edu
www.woodbury.edu

San Diego
Woodbury University
School of Architecture
2212 Main St.
San Diego, CA 92113
www.woodbury.edu

STUDENT AND FACULTY DEMOGRAPHICS

% of Female Students	35
% of International Students	4
% of Minority Students	54
% of Out-of-State U.S. Students	
No. Full-Time Faculty	11
No. Part-Time Faculty	95
No. Full-Time Students	454
No. Part-Time Students	66

FINANCIAL INFORMATION

Main Source of University Funding	Private
Annual Tuition & Fees (graduate, resident)	$29,205
Annual Tuition & Fees (graduate, nonresident)	$29,205
Annual Tuition & Fees (undergraduate, resident)	$27,992
Annual Tuition & Fees (undergraduate, nonresident)	$27,992
% Students Receiving Federal Financial Aid	79
% Students Receiving University Financial Aid	68
% Students Receiving Departmental Financial Aid	38
% Students Receiving Scholarships (assistantships or fellowships)	6
Average Annual Scholarship for Department	

ACADEMIC SESSIONS

Fall Semester: August to December; Application Deadline: March 1
Spring Semester: January to May; Application Deadline: October 1

ARCHITECTURE AND RELATED DEGREE PROGRAMS							
Degree	Yrs. to Complete	Professional Accreditation	# of FT Students	# of PT Students	# of First-Year Students	# of Degrees Conferred	Admissions Requirements
Architecture							
B. Arch	5	NAAB	457	66	48	70	
M. Arch. RED	1.5		7	0	0	6	Undergraduate Architecture degree
M. Arch 2009)	2	pending	0	0	0	0	4-year Architecture degree

ARCHITECTURE PROGRAM SUMMARY

Woodbury University's School of Architecture is committed to investigating and extending the social, urban, economic, environmental, technological, and formal dimensions of architecture. The School emphasizes, analyzes, and debates the role of the architect/citizen as cultural communicator and builder responsive to societal and environmental challenges. We integrate into the design curriculum recent innovations in computer aided design, multi-media, and sustainable technologies. We provide students with a strong skill base, rich interdisciplinary dialog, and generous support resources.

B. Arch Program

The Department of Architecture offers a five-year, nationally accredited professional Bachelor of Architecture degree. An education in architecture at Woodbury combines critical thinking, creative design, clarity in communication, technological literacy, and responsible, ethical behavior.

M. Arch 1 Program

Building on the success of the undergraduate program's emphasis on direct encounters with the realities in architecture and urbanism in the issue-oriented design studios, and the transformative value of the study–away programs, in fall of 2009 Woodbury will introduce a 2-year M.Arch.I program that has a field-work-oriented curriculum. The curriculum addresses urgent issues grounded in reality and contemporaniety and will prepare architects to effect positive change in the built environment while remaining intrepidly responsive to shifting theoretical debates. Woodbury's 4+2 M.Arch. 1 program has a clear emphasis on landscape urbanism, building technology, and entrepreneurship, unique in Southern California. Taking advantage of the diverse research opportunities in Southern California, the program will stimulate its graduates with the expertise to realize their visions as critically effective builders, trained to invent, craft, and inspire wonder while addressing the architectural, environmental, and urban challenges of the contemporary world. The 70 to 73-unit first-professional degree graduate program includes 15 to 18 electives and a summer "field-study" semester between the first and second year.

M. Arch Red Program

A program to equip architects with the expertise necessary to realize their ethical visions as effective entrepreneurs. Under the direction of architect-developer Ted Smith, of Smith and Others, the M.Arch RED program is a three-semester studio-based program offered to individuals holding a professional degree in architecture (B.Arch, M.Arch or D.Arch). The twelve-month program provides hands-on professional experience in real estate and project development for architects.

UNIVERSITY SETTING

Woodbury University is located within the southern California region—stretching from Los Angeles through San Diego to Tijuana. This Pacific Rim setting presents a vital and diverse context within which to examine architecture, urbanism, culture, and the natural environment. The Los Angeles campus is set at the foot of the Verdugo Hills and features a tranquil setting for study that offers a contrast to the stimulating urbanity of the campuses in Hollywood and San Diego. The San Diego campus is in an urban setting adjacent to downtown and the harbor.

SCHOOL PHILOSOPHY
WOODBURY : ARCHITECTURE : TRANSFORMS

We believe in architectural education as transformative.

We believe in the radical possibilities of architecture's relevance, socially, environmentally, and formally.

We are architects and critical thinkers who produce other architects and critical thinkers.

Woodbury's students, faculty, and graduates are committed to architecture that is:

- Intelligent—articulates a critical position
- Effective—addresses the challenges of contemporary life; and
- Beautiful—fully vested in the transformative power of beauty

Woodbury students distinguish themselves in local, regional, and national design competitions and scholarship awards; are valued in the workplace; and often go on to elite graduate schools. Woodbury School of Architecture delivers a strong and effective education that has garnered much regional attention and is poised to gain national prominence.

The department sees its vital and diverse student population, as well as its dynamic faculty, as its greatest asset. Thus, the pedagogical approach is to provide an excellent architectural education in an open, creative, and spirited environment that recognizes and promotes the potential of its students and faculty. Woodbury University's mission is to prepare graduates who are articulate, ethical, and innovative life-long learners.

PROGRAM DESCRIPTION

The themes of the architectural curriculum—critical thinking, design, building technology, representation, and professionalism—are each developed simultaneously throughout the program: proceeding from basic to specialized. Woodbury integrates into the design curriculum recent innovations in computer-aided design, multimedia, and sustainable technologies—encouraging student participation in architecture and university committees. The program combines architectural education with comprehensive foundation of humanist scholarship preparing students intellectually to perform effectively and ethically in an ever-changing global society. Students test, practice, and apply course content and possible interrelationships in a design studio every semester of the five-year sequence. The spring semester of their fifth year, students complete a final degree project. The subject and scope of this project emerges from the students' own interest and reflects accumulated growth during their five-year enrollment at Woodbury. Both the Los Angeles and San Diego campuses accept first-year and transfer students into the Department of Architecture. All B.Arch students are required to complete 300 hours of work experience with an approved architect or allied professional. Woodbury University is in the process of inaugurating a post-professional graduate program. Please contact the department chair for further information about this development.

AREAS OF FOCUS

The Woodbury architecture program encourages investigation of plural viewpoints within each campus location. For example, understanding border issues is a focus of studios and seminars in San Diego, mapping historical and contemporary ethnic neighborhoods,

proves a basis for research and analysis in Burbank-LA and Hollywood studios and seminars. Understanding European urbanism to see southern California issues more clearly is the foundation of the summer study-abroad program. The department has recognized the need to address globalization and environmental sustainability throughout the curriculum at the broadest level as part of the domain of the responsible architect.

SPECIAL ACTIVITIES AND PROGRAMS

The Department of Architecture actively seeks real-world projects to engage our students and faculty in the community. Recent community-based projects have included designing and building a mobile environmental studies laboratory for the City of Los Angeles, doing schematic designs for a community garden, and designing the Community center for a public art collective. The Hollywood Center for Community Research and Design (CCRD) offers public lectures and exhibits.

FACILITIES

Woodbury's facilities include a library, student cafeteria, student housing, career counseling and placement office, financial aid office, metal and wood shop, lecture facilities, exhibition space, photo darkroom, materials resource room, and computer labs (Mac & PC). All students have dedicated studio space accessible 24 hours a day. The library offers an extensive collection of books, slides, DVDs, multimedia equipment, and on-line research links. Student housing in Los Angeles includes two residence halls that accommodate a total of 203. The university also offers student support through campus security, food service, health services, international student programs, residence life, student activities, and orientation programs.

SCHOLARSHIPS AND FINANCIAL AID

Financial aid includes subsidized and unsubsidized student loans, grants, federal work-study, scholarships and awards. Scholarships are awarded based on scholarship–specific criteria that may include academic merit, personal achievement, and financial need, among others. There are scholarships designated for Woodbury architecture students only. Woodbury students have been recipients of scholarships available to students in the local architecture/design programs, as well as scholarships awarded by local and national professional and community associations.

ADMINISTRATION

Norman Millar, AIA; Director
norman.millar@woodbury.edu

Ingalill Wahlroos-Ritter; Associate Director,
Los Angeles Campus
ingalill.wahlroos-ritter@woodbury.edu

Catherine Herbst; Associate Director,
San Diego Campus
catherine.herbst@woodbury.edu

YALE UNIVERSITY

ADDRESS

Main
Yale University
School of Architecture
P.O. Box 208242 (180 York St.)
New Haven, CT 06520-8242
Tel.: 203.432.2288
Fax: 203.432.7175
www.architecture.yale.edu

STUDENT AND FACULTY DEMOGRAPHICS

% of Female Students	42
% of International Students	2
% of Minority Students	2
% of Out-of-State U.S. Students	100
No. Full-Time Faculty	18
No. Part-Time Faculty	78
No. Full-Time Students	100
No. Part-Time Students	0

FINANCIAL INFORMATION

Main Source of University Funding	Private
Annual Tuition & Fees (graduate)	$34,950
Annual Tuition & Fees (undergraduate)	
% Students Receiving Federal Financial Aid	62
% Students Receiving University Financial Aid	78
% Students Receiving Departmental Financial Aid	78
% Students Receiving Scholarships (assistantships or fellowships)	78
Average Annual Scholarship for Department	

ACADEMIC SESSIONS

Fall Semester: August to December
Spring Semester: January to May

ARCHITECTURE AND RELATED DEGREE PROGRAMS

Degree	Min. Yrs. to Complete	Professional Accreditation	# of FT Students	# of PT Students	# of First-Year Students	# of Degrees Conferred	Admissions Requirements
Architecture							
M. Arch—2 years	2	NAAB	28	0	15	14	
M. Arch—3 years	3	NAAB	180	0	60	67	Undergraduate degree, GRE, TOEFL, Portfolio, Rec. Letters, Essay
PhD Program to begin Fall 2009							Undergraduate degree, Prof. Architecture degree
Environmental Design							
M Env Design	2		7	0	3	2	

SPECIALIZATIONS

Architectural Design

UNIVERSITY SETTING

The School of Architecture offers professional and post-professional programs leading to an M.Arch. degree at the graduate level for recipients of baccalaureate degrees from accredited colleges. A non-professional, two-year research degree, the Master of Environmental Design, is also offered. Yale College also offers a non-professional undergraduate major in architecture. The school is one of the twelve graduate and professional schools, that along with Yale College, make up Yale University. A major private institution of higher learning since 1701, Yale has a strong historic commitment to the arts. The institutional and physical context of the School of Architecture includes internationally recognized Schools of Music, Drama, and Art, as well as major university art museums and professional theatres. The arts, humanistic scholarship, and scientific research are all recognized as integral components of the university community. Yale University is an urban institution, now spreading over 200 acres, but still focused on the historic New Haven Green, dating from the original 1638 plan. Students live on campus in university housing or off campus in city neighborhoods adjacent to the university. In addition to its own considerable cultural resources, New Haven is 90 minutes by train from New York City and 3 hours from Boston.

The School of Architecture maintains a student enrollment from a variety of undergraduate backgrounds. While admission is very selective, the School actively seeks a diverse student body. Highly-motivated and independent students have been the greatest strength of the School, organizing a wide range of events and publications, working in the local community, and creating an atmosphere of exceptional intensity and creativity. The alumni of the School include a high percentage of internationally recognized practicing architects, many of whom remain active and involved in the life of the School.

SCHOOL PHILOSOPHY

Undergraduate Philosophy

Architecture is studied in Yale College in the context of rigorous and broadly-based liberal arts education. The undergraduate major in architecture is designed to support the study of architecture by students with a wide range of interests who have not necessarily decided to pursue professional education in the field. Architecture and architectural design are seen as part of the culturally and socially based production of meaning also studied by the humanities and social sciences, and students are encouraged to combine their study of architecture with continuing interdisciplinary studies throughout the college.

Graduate Philosophy

The School of Architecture is committed to a professional education, and to research and scholarship, based upon the understanding of architecture as an expression of human values and as a setting for human activity. The situation of the School within a major university supports and reflects its understanding of the discipline of architecture as part of the larger pursuit of knowledge and the making of culture. At the School of Architecture, that commitment has been expressed by an educational philosophy of critical pluralism. The School has a special commitment to the study of architecture within an urban setting and to the inseparability of architectural ideas, their representation, and their realization as built form.

PROGRAM DESCRIPTION

The undergraduate major in architecture is open only to students enrolled in Yale College. As with other undergraduate majors, prerequisite courses are taken in the freshman and sophomore years, and concentration is developed in the junior and senior years after admission to the major. Students may pursue studies in two tracks: Spatial Language in Design or Theory and Criticism of Architecture. Graduate-level courses are open to qualified undergraduates.

The three-year M.Arch. program is designed to provide students pursuing the first-professional degree with a thorough and rigorous professional education leading to the practice of architecture. Required courses in drawing, history and theory, structures, materials and construction, and environmental controls are concentrated in the first four semesters of the program. These semesters include a four-term sequence of required studios set up to introduce design issues and methods at a variety of scales and through a variety of building types. Students who have previously completed courses at other institutions which satisfy requirements may be waived from required courses, increasing their number of elective credits available. Required courses provide a base not only for professional education and practice, but also for advanced study and research in support of an individual student's personal interests and career goals. Elective courses, advanced studios, and independent study are important components of a professional education and allow a student at Yale to work with leading scholars and professionals in architecture and a variety of fields. Interdisciplinary studies are encouraged by the School and by the university. The design studio requirement for the final two semesters of the three-year program may be satisfied by two of the advanced studios offered by distinguished visiting faculty or the senior faculty of the School, or by one advanced studio and one independent studio proposed by the student.

Students enrolled in the two-year post-professional M.Arch. program pursue a course of study consisting entirely of elective courses and advanced or independent studios. These students are encouraged to pursue not only advanced explorations in architectural design, but also theoretical and research interests which may lead to careers in specialized areas or in teaching. The curriculum of the School is organized according to the following areas of study: architectural design; structures; environmental control systems; architectural practice and construction; architectural history and theory; visual studies; computer-aided design; and planning, design, and development of the urban landscape.

SPECIAL ACTIVITIES AND PROGRAMS

The design curriculum at the School of Architecture is enhanced by four endowed visiting professorships in architectural design, which normally bring eight distinguished practitioners to the School each year to teach advanced studios. There is a lively program of exhibitions and lectures. The School offers a joint degree program with the Yale School of Organization and Management. Students in either the three-year professional M. Arch. or the two-year post-professional M.Arch. programs may apply for admission to the School of Organization and Management and complete both degrees in one additional year of study.

The School also offers a two-year research degree, the Master of Environmental Design. The program is directed at graduates of both architecture programs and programs in related fields, practicing architects, and other mid-career professionals. Students pursue a program of coursework and independent study and write a substantial research-based thesis. Student publications include *Perspecta*, the oldest student architectural journal, *Retrospecta*, an annual publication documenting the work of the school, the new *Yale Journal of Architecture and Feminism, Rapsheets*, an occasional publication of opinion and criticism, and *Constructs*, a twice-yearly newsletter of the School. Recent exhibitions and symposia have focused on "New Blue," the work of recent alumni, "Saving Corporate Modernism," "The Charles Moore Years at Yale in the 1960s," "Women," "Family and the Practice of Architecture," and "Informed Terrain: Art, Architecture & Cartography in the Age of Digital Media." Students sit on all major committees of the School, including admissions, lectures, and exhibitions. The School annually awards a number of prizes, fellowships, and honors, including two endowed traveling fellowships. Since 1968, students in the spring term of the first-year of the three-year M.Arch. program have participated in the design and construction of a small building for a community or non profit client. Graduate students in all programs may be eligible to gain teaching experience as teaching assistants in undergraduate courses and studios.

FACILITIES

Since 1963, the School of Architecture has occupied the Art and Architecture building designed by Paul Rudolph. In addition to the Art and Architecture Library, the work of the school is supported by the Computer Laboratory, a woodworking shop, a structures laboratory, a metal shop, photographic darkroom and print room, Hastings Auditorium, and exhibition gallery. Adjacent facilities include the Yale Art Gallery and British Art Center, both in significant buildings by Louis Kahn, and a major collection of slides and photographs in Street Hall.

ADMINISTRATION

Robert A. Stern: Dean
John Jacobson: Associate Dean
Keith Krumwiede: Assistant Dean, Student Affairs
Bimal Mendis: Assistant Dean,
    Student/Career Development

ACSA AFFILIATE MEMBER SCHOOLS

ACSA's Affiliate Member roster is composed of more than 70 schools and institutions throughout the world. Listings are classified into three categories:

Affiliate Members: Schools and institutions offering programs or courses in architecture or related disciplines within the United States & Canada, which do not qualify for full or candidate membership.

International Associate Members: Schools and institutions offering professional degree programs in architecture outside the United States and Canada which are officially recognized as such by the appropriate authorities of their country.

International Affiliate Members: Schools and institutions offering programs or courses in architecture or related disciplines outside the United State and Canada.

NEW VISIONS OF SECURITY: RE-LIFE OF A DFW AIRPORT TERMINAL, 2007–08
ACSA/U.S. Department of Homeland Security Student Design Competition
First Place Winner
Students: Blake Burton & Tristan Phillip Hall, Georgia Institute of Technology
Faculty Sponsor: Harris Dimitropoulos, PhD, Georgia Institute of Technology
Project Title: Re-life of a Terminal

ACSA AFFILIATE MEMBER SCHOOLS

ANNE ARUNDEL COMMUNITY COLLEGE

Department of Architecture and Interior Design
School of Business, Computing and Technical Studies
101 College Parkway, CALT 234
Arnold, MD 21012-1895

Tel: 410/777-2442
Fax: 410/777-2445
mdryan@aacc.edu
www.aacc.edu/architecture
Contact: Michael Ryan, Department Chair

Degrees/Certificates Offered
Associate of Applied Science (AAS)
FT students: 475
FT faculty: 7

Admission Requirements
High School Transcript/GED, SAT/ACT

Tuition & Fees
$86/credit hour in county resident
$165/credit hour out-of-county resident
$292/credit hour out-of-state resident

Program Description
The Architecture program serves two fundamental groups: those who plan to transfer and those who seek immediate employment. The emphasis is on design, technology, sustainability and computer-aided drafting and design. Students are prepared for transfer to a university and/or placement in the work force.

The department offers three primary disciplines: architecture, interior design, and construction management. Additionally, there is a certificate in landscape design. Each offers an option for obtaining a two-year associate of applied science degree, as well as certificates which target specific skills for immediate employment or professional development. Courses in certificate programs may also be applied toward one of the degree options.

Award-winning full and part-time faculty members are locally and nationally certified as licensed, practicing professionals. Several faculty are graduates of the program.

Many student projects, based on real situations, are actually built. Active architecture interior design and construction management clubs provide opportunities to meet socially and network with outside organizations. Students have participated in and won design contests, often beating upper-level university students and practicing professionals in the field. The program and its students continue to receive awards from community, governmental and national organizations.

BOWLING GREEN STATE UNIVERSITY

Architectural & Environmental Design Program
College of Technology
Architecture Studies Building
Bowling Green State University
Bowling Green, OH 43403

Tel: 419/372-9885
Fax: 419/372-6066
Email: guidera@bgnet.bgsu.edu

Web: www.http://www.bgsu.edu/colleges/technology/
undergraduate/arch/index.html
Contact: Stan G. Guidera

Degrees/Certificates Offered
Undergraduate: B.S. in Technology, with major in Architecture & Environmental Design Studies
Graduate: M.Arch in planning stage
FT Students: 160
FT Faculty: 7

Admission Requirements
University admission requirements

Tuition & Fees
Undergraduate per semester: $4,530 resident
$8,184 non-resident

Program Description
The Architecture/Environmental Program at BGSU is a pre-professional program for students interested in pursuing a career in architecture or a related field, such as urban design, computer-aided design, and/or historic preservation. The program goal is to balance the development of technical knowledge and skills with the cultivation of professional values and leadership abilities necessary for success in our knowledge and innovation-based technology. The curriculum is structured around the study of the theoretical, technical, and professional parameters of architecture integrated with a liberal education at a university recognized for its leadership in the liberal arts. The program emphasizes interaction with the professional design community and maintains an ongoing working relationship with the Toledo Design Center, an architecture and urban design resource center located in Toledo's downtown business district, providing opportunities for community-based studio projects linking theory and practice. The undergraduate curriculum is structured around a six- semester studio sequence following first year coursework that includes design representation, introductory CAD and digital technologies, and general education. In addition to the studio sequence and technical coursework, the program provides opportunities to study advanced digital technologies, historic preservation, and materials and construction technologies. Some program features include a very active AIAS chapter, co-operative education courses, a lecture series, and summer study-abroad opportunities.

BGSU graduates currently earn the Bachelor of Science in Technology degree and must subsequently obtain a master of architecture degree from an accredited institution to become a licensed architect. Approximately 70% of our graduates pursue graduate studies, which generally takes two to three years to complete. BGSU architecture graduates are regularly accepted to graduate programs across the nation. A Master of Architecture degree offered by BGSU is currently under development.

Bowling Green State University, located in Bowling Green, Ohio, has approximately 21,000 students from 49 states and about 85 foreign nations.

BROWARD COMMUNITY COLLEGE

Department of Architecture & Design
225 E. Las Olas Boulevard
331423
Ft. Lauderdale, FL 33301

Tel: 954.201.7396
Fax: 954.201.7379
Contact: Ken Williams, Center Administrator

Degrees/Certificates Offered
AS Architectural Design & Construction Technology
AA Architecture

Tuition & Fees
$2,500 per year

Program Description
The Advanced Technical certificate in Interior Design, offered at the Higher Education Complex (Willis Holcombe Center), is designed as a specialized extension to the Associate in Science degree in Architectural Design and Construction Technology program. Graduates from this program will gain supplemental skills in areas of architecture, construction, and interior design. Students will gain an understanding of the interdisciplinary nature of these fields. Coursework focuses on understanding the technical and aesthetic principles essential to the planning of interior spaces, color, and design theory, selection and specification of interior materials and finishes, drafting and interdisciplinary communication standards, business practices and marketing. This program is aimed at architects and those ancillary fields in architecture, construction, and interior design.

CALVIN COLLEGE

Department of Art and Art History
3201 Burton SE
Grand Rapids, MI 49546
Tel: 616.526.6744
ya22@calvin.edu
www.calvin.edu/academic/art/programs/pre-arch
Contact: You-Kyong Ahn, Assistant Professor of Art and Architecture

Degrees/Certificates Offered
B.A. degree major in any field or an interdisciplinary group major with specialization in architecture (required qualifying courses for graduate professional programs).

Admission, Tuition, and other general information is available from www.calvin.edu

Program Description
Calvin College is a Christian liberal arts college whose rigorous thirty-year old pre-architecture program primarily prepares students for graduate M. Arch. Programs. Graduate Professional programs at Harvard, Columbia, Michigan, Illinois, Rice, Virginia, University of California, Berkeley as well as others ranked in the top twenty programs have admitted our graduates to both their programs in architecture as well as in urban planning. The AIAS chapter is active both on campus as well as with the regional AIA Grand Valley and the AIA Michigan chapters.

CENTRAL PIEDMONT COMMUNITY COLLEGE

Architectural Technology Programs
Central Campus, IT 2110
P.O. Box 35009
Charlotte, NC 28235-35009

Tel: 704/330-6548
Fax: 704/330-6913
mick.campbell@cpcc.edu
http://arts.cpcc.edu/academics/architectural-technology
Contact: Mitchell W. Campbell, AIA, Program Chair

Degrees/Certificates Offered

AAS in Architectural Technology
AAS in Interior Design
Pre-architecture Diploma
Certificate in Computer-Aided Drafting and Design
Certificate in Residential Technology

Admission Requirements

High School Diploma or Equivalent
Placement tests in English & Mathematics

Program Description

The Architectural Technology curriculum prepares individuals with knowledge and skills that can lead to employment in the field of architecture or one of the associated professions. Students receive instruction in construction document preparation, materials and methods, environmental and structural systems, building codes and specifications, and computer applications, as well as the completion of a design project.

Upon completion, graduates have career opportunities within the architectural, engineering, and construction professions as well as positions in industry and government.

The programs at Central Piedmont Community College include emphasis on computer-aided drafting (CAD) and related computer courses to prepare graduates for employment in the expanding CAD area within the field of Architectural Technology.

Interior Design—The Interior Design curriculum is designed to prepare students for a variety of job opportunities in the field of both residential and non-residential interior design. The focus of the studies is technical knowledge, professional practices, graphic presentations and general education courses. Graduates should qualify for a variety of jobs including residential and commercial interior design, set design, showroom design, and sales positions for furniture, textiles and accessories, and all businesses dealing with interiors.

COLLEGE OF DUPAGE

Department of Architecture
425 22nd Street
IC 1028 Leary
Glen Ellyn, IL 60137-6599

Tel: 630/942-2502
Fax: 630/858-5409
learyd@cdnet.cod.edu
www.cod.edu/
Contact: David Leary

Degrees/Certificates Offered

Associate in Arts, Associate in Science,
Associate in Applied Science
FT Students: 75
FT Faculty: 3

Admission Requirements

Admission is open to anyone who is a high school graduate or is at least 18 years old

Tuition & Fees

$27/credit hour in-district
$83/credit hour out-of-district
$107/credit hour non-Illinois resident

Program Description

Architecture is a manifestation of cultural aspirations embedded in physical form. Our daily experience of the world, that which is constructed by human hands, and that which is naturally occurring, is an unavoidable human condition. The design studio sequence is primarily concerned with speculations... philosophical, religious, scientific, literary, architectural... these repositories of illumination have transformed concepts of the universe throughout time. Probing the depth of visual traditions and their artifacts, in turn based upon intellectual constructs, reveal those attempts to impart meaning to the physical realm. A familiarity with, and a response to, these fundamental yet profound questions, permeate the primary academic investigations within which an education in architecture commences.

The study of architectural design at DuPage is an immersion in architectural making and thought as it is externally presented. More importantly, the design studios are structured to provoke and challenge the individual student's analysis and digestion of this culture. These investigations form the foundation upon which the student begins to have a personal response to the contemporary world of architecture, and if it be their desire, their eventual place within it. This method of primary architectural education has facilitated transfer of our students to university architecture programs throughout the country.

CONNECTICUT COLLEGE

Department of Art History and Architectural Studies
Connecticut College
270 Mohegan Avenue
New London, CT 06320-4196

Tel: 860/439-2740
Fax: 860/439-5339
jdalc@conncoll.edu, aavan@conncoll.edu
www.conncoll.edu/academics/departments/
     arch_studies
Contact: Abigail A. Van Slyck: Director

Degrees/Certificates Offered

B.A. with a major in Architectural Studies.
FT students: 37
FT faculty: 2.4

Admission Requirements

Average rank and GPA are top 20% and A-. ACT or 3 SATIIs are required.

Tuition & Fees

Undergraduate: $37,900

Program Description

Architectural Studies allows students to pursue specific interests in architecture as part of a general liberal arts education. Students may choose to develop a particular focus through their selection of courses or prepare for a professional career in architecture, urban planning, historic preservation, interior design, or other allied fields.

The major in Architectural Studies consists of twelve classes. In addition to four core courses and seven electives in the arts, humanities, sciences, and social sciences, each student also completes an integrative project either as an independent study project, as an honors thesis, or through a local internship.

CUESTA COLLEGE

Department of Architecture
P.O. Box 8106
San Luis Obispo, CA 93403-8106

Tel: 805.546.3100
Fax: 805.546.3963
Contact person: Bruce A. Silverberg, R.A.

Degrees/Certificates Offered

A.S., Architectural Technology
Certificate of Proficiency, Architectural Drafting
FT Students: 117 full-time architecture majors; 139 full-time students enrolled in at least one architecture course
FT Faculty: 2
PT Faculty: 5

Admission Requirements

Cuesta College offers "open door" admission for:
- Any person with a high school diploma;
- Any person 18 years of age or older who does not hold a high school diploma or the equivalent to a high school diploma;
- Any person who has passed the California State Proficiency Exam or equivalent. A copy of the certification is required if under 18.
- Transfer students from colleges, universities, and other post-secondary programs;
- Any person who has served in the Armed Forces of the United States;
- Students interested in completing postsecondary coursework for personal development, vocational training, and/or transfer to a four-year educational institution;

Minors, known as Enrichment students, currently enrolled in grades K-12, who in the opinion of their school principal, would benefit from concurrent enrollment in "advanced scholastic" or "vocational" college coursework. The following is required:
- A Permit to enroll with specific courses identified and approved by the school principal, along with the parents' signature is required prior to registration.
- Minors, grades K-8, will need to meet with the Director of Admissions and Records, or designee, prior to registration.
- Enrichment students may not enroll in more than 11 units each semester (4 units in summer session) and may not be approved to take physical education courses.

- Students enrolled in home school must attach a copy of a current Private School Affidavit to the Permit to Enroll.

Tuition & Fees
In State: Enrollment Fee: $20 per unit
Additional college fees apply
Out-of-State: Enrollment Fee: $20 per unit, plus
Tuition: $181.00 per unit
Additional college fees apply

Program Description
The Architecture program at Cuesta College, prepares individuals for challenging careers in the architecture profession and its related design and technical fields. An acknowledged leader in architectural education among California's community colleges, Cuesta strives to offer its students the best foundation for transferring to a university program or entering the workforce. The program offers three pathways for the pursuit of these goals:

- University Transfer: Most architecture courses offered at Cuesta are articulated with either or both of California's state university systems, CSU and UC, for transfer credit to meet their lower-division course requirements in architecture and related environmental design disciplines. The vast majority of Cuesta's architecture students pursue this option.
- Associate of Science Degree in Architectural Technology: Preparing students for employment as Production Technicians in Architecture and related field, the A.S. degree is closely aligned/articulated with the CSU Architecture lower division requirements, giving students the option to either apply for transfer or to enter the workforce directly as architectural production technicians. A total of 34 major-related course units are required for completion of the A.S. program, and students must chose a concentration in one of the following areas: (1) Computer Applications (Computer Aided Drafting); or (2) Structural Engineering (Statics, Strength of Materials, and Structural Systems).
- Certificate of Proficiency: The Architectural Technology Certificate of Proficiency Program is designed to give students the entry-level skills required for employment as Architectural Drafting Technicians. The curriculum is vocational and mandates the completion of 21.5 units of study in construction methods, architectural and environmental design, architectural practice, visual communication, computer-aided design and building information management. A total of 27.5 units are required for completion of the program.

DUTCHESS COMMUNITY COLLEGE
53 Pendell Road
Poughkeepsie, New York 12601

Tel: 845-431-8410
Fax: 845-431-8996
freeman@sunydutchess.edu
enact.sunydutchess.edu
Contact: David Freeman A.I.A.
845-431-8410

Degrees/Certificates Offered
Architectural Technology AAS
FT students: 85 in program
FT faculty: 3 in program

Admission Requirements
Open Enrollment

Tuition & Fees
Full-Time Tuition $2900.00 (lowest New York State Community College tuition)

Program Description
The Architectural Technology Program prepares the graduate for employment opportunities in the field of architecture. Dutchess Community College graduates are also able to transfer many of their credits to accredited architectural colleges.

First-year students are introduced to design, hand drafting and computer aided drafting. Student design projects include residential and small-scale commercial design. The students study construction materials and methods of construction in wood frame residential buildings in the first semester and commercial construction in the second semester.

Second-year students continue to develop their understanding of design by taking on more complex residential and commercial building types. Students also expand their drawing and organizational skills by learning to prepare construction drawings of commercial building types.

FAIRMOUNT STATE UNIVERSITY
Architectural Engineering Technology
1201 Locust Avenue
Fairmont, WV 26554

Tel: 304/367-4156
Fax: 304/367-4791
kmorphew@mail.fscwv.edu
www.fscwv.edu/schools/tech/architectural/arch_welcome.html
Contact: Kirk Morphew

Degrees/Certificates Offered
Undergraduate: Associate of Science and Bachelor of Science
Graduate: N/A
FT students: 100
FT faculty: 3

Admission Requirements
Admission to A.S. degree is open to all graduates of approved high schools. Admission to B.S. requires 2.75 HS GPA, 19 ACT or 910 SAT

Tuition & Fees
Undergraduate:
A.S. Program tuition for full-time resident: $2,508
A.S. Program tuition for full-time non-resident: $5,904
B.S. Program tuition for full-time resident: $2,766
B.S. Program tuition for full-time non-resident: $6,340

Program Description
The Architectural Engineering Technology program couples the development of a hands-on technology

background with the specific activity of designing built forms. The curriculum is structured with two primary objectives, which are reflected in the 2+2 study plan:
1) To develop a programmatically sound foundation, leading to the associate degree.
2) To deliver a pre-professional curriculum in architecture, leading to the baccalaureate degree.
The first objective enables students to develop an understanding of architectural technology and the basic concepts of building construction. The second objective enables students to concentrate on the integration of architecture within the context of the built environment, as well as within the theoretical construct.

Upon completion of years 1 and 2, students with the associate degree can seek employment as entry-level technicians or continue to pursue the baccalaureate degree.

As a pre-professional degree, the program prepares students for a variety of positions in architecture and related fields and/or academic opportunities. Since this is not a professional degree program (B.Arch), the content reflects the expectation that a portion of the students will continue to pursue their studies at the graduate level in order to obtain their professional degree in architecture or related disciplines.

FITCHBURG STATE COLLEGE
Industrial Technology Department
Architectural Technology Concentration
160 Pearl Street
Fitchburg, MA 01420

Tel: 978 665-3051
Fax: 978 665-4435
www.fsc.edu/indtech/architecttech.cfm
Contact: D. Keith Chenot, AIA
kchenot@fsc.edu

Degrees/Certificates Offered
BS Industrial Technology
Architectural Technology Concentration
FT Students: 250 Industrial Technology
90 Architectural Technology
FT Faculty: 8 Industrial Technology

Admission Requirements
Go to: http://www.fsc.edu/enrollsrv/freshman.cfm

Tuition & Fees
In-State (if applicable): $13,654 Full Time Fall '08
Out-of-State (if applicable): $19,734 Full Time Fall '08

Program Description
Architectural Technology at Fitchburg State College is a pre-professional program that provides a foundation of architectural and technology undergraduate studies. It is based on a strong exposure to the many facets of architecture and architectural design that include residential, commercial, urban, and sustainability issues.

Equal emphasis is placed on technological components such as drawing, computer aided drafting (CAD), 3D building information modeling (BIM), site planning, construction and materials technology, energy and sustainability, mechanical and electrical systems, and architectural professional practice.

These courses are interwoven with a comprehensive education in the liberal arts and sciences which includes writing, literature, behavioral sciences, history of architecture, art, technical calculus, and physics.

The program is structured to prepare students with a focused knowledge base and, with the introduction of design, a combination of both linear and creative thinking skills. The curriculum requires approximately 122 semester hours and follows a relatively prescribed four-year course of study. This leads to a degree of Bachelor of Science in Industrial Technology with a concentration in Architectural Technology.

Graduates are prepared to enter the design/building industry or proceed to graduate programs in architecture or other related design and construction programs. Job opportunities include working in architectural offices and many design and building industry related positions.

GEORGE BROWN COLLEGE

Faculty of Technology
146 Kendal Avenue
Toronto, Ontario M5T 2T9
Canada

Tel: 416.415.5000
Fax: 416.415.4515
www.georgebrown.ca
Contact: Steffanie Adams

Degrees/Certificates Offered
Diploma in Architecture Technology

Admission Requirements
Ontario Secondary School Diploma or Equivalent
OAC or General Math, English

Tuition & Fees
$2,608

Program Description
Skylines, suburbs and structures of all kinds continue to change. As an Architectural Technology graduate, you can influence that change with environmental responsibility. The Architectural Technology three-year program at George Borwn College prepares you to work as a team member with architects, engineers, designers and project managers to design our living and working environments, using sustainable building practices.

Working in modern studios that resemble architectural offices, you will develop a solid foundation of architectural technical and administrative skills and sustainable design reflecting current green principles. The program prepares you to apply current business aspects of the architectural industry, including construction law, contracts and specifications, project design and quantity surveying (estimating the labour, materials and equipment required for a project). You will also develop and practice skills in computer-aided drafting and design, building codes, architectural presentation (including perspective drawing, modelling), and design.

Our Work Experience/Capstone Project provides hands-on work placement in a job related to your future career. Teamwork and projects simulate an office environment and whenever possible, projects involve designs and proposals for buildings or other properties that you visit as part of your fieldwork.

HOBART AND WILLIAM SMITH COLLEGES

Architectural Studies
Art Department
Geneva, NY 14456

Tel: 315.781.3487
Fax: 315.781.3689
mathews@hws.edu
academic.hws.edu/arch
Contact: Stanley Mathews, Chair

Degrees/Certificates Offered
BA Architectural Studies
FT students: 15
FT faculty: 2

Admission Requirements
Candidates for admission are expected to complete a secondary school program with a minimum of four academic subjects each year. At a minimum that program should include four years of English, three or more years of mathematics, three or more years of social science, three or more years of science, and two or more years of a foreign language. A design portfolio is not required.

Tuition & Fees
$48,546 per year

Program Description
Architectural Studies at Hobart and William Smith Colleges offers a multi-disciplinary, holistic approach to design education, embracing a liberal arts philosophy. Unlike the pre-professional training offered in many undergraduate professional degree programs, Architectural Studies at Hobart and William Smith Colleges is broad-based, varied, flexible, and centered in the liberal arts. Students may, along with their advisor, tailor the major to suit their particular academic interests. While our program does not offer a professional degree, many of our graduates choose to complete a professional architecture degree at the graduate level.

ILLINOIS CENTRAL COLLEGE

One College Drive
East Peoria, IL 61635-0001

Tel: 309/694-5734
Fax: 309/694-5735
www.icc.edu
Contact: Frank Corso, AIA

Degrees/Certificates Offered
Associate in Arts and Science - Architecture
Associate in Applied Science - Architectural Construction Technology
Certificate - Architectural Drafting
FT students: 120
FT faculty: 3, ADJUNCT : 6

Admission Requirements
High School Diploma, 4 units English, 3 units math, 2 units each of social science, laboratory science, foreign language, fine arts or vocational education and electives.

Tuition & Fees
In-district: $82/credit hour
Out-of-district: $180/credit hour
Out-of-state: $180/credit hour

Program Description
Illinois Central College students number over 12,000 on its Peoria and East Peoria campuses. The college is ideally located midway between St. Louis, Missouri, and Chicago, Illinois, to take advantage of the opportunities and architectural treasures from these two great cities.

The architectural curriculum is a two-year Associate Degree program articulated with the University of Illinois, Urbana-Champaign, and with transfer options to other college and university architectural schools. Students may complete courses in basic design studio, freehand drawing, introduction to architectural history, and building materials and methods of construction, as well as general education degree requirements. Computer-Aided Drafting and Design (CADD) and architectural illustration are integrated into the program. Students have access to state-of-the-art computer labs, photographic studio, and construction lab, all within the same building. Students may participate in the Study Abroad program with the University of Illinois at Versailles, France, with the assistance of a transfer scholarship provided by the college.

Illinois Central College also provides continuing education credits through its Professional Development Institute. Program offerings range from Code Compliance to Indoor Air Quality and numerous computer-training workshops to enhance and upgrade skills of local professionals.

JAMES MADISON UNIVERSITY

School of Art & Art History
820 South Main Street
MSC 7101
Harrisonburg, VA 22807

Tel: 540/568-6216
Fax: 540/568-6598
www.jmu.edu/artandarthistory
Contact: Leslie Bellavance, Director

Degrees/Certificates Offered
B.A., studio art or art history
B.S., studio art of industrial design
B.F.A., studio art (emphasis in fine arts, graphic design, interior design)
M.A., art, art history, art education
M.F.A., studio art
FT students: 700 art and art history majors
18,000 general enrollment
FT faculty: 30

Admission Requirements
Admission is competitive and selective. Contact the JMU Office of Admissions at: 540/568-5681 for details.
Tuition & Fees
Current tuition fees can be located on the JMU Student Financial Services Web site at: www.jmu.edu/stufin.

Program Description

JMU is committed to preparing students to be educated and enlightened citizens who will lead productive and meaningful lives. Established in 1908, JMU has grown to become a selective, co-educational, and comprehensive public university serving approximately 18,000 students. The School of Art and Art History is NASAD and CIDA accredited and is located in the College of Visual and Performing Arts. The visual arts program enrolls over 700 undergraduate and graduate art and art history majors, and is served by a teaching faculty of 50 professionals.

KEENE STATE COLLEGE

Technology, Design and Safety
229 Main Street
Keene, NH 03435-1901

Tel: 603.358.2312
Fax: 603.358.2871
www.keene.edu/programs/arch
Contact: Larry McDonald, Department Chair

Degrees/Certificates Offered

Bachelor of Science in Architecture
FT students: 25
FT faculty: 2

Admission Requirements

General Application to Keene State College

Tuition & Fees

NH resident: $7,800
Out-of-state: $15,100

Program Description

The Architecture major at Keene State College is a pre-professional four-year program designed to give students a solid foundation in the artistic, scientific, and technical aspects of architecture. The curriculum offers a range of courses in studio design, building science, sustainable design, history/theory, digital technology, and practice.

The education of KSC architecture majors, grounded in the liberal arts, focuses on teaching students to become effective, creative problemsolvers with the tools to adapt and evolve their career paths to meet the needs of a rapidly changing world. Graduates in architecture are prepared to pursue graduate study or transition directly into careers in architecture, planning, building science, construction management, environmental design, design-build, or other related professions.

LEHIGH UNIVERSITY

Department of Art and Architecture
17 Memorial Drive East
Bethlehem, PA 18015

Tel: 610/758-3610
Fax: 610/758-6551
www3.lehigh.edu/arts-sciences/casuart.asp
Contact: Anthony Viscardi, Chair

Degrees/Certificates Offered

Bachelor of Arts in Architecture
FT Students: 140
FT Faculty: 12

Admission Requirements

Admissions to Lehigh University of College of Arts and Sciences.

Tuition & Fees

$49,540

Program Description

The Department of Art and Architecture is part of the College of Arts and Sciences. The degree granted by the university is a liberal arts BA with a major in architecture.

A major in architecture is designed to give the student a strong liberal education related to the issues of the built environment. The major requirements include 22 credits in architectural design, 12 credits in art studio, and 18 credits in history, theory and related disciplines. Courses in calculus (8 credits) and physics (5 credits) are also required.

Other courses related to architecture offered by the Division of Urban Studies, Classical Studies, and Technology are recommended. It is the interaction of these areas and a strong design base that defines the character of architectural education at Lehigh. This program is intended primarily for students who plan to attend graduate schools of architecture and stresses design as the architect's essential skill.

The major is also open to students admitted to the College of Engineering who may take a dual degree of five years and earn a BA (Architecture) and BS (Civil Engineering).

MARYLAND INSTITUTE COLLEGE OF ART

Environmental Design
1300 Mount Royal Avenue
Baltimore, MD 21217

Tel: 410.225.2240
Fax: 410.225.2240
www.mica.edu
Contact: Peter Chomowicz, Department Chair

Degrees/Certificates Offered

Bachelor of Arts in Environmental Design

Program Description

In the Environmental Design Department we believe that designers will increasingly find themselves at the center of converging professional disciplines. The historic barriers between design and nearly all other professional disciplines are quickly dissolving away. In their place are new paradigms that put the designer in a crucial role to integrate diverse expertise in pursuit of solving complex social issues.

This is hugely important because nearly everything in your life is designed. The page you are reading, the chair you are sitting in, the room, building, block and city around you, even the airplane above your head and the train below your feet were all ideas turned into form. Each began as a question, "why isn't there a ..." and ended with a solution that changes how we live, work

and play. A solution that changes the world.

The goal of the environmental design department is to create informed, critical, and passionate investigators of built form. From the smallest prototyped object, to furniture, to interior spaces to architecture to entire cities, environmental design is deeply concerned with addressing societal dilemmas through the exploration of form and materials.

The exploration of ideas, forms, drawings, and tools is a holistic process, requiring mastery of different mediums, concepts and methods. Students develop through visualizing and constructing their ideas. In Environmental Design this means acquiring comfort across the full spectrum of available techniques. From traditional hand and power tools to advanced rapid prototyping and remote sensing, from freehand sketching to 3D animations, MICA students gain the necessary training to fully realize their ideas.

By equipping students with the technical and conceptual tools demanded by today's professional design firms, our students are well prepared to utilize their talents under a broad range of project types, sizes and locations.

Graduates of MICA's environmental design program have been accepted into the highly competitive master's of architecture programs at Yale University, the University of Pennsylvania, Catholic University, Syracuse University, and the University of Maryland, College Park. Others are working in architecture and industrial design firms in across the US. A wide array of internships has been developed for MICA students in environmental design, including an industrial design internship at Baltimore-based Black & Decker.

NEW ENGLAND INSTITUTE OF TECHNOLOGY

Department of Architectural and Building Engineering Technology
2500 Post Road
Warwick, RI 02886

Tel: 401/467-7744
Fax: 401/738-5122
Contact: Philip C. Marks, Chairman

Degrees/Certificates Offered

Associate and Bachelor's degrees
FT students: 75

Program Description

The Architectural and Building Engineering Technology Program at New England Institute of Technology combines the art of designing buildings in the context of their fundamental systems and components with the engineering and technical concepts of construction.

The program is based upon the premise that buildings are designed and built using the team concept. As an integral member of that team, the architectural engineer must have the ability to create buildings that will answer the economic, safety, technical and aesthetic requirements of a project. This program allows the student to develop those necessary abilities by emphasizing the fundamentals of architectural design combined with the scientific and engineering aspects of planning, structures, environmental systems and construction. The program is also designed to instill within the student a sense of professionalism and a desire to serve and contribute to society by way of solutions which are technically, environmentally and socially acceptable.

In the associate degree program, students develop the basic skills in drafting, graphic communications, design, CAD, construction documents, construction techniques and concepts, and materials. Upon successful completion of the associate degree program, students may be accepted into the bachelor program. Graduates of other two- and four-year architectural/ engineering programs are also encouraged to apply.

The bachelor degree program is firmly based upon the engineering concepts of architectural design and building sciences. In the bachelor program, students study structural design using wood, steel, masonry and concrete, advanced environmental and mechanical systems, site planning, and building design. The program culminates with an independent directed-studies course. In this final quarter, students must demonstrate their understanding and ability to utilize and synthesize the technical and engineering concepts they developed throughout their New England Tech experience.

NORTHAMPTON COMMUNITY COLLEGE

Architecture Department
3835 Green Pond Road
Bethlehem, PA 18020

Tel: 610/861-5332
Fax: 610/691-9884
ktrionfo@northampton.edu
www.northampton.edu
Contact: Prof. Ken Trionfo, Director

Degrees/Certificates Offered
AAS degree
FT students: 100
FT faculty: 7

Tuition & Fees
$80/credit hour

Program Description
Our Architecture program is designed to prepare students to transfer to a Baccalaureate degree school of architecture.

Northampton's program offers a balance of academic, design and advanced computer technology coursework that forms the foundation needed for transfer. The four-semester design studio sequence with supporting coursework in history, graphics and building technology emphasizes the development of skills in conceptualization and understanding of design vocabulary and design process. A balance of both traditional graphic and model making is emphasized.

Our architecture curriculum has as its goal to stay on the leading edge of changes in computer technology by integrating technology across the curriculum as a design and research tool.

Northampton's faculty consists of practicing, registered architects who are members of the American Institute of Architects. The program boasts a strong active chapter of the AIAS, providing students with leadership opportunities at both the local and national levels.

Some features that make Northampton an attractive place to begin your architectural education are: our location midway between New York and Philadelphia; diverse student body represented by students from numerous states and foreign countries; the only community college in Pennsylvania providing on-campus student housing. Some schools that NCC students have transferred to are: University of Miami; University of Maryland; University of Arizona; University of Michigan; Drexel University; BAC; Temple University; Lehigh University; Penn State; Florida Atlantic University; NJIT; NC State.

OHIO UNIVERSITY

Interior Architecture Program
W 324 Grover Center
Ohio University
Athens, OH 45701

Tel: 740/593-2880
Fax: 740/593-0289
matthej3@ohio.edu
www.ohiou.edu/design/main.html
Contact: David Matthews

Degrees/Certificates Offered
Bachelor of Science
FT students: 100
FT faculty: 3

Admission Requirements
Open admissions first year, selective admissions second year based on portfolio review.

Tuition & Fees
For information on fees go to:
www.ohiou.edu/admissions

Program Description
The Ohio University Interior Architecture program involves the study and practice of designing interior architectural environments. The program emphasizes the studies within a synthesized context of architecture and the decorative arts. Students are involved in the study and designing of space, form, materials, finishes, furnishings, construction methods, building codes, social, cultural, and aesthetic issues directly related to the interiors of buildings.

The program provides a strong understanding of the overall architectural context of the building environment combined with intensive investigations in the decorative arts often associated with traditional interior design programs. The Ohio University Interior Architecture Program received a renewal of FIDER (Foundation for Interior Design Education Research) accreditation in the spring of 2001. Interior architecture students at Ohio University are prepared for entry-level positions in interior architecture and interior design. The program also prepares students with the skills and knowledge which will allow for lifelong professional development in the design industry.

ONONDAGA COMMUNITY COLLEGE

Architecture + Interior Design
4585 West Seneca Turnpike
Syracuse, New York 13215

Tel: 315/498-2687
Fax: 315/498-2713
www.sunyocc.edu
Contact: James E. Ruddock, AIA

Degrees/Certificates Offered
Architectural Technology AAS
Interior Design AAS
FT Students: 172
FT Faculty: 3

Admission Requirements
In addition to your completed application we will need one of the following:
*   an official high school transcript showing proof of graduation from high school (applicants still in high school should send most recent transcript at time of application and a final is required when available) (OR)
*   an official GED score report

Tuition & Fees
In-State (if applicable) $1696/$132 per hour
Out-of-State (if applicable) $3392/$264 per hour

Program Description
Architecture: Graduates of the Architectural Technology program have acquired the knowledge and skills to pursue a wide variety of employment opportunities in the design and construction industry and are well-prepared to pursue a bachelor's degree at a four- or five-year college or university.

The faculty is composed of practicing architects and engineers who are in contact with today's materials and construction methods and computer technology. The Architecture department is held in high regard in the Central New York architectural community for its ability to challenge its students and instill essential technical skills that employers look for. The program stresses the fundamentals, beginning with a three course foundation semester and continuing with three-semester studio course sequences available in both design and drafting. Students in the program have the opportunity to sample a variety of interest areas within the discipline including interior architecture, building design, graphics, computer drafting, materials and construction technology, architectural history, environmental controls, office practice, and structures. Green/ sustainable practices are infused throughout the curriculum. You may begin either fall or spring semester.

The NYS Education Department Division of Professional Licensing recognizes the A.A.S. in Architectural Technology as equivalent to two years of experiential credit toward architectural licensure.

Students in the program will be required to create, transmit and present assignments using computers and other digital technology. After the completion of the first semester required classes (ARH 101, ARH 150, ARH 170), students will be required to provide their own laptop computer and software for all classes in the program. The laptop computer must be capable of running the required software as designated for each course.

Individual courses are available to practicing professionals who wish to update skills and to satisfy continuing education requirements.

Interior Design: The Interior Design program emphasizes the design of functional, aesthetic, and technically proficient environments that meet the needs of people in spaces that are both safe and universally accessible. Green/sustainable practices are infused throughout the curriculum. As an interior design professional, you will work collaboratively with architects and engineers in design teams lending your particular expertise to the design and construction process. Given these close professional ties, you should not be surprised to find yourself in studios and classes with architecture students.

As a prospective interior design student, you should not confuse this program with interior decoration, although elements of decoration are inherent in any interior design program. To ensure a more positive understanding of the program, please note that similar programs at other schools are identified as programs in interior architecture.

Onondaga's Interior Design faculty is composed of practicing interior designers, architects, and engineers with up-to-date design and construction experience in a variety of residential and commercial projects including historic preservation, additions and renovations, and contemporary new construction.

Admission requirements are flexible. Evidence of studio courses in art or three-dimensional design is desirable, but not mandatory. A personal interview is recommended. You may begin in either the fall or spring semester.

The work of the interior designer has taken on new significance as many states, including New York, have established interior design as a licensed profession. The Interior Design curriculum at Onondaga is one of the registered A.A.S. programs recognized by the NYS Education Department as creditable toward the education/experience requirement necessary for certification to use the title "certified interior designer." The Interior Design Curriculum closely matches the NYS Ed. Dept. list of content areas required for associate degrees as follows:

- drafting and presentation techniques;
- fundamentals of space planning and design;
- materials and methods of construction;
- furniture, finishes, and equipment;
- history of architecture and the decorative arts;
- codes – construction, fire, safety and accessibility.

Students in the program will be required to create, transmit and present assignments using computers and other digital technology. After the completion of the first-semester required classes (IND 101, IND 150, IND 170), students will be required to provide their own laptop computer and software for all classes in the program. The laptop computer must be capable of running the required software as designated for each course.

Courses in color theory, computer drafting, environmental controls, and professional practice are also available. Individual courses are available to practicing professionals who wish to update skills and to satisfy continuing education requirements.

OTIS COLLEGE OF ART AND DESIGN

Department of Architecture/Landscape/Interiors
9045 Lincoln Boulevard
Los Angeles, CA 90045

Tel: 310.665.6867
Fax: 310.665.6853
www.otis.edu

Contact: Linda Pollari, Chair, Architecture/Landscape/Interiors

Degrees/Certificates Offered
BFA in Architecture/Landscape/Interiors
FT Students: 50
FT Faculty: 2
PT Faculty: 15

Admission Requirements
Portfolio
Essay
SAT or ACT test scores if applying when in high school
Official transcripts from high school and all colleges attended

Tuition & Fees
In-State (if applicable) $30,414
Out-of-State (if applicable) $30,414

Program Description
The Architecture/Landscape/Interiors (A/L/I) Department seeks to contribute to the emergence of imaginative, contemporary practices through a synthetic curriculum of the spatial design fields: architecture, landscape and interiors.

The department promotes critical reflection on these fields while creating opportunities for inventive design solutions within the myriad cultural, economic, and material contingencies that condition design. Its focus on design, rather than craft, trains future architects and designers to communicate and collaborate with builders, crafts persons, and artisans working in any scale, material or technique.

At the core of the curriculum are six comprehensive studio courses that combine or alternate between the related disciplines. Technologies + Ecologies courses provide knowledge of the materials and methods of building, landscape, and interior construction. Digital Media courses focus on digital communication skills (drafting, modeling, rendering, and fabrication) as well as digital 2D design and typography. History + Theory courses provide the cultural and intellectual framework necessary for informed and articulate design proposals. This sequence of courses supports the development of studio projects that exhibit technical precision, aesthetic sophistication, and conceptual rigor.

The department provides both graduates and students with skills necessary to enter any of its allied design fields. Many A/L/I students work in professional architecture, landscape or interior design offices while training in the program, often as early as sophomore year. Graduates are prepared to enter competitive graduate programs such as Master of Architecture, Master of Landscape Architecture or Master of Interior Architecture. OTIS A/L/I alumni may become licensed architects through work experience and testing in California, with no additional education.

Architecture/Landscape /Interiors alumni are working at Atelier Bow-Wow, Behnisch Architects, Bennitt + Mitchell, Clive Wilkinson Architects, Ellerbe Becket,

GRAFT, Griffin Enright Architects, Hodgetts + Fung, Mansilla + Tuñón, REX, Shubin-Donaldson, Stan Allen Architect, and Visual Terrain, among others. Architecture/Landscape /Interiors alumni currently are pursuing or have received graduate degrees from Harvard, Pratt, Princeton, UCLA, USC and Yale.

PALM BEACH COMMUNITY COLLEGE

Department of Architecture
4200 Congress Avenue
Lake Worth, FL 33461-4796

Tel: 561.868.3326
Fax: 561.868.3327
www.www.pbcc.edu
Contact: Stafford Mooney, Associate Dean

Degrees/Certificates Offered
Associate of Arts
FT students: 90
FT faculty: 1

Admission Requirements
High school graduate

Tuition & Fees
$55/credit for 65 credits ($3,575)

SAN ANTONIO COLLEGE

Architecture Program
1300 San Pedro Avenue
San Antonio, TX 78212-4299

Tel: 210/733-2856
Fax: 210/733-2133
rarmstrong@mail.accd.edu
www.accd.edu/sac
Contact: Richard Armstrong, Program Coordinator

Degrees/Certificates Offered
Associates of Art in Architecture
FT students: 125
FT faculty: 6

Admission Requirements
High school graduate or GED

Tuition & Fees
15 hours tuition & fees: $765 (in district),
$1425 (in-state), $2745 (out-of-state)

Program Description
Established in 1958, the program provides the first two years of a professional education in architecture and interior design. Our primary objective is to prepare students for transfer into both four and five-year programs; our curriculum is modeled after the traditional five-year B.Arch. degree.

We offer four semesters of design studio, two survey courses in architectural history, materials and methods of construction, structures, an introduction to landscape architecture and six courses in visual communications. There are six full-time faculty and, depending on enrollment, between 8–12 adjunct instructors.

Students interested in part-time employment in area firms are encouraged and aided by faculty. Opportunity for travel is provided by faculty-led field trips and tours to Europe. We are scheduled to teach 2 classes in Italy this summer. The freshman class varies in size between 85–110. Between 25–35 students a year successfully transfer into an accredited professional design program.

SMITH COLLEGE

Hillyer Hall
Department of Art
Northampton, MA 01063

Tel: 413.585.3100
Fax: 413.585.3119
www.smith.edu/art
Contact: Barbara Kellum, Chair

Degrees/Certificates Offered
BA in Architecture and Urbanism
FT students: 10
FT faculty: 6

Admission Requirements
Admission to Smith College

Tuition & Fees
$38,000

Program Description
The architecture major is built on a mix of both studio and art history courses.

The art history courses examine the interrelated artistic, historic, and cultural forces that create architecture and the built environment. Likewise, the studios explore the built environment "as a person experiences it," integrating traditionally separate aspects of landscape and architecture, building and city in the active "laboratory" of the design studio.

The major serves multiple audiences, and stems from the premise that the built world is shaped by many different people. One audience is those students who want to become design professionals—architects, landscape architects, and urban designers and planners. For them the major aims to provide a rigorous and creative base for graduate study. The other audience is equally important; these are the students who will go on to become doctors, politicians, academics, lawyers, or members of neighborhood design review boards. ALL students will eventually play a significant role in shaping our built environment, no matter what career path they choose.

STATE UNIVERSITY OF NEW YORK AT ALFRED STATE COLLEGE

10 Upper College Drive
Alfred, NY 14802

Tel: (607) 587-4696
Fax: (607) 587-4620
www.alfredstate.edu
Contact person: William C. Dean, RA, AIA
                Associate Professor and Chair

Degrees/Certificates Offered
BS in Architectural Technology
AAS in Architectural Engineering Technology
AAS in Interior Design
FT Students: 277
FT Faculty: 10

Tuition & Fees
In-State: $5,498
Out-of-State: $8,358

Program Description
Architecture at Alfred State

Since 1972, the architectural program has pioneered a unique educational approach to the integration of building technology and architectural design. Two sequential degree programs are offered within the department of Computer Imaging and Architectural Engineering Technology: a two-year Associate of Applied Science in Architectural Engineering Technology (AAS), and a four-year Bachelor of Science in Architectural Technology (BS). The AAS degree is accredited by the Technology Accreditation Commission, Accreditation Board for Engineering Technology, Inc. (TAC/ABET). While many graduates opt to seek advanced professional degrees in architecture, career placement is the principle goal of both programs as we seek to provide the profession with highly-skilled technicians and intern architects.

The AAS Degree

Consistent with the technology-based mission of the College, the two-year architectural curriculum emphasizes fundamental skills and technical competency required for entry-level positions in the architectural office. Architectural graphics, design methodology, computer applications and building technology form the core of the curriculum, with supplemental offerings in architectural history, professional practice, the humanities and the sciences. Graduates of the AAS degree may matriculate seamlessly into the BS degree program.

The BS Degree

Building upon the core skills of the AAS degree, the four-year program provides our graduates with a comprehensive architectural education, integrating the philosophy of building design with an applied technical knowledge of construction systems and materials. The technically oriented, upper-level studio sequence includes courses in design and construction, historic preservation and urban design. There is also a capstone design project in the final semester.

STATE UNIVERSITY OF NEW YORK AT DELHI

Technology Division
2 Main Street
Delhi, NY 13753

Tel: 607.746.4070
Fax: 607.746.4224
hubbarpg@delhi.edu
www.delhi.edu
Contact: Philip Hubbard, Division Dean

Degrees/Certificates Offered
BT in Architectural Design and Building
AAS in Architectural Technology
AAS in Construction Technology
FT students: 204
FT faculty: 9

Admission Requirements
GPA 2.3, previous college work plus portfolio review

Tuition & Fees
$5,648 per year

Program Description
The Architectural Technology Department at SUNY Delhi offers the Associate in Applied Science (A.A.S.) degree, and the Bachelor of Technology Degree (B.T.)—The vast majority of core courses feature hands-on performance in the laboratory or studio supported by classroom theory. All of the core courses are taught by architects, engineers, and construction professionals with extensive work experience.

The Architectural Technology program places equal emphasis on the preparation of detailed residential and commercial construction drawings; on the creative process of rendering and designing buildings; and on the understanding of building methods, materials, structure, and mechanical systems. The drawing instruction, in turn, is equally divided between conventional design and drafting media, and computer-generated design and drafting.

The Architectural Technology program is distinguished by its range of fully equipped construction laboratories and fully equipped drafting and computer studios for hands-on instruction.

STATE UNIVERSITY OF NEW YORK AT MORRISVILLE

College of Agriculture and Technology
Architectural Studies and Design Program
Engineering Technologies Department
School of Science and Technology
P.O. Box 901
Morrisville, NY 13408-0901

Tel: 315/684-6281 or 6079
Fax: 315/684-6024
Englotas@Morrisville.edu or kellybj@Morrisville.edu
www.morrisville.edu/architecture
Contact: Anne S. Englot, PhD or Brian J. Kelly Jr., AIA

Degrees/Certificates Offered
Undergraduate: Associate in Science
FT students: 25
FT faculty: 2

Admission Requirements

Two-year advising sequence: Required: Minimum high school average in the C+ to B range, 3 units of defined math, 2 units of defined science including physics and a minimum C+ to B- (minimum 78%) high school average in English. Desired: Additional unit of defined math, art sequence, computer-aided drawing, architectural drawing, additional English, history and a portfolio.

Three-year advising sequence: Required: Minimum high school average in the C to C+ range, 2 units of defined math, 2 units of defined science and English. Desired: Art sequence, computer-aided drawing, architectural drawing, additional English, history and a portfolio. Students lacking one or more requirements for the two-year advising sequence will be considered for the three-year advising sequence.

Tuition & Fees

Undergraduate: NY state resident: $2,175 per semester
Out-of-state resident: $3,605 per semester

Program Description

The Architectural Studies and Design Program is geared to the needs of the student planning to continue his/her education in architecture following graduation. The program does this by providing the student with a strong foundation to transfer into a pre-professional or professional architectural degree program. The core of the studio-centered curriculum is the four-semester architectural design (studio) sequence. The knowledge gained in courses like architectural graphic communications, architectural history, and architectural technology are applied within the architectural design (studio) sequence to provide a sound preparation. Computer technology is also integrated into all parts of the studio-center curriculum.

This rigorous program has resulted in successful transfer opportunities for graduates. Morrisville graduates have excellent reputations at other academic institutions and universities. Should a student decide not to transfer after earning the Associate of Science degree, there are employment opportunities in architectural firms and architectural related industries as an entry-level employee.

The Architectural Studies and Design Program is a Thinkpad University curriculum in which the use of laptop computers is integrated into courses.

TIDEWATER COMMUNITY COLLEGE

Architectural Drafting
Tidewater Community College
1700 College Crescent
Virginia Beach, VA 23453-1999

Tel: 757/822-7179
Fax: 757/822-7334
sdolgalev@tcc.edu
www.tcc.edu
Contact: Sergei Dolgalev; PhD

Degrees/Certificates Offered

Associate in Applied Science (AAS) in Architecture;
Certificate in Architectural Drafting
Undergraduate faculty: 10
FT Students: 80

FT Faculty: 2

Admission Requirements

High school or equivalent

Tuition & Fees

Undergraduate: $63 per credit hour

Program Description

The architectural drafting program prepares you to work with architects and engineers in architectural firms, marine- or design-oriented industry, or civil service. The certificate program trains you as a board/CAD drafter for an architectural or civil engineering firm, capable of producing a set of high-quality working drawings. The certificate program takes three semesters to complete. The associate's degree prepares you for immediate employment as an advanced draftsperson for an architectural or civil engineering firm. You are also qualified to transfer to a school of architecture. The Associate in Applied Science degree requires four semesters of full-time study. In addition to the college's general admission requirements, students are required to complete Student Assessment Program (placement) tests in reading, composition, and mathematics. Students may include related work experience as part of their education. The college's cooperative education program allows you to earn income while gaining work experience and academic credit.

TRITON COLLEGE

2000 Fifth Avenue
Oak Park, IL 60171

Tel: 708/456-0300 ext. 3007
fheitzma@triton.edu
academics.triton.edu/faculty/fheitzman/arch.html
Contact: JoBeth Halpin, Director

Degrees/Certificates Offered

Undergraduate: Associate of Arts Degree and Associate of Applied Science Degree
FT students: 150
FT faculty: 2

Tuition & Fees

Undergraduate: $2,200.00/year

Program Description

The Associate of Arts Degree program at Triton College will enable the student to receive a two-year degree in Architectural Studies. It was created to duplicate the first two years of state baccalaureate architectural programs such as at the University of Illinois. Its purpose is to prepare students for entry into the profession or to enable students to competently transfer to baccalaureate architectural programs as a Junior to complete a B.A. or a B.S. in Architectural Studies.

Courses Required:
Fundamentals of Architectural Drafting
Fundamentals of Architectural Drawing and Models
Architectural Design I
Architectural Design II
Introduction to the History of Architecture
Introduction to Architectural CADD
Wood and Masonry Construction Technology

Steel Construction Technology
Calculus & Analytic Geometry I
Freshman Rhetoric & Comp I
Freshman Rhetoric & Comp II
Principles of Effective Speaking
Life Science Elective
Humanities Electives
Introduction to Sociology
Introduction to Psychology
General Physics
Total credits required for graduation: 63

UNION COUNTY COLLEGE

Engineering/Technology/Architecture Department
1033 Springfield Avenue
Cranford, NJ 07016

Tel: 908.709.7559
www.ucc.edu
Contact: Nicholas Gilbert, Chair

Program Description

This program is designed to prepare students who plan for a career in architecture to transfer to a five- year baccalaureate program.

The specific objectives of this program are that the graduate must be able to demonstrate:

- critical thinking and problem solving skills in science, mathematics, and fundamentals of architecture;
- computer literacy in programming and use of word processing, and other software applications;
- an ability to use technology and library resources to research information related to architecture, mathematics, engineering, the humanities, and social science;
- an ability to communicate effectively by written, oral and graphical methods;
- an understanding of materials and methods of building construction, basics of structural analysis/design related to architecture, collect and analyze relevant data, and work as a member of a team;
- an appreciation of the need for a broad and liberal education and understand the impact of architectural solutions in a global/societal context;
- implementation of skills learned in architecture, science, social sciences, and the humanities into collaborative design projects for/with local communities;
- an ability to learn independently and an appreciation of the need for lifelong learning in the architectural field.

UNIVERSITY OF MISSOURI-COLUMBIA

Department of Architectural Studies
137 Stanley Hall
Columbia, MO 65211-7700

Tel: 573.882.7224
Fax: 573.884.6679
TofleR@missouri.edu
www.missouri.edu/~envugwww
Contact: Ruth Tofle

Degrees/Certificates Offered
B.Sc. HES Architectural Studies, M.A. and M.SC. in Architectural Studies, Ph.D. in Human Environmental Sciences

Admission Requirements
Portfolio for undergraduate and portfolio, statement of objective, letters of reference for graduate admission.

Tuition & Fees
Undergraduate: Resident @ $141/credit hr.
Non-resident @ $423/credit hr.
Graduate: Resident @ $179/credit hr.
Non-resident @ $538/credit hr.
Activities fees: $122 per semester in residence

Program Description
Architectural Studies describes the processes, procedures, observations and techniques essential to the development of designs of human living, leisure, and work environments. The program synthesizes the functional, technological, aesthetic and symbolic attributes of interior design and architecture. As a college within the college of Human Environmental Sciences, emphasis is placed on planning and design of physical environments that support human needs and aspirations. The two declared graduate niche areas are:

*   Environment-behavior design focusing on the physical settings responsive to culture, income and life-span diversity of people.
*   Design with digital media focusing on graphic ideation and application of computer technology integral to the design process.

The program addresses the teaching, research and outreach missions of the university of Missouri with a Council of Interior Design Accreditation (CIDA) accredited interior design undergraduate program.

UNIVERSITY OF MISSOURI—KANSAS CITY

Department of Architecture, Urban Planning & Design
213 Epperson House
5200 Cherry
Kansas City, MO 64110

Tel: 816/235-1725
Fax: 816/235-5226
swallowj@umkc.edu
Contact: Joy D. Swallow, AIA

Degrees/Certificates Offered
Architectural Studies at UMKC is a collaborative program with Kansas State University. After the first two years of study at UMKC, students transfer to KSU for completion of the accredited B. Arch degree.
FT students: 50
FT faculty: 2

Admission Requirements
Applicants must meet or exceed specified values for high school class rank percentile and ACT score.

Tuition & Fees
$162.40/credit hr., Missouri residents
$467.50/credit hr., Non-Missouri residents

Program Description
UMKC and Kansas State University offer a unique opportunity for students who want to study architecture and environmental design. Under the five-year program, students spend the first two years at UMKC completing an environmental design curriculum patterned after KSU's program. The next three years are spent at KSU. The College of Architecture and Design at KSU is one of the few truly comprehensive architecture schools in the region. The college grants accredited degrees in three professional areas: architecture, interior architecture, and landscape architecture.

Starting your studies at UMKC allows you to take advantage of a ready-made urban laboratory. The university is located in the heart of Kansas City, a city rich in varying architecture. A high concentration of design firms in the area enables UMKC to maintain ties with the professional community. Practicing architects often visit campus to act as studio critics. Small class sizes ensure you receive individualized attention during the first two years. The average number of first-year architecture students entering UMKC is 36. Studying in the city gives you advantages you won't find in other environments. UMKC also offers a four-year degree in Urban Planning and Design. Call us for more information.

UNIVERSITY OF PITTSBURGH

Architectural Studies Program
History of Art and Architecture Department
104 Frick Fine Arts Building
Pittsburgh, PA 15260

Tel: 412.648.2401
Fax: 412.648.2792
ksa@pitt.edu
www.pitt.edu/~arthome
Contact: Drew Armstrong, Director, cda68@pitt.edu;
Gretchen Bender, Director of Undergradute Advising, ghb1@pitt.edu

Degrees/Certificates Offered
BA Architectural Studies
FT students: 100
FT faculty: 7

Admission Requirements
None other than those for general admission to the School of Arts and Sciences at the University of Pittsburgh

Tuition & Fees
In-State: $13,000
Out-of-State: $23,000

Program Description
Learning to think about architecture as both the product of a creative process and as a historical phenomenon are the principal goals of Pitt's BA program in Architectural Studies. We endeavor to create a rigorous curriculum and a supportive learning environment, allowing students to build skills and knowledge while developing close working relationships with peers and faculty. Students will gain a broad understanding of the complexity of architecture as a profession and as an academic discipline, and will be well-positioned by their senior year to apply to accredited, graduate programs in architecture or historic preservation at universities in the United States and Canada. Students considering careers in architecture and historic preservation are encouraged to apply to Architectural Studies by the end of their freshman year at Pitt .

The Architectural Studies curriculum draws primarily on courses offered in the Department of History of Art and Architecture and the Department of Studio Arts. Students are encouraged to explore related interests through course work in other departments, through off-campus study, and through a range of undergraduate teaching and research opportunities available through Pitt's Office of Experiential Learning. Students may also opt to complete certificate programs in civil engineering or historic preservation as a complement to Architectural Studies.

UNIVERSITY OF WYOMING

Civil & Architectural Engineering
Dept. 3295, 1000 E. University Avenue
Laramie, WY 82071-2000

Tel: 307.766.5255
Fax: 307.766.4395
tdenzer@uwyo.edy
www.uwyo.edu/architectural
Contact: Tony Denzer

Degrees/Certificates Offered
BS in Architectural Engineering
FT students: 200
FT faculty: 12

Program Description
Architectural engineering is a rapidly expanding profession that deals with the myriad aspects of buildings and their design, construction, and operation. Architectural engineers are typically specialists, responsible for the design and integration of such building elements as the structural, heating and air conditioning, or lighting and electrical systems. The curriculum in architectural engineering is designed to acquaint students with the various aspects of the building process and exposes them to a variety courses dealing with different building materials and systems. The curriculum also includes course work in the humanities and social sciences, both to enrich the student's academic experience and assist in dealing with and contributing to society. The program leads to a Bachelor of Science in Architectural Engineering, preparing graduates to engage in practice as Professional Engineers upon completion of post-graduate registration requirements. Additionally, further study can be pursued in allied areas such as architecture, business and other engineering fields.

Students choose from an area of emphasis in either structural or mechanical/electrical systems and select courses from approved electives, usually beginning their elective sequence in the second semester of their junior year.

VALENCIA COMMUNITY COLLEGE

Arch., Bldg./Constr. Technology Program
1800 South Kirkman Road, MC 4-41
Orlando, FL 32811

Tel: 407.299.5000
http://valenciacc.edu/west/engineering/
Contact: Andrew Ray, R.A.: Director

Degrees/Certificates Offered

AS Building Construction Technology

Program Description

The program has been planned to provide theoretical and classroom experience which closely parallels on-the-job activities. The Building Construction program is designed to train competent technicians capable of working with architects, engineers, contractors, building officials and others. The program will accommodate architectural drafting, construction estimators, schedulers, and supervisors, as well as persons just entering the field of construction.

WESLEYAN UNIVERSITY

Department of Art and Art History
Middletown, CT 06459

Tel: 860/685-3526
Fax: 860/685-2061
www.wesleyan.edu
Contact: Martha Añez

Degrees/Certificates Offered

B.A. - studio arts major (architectural concentration)
FT students: 10
FT faculty: 1

Tuition & Fees

$34,900

Program Description

Architecture at Wesleyan is a concentration within the Studio Arts Program. It consists of introductory design courses supported by drawing and architectural history classes. In the architecture concentration, emphasis is placed on developing the students' ability to examine the relationship between production (the process of creating things) and expression (the conveying of ideas and meaning) involved in the making of architecture. Students engage in an intensive exploration of the language of architecture as it relates to the situations of placemaking, human habitation, and cultural interaction. All studio arts majors are required to engage in a year-long thesis project in their area of concentration. At this stage, architecture students are highly in traditionally focused studies in architecture, as well as interdisciplinary experimentation with painting, photography, printmaking sculpture, and typography. In general, the architecture concentration aims at developing the students' awareness and understanding of the built environment as a result of the investigations, observations, and inquiries generated in the studio.

YESTERMORROW DESIGN/BUILD SCHOOL

189 VT Route 100
Warren, VT 05674

Tel: 802/496-5545
Fax: 802/496-5540
designbuild@yestermorrow.org
www.yestermorrow.org
Contact: Kate Stephenson

Degrees/Certificates Offered

Certificate in Sustainable Building and Design
Natural Building Certificate
Yestermorrow is not a degree-granting institution

Admission Requirements

Portfolio for undergraduate and portfolio, statement of ojjective, letters of reference for graduate admission.

Tuition & Fees

Programs vary; $300 for 2 days to $1,400 for 12 days, plus room and board

Program Description

Yestermorrow Design/Build School inspires people to create a better, more sustainable world by providing hands-on education that integrates design and craft as a creative, interactive process.

Yestermorrow is unique in its professional field. Since 1980 our nationally recognized instructors have been teaching all aspects of the building arts and trades to present and future members of the design/build team: student, homeowner, designer and builder. Courses are intensive and constantly engaging, challenging students to solve complex design problems through the integration of the design and construction processes. We offer a low student-to-instructor ratio, allowing individualized instruction and personal attention. Our instructors and staff consist of over one hundred professional architects, builders and artisans who come from across the nation to the mountains of central Vermont to share their expertise with our students.

Yestermorrow's courses are specifically designed to demystify the designing and building processes using hands-on, experiential learning to teach students the art and wisdom of good design and the skill and savvy of enduring craftsmanship as a single, integrated process.

Combining design and building offers numerous advantages and promotes the creation of intentional and inspired buildings and communities that enhance our world. From the professional design/builder to the do-it-yourself design/build homeowner, every designer should know how to build and every builder should know how to design. This philosophy sets Yestermorrow apart from other educational institutions.

The Yestermorrow Design/Build School is approved by the Vermont Department of Education but is not a degree granting institution. Select courses are available for college credit through the University of Vermont, and by special arrangement through other colleges and universities. In addition, a number of Yestermorrow courses are available for Continuing Education Units through the American Institute of Architects.

ARCHITECTURAL ASSOCIATION

School of Architecture
34-36 Bedford Square
London, WC1B 3ES United Kingdom

Tel: 44-207-887-4000
Fax: 44-20-7414-0782
info@aaschool.ac.uk
www.aaschool.ac.uk
Contact: Brett Steele, AA Dipl. Director

Degrees/Certificates Offered
Undergraduate: AA Intermediate Examination (RIBA/ARB Part 1); AA Final Examination (RIBA/ARB Part 2); AA Diploma.
Graduate: M.A. / MSc. / M.Arch./ M.Phil./ Ph.D./ AA Graduate Diploma.
FT students: 350 undergraduate full-time students; 240 graduate full-time students; 17 graduate day-release students.

Admission Requirements
(Full details on the AA website)
Undergraduate overseas students: equivalent to 2 'A' levels plus 5 GCSEs and a design portfolio. Graduate School: entry requirements according to the programme and degree awarded.

Tuition & Fees
2008-09 academic year: undergraduate tuition fees: £14,475; graduate tuition fees: £16,656: 12-month programmes
£22,231: 16-month programmes
£14,925: M.Phil/Ph.D. programmes
£ 4,869: Building Conservation programme

Program Description
The school's undergraduate programmes consist of the AA Foundation Open Studio course and the 5-year RIBA/ARB-recognized course leading to AA Intermediate Examination (RIBA/ARB Part 1), AA Final Examination (RIBA/ARB Part 2), and the AA Diploma. First Year is organized as a studio-based programme of design projects. In the Intermediate and Diploma Schools teaching is within the design units, all of which have very different characters and concerns. The design studio projects are supplemented by Technical Studies, History & Theory Studies and Media Studies, as well as a rich programme of lectures, workshops, conferences, exhibitions, and publications. In addition, the AA offers Visiting Student Programmes (full details on the AA website).

The Graduate School currently offers eight programmes:
- MSc. / MArch. courses in Sustainable Environmental Design
- M.A. in Histories and Theories
- M.A. in Housing and Urbanism
- M.Phil./ Ph.D. research degrees

Graduate Design studio-based programmes:
- M.A. in Landscape Urbanism
- MSc./ MArch. in Emergent Technologies + Design
- MArch. in Architecture & Urbanism (DRL)
- Part-time/day release course in Building Conservation leading to an AA Graduate Diploma

Further information on all courses can be obtained from the AA's website: www.aaschool.ac.uk.

CHIANG MAI UNIVERSITY

Faculty of Architecture
Chiang Mai 50202 Thailand

Tel: 66-53/94-2811
Fax: 66-53/22-1448
somchai@mail.arc.cmu.ac.th
www.arc.cmu.ac.th
Contact: Sombat Thiratrakoolchai

Degrees/Certificates Offered
Bachelor of Architecture (5-Year B.Arch)
Master of Architecture (2-Year M.Arch)
M. Arch offered beginning June 2004
Undergraduate Faculty: 54
Graduate Faculty: 4
FT Students: 211
FT Faculty: 27

Admission Requirements
M.Arch—any nationality, written & oral exam, resume, portfolio. B. Arch—Tai citizens only

Tuition & Fees
US $1,100 approx. Baht 46,000
US $1,714 approx. Baht 72,000

Program Description
Bachelor of Architecture (B.Arch) is a five-year degree program consisting of 178-credit hours. Exchange students may contact the International Office through the Faculty's website for admission requirements. Beginning in June 2004, the Faculty of Architecture will offer a Master of Architecture (M.Arch) program open to students of all nationalities. The Master's program is a two-year program consisting of 36 credit hours. Nine credit hours of core courses, 12 hours of major courses, 3 hours of free electives and 12 credit hours dedicated for the student's thesis project. This Master's program is research oriented and designed to strengthen the integrative study of local intelligence and global technology in architecture.

The Faculty also offers a Joint Sandwiched Graduate Program. This Joint Sandwiched Master of Architecture is a new program, which allows students to exchange with other universities during the 2nd and 3rd semesters. Students are required to fulfill the core course requirements at CMU and then it allows them to choose to exchange 18 credit hours, or equivalent, with other universities. These 18 credit hours can be tailored to fit in with courses offered at various universities. A list of exchange programs can be obtained from the website.

NATIONAL UNIVERSITY OF SINGAPORE

Department of Architecture
School of Design and Environment
4 Architecture Drive
Singapore 117566
Tel: (65) 6516 3452
Fax: (65) 6779 3078
www.arch.nus.edu.sg
Contact Person: Associate Professor WONG Yunn Chii

Degrees/Certificates Offered
BA Interior Design
BA Architecture
M. Arch

Admission Requirements
Good 'A'–level passes or equivalent and at least an 'O' grade in one of the following: Math/Physis/Physical Science/Chemistry, obtained at 'A'–level examination.

Tuition & Fees
Subsidized: $6,360(local), $9,540(international)

Program Description
BA Interior Design—The Industrial Design programme focuses on issues which support the sustainability of global environment. The unique quality of the programme is its pedagogic emphasis on a holistic approach to design thinking and practice. Close collaboration with the industry in the formulation and execution of projects enables students to develop the high level of professionalism required by industry. The programme is fully supported by extensive resource in traditional workshop facilities as well as equipment for digital media application and prototyping.
BA Architecture—The Bachelor of Arts (Architecture) is a 4-year direct honours programme. The BA Arch (Hons) operates under the modular system which requires students to complete Essential Modules, General Education Modules (GEM), for a strong foundation programme in architectural studies under NUS policy. GEM, SS, Breadth and UEs widen the scope of intellectual pursuit. The course curriculum therefore comprises the University, School and Department programme requirements.
M. Arch—This is the final year of the architecture course following a 4-year undergraduate programme in architecture. Students with relevant requisites could also opt to be considered for entry to specialization in Urban Design or Design Technology and Management under this programme. The strategic objective of the M Arch programme is to prepare students for a professional career in architecture in a rapidly changing global context. Design is the central core discipline. It is complemented by other courses that focus on the technological, ethical and professional and management aspects of architecture. Design constitutes approx two thirds of the M Arch course content.

PROVINCIALE HOGESCHOOL LIMBURG
Departement Architectuur en Beeldende Kunst
Universitaire Campus
Gebouw E, B-3590 Diepenbeek Belgium

Tel: 00 32 (0) 11 24 92 00
Fax: 00 32 (0) 11 24 92 01
architectuur@phlimburg.be
www.phlimburg.be

Degrees/Certificates Offered
Candidate in Architecture
Architect
Interior Architect
Undergraduate faculty: 24
Graduate faculty: 16

FT Students: 340
FT Faculty: 26

Admission Requirements
Candidate in Architecture: humanities
Architect: candidate in architecture
Interior Architect: candidate in architecture

Tuition & Fees
Undergraduate: 495 Euro for EC citizens/EC exchange
students
(Socrates-Erasmus, Tempus bilateral programmes):
no fees/1200 Euro for non EC citizens
Graduate: 495 Euro for EC citizens/EC exchange students
(Socrates-Erasmus, Tempus bilateral programmes):
no fees/1200 Euro for non EC citizens

Program Description
Language: Dutch
Studies in the Section of Architecture are divided
into two cycles. The first cycle lasts two years and leads
to a Candidate Architect diploma. The second cycle
lasts three years and leads to an Architect diploma (AR)
or two years for an Interior Architect diploma (IAR).
Courses are subdivided under the following headings:
- Architectural Design: architectural design, visual
communication and design, environmental sciences, theory of design and design methods;
- Building technology: exact sciences, architectural
engineering and technology;
- Cultural sciences: humanities, philosophy, architectural history and theory.
In the second AR-cycle, students can take an optional
course (8 ECTS) chosen from the following: Architectural Design, Architectural Theory and critics, Building
physics and Technology in Design, Urban ecology.
In direct line with this optional course, the students write during the last two years a dissertation
on a theoretical topic related to architecture/interior
architecture.
English Language Program
January/February through June/July
BelArch (Belgian Architecture) is an English-language program set up especially for foreign students.
The program is conducted in the second semester of
each academic year. For more information: www.phlimburg.be go to: "international."

THAMMASAT UNIVERSITY
Faculty of Architecture
Rangsit Center
99 Mhu 18, Paholyothin Rd.
Khong Luang
Pathum Thani 12121
Thailand

Tel: +66 (0) 2986 9605-6
Fax: +66 (0) 2986 9434 Ext. 703
info@arch.tu.ac.th
www.arch.tu.ac.th
Contact: Dr. Vimolsiddhi Horayangkura, Dean

Degrees/Certificates Offered
Bachelor of Science in Architecture
Master of Architecture
Bachelor of Interior Architecture
Bachelor of Urban Environmental
Admission Requirements
High school graduate or equivalent and pass either (1)
Nationale entrance examination by the Office of the
Commission of Higher Education, or (2) Examination
organized by Thammasat University.

Tuition & Fees
Contact school

Program Description
The 4+2 Architecture Program
Architects are involved in the design of buildings of
all kinds from houses to large public buildings as well
as the shaping of cities of the future. It is a demanding
and challenging profession, requiring a range of skills
and strong dedication and commitment. It requires an
integration of creativity as well as practical, analytical
and management ability as well as technological expertise. Architecture requires the ability to think in three-dimensional space in order to create a better environment for people.
The 4-year Undergraduate Program
Design studios are the core of the program, in
which you are encouraged to develop your creative and
analytical skills through various projects. There are
also other course works covering various topics such as
structure, material and construction, building technology, history and theory as well as management that are
aimed to complement and support your design work. The
first year of the program introduces the fundamentals
of design, visual and technical communication techniques. During your second year, you will start your first
architecture design studio class. Studio-based small-scale projects of a livable space will encourage you to
experiment with the notion of space. In the third year,
you are encouraged to explore, analyze and incorporate
conceptual thinking of various themes such as building
materials, socio-political factors and cultural thinking
process into your design. In your fourth year, you will
tackle more advanced and complex architectural and
urban design issues. You are expected to explore, analyze and integrate different specific knowledge in architecture such as building technologies and services,
structure and management.
The 2-year Master of Architecture Program
The Master of Architecture Program offers the
first professional degree in architecture. You will be
focused on your research capabilities. You will choose
one of our following four specialized paths; Architecture
Design and Theory, Building Technology, Information
Technology in Architecture and Architectural Manage-

ment. During your first three semesters, you will learn
about research methods and related specific knowledge
through lectures and seminars. In your final year, you
will produce a thesis, which is your own investigation
into a topic of your own. Your thesis will be assessed by
a panel of internal and external examiners.

UNIVERSIDAD ANAHUAC MÉXICO NORTE
School of Architecture
Avenida Universidad Anáhuac 46
Lomas Anáhuac
Huixquilucan, Estado de México,
México 52786

Tel: 52-5/627-0210 Ext. 8515
Fax: 52-5/627-0210 Ext. 8414
Contact: Dr. Manuel Aguirre-Osete, Academic Head

Degrees/Certificates Offered
Architect title
FT Students: 362
FT Faculty: 12 (+53 PT)

Admission Requirements
General Admission test, Personal interview & high
school certificate.

Tuition & Fees
Tuition: US $7,100 per year
Fee: US $2,200 per year

Program Description
Students in the School of Architecture enjoy the benefits
of its small size and full integration into the larger Anahuac University community. In recent years, the school
has had an enrollment of approximately 130 undergraduates per year. Design studios range in size from
10–18 students depending on the studio level. Interaction between students and faculty is encouraged at all
levels. A shared building with the Schools of Industrial
and Graphic Design and the School of Communication
offers students a wide range of contact with other design and communication disciplines.
Faculty and students are interested in examining
alternative ways of designing and seeing and alternative technologies. There is an increasing concern with
research, both academic and practical. Emphasis is
placed on the role of leadership and management that
the architect plays as a part of a very wide team of work
depending on the size of the project.
The undergraduate architecture degree and licensing is normally awarded after 5 years of study.
Our program is nationally accredited by the COMAEA
(Comite Mexicano de Acreditación de la Enseñanza de
la Arquitectura, AC) There are two design studios in the
ninth & tenth semesters that concentrate and integrate
all the knowledge in a community design problem. This
becomes the base for the professional oral examination with a group of 3 juries. Coursework is distributed
across several areas: design; communication aids;
geometry and perspective; theory and history; construction and structures; environmental control systems;
administration; computer-aided systems; and urban
design/planning. The school also offers a real estate
and construction management master diploma after
completing the program.

UNIVERSIDAD DE LA SALLE BAJÍO

Escuela de Arquitectura
Avenida Universidad 602 Colonia Lomas Del Camp-
estre
Leon Guanajuato, México

Tel: 55 477 7108580
Fax: 55 477 7185511
dcabrera@delasalle.edu.mx
www.delasalle.edu.mx
Contact: Juan Roberto Lopez Gonzalez, Rector

Degrees/Certificates Offered
Licenciatura en Arquitectura

Admission Requirements
Diploma of Bachillerato of Educacion Media Superior,
entrance exam, entrance interview, leveling course.

Program Description
With recognition of Official Validity of Studies according to the agreement Not. 2002190 with date August
18, 2000 before the Office of the secretary of Public
Education.

The Architect is a professional that designs and he
transforms the habitable spaces of respectful, sensitive, and creative form of the environment, recognizing,
interpreting and controlling the factors that participate
in the the materialization of the architectural object.

If you are sensitive to the art and to the design,
consider interest the environment and your city, you
would like to work as a designer architectural, designer
of interiors, construction, supervisor or administrator
of work and besides are a capable leader to work in
multidisciplinary teams and to make decisions with
a high sense of social responsibility, we invite you to
study with us.

UNIVERSIDAD FRANCISCO MARROQUIN

Facultad de Arquitectura
Sexto piso. Edificio Académico Guatemala

Tel: (011-502) 338-7708
Fax: (011-502) 361-1991
epocas@ufm.edu.gt; eaguilar@ufm.edu.gt
www.arquitectura.ufm.edu.gt

Contact: Ernesto Porras C.; Dean or Dr. Eduardo Agui-
lar; Secretary

Degrees/Certificates Offered
License in Architecture. According to Guatemala's law,
this suffices for liberal practice of architecture within
the country.
Undergraduate faculty: 35
Graduate faculty: N/A
FT Students: 150
FT Faculty: 0

Admission Requirements
Total College 1150 score minimum; Otis I.Q. 90%; High
school grades above 80%; Personal interview with academic authorities.

Tuition & Fees
Undergraduate: Q.750 (US $95) per semester credit
hour; Q450 ($57) Design studio fee; Q1625 ($205)
Computer lab fee; Q800 ($100) parking, ID, and Internet
access, per semester.

Program Description
A five-year program with one additional non-present
year for thesis work and professional internship. The
first three years offer consecutive design studios with
fixed faculty. The last two offer four advanced design
platforms where the student can choose theme and
faculty.

Summer programs offer advancement and elective
courses taught by own faculty or visiting professors.
Students with high GPAs are eligible to participate in
Student Exchange Summer Programs with Texas A&M
University or Tulane University. Some students have
been chosen for semester-long exchange at Tulane.

Professional internship can be completed at Gua-
temalan architectural firms. When available, those students with high GPAs can do their internship at several
architectural firms in the U.S. or Europe.

THE UNIVERSITY OF HONG KONG

Department of Architecture
3/F Knowles Building
The University of Hong Kong
Pokfulam Road, Hong Kong. China

Tel: 852/2859-2133
Fax: 852/2559-6484
dept@arch.hku.hk
http://arch.hku.hk
Contact: Head of Department

Degrees/Certificates Offered
BA(Arch Studies); MArch; MLA;
MSc/PDip(Conservation)
FT Students: 400
FT Faculty: 27

Admission Requirements
BA(AS) — Academic achievements in accordance with
standards and regulations of HKU.
MArch — BA(AS) or equivalent.

Tuition & Fees
Undergraduate: HK $42,100.00
Graduate: HK $42,100.00

Program Description
BA(AS) — The Bachelor of Arts in Architectural Studies
Degree is a three-year, full-time curriculum, organized
with strong emphasis on the development of creativity,
innovation and analytical skills through studio/project-
based learning.

The Design Studio is supported by education and
training in visual communications, history and theory,
building technology and CAD methods. The studio design programmes are based on topical issues while
encouraging diversified approaches to give exposure to
different environmental, contextual and problem solving challenges.

MArch — The Master of Architecture is a two-year,
full-time accredited professional programme. The
curriculum is organized into three areas of emphasis: History and Theory, Architectural Management
and Technology/CAAD. Special importance is placed
on inter-disciplinary learning and research through
collaborations with urban design, landscape design,
conservation, arts and humanities, social sciences and
other creative disciplines. Strong ties with the professions are maintained throughout to enhance advanced
partnering with society and the associated creative and
construction industries.

UNIVERSITY OF NEWCASTLE

School of Architecture and Built Environment
University Drive
Callaghan, Newcastle
New South Wales 2308, Australia

Tel: 61-2/4921-5771
Fax: 61-2/4921-6913
archbe@newcastle.edu.au
www.eng.newcastle.edu.au/abe/
Contact: David Stafford; Prof. Steffen Lehmann

Degrees/Certificates Offered
B.Des. (Arch.) + MArch. (3+2 years full-time)
FT students: 320
FT faculty: 15

Admission Requirements
Year 12 or alternate entry by special application

Tuition & Fees
Program - International student enrollment
Courses - International student enrollment or exchange
student enrollment

Program Description
The program partially simulates the problem-solving
situations faced by a working architect. Students learn
using 'Integrated Problem-Based Learning,' whereby
all areas of study are covered through a series of design projects. Students are facilitated in developing a
holistic view of the architecture process in a realistic
context, integrating content material from the professional and user studies, theoretical studies, technical
studies, environmental studies, and communication
skills areas.

Students immediately begin work in problem-based
situations and are presented with a series of 'Design
Integrations,' or problems which bring industry problems into the academic environment. The assignments
increase in complexity and duration as the program
progresses, culminating in the submission of a major
project in which students elect their own site, design
project and work with a mentor chosen from within
the School of Architecture and Built Environment. The
complexity of the design problems increases with each
year.

All programs have been fully accredited by the RAIA
and UIA.

Bachelor of Design (Architecture)
- Year 1 — Problems of the Personal Context (Developing Basic Skills)
- Year 2 — Problems of the Residence (Creative Problem-Solving)
- Year 3 — Problems of Public Places (Challenge and Justification)

Master of Architecture
- Year 4 — Problems of the City
- Year 5 — Problems of Architectural Practice (Student Elective Program)

WARSAW UNIVERSITY OF TECHNOLOGY

Faculty of Architecture
ul. Koszykowa 55
Warsaw 00-659 Poland

Tel: 48-22/6282887
Fax: 48-22/6283236
www.pw.edu/pl
Contact: Stefan Wrona; Dean

Degrees/Certificates Offered
MS in Architecture and Urban Design
FT Students: 1,033

Admission Requirements
Portfolio, a qualifying interview and a two-part written evaluation, including a test and drawing.

Program Description
The Faculty of Architecture is one of the largest of Warsaw University of Technology. The student/faculty ratio is very advantageous, with an academic staff of 156, including 23 professors, many of whom are nationally-recognized architects. This is the largest faculty of architecture in the country, established in 1915 and originally housed in the Warsaw School of Fine Arts.

The "Warsaw School" of modern architecture, which developed between the wars, may be characterized by its creativity within the boundaries of rational design, and this tradition is carried on today. It includes strong emphasis on practice as part of a student's education and many of the faculty continue to be actively engaged in the profession. In addition, research is conducted in such areas as history of architecture and city planning, preservation, and urban and special planning, as well as CAD techniques.

Studies last five years (10 semesters). From the third year on, students choose elective projects, seminars, and lectures which complement their required course syllabus. The last semester is dedicated to a student's thesis project and an examination.

AARHUS SCHOOL OF ARCHITECTURE

Noerreport 20
8000 Aarhus C
Denmark

Tel: 45-/8936-0000
Fax: 45-/8613-0645
Contact: Jørgen Helstrup, International Coordinator
www.aarch.dk

Degrees/Certificates Offered

Bachelor of Arts in Architecture, Master of Arts in
Architecture, Ph.D.
FT Students: 800
FT Faculty: 90

Admission Requirements

Danish Upper Secondary School Leaving Examination or
equivalent, Danish Test 2. Admission is restricted; about
one in three applicants are admitted. For more information regarding the application procedure, please refer
to: www.ciriusonline.dk/Default.aspx?ID=3597

Program Description

The Aarhus School of Architecture (AAA) is an institution of higher education under the Danish Ministry
of Culture. The AAA was established in 1965 and is,
together with the School of Architecture at the Royal
Danish Academy of Fine Arts, the only institution which
educates architects in Denmark.

Bachelor programme at the Aarhus School of Architecture

The Bachelor programme is organised as term courses
in study units.

The first year of study is organised as two coherent
term courses and aims at developing the students' basic academic skills. It deals with the general contents,
methods and requirements of the profession. The students' academic abilities are assessed after the first
year of study.

The second year of study consists of two alternating term courses in architectural planning and architectural design respectively. Here, the students develop
their general disciplinary skills and are introduced to
knowledge, methods and supporting tools in relation to
the central fields of the profession.

The third year of study constitutes two chosen term
courses within the subject area of the departments at
the Aarhus School of Architecture. The students broad-
en their general specialised insight and design competence, and develop basic subject specific knowledge,
methods and skills.

Assessment of the Bachelor project takes place after the third year of study. The assessment is based on a
Bachelor project within one of the subject areas.

Master programme at the Aarhus School of Architecture

The Master programme is carried out within one of the
Master courses offered by the departments at the Aarhus School of Architecture.

Education at the Master level is provided by one of
the specialised departments or in cooperation between
the departments:

- Department of Architecture and Aesthetics
- Department of Landscape and Urbanism
- Department of Architectural Heritage
- Department of Design
- Department of Architectural Design

During the Master programme, the students expand
their Bachelor education with advanced studies within
a defined subject area. The education qualifies for
practicing the profession. The course of the Master programme is an entity of two years of term courses with
compulsory and optional elements of courses, seminars
and projects. A few educational elements can be completed in connection with studies abroad and trainee
service. Assessment of the Master project is based on a
Master Project within the chosen educational field.

Way of studying

Problem-oriented project work is the central element
of the education. It reflects the practical and action-
oriented character of the profession. Openly formulated
presentations of problems related to the surrounding
society form the basis of the projects.

Project work is done in dialogue between instructors and fellow students and requires daily presence
in the studio. The work is done in groups as well as
individually. Typically, joint pilot studies and analyses
are followed up by individual development of synthesis.
Exercises and assignments improve the students' abilities to read and analyse, to relate to and put a given
problem into perspective, and to prioritise, make choices and sum up a solution. Apart from this, the students
are trained in the ability to cooperate, and in taking
part in innovative, interdisciplinary projects.

Assessment

All educational elements of the education are assessed. Assessment usually takes place at the end of
a term.

ECTS points

All educational elements give a fixed number of ECTS
points. ECTS stands for European Credit Transfer and
Accumulation System. Active full-time studies for one
term give 30 ECTS.

Marking

Most major and a few smaller educational elements are assessed with grades (7-point grading
scale), whereas the others are assessed as passed/not
passed or approved/not approved.

ASSUMPTION UNIVERSITY

Department of Architecture
592 Ramkhaheam Road 24
Huamak, Bangkapi, Bangkok
Thailand 10240

Tel: (662) 3004553-62
Fax: (662) 7191531
arch@au.edu
www.arch.au.edu
Contact: Karan Paibullert

Degrees/Certificates Offered

Bachelor of Architecture
FT Students: 80
FT Faculty: 33

Admission Requirements

- Photocopy of M.6 Certificate or its equivalent
- Two 3 x 4 cm. photographs
- Application fees of 300 Baht
- Copy of residential registration
- Copy of identify card
- Copy of passport (non-Thai)

Program Description

The programs for both Architecture and Interior Architecture were approved by Ministry of University Affairs
in 1997. The first students for both departments were
enrolled in June 1997. The curriculum is a five-year program. The graduating students are granted a Bachelor
of Architecture (B. Arch.) degree, which entitles them to
apply for a professional license in order to practice in
the design field.

The curriculum also promotes graduate studies
in master's programs for architecture or other related
fields of design; for example landscape design, environmental design, event design, exhibition design,
interaction design, urban design, city and regional
planning, real estate development, construction management, facility management, etc.

CENTRE FOR ENVIRONMENTAL PLANNING & TECHNOLOGY

School of Architecture
Kasturbhai Lalbhai Campus
University Road
Navrangpura, Ahmedabad, 380 009 India

Tel: 91-79/6442452
Fax: 91-79/6442075
Contact: Kurula Varkey, Director

Degrees/Certificates Offered

Diploma in Architecture after 5 years of full-time study
(equivalent to B Arch) recognized by the Council of
Architecture, India and the Commonwealth Board of
Architectural Education.
FT students: 150
FT faculty: 12

Admission Requirements

12 years high school with math, science, and English
with 55% minimum, aptitude tests in perception, logic,
drawing skills, and creativity.

Tuition & Fees

Undergraduate: Rs. 3,500 per semester
Post-Graduate: Rs. 4,00 per semester

Program Description

The School of Architecture was founded in 1962, under
the aegis of the Ahmedabad Education Society, and is
funded by the Government of Gujarat. Current concerns
of the program include the relationship between architecture and urbanism and issues of regionality and
modernity.

Courses are organized around laboratory studies
and model making. In addition, site visits are organized
to complement the class work. In senior years, regular
involvement of professionals and experts is emphasized
in teaching as well as design exercises. On successful completion of all the formal course requirements,

students are required to undertake an approved and independent investigation for a period of six months in architectural (or related) theory, methods, practice, or criticism.

Faculty include prominent practitioners supplemented by a wide group of visiting faculty. Foreign students are accepted for winter semester at fourth-year level as guest students.

Post-graduate programs are offered in urban design and landscape architecture (School of Architecture); and in urban and regional planning, housing (School of Planning). Other five-year undergraduate programs are offered by the School of Building Science and Technology.

DANISH INSTITUTE FOR STUDY ABROAD

Architecture and Design
Vestergade 7
Copenhagen K, DK-1456 Denmark

Tel: 45/33-11-01-44
Fax: 45/33-93-26-24
www.dis.dk
Contact: Johanne Riegels Ostergaard

Admission Requirements

The AD program is open to students from professional schools and departments of architecture, landscape architecture, urban design, interior architecture, or design at the junior, senior and graduate level. Admission is competitive.

Program Description

The DiS Architecture & Design program offers you the opportunity of studying architecture, landscape architecture, urban design, or interior design. Each of the programs is an integrated whole, in which studio work, lecture courses, seminar courses, field work, and study tours are combined to give you a thorough understanding of the theory, aesthetics, methodology, and actual works of contemporary Scandinavian and European architectural design.

If you do not have a background in architecture and design, but one in fine arts, studio arts, or similar fields, plus the necessary drawing skills, you can choose to study prearchitecture by selecting the course "Foundation Architecture Studio." Students choosing this option participate in AD field studies and required study tours.

The objectives of the Architecture & Design programs are: to expand professional skills through interaction with Danish architects and designers in studio, coursework, and on field studies and study tours; to familiarize you with contemporary Danish, Scandinavian, and European architecture, architectural theory, and design; and to enable you to recognize and analyze the effects of European cultural, economic and political life on architecture and design.

DEAKIN UNIVERSITY

School of Architecture and Building
1 Gheringhop Street
Geelong, Victoria 3217 Australia

Tel: 61-3/522-78300
Fax: 61-3/522-78341
alan.young@deakin.edu.au
www.ab.deakin.edu.au
Contact: Pam Brebner, Executive Officer

Degrees/Certificates Offered

BA Arch, B Arch
FT students: 398
FT faculty: 25

Admission Requirements

Satisfactory completion of Victorian Certificate of Education and work requirements in Units 3 & 4 of English.

Tuition and Fees

$260 general service fee and overseas tuition fee

Program Description

The Bachelor of Arts in Architecture degree is a three-year, full-time course of study comprising 24 units, six of which are elective units. This on-campus course is designed to meet the needs of students who ultimately intend to practice architecture, but alternative units may be taken by those students who wish to pursue different career directions. The Bachelor of Architecture degree follows the BA Arch course and consists of a two-year on-campus course (16 units) of professional studies with main areas of study in architectural design and building technology at an advanced level, architectural management and professional practice, building documentation, and building economics.

Each of these degrees may be awarded at either pass or honors level. Although most students complete the full course, the BA Arch is designed to stand alone as a non-professional study of architecture. The B Arch course is designed to lead to professional recognition by the Royal Australian Institute of Architects and the Architects Registration Board of Victoria, and can be entered on successful completion of the BA Arch degree.

KUWAIT UNIVERSITY

Bachelor of Architecture, Dept. of Architecture, College of Engineering and Petroleum Kuwait

Tel: 965/481-90 94
Fax: 965/484-28 97
arch_dept@yahoo.com
ecealpha.ece.eng.kuniv.edu.kw:8080/~automate/architect/archi.html

Degrees/Certificates Offered

Bachelor of Architecture
Undergraduate faculty: Eight (8)
Graduate faculty: N/A

Admission Requirements

Female students minimum high school equiv. GPA 91%, for male students minimum 82%.

Tuition & Fees

Undergraduate: KD 10/= (approx. US $30) per course

Program Description

The curriculum of the program of architecture is a 5-years 166 semester credits program leading to the degree of Bachelor of Architecture (B.Arch). The program is designed according to reputable international standards as outlined by NAAB adapting to Kuwaiti needs and goals.

LUND INSTITUTE OF TECHNOLOGY AT LUND UNIVERSITY

Programme of Architecture
Box 118
22100 Lund
Sweden

Tel: 46 46 222 00 00
Fax: 46 46 222 0411
abelardo.gonzalez@arkitektur.lth.se
www.lth.se
Contact: Aberlardo Gonzalez

MANIPAL INSTITUTE OF TECHNOLOGY

Faculty of Architecture
Manipal-576104 Karnataka India
Tel: +91-820-2571061
Fax: +91-820-2571071
Email: architecture@manipal.edu
Web: www.manipal.edu/manipalsite/Users/Colsubpage.aspx?PgId=334&ID=1&collegeId=3#arch

Degrees/Certificates Offered

Bachelor of Architecture (B.Arch.): A five-year professional course recognized by the Council of Architecture, New Delhi, the Indian Institute of Architects, Mumbai, and the Commonwealth Association of Architects, London.
Master of Architecture (M. Arch.)
Doctor of Philosophy (Ph. D.)
Faculty: 26 core faculty + 11 visiting faculty
FT Students: 294 undergraduate and 2 graduate
FT Faculty: 26

Admission Requirements

10+2 with Physics, Mathematics and English with Chemistry or Biology or Computer Science or Engineering Drawing as optional subjects for admission and a minimum of 50% marks in Physics, Mathematics and any one of the options and appear for an entrance test which includes aptitude test in Architecture.

Tuition & Fees

Undergraduate: Rs. 151,500 for Indian students
US $6,300 for International students
Graduate: Rs. 162,500

Program Description

The Faculty of Architecture is committed to excellence in architectural education through innovation and teamwork. It strives to create a symbiotic relationship with the region around.

The objectives of the program are:

- To provide quality architectural education leading to the degrees of Bachelor of Architecture, Master of Architecture and Doctor of Architecture.
- To facilitate architectural education through a 'state of the art' Architectural Design Centric Studio

The undergraduate program is divided in two stages, viz., stage-I comprising of basic course involving skill development and stage-II comprising of complete projects having complexity of all the layers.

The Department has a firm belief in a dynamic and competitive world with innovations taking place for human development. A strong academic exchange program supports this. Exchanges of faculty and students has taken place with Rangsit University, Bangkok and University of Chile, Santiago. MoU's for academic exchange are in place with Kagoshima University, Japan and University of Sydney, Australia.

NORTH SOUTH UNIVERSITY

Department of Architecture
12 Kemal Ataturk Avenue, Banani
Dhaka 1213, Bangladesh
Bangladesh

Tel: 9885611-20,8812951
Fax: 880-28823030
hrashid@northsouth.edu
www.northsouth.edu/html/architecture.html
Contact: Haroon Rashid, Chair

Degrees/Certificates Offered
Bachelor of Architecture

Program Description
The architecture program at the North South University with strong philosophical grounding pivots on local tradition, culture, building materials and modern means. It presents a great expectation and promise, harnesses pedagogical learning, and responds to the social and professional needs by aiming to produce a brand of thinkers and makers. The School manifests a culture by offering paradigm to root architecture for the locality. The program stresses the theoretical, historical, cultural, creative, disciplinary and intellectual forces shaping the work and research of the contemporary building profession. It negotiates alteration of the social, cultural and economic landscape that describes the prophetic, utopic, and therapeutic dimensions of the imaginary.

The North South Architecture School commits to the value of design supported by the mutually reinforcing aspects of creativity, investigation and technology. Steadfast in providing professionally relevant, socially aware, and environmentally sensitive directions to learning, it actively engages with the changing needs of modern society. The Program aims to create socioculturally and environmentally aware building professionals for this century who will bring order, vitality and beauty to the built environment. The brilliant young academics encourage creativity, hands-on learning, integrated theory and studio, and contextual response.

PAPUA NEW GUINEA UNIVERSITY OF TECHNOLOGY

Department of Architecture & Building
Private Mail Bag
Lae, 411
Papua, New Guinea

Tel: 675-473-4501
Fax: 675-473-4520
aernest@arch-bldg.unitech.ac.pg
www.unitech.ac.pg
Contact: Rahim Milani

Degrees/Certificates Offered
Bachelor of Architecture (5 years)
FT students: 72
FT faculty: 11

Admission Requirements:
High school (grade 12) certificate

Tuition & Fees:
Kina 7,642 (US $1,900) per year

Program Description
The B.Arch. is a five-year undergraduate program designed for students intending to pursue an architectural career with particular focus on conditions in PNG and the Pacific Region in general. The first three years lead to the award of a Diploma in Architecture. Upon successful completion of the diploma, students who wish to pursue a professional degree are required to undertake an additional two years of coursework.

The department also runs a two-year joint program with the University of Papua New Guinea, Port Moresby, leading to the award of a Postgraduate Diploma in Physical Planning.

Over the years, research activities in the department have focused on the following:

1. "PNG Architectural Heritage Project" involves a long-term study of the traditional settlement and shelter patterns of the numerous cultural areas of the country.

2. Research involves a variety of initiatives falling under the broad category of "Tropical Architecture" and includes research into climatic, social, cultural, and economic factors influencing the design of buildings in the region and the production of durable building materials from locally available resources.

ROYAL DANISH ACADEMY OF FINE ARTS

School of Architecture
Philip de Langes Allé 10
1435 Copenhagen K, Denmark

Tel: 45 32 68 60 26
Fax: 45 32 68 60 31
inger.bak@karch.dk
www.karch.dk
Contact: Inger Merete Bak

Degrees/Certificates Offered
BA, Diploma in Architecture (MA), PhD
FT students: 1,200
FT faculty: 117

Admission Requirements
Danish Upper Secondary School Leaving Certificate or equivalent. Good command of Danish. Admission is restricted.

Tuition & Fees
No fees

Program Description
The School of Architecture at the Royal Danish Academy of Fine Arts is one of the world's oldest schools of architecture. Founded in 1754 as 'The Royal Danish Painting, Sculpture and Building Academy,' the purpose was to educate artists and craftsmen in the three disciplines under the same roof. In the 1960s the school became an independent unit with its own management and achieved the status of an institution of higher learning, issuing a diploma equal to a university Master's degree in architecture, while maintaining its artistic and professional status within the Royal Danish Academy of Fine Arts.

The school educates architects in the fields of architectural design and restoration, urban and landscape planning, and industrial, graphic, and furniture design. Design work is carried out through studio projects covering all the learning components and forms the heart of the course. The complexity and requirement of artistic and technical skills of the students' projects increase throughout the studies.

As an institution of higher learning the School of Architecture carries out artistic development and scientific research in the field of architecture. The transfer of research results in the basic education is a prerequisite to ensure the quality of the architectural education.

SUSHANT SCHOOL OF ART AND ARCHITECTURE

Sector 55
Ansal Institute of Technology Campus
Gurgaon – 122 003 India

Tel: 91-124-2570317, 2570318, 2570319
Fax: 91-124-2570316
sushant@nde.vsnl.net.in
www.sushantschool.org

Degrees/Certificates Offered
Bachelor of Architecture (B.Arch.)
Undergraduate faculty: 37
FT Students: 200
FT Faculty: 12

Admission Requirements
Senior school certificate (10+2) or equivalent with Physics, Math and English as a subject with aggregate 50% marks.

Tuition & Fees
Undergraduate: For Indian Nationals: Rupees 45,000/- per annum (approximately US $1,000)
For Foreign Nationals & NRIs: Fees are usually different and decided from time-to-time

Program Description

Sushant School of Art and Architecture is affiliated to G.G.S. Indrapasta University, New Delhi, for the Five-Year undergraduate program in Architecture, leading to a B.Arch degree. In the new curriculum, architectural design emerges as the core subject, supported by lateral inputs from other allied subjects. Each year of study at the School concentrates on a thematic base, addressed programmatically in the design studio and supported by theoretical understanding and related technological knowledge. Rural and urban process settlement, social housing community structure and cultural fabric, urban process and architecture of the city are some of the themes, synchronically connected with each other at various levels of the five years of study.

Students are encouraged to develop their individual design approach with an understanding of making of architecture through the analysis of history of ideas, theories and cultural agendas, which constitute the base for an architectural outcome of a particular time. At the end of the five years of study, students undergo a metamorphosis, from thinking in the metrical space of wholesomeness, from concepts of dogmatized popular architecture to those of diverse forms, which will drive their imagination to build—the sole dream of an architect.

TAMPERE UNIVERSITY OF TECHNOLOGY

Faculty of Built Environment
School of Architecture
P.O. Box 600
FIN-33101 Tampere
Finland

Tel: +358 3 3115 3203
Fax: +358 3 3115 3206
architecture@tut.fi
www.tut.fi/ark

Degrees/Certificates Offered

Bachelor's Degree as the Bachelor of Science in Architecture (BSc Arch) (3 years, 180 credits)
Masters Degree as the Master of Science in Architecture (MSc Arch) (2 years, 120 credits)
Doctoral Degree as the Doctor of Science in Architecture (70 credits and a doctoral dissertation)
International programs with no degree

Program Description

Originally the Department of Architecture was founded in 1969. Due to a major administration and organization change in the beginning of the year 2008, the former departments were re-arranged into five new faculties. The School of Architecture (former Department of Architecture) is now together with the Department of Civil Engineering forming the new Faculty of Built Environment.

Teaching at the school of architecture is divided among three institutes: The Institute of Theory and History of Architecture, The Institute of Architectural Design, and The institute of Urban Planning and Design. The school has also a Media Laboratory for studies of computer-aided design and planning and visualization of architecture.

Students to the Bachelor's Degree are chosen through entrance examinations. High School diploma or

equivalent is required. The number of new students has been limited to about thirty students per each new academic year. Students in Bachelor's Degree Program are given the right to study in the Master's Degree Program. The Bachelor's Degree takes three years to complete with 180 credits to be earned. The Bachelor's Degree consists of common basic studies (as courses in art and languages together with practical training), professional studies and elective studies in the field of architecture.

Students to the Master's Degree Program are coming directly from the Bachelor's Degree program or chosen through applications and portfolio viewing. Bachelor's Degree in Architecture is required. The Master's Degree takes two years to be completed with 120 credits to be earned. The Masters Degree consists of professional, advanced and elective studies in the field of architecture. A Diploma thesis project concludes the studies and leads to the Master of Science in Architecture Degree.

It takes about three to five years to complete a doctoral degree. Doctoral programmes can be taken in English. Master's Degree is required. Applicants to the doctoral degree are expected to find a professor at TUT in the field of the applicant's research interest before applying. In order to complete the postgraduate studies the student must complete scientific postgraduate studies worth of 70 credits in the major subject and supporting subjects and prepare a doctoral dissertation and its presentation for public defence and criticism.

UNIVERSIDAD DE NAVARRA

Escuela Técnica Superior de Arquitectura
Campus Universitario, S/N
31080 Pamplona (Navarra)
Spain

Tel: 34-948 42 56 27
Fax: 34-948 42 56 29
www.unav.es/arquitectura

Degrees/Certificates Offered

Arquitectura Superior, Arquitectura Técnica; Doctorado, Máster en Diseño Arquitectónico (MDA); Especializaciones Paisajismo, Rehabilitación, Planeamiento Urbano.

Admission Requirements

School admission exam; state exam

Tuition & Fees

Arquitectura Superior: 13.311,30 €
Arquitectura Técnica: 9.172,80 €
MDA: 13.000 €

UNIVERSIDAD DEL ISTMO, GUATEMALA

Facultad de Arquitectura y Diseño
7a Avenida 3-67, zona 13
Guatemala City 01013
Guatemala C.A.

Tel: PBX (502) 24291400 Ext. 173
Fax: (502) 24752192
www.unis.edu.gt
Contact: Ana María de García, Dean

Degrees/Certificates Offered

Department of Architecture
Bachelor of Architecture
Bachelor of Interior Architecture
Licenciatura en Arquitectura
Master of Architecture
Master of Interior Architecture

Department of Design
Bachelor of Graphic Design for Communication and Advertising
Licenciatura en Diseño Gráfico en Comunicación y Publicidad
Master of Graphic Design for Communication and Advertising
Bachelor of Industrial Apparel Design
Licenciatura en Diseño Industrial del Vestuario

FT Students: 503
FT Faculty: 20 FT Faculty and 65 PT Faculty

Admission Requirements

A completed UNIS application form
Identification papers
An official high school transcript
Successfully passed admission tests
Personal interview

Tuition and Fees

Tuition Q.1500.00 (US$. 197.36)
Fees Q.2375.00 (US$. 312.50)

Program Description

The program is structured in accordance to the European Bologna process, to permit student mobility and title recognition.

Our architecture program enables our graduates to design as well as build, according to laws in Guatemala. In all our departments, we emphasize subjects related to the better understanding of the human being and we prepare our students to successfully incorporate in the business world through a solid group of courses related to administration and finance.

UNIVERSIDADE LUSOFONA DE HUMANIDADES E TECHNOLOGIAS

Av. Campo Grande, 376
Lisboa Portugal

Tel: +3512175155 65
Fax: +3512175155 34
a.bramdao@ulusofona.pt
www.ulusofona.pt

Program Description

The Integrated Masters in Architecture Course of the Lusófona University is designed to train Master's Graduates in Architecture, in accordance with Decree-Law 74/2006 of 24 March, and the principles set out by the

International Union of Architects (Union Internationale des Architectes or UIA), while making young future architects aware of issues in Architecture and in the Tropico-Equatorial Territory, in the context of Lusofonia, where the university is found.

It is therefore expected that the trained young architects:

- Will be sufficiently equipped, with senior help, to be able to design and develop an Architectural project, taking into consideration the various elements and constraints specified. From the selection and survey of the site, development and handling of the conceptual model, after interpretation of the programme, the legal-framework system, to the organisation and completion of the process —in relation to specialisation, span and finishing charts, contract specifications, measurements and budget estimates, technical work assistance, etc.—they will also be expected to have control over the various phases, the complexity of the works, the inherent responsibilities and costs, and inherent negotiating capabilities;
- Will be able to handle various construction systems, according to their project options, to know how and when to obtain technical information and integrate it in a consistent manner, into the project;
- Will have solid and reliable knowledge of the History and Theory of Architecture, expressive ideas on the conditioning that the culture, economy, history, and geography of the territories and communities confer to the project perspective, particular with respect to Portuguese territory and the Lusophone Space (Espaço Lusófono);
- Will know how to work with urban territory of different dimensions and scopes: buildings, complexes, detailed planning, the land subdivision project, and the urban-development plan;
- Will understand the various domains of professional action of the Architect, in addition to designing buildings: rehabilitation of buildings and sites, urban management and legal resources for project licensing, Architectural critical observation, management and preparation of works, Architectural instruction, participation in cross-discipline teams in Land Use Plans, in Environmental Impact Studies, in Building evaluation processes, in Architectural Tender Jury Panels, in integration processes of the other Architectural Trades and in the City, and in the physical management of the running of cities and other human settlements;
- Will have knowledge of the use and pathologies of some materials, as well as old, vernacular, and contemporary structures, and also safety systems, heating and acoustic framework of buildings, particularly in Portuguese territory and in the Lusophone Space.

UNIVERSIDAD PRIVADA DE SANTA CRUZ DE LA SIERRA

Facultad de Arquitectura, Diseño y Urbanismo
(School of Architecture, Design and Urbanism)
Campus: Av. Paragua y Cuarto Anillo
Casilla de Correo: 2944
Santa Cruz – Bolivia

Tel: (591) (3) 346.4000
Fax: (591) (3) 346.5757
victorlimpias@upsa.edu.bo
www.upsa.edu.bo
Contact: Victor Hugo Limpias Ortiz, Dean

Degrees/Certificates Offered
Licenciado en Arquitectura
Undergraduate faculty: 32
FT Students: 291
FT Faculty: 6

Admission Requirements
Interview, high school grades

Tuition & Fees
Undergraduate: $1,000 per semester

Program Description
The architecture program is focused on the production of competitive, self-conscious architects, able to respond effectively and responsibly to the spatial demands of the community they form part of. His/her professional behavior and acts should promote community interactions and the quality of life, within the framework of positive political, social and environmental ethics. The Architecture program leads to a professional degree that allows graduates to become registered architects, once they successfully defend a thesis work, which can be an applied architecture design project, urban plan, technological research, preservation project or a theoretical analysis.

An active Community Design Program allows students to develop design projects, either architectural or urbanistic, to small communities and non-profit organizations. Prominent international architects present their work on a regular basis. Field trips are programmed along the studies in different courses, visiting literally the entire country. International architecture trips are also programmed yearly to Latin American countries, the United States of America or Europe. During summer and winter breaks, the School offers off-campus architecture design courses, held in different Bolivian cities, and in Argentina and Chile. There are different student exchange programs with several Latin American, North American and European universities.

UNIVERSITÉ CATHOLIQUE DE LOUVAIN (UCL)

Architecture Unit
Place du Levant, 1
Louvain-la-Neuve, B-1348 Belgium

Tel: 32-1047-2341
Fax: 32-1047-4544
francoise.daoust@uclouvain.be
www.uclouvain.be/prog-2008-arch2m.html
Contact: Head, Architecture Unit

Degrees/Certificates Offered
5-year first professional degree ("Ingénieur civil architecte"); Doctorate
FT students: 150 undergraduate, 30 graduate
FT faculty: 5
PT faculty: 13

Admission Requirements
Undergraduates: high school diploma, entrance examination.
Graduate students: letter of intent, transcripts, support of a faculty member.

Tuition & Fees
Basic tuition varies between 100 and 700 Euros per year. Other fees may apply in the case of specific programs.

Program Description
The Université Catholique de Louvain (UCL), a nearly 600-year old comprehensive university, has been involved in architectural education since 1877. Since 1972, the French-speaking faculty and students work in a new town and campus that is in itself a laboratory for architecture and urban design, called Louvain-la-Neuve. Holders of the first-professional degree, thanks to a series of master's-level options in the fourth and fifth years, find work in a variety of spheres, including architectural design, engineering, industry, and government. Options for research degrees at the master's level include Bioclimatic Architecture, Structural Design, and Theory/History. The doctoral program provides opportunities for advanced research and teaching experience. The language of instruction is primarily French, but international graduate students find it particularly easy to function in Belgium's naturally multi-lingual environment, a crossroads of European and world cultures.

UNIVERSITY OF ADELAIDE

School of Architecture
5005 AUSTRALIA

Tel: +61 8 8303 5836
Facsimile: +61 8 8303 4377
rebecca.zweck@adelaide.edu.au
www.architecture.adelaide.edu.au

Tuition & Fees
Commonwealth-supported place: $7,412

Program Description
Design is an activity that requires creativity, critical thinking and the ability to understand and respond to the needs and aspirations of people and the possibilities of our environment. Design in the Bachelor of Design Studies degree focuses on the way humans create places through architecture, landscape architecture and urban design.

The three-year Bachelor of Design Studies degree can be taken alone or as the first part of the professionally accredited academic programs of Master of Architecture or Master of Landscape Architecture. Alternatively, the Bachelor of Design Studies program provides a study pathway for students who wish to undertake the Master of Design in Digital Media program.

The program involves the arts and the sciences, writing and graphics, design and analysis, management and engineering, together with architecture, landscape architecture and urban design. Students will find themselves involved in practical aspects of the program, such as designing, making models, visiting building sites and gardens, visiting art galleries and exhibitions, and absorbing aspects of the society in which people live and formulating proposals for improving the environment.

UNIVERSITY OF AUCKLAND
School of Architecture and Planning
National Institute of Creative Arts and Industries
Private Bag 92019
Auckland New Zealand

Tel: 64-9/373 7599 extension 88134 or 88596
Fax: 64-9/373 7694
Web: info-archplan@auckland.ac.nz
School Manager: Martine Davis
Head of School: Professor Jenny Dixon

Degrees/Certificates Offered
Bachelor of Architectural Studies BAS (3 years);
Master of Architecture (Professional) MArch(Prof) (2 years);
Master of Architecture MArch (1 year);
Master of Architecture MArch – in Sustainable Design (1 year);
Postgraduate Diploma in Architecture PGDipArch (1 year):
PhD. (3-4 years)
Undergraduate students: 420
Postgraduate students: 124
FT faculty: 33

Admission Requirements
BAS: New Zealand university entrance or equivalent
plus a portfolio of creative work
MArch(Prof): BAS or equivalent with a minimum average grade of B- over 90 points in stage 3
Other Postgraduate: appropriate qualification
Tuition & Fees
BAS:
NZ citizens and permanent residents: NZ $4,465 – $5,741
International students: NZ $19,478 - $24960
Postgraduate:
NZ citizens and permanent residents: NZ $4,759 – $6,598
International students: NZ $23,243 - $26,514
PhD:
NZ citizens and permanent residents: NZ $4,295
International students: NZ $4,295

Program description
The BAS provides a general introduction to architecture and related aspects of design. It forms the first part of the two-tiered programme and is a prerequisite degree for entry into the professional qualification the Master of Architecture (Professional)* (MArch(Prof)).

In the first and subsequent years students will:
* Undertake design projects in studio courses
* take a number of core courses including Architectural Media, History and Theory of Architecture and Urbanism, and Architectural Technology
* select from electives in Architectural Media
The MArch(Prof) is the second part of the two-tiered professional architecture programme and follows on from the Bachelor of Architectural Studies (BAS). It is the qualification that is required to apply for registration as a professional architect*.

The first year of the programme comprises of a number of taught seminars, professional studies courses and studio design topics. Students have the opportunity to select their main areas of study from the following four thematic clusters:
* Sustainable Design
* Urban Design
* Material and Digital Fabrication
* Maori and Cultural Studies
The second year requires the completion of a 120 point research-based design thesis on a topic of specific interest. The thesis involves research on a specific

architectural issue, proposition or hypothesis investigated and explored through design.

Recognised by the New Zealand Registered Architects Board (NZRAB), the New Zealand Institute of Architects (NZIA) and the Commonwealth Association of Architects.

UNIVERSITY OF EDINBURGH
Department of Architecture
Minto House, 20 Chambers Street
Edinburgh, EH1 1JZ
United Kingdom

Tel: +44 (0) 131 650 2306
Fax: +44 (0) 131 650 8019
architecture@ed.ac.uk
www.architecture.ed.ac.uk
Contact: Dr Stephen Cairns, Head of Architecture

Program Description
Architecture is the art of building. So significant are buildings in contemporary society that this definition implies a wide range of conditions: from the most intimate spaces of a dwelling, to the heterogenous fabric of a city.

This scope brings architecture into contact with other disciplines concerned with buildings and cities, such as engineering, construction, urban planning, landscape architecture, environmental science, art history, and sociology.

Architecture necessarily engages with all of these neighbouring disciplines, but is the only one of them that has design as its specialist skill and knowledge base. Design is a mode of thinking and practice that combines historical and environmental knowledges, logical analysis and creativity. The Department of Architecture at Edinburgh treasures the distinctiveness of design, and seeks to put it to work in critical, responsible, and creative ways in the diverse conditions of contemporary metropolitan life.

In this work our Department is nourished and supported by Edinburgh itself, a city widely acclaimed as one of the most beautiful in the world.

UNIVERSITY OF NEW SOUTH WALES
School of Architecture
Sydney, NSW 2052 Australia

Tel: 61-2/9385-4796
Fax: 61-2/9662-1378
www.fbe.unsw.edu.au
Contact: Jon T. Lang

Degrees/Certificates Offered
B Arch, B Int Arch, M Arch (History and Theory), M Arch (Computing), M Arch (Design)
FT Students: 700
FT Faculty: 30

Admission Requirements
Undergraduate: High school certificate
Graduate: Appropriate degree

Tuition & Fees
$10,500 for international students

Program Description
The University of New South Wales is one of the East Pacific region's leading research and teaching institutions. The School of Architecture follows suit with major research efforts to supplement its teaching endeavors. It has research units in Sustainable Development (SOLARCH) and lightweight structures which have been augmented in the past five years with an emphasis on history and theory, Asian architecture, and urban design. As an educational institution, the school is one of the largest in Australia, with full-time students and staff aided by over a hundred people drawn from professional practice on a part-time basis. The school offers education at both an undergraduate and graduate level.

About 30% of the students enrolled in the school are international students drawn predominantly from Southeast Asia, but also from East and South Asia, the Americas, and Europe. The international nature of the school is reinforced through exchange programs with universities throughout Asia, Europe, and the Americas.

The professional architectural degree course is the 5.5-year B Arch program, and the interior architecture course leads to the award of a B Int Arch degree in four years of study.

Graduate education is becoming an increasingly important component of the school's educational endeavors. There are also master's and Ph.D. research programs. The predominant teaching mode throughout is the lecture, seminar and design tutorial. The school also offers refresher courses to graduates seeking professional registration and continuing education courses to practitioners.

THE UNIVERSITY OF QUEENSLAND
Department of Architecture
School of Geography, Planning and Architecture
Zelman Cowen Building
The University of Queensland, Brisbane Qld 4072
Australia

Tel: 61 7 3365 3537
Fax: 61 7 3365 3999
architecture@uq.edu.au
www.architect.uq.edu.au
Mr. Peter Skinner, Head of Department of Architecture

Degrees/Certificates Offered
BArch, MDesign Studies, Mphil, PhD
FT Students: 353

Admission Requirements
Undergraduate: Admission through Queensland Tertiary Admissions Centre with a pass in Year 12 English.
Postgraduate: Previous degree(s) in architecture

Tuition & Fees

Undergraduate: Aust. & NZ citizens (HEC S2003): $5,242/year (deferred); $3,931/year (upfront). International (2003): AUD $20,000/year.

Program Description

This is the longest-established Architecture course in Queensland. The undergraduate course focuses on the teaching of architectural design skills. Studio-based Architectural Design courses constitute 50% of the program, supported by lecture streams in Technology (Structures, Construction, Environmental Design, Professional Studies) and Humanities (History, Theory, People/Environment Studies) and a final year Thesis.

The undergraduate Bachelor of Architecture program is a professionally-oriented degree and students must successfully undertake the equivalent of five years of full-time study, plus 10 months of practical experience between Years 3 and 4.

The BArch is a professional qualification fully-recognized by the Royal Australian Institute of Architects and by the State Boards of Architects as an appropriate educational qualification for registration and practice as an architect in Australia. Students who have successfully completed 3 years of the BArch program are eligible to receive the Bachelor of Design Studies degree.

At the postgraduate level, Master of Philosophy (Architecture), Master of Philosophy (Design Studies) and PhD are research degrees awarded on the basis of a thesis resulting from individual self-directed research under the supervision of a staff member. Usually master's degrees take two years full-time to complete, while doctoral degrees normally require three years of full-time study.

UNIVERSITY OF SAN CARLOS

College of Architecture and Fine Arts
University of San Carlos
Talamban Campus
Cebu City, Philippines 6000

Tel: (063-32) 3443801/3461128 local 707
Fax: (063-32) 3460351
Email: cafadean@usc.edu.ph or
archdept@usc.edu.ph or
usc.cafa@yahoo.com
Web: www.usc.edu.ph
Contact: Archt. Omar Maxwell P. Espina

Degrees/Certificates Offered

Master of Architecture majors in:
Architectural Science
Landscape Architecture and Urban Design
Bachelor of Science in Architecture
Bachelor of Science in Landscape Architecture
Bachelor of Science in Interior Design
Bachelor of Fine Arts majors in:
Advertising Arts and Painting
Certificate of Draftsmanship
Certificate of Building Technician
Undergraduate faculty: 58
Graduate faculty: 7
FT Students: 1,205
FT Faculty: 37

Admission Requirements

1. Accomplished Application or Admission form
2. Birth Certificate
3. Two sets of 50mm x 50mm ID pictures
4. Statement of Good Moral Character from the school attended
5. Must pass the College Entrance Examination and Interview
6. Two accomplished recommendation forms from professors and/or current employer (for Graduate Program applicant only)
7. Official transcript of records or Certificate of Transfer Credentials (for Graduate Program applicant only)
8. For USC Graduates: Clearance from Bursar's Office and Student Affairs Services Office (for Graduate Program applicant only)
9. For Foreign Applicants:
   i. Certificate of English Proficiency (TOEFL) if medium of instruction is not English
   ii. Clearance/Recommendation from Foreign Student

Tuition & Fees

Undergraduate: $665 per student per semester
Graduate: $385 per student per semester

Program Description

Master of Architecture (2 years) majors in:
Architectural Science
Landscape Architecture and Urban Design
The program is intended for persons with professional undergraduate degree who are already competent in most aspects and therefore do not require broad coverage of the field, and for individuals from the academe and any related discipline who will pursue research and advance knowledge in architecture.

B.S Architecture Program (5 years)
The B.S. Architecture program of the University of San Carlos span the 3-year Building Construction program plus 2 more years of higher studies in Architecture theory and design. These professional courses place emphasis on design approaches sensitive to local conditions, utilizing basic and empirical data as starting point for design. Placement and time slot for a 2-year practicum are built-in features of the 5-year ladder type program. In the terminal year, a range of electives plus an undergraduate thesis complete the requirement for the B.S. Architecture degree.

B.S Landscape Architecture Program (4 years)
The B.S. Landscape Architecture Program of the University of San Carlos is a 4-year course program which equips students with theoretical grounding as well as practical skills through training in architectural principles, planning and design, site engineering principles, geology and soil sciences, plant materials, ecology, drafting, surveying and mapping, construction detailing, water science and irrigation, natural and social sciences, preparing contracts and specification documents. Students graduate from the program with the excellent capacities to render professional services in landscape design as well as implementing aesthetically attuned landscape architecture projects.

The course curriculum shall be an integration of subjects offered under the Departments of Engineering, Arts and Sciences, and Architecture.

B.S. Interior Design Program(4 years)
The B.S. Interior Design Program of the University of San Carlos covers design concepts and methods for building interiors based on the fundamental criteria of

comfort, beauty and integrity with the building character. In addition, students learn skills in furniture and product design, photography, fashion and other crafts, with emphasis on concepts of expression of cultural identity. A terminal design project in the 4th year is a pre-requisite for graduation.

Bachelor of Fine Arts major in Advertising Arts (4 years)
The core of the Bachelor of Fine Arts major in Advertising Arts Program of the University of San Carlos are visual presentation skills, commercial arts technique and advertising approaches. Innovative projects expose students to actual involvement in current technical issues and methods for expressing international trends as well as native traditions and lifestyles.

Bachelor of Fine Arts major in Painting (4 years)
The main focus of the Bachelor of Fine Arts major in Painting Program of the University of San Carlos is the special skills training in painting. The painting courses place emphasis on the painting techniques and development of the student's abilities in painting. Aside from providing them with the knowledge, skills and proficiency in developing their painting abilities, students also learn other skills in photography, illustration, cartooning and other elective advertising arts.

UNIVERSITY OF SOUTH AUSTRALIA

City West Campus, North Terrace
Adelaide, SA 5000 Australia

Tel: 61-8/8302-0201
Fax: 61-8/8302-0211
www.unisa.edu.au/arc
Contact: Professor Mads Gaardboe; Head of School

Degrees/Certificates Offered

B.Arch.Stud., M.Arch, B.Int.Arch., B.Ind.Des, M.Sust. Des., master's and doctoral degrees by research
FT Students: 770
FT Faculty: 38

Admission Requirements

Year 12, TAFE, STAT or Tertiary Transfer.
All applications should be made through the South Australian Tertiary Admissions Centre. Confirmation should be sought on detail requirements.

Tuition & Fees

$7,240 per year (Commonwealth Supported undergraduate and post-graduate course work degrees)
$18,600 per year (International students)
Higher Degree by Research student fees vary. Information is available from the University.

Program Description

The B.Arch.Stud consists of three years (6 semesters) of full-time study organized into three levels: Level 1 (semesters 1 and 2) is an introduction to the basic principles of architecture; Level 2 (semesters 3, 4, 5, and 6) develops competence in core subject streams. This is a non-professional architecture degree that gives access to the professional Master of Architecture.

M.Arch consists of two years full study (semesters 7, 8, 9, and 10), and can be accessed from the Bachelor Degree or directly with similar prerequisites. It expands the intellectual and professional areas of the program and provides scope for specialization. With some practice experience, the M.Arch leads to professional registration as an architect and permission to use the title Architect.

The total five-year course sequence (B.Arch.Stud. + M.Arch.) is organized into the following core subject streams:

- Design Studio – the major focus for the integration of all subject streams in the course;
- Communication and Documentation – includes technical, graphic, and verbal communication skills, and CAD;
- Technical Systems – includes services, environmental science, structural systems, building economics, and legislation;
- Environmental Studies – includes architectural history and theory, sustainability, and urban ecology; and
- Practice Management

Through elective studies, the school is uniquely involved in design and construction of buildings that has won national acclaim.

All academic staff are involved in research and consultancy activities supporting the advancement of the design professions.

The school is located on the City West Campus in the heart of Adelaide in recently completed award-winning buildings, offering dedicated studios, lecture theaters, tutorial rooms, and a well equipped, contemporary workshop. The library's art and design collection is nationally recognized, and the School is home to Australia's only dedicated Architecture Museum.

UNIVERSITY OF TECHNOLOGY, SYDNEY

Architecture Program
Faculty of Design
Architecture and Building
PO Box 123 Broadway NSW 2007 Australia

Tel: 61-2-9514 8024
Fax: 61-2-9514 8078
Kerryn.Stanton@uts.edu.au
www.dab.uts.edu.au/architecture
Contact: Kerryn Stanton; Program Assistant

Degrees/Certificates Offered
Bachelor of Arts (Architecture), Bachelor of Architecture, Master of Architecture and PhD
FT Students: 220
FT Faculty: 14

Admission Requirements
- NSW Higher School Certificate or Australian equivalent, UAI e 85, or
- Australian TAFE, Tertiary or approved overseas qualification

Tuition & Fees
Undergraduate: HECS (Higher Education Contribution Scheme) for Australian citizens and permanent residents. $15,000 per year for international students.

Program Description
Already one of the most highly-respected courses in Australia because of its links with industry and orienta-

tion toward the architectural profession, we emphasize quality of education and self-directed learning. The aims of the Architecture course are to equip students with sufficient skills and knowledge for the practice of architecture, and equally to develop students' capacity for critical thought and understanding of the humanistic and socio-cultural dimensions of architecture.

The Architecture course at UTS is structured into two parts. Students first undertake a Bachelor of Arts in Architecture (BA), which is a three-year, full-time (or equivalent) degree. Following completion of the BA, students progress to the Bachelor of Architecture (BArch), which is a two-year full-time (or equivalent) degree. In general terms, the BA can be seen as a liberal introduction to the study of architecture as a discipline. This degree can stand alone, and equips students well to join other design fields or related disciplines, or to go on to further academic research and study. It also has an important role in preparing students for the BArch degree. In this second degree, the emphasis lies in educating students for the practice of architecture as a profession. Together, the two degrees acknowledge the nature of architecture as both a discipline and a profession.

VICTORIA UNIVERSITY OF WELLINGTON

School of Architecture
139 Vivian Street
Wellington
New Zealand

Tel: (04) 463 6200
Fax: (04) 463 6204
www.arch.vuw.ac.nz
Contact: Gordon Holden, Head of School

Degrees/Certificates Offered
Bachelor of Architecture
Bachelor of Design (Interior Architecture)
Bachelor of Design (Landscape Architecture)
Bachelor of Building Science
Bachelor of Arts (Architectural Studies)
Bachelor of Arts (Design Studies)
Master of Architecture
Master of Design
Master of Building Science
PhD

Program Description
Bachelor of Architecture
The Bachelor of Architecture (BArch) degree is a five-year programme of full-time study that provides students with the skills, practical knowledge and theoretical approaches required in the architecture profession. This degree consists of 600 points, comprising 126 points from First Year Architecture, followed by a further four-year specialised study. It satifies the academic requirements for registration as an Architect.
Bachelor of Design (Interior Architecture)
The BDes (Interior Architecture) degree is a four-year programme of full-time study that provides students with the skills, practical knowledge and theoretical approaches required in the profession of Interior Architecture. This degree consists of 482 points, comprising 126 points from First Year Design or First Year Architecture, followed by a further three-year spe-

cialised study.
Bachelor of Design (Landscape Architecture)
The BDes (Landscape Architecture) degree is a four-year programme of full-time study that provides students with the skills, practical knowledge and theoretical approaches required in the profession of Landscape Architecture. This degree consists of 482 points, comprising 126 points from First Year Design or First Year Architecture, followed by a further three-year specialised study.
Bachelor of Building Science
The Bachelor of Building Science (BBSc) degree is a three-year programme that provides a thorough grounding in the science and technology of building and an understanding of architecture. This degree consists of a minimum 360 points, comprising of 126 points from First Year followed by a further two years of 120 points each.
Bachelor of Arts (Architectural Studies)
The BA major in Architectural Studies - BA (ARCS) offers an attractive option for students who are interested in Architecture but do not wish to pursue a professionally oriented degree.
Bachelor of Arts (Design Studies)
The BA major in Design Studies - BA (DESS) offers an attractive option for students who are interested in Interior Architecture or Landscape Architecture but do not wish to pursue a professionally oriented degree.
Conjoint Bachelor of Arts (Design Studies) / Bachelor of Teaching
The four-year conjoint BA (Design Studies) / BTeach degree is offered for students who are interested in teaching. Students must complete a BA major from a list of approved teaching subjects, and must take a second teaching subject to 200-level. Students who major in Design Studies are eligible to teach in the areas of visual arts, design and technology, subjects which have become a significant part of the contemporary school curriculum.
Master of Architecture
The Master of Architecture (MArch) degree is undertaken as the writing of a thesis, the result of detailed research of an architectural subject of interest for which the candidate has adequate training and ability.
Master of Design
The Master of Design (MDes) degree normally requires a minimum of three trimesters full-time or six trimesters part-time research-based study. It is currently available for the study of Interior Architecture and Landscape Architecture, as well as Industrial Design and areas which link Design with Architecture, Building Science or certain areas of the Arts and Humanities and general design topics.
Master of Building Science
The Master of Building Science (MBSc) is a two-year full-time, or up to four-year part-time, degree consisting of coursework and a thesis.
PhD
The PhD is examined by thesis after a period of a minimum of two years of supervised research at Victoria. The PhD thesis is a major piece of original research.

The following list of worldwide schools of architecture are grouped by the following regions:

8th Annual ACSA/AISC Steel Design Student Competition, 2007–08
Second Place Winner —— Assembling Housing
Students: David Schellingerhoudt & Lindsey Nette, University of Waterloo
Faculty Sponsor: Terri Meyer Boake, University of Waterloo
Project Title: Community Building

SCHOOLS OF ARCHITECTURE WORLDWIDE

AFRICA

Centre Universitaire de Biskar
Institut d'Architecture
Alexandria 07000 **Algeria**

Ecole Polytechnique d'Architecture et
Urbanisme (APAU)
B.P. n. 2, El Harrach
Algiers **Algeria**

Institut d'Architecture
USTO, BP 1505 Oran
Elm'nouar **Algeria**

Institut d'Architecture de Bechar
Bechar **Algeria**

Institut d'Architecture de Tizi-Ouzou
Tizi-Ouzou **Algeria**

Universite de Blida
Institut d'Architecture de Blida
Blida **Algeria**

Universite de Constantine
Institut d'Architecture, d'Urbanisme et
Construction (IAUC)
Constantine **Algeria**

Universite de Setif
Institut d'Architecture de Setif
Setif **Algeria**

Universite Nouvelle du Zaire
I.B.T.P.
B.P. 8249
Kinshasha **Democratic Republic of the Congo**

Ain Shaims University, Faculty of Engineering
Department of Architecture
Midan Abdou Basha
Cairo-Abbasia **Egypt**

Al-Azhar University, Faculty of Engineering
Department of Architecture
Cairo-Nasr City **Egypt**

Tel: +20-2/291-805

Al-Mansoura University
Faculty of Engineering
Department of Architecture
Al-Dakhalia Governorate
Mansoura **Egypt**

Al-Menia University
Faculty of Engineering and Technology
Department of Architecture
Al-Menia Governorate
Al-Menia **Egypt**

Al-Menofia University, Faculty of Engineering
Department of Architecture
Al-Menofia Governorate
Menofia **Egypt**

Alexandria University, Faculty of Engineering
Department of Architecture
Gamal Abdel-Naser Road
Alexandria **Egypt**

Assuit University, Faculty of Engineering
Department of Architecture
Assuit Governorate
Assuit **Egypt**

Cairo University, Faculty of Engineering
Department of Architecture
Giza **Egypt**

Helwan University, Faculty of Fine Arts
Department of Architecture
Cairo-Zamalek **Egypt**

Mataria-Helwan University,
Faculty of Engineering and Technology
Department of Architecture
Giza **Egypt**

MISR International University,
Faculty of Engineering
Department of Architecture
Giza **Egypt**

Tel: +20-2/349-3110

Tanat University, Faculty of Engineering
Department of Architecture
El-Gharbia Governorate
El-Gharbia **Egypt**

Zagazig University, Faculty of Engineering
Department of Architecture
Banha Branch
Cairo-Shoubra **Egypt**

Addis Ababa University
Dept. of Architecture & Urban Planning,
Faculty of Technology
P.O. Box 518
Addis Ababa **Ethiopia**

University of Science and Technology
Faculty of Environmental and Development Studies
Kumasi **Ghana**

Tel: +233-51/60309

University of Nairobi
Department of Architecture
PO BOX 30197
Nairobi **Kenya**

Tel: +254-2/724-528
Fax: +254-2/718-549

Jomo Kenyatta University of Agriculture
and Technology
Department of Architecture
PO BOX 60000
Nairobi **Kenya**

Tel: +254-1512-2646
Fax: +254-1512-1764

Universite d'Antananarivo
Filiere Batiment/Travaux-Publics, Ecole
Superieure Polytechnique
B.P. 562
Antananarivo 00101 **Madagascar**

University of Lagos
Department of Architecture and Design
Faculty of Environmental Sciences
Lagos Akoka-Yaba **Nigeria**

Bendel State University
Dept. of Architecture & Town Planning
Faculty of Environmental Design, PMB 14
Bendel State Eknoma **Nigeria**

University of Nigeria
Dept. of Architecture
Faculty of Environmental Studies
Anambra State Enugu Campus **Nigeria**

Obafemi Awolowo University
Department of Architecture
Fac. of Environmental Design and Management
Osun State Ile-Ife **Nigeria**

Abia State University
School of Architecture
P.M.B. 2000
Okigwe **Nigeria**

Ahmadu Bello University
Department of Architecture
Faculty of Environmental Design
Kaduna State Zaria **Nigeria**

University of the Free State
Department of Architecture
P.O. Box 339
Bloemfontein 09300 **South Africa**

Tel: +27-51/401-2332

Cape Technikon
Dept. of Architecture, School of Arch. and Building
P.O. Box 652
Cape Town 08000 **South Africa**

Tel: +27-21/460-3029

University of Natal
School of Architecture
King George V Avenue
Durban 04001 **South Africa**

Tel: +27-31/260-2699

University of Witswatersrand
Faculty of Architecture
P.O. Wits
Johannesburg 02050 **South Africa**

University of Port Elizabeth
Faculty of Architecture
P.O. Box 1600
Port Elizabeth 06000 **South Africa**

Tel: +27-41/504-2552

University of Pretoria
Dept. of Architecture and Landscape Arch.
Div. Of Environmental Design & Management
Pretoria 00001 **South Africa**

Tel: +27-12/420-2550

University of Cape Town
School of Architecture and Planning
Rondebosch Cape 07701 **South Africa**

Tel: +27-21/650-2374

R.S.B.C.A.
P.O. Box 720
Khartoum **Sudan**

University of Khartoum
Department of Architecture
P.O. Box 321
Khartoum **Sudan**

Ecole Africaine et Mauricienne
d'Architecture et d'Urbanisme
B.P. 2067
Lome **Togo**

Institut Technologique d'Art, d'Arch.
Et d'Urbanisme (ITAAU)
Section Architecture et Urbanisme
Route de l'Armee Nationale
Tunis Bab Souika 01006 **Tunisia**

Ecole Nationale d'Architecture et d'Urbanisme
16, rue Mikhaïl Noaïma/ 23-25 Bouleverd
Hédi Saïdi
El Omrane 1005 Tunis **Tunisia**

Tel: +216-1/891-333
Fax: +216-1/571-861

The Copperbelt University
School of Environmental Studies
P.O. Box 21692
Kitwe **Zambia**

ASIA, OCEANIA, & MIDDLE EAST

Afghan Institute of Technology
Department of Building Construction
Kabul **Afghanistan**

University of Adelaïde
Dept of Architecture
North Terrace
Adelaide SA 5000 **Australia**

Tel: +61-8/303-5836
Fax: +61-8/303-4377

University of South Australia
Faculty of Art, Architecture & Design
GPO BOX 2471
Adelaide SA 5001 **Australia**

Tel: +61-8/302-0333
Fax: +61-8/302-0334

University of Canberra
Faculty of Environmental Design
P.O. Box 1
Belconnen ACT 2616 **Australia**

Tel: +61-6/201-2178
Fax: +61-6/201-5034

Curtin University of Technology
School of Architecture, Construction & Planning
Kent Street
Bentley WA 6102 **Australia**

Tel: +61-9/351-7258
Fax: +61-9/351-2711

University of Technology Sydney
Faculty of Design, Architecture & Building
P.O. Box 2007
Broadway NSW 2007 **Australia**

Tel: +61-2/330-8913
Fax: +61-2/330-8877

Queensland University of Technology
School of Architecture, Interior and Industrial Design
G.P.O. Box 2434
Brisbane QLD 4001 **Australia**

Tel: +61-7/864-2670
Fax: +61-7/864-1528

University of Queensland
Department of Architecture
Brisbane QLD 4072 **Australia**

Tel: +61-7/365-3790
Fax: +61-7/365-3999

The University of Newcastle
Faculty of Architecture
University Drive
Callaghan NSW 2308 **Australia**

Tel: +61-4/921-5771
Fax: +61-4/921-6913

Canberra College of Advanced Education
School of Environmental Design
Opost Office Box 381
Canberra ACT 2601 **Australia**

University of Canberra
Faculty of Environmental Design,
Dept. of Architecture & Building
P.O. Box 1, Belconnen
Canberra ACT 2616 **Australia**

Deakin University
School of Architecture & Building
Geelong VI 3217 **Australia**

Tel: +61-5/227-8300
Fax: +61-5/227-8341

Gordon Technical College
Architectural Drafting
Private Bag No. 1
Geelong VI 3221 **Australia**

University of Tasmania
School of Architecture & Engineering
P.O. Box 1214
Launceston TAS 7250 **Australia**

Tel: +61-3/6324-3464
Fax: +61-3/6324-3557

Royal Melbourne Institute of Technology
Dept. of Architecture
GPO 2476V
Melbourne VI 3001 **Australia**

Tel: +61-3/9660-2716
Fax: +61-3/9660-3507

Oceanic Polytechnic
Faculty of Art & Architecture
54, La trobe Street
Melbourne VI 3000 **Australia**

Tel: +61-3/9663-3129
Fax: +61-3/9639-2676

Murdoch University
School of Environmental and Life Science
Dept. of Architecture
Murdoch WA 6150 **Australia**

University of Western Australia
Faculty of Architecture Building & Planning
Nedlands WA 6009 **Australia**

Tel: +61-9/380-2582
Fax: +61-9/380-1082

University of Melbourne
Dept. of Architecture & Building
Parkville VI 3052 **Australia**

Tel: +61-3/9344-6429
Fax: +61-3/9344-5532

University of New South Wales
School of Architecture
Sydney NSW 2052 **Australia**

Tel: +61-2/385-4792
Fax: +61-2/9662-1378

University of Sydney
Dept. of Architecture
Sydney NSW 2006 **Australia**

Tel: +61-2/351-3248
Fax: +61-2/351-3031

James University of North Queensland
Faculty of Science and Engineering
School of Engineering
Townsville QLD 4811 **Australia**

Gulf Technical College
Department of Building and Civil Engineering
Isa Town Bahrain

University of Bahrain
Dept. of Civil & Arch. Engineering
P.O. Box 32038
Isa Town **Bahrain**

Tel: +973-688-334

Bangladesh University of Engineering & Technology (BUET)
Faculty of Architecture & Planning
Dhaka-1000 **Bangladesh**

Tel: +880-2/863338

SCHOOLS OF ARCHITECTURE WORLDWIDE

Arts & Science University
University P.O.
Mandalay **Burma**

Rangoon Institute of Technology
Department of Architecture
Gyogone, Insein P.O.
Rangoon **Burma**

Universite Royale des Beaux Arts
Faculte d'Architecture
Boulevard de l'URSS
Phnom-Penh **Cambodia**

Universite Technique
Faculty of Civil Engineering
Angle Vithei Moat Chrouk et Hing Pen
Phnom-Penh **Cambodia**

Vithei Samdech Ouk
Faculte d'Architecture et d'Urbanisme
Phnom-Penh **Cambodia**

Beijing Polytechnic University
Jiulongshan
Beijing 100022 **China**

Tel: +86-10/6739-1513

Baotou University of Iron & Steel Technology
Kun District
Inner Mongolia 014010 Baotou **China**

Beijing Institute of Architecture and Engineering
Department of Architecture
1, Zhanglanlu
100044 RP de Chine Beijing **China**

Tel: +86-10/6835-2495
Fax: +86-10/6836-445

Tsinghua University
School of Architecture
Haidian District100084 RP Chine Beijing **China**

Tel: +86-10/6278-4519
Fax: +86-10/6256-4174

Hua Nan Polytechnic Institute
Department of Civil Engineering and Architecture
Canton **China**

Jilin Architectural and Engineering Institute
Hongcqi Street
Hunan Changcun **China**

Hunan University
Department of Architecture
Yuelushan
410082 Changsha **China**

Tel: +86-731/882-2979

Southwest Jiaotong University
Sichuan 610031 Chengdu **China**

Chongqing University of Architecture
School of Architecture and Urban Planning
Shapingba
630045 Chongqung **China**

Tel: +86-23/696-1985 ext.2102
Fax: +86-23/986-6121

Dalian University of Technology
Lingshuihe
Liaoning Dalian **China**

South China University of Technology
Department of Architecture
Wushang
510641 Guangzhou **China**

Tel: +86-20/711-1335
Fax: +86-20/551-1676

Hebei Coal and Architectural
Engineering Institute
No. 199 Guangming South Road
Hebei Handan **China**

Zhejiang University
Department of Architecture
20, Yugulu
310027 Hangzhou **China**

Tel: +86-571/795-1569
Fax: +86-571/704-3358

Harbin University of Architecture
Department of Architecture
West Dazhijie
150006 Harbin **China**

Tel: +86-451/628-1132
Fax: +86-451/363-5700

Harbin Architectural Engineering Institute
Dazhi Street
Nangang District
Heilongjiang Harbin **China**

Hefei University of Industrie
Department of Architecture
Tunxilu, 59
230009 Hefei **China**

Tel: +86-551/465-5210 ext.2307

Anhui Architectural and Engineering Institute
Nanqili
Anhui Hefei **China**

University of Hong Kong
Department of Architecture
Knowless Building, Pokfulam Road
Hong Kong **China**

Tel: +852-2/859-2133
Web: www.arch.hku.hk

Chinese University of Hong Kong
Department of Architecture
Room 514 Wong Foo Yuan BuildingShatin,
New Territories
Hong Kong **China**

Tel: +852-2/609-6517
Fax: +852-2/603-5267
Web: www.arch.cuhk.hk

Inner Mongolia Institute of Technology
Aimin Road
Inner Mongolia Huerhot China

Shandong Architectural and Engineering Institute
Heping Road
Shandong Jinan **China**

Yunnan Institute of Technology
Department of Architecture
Xiziying
Yunnan 650051 Kunmimg **China**

Nanchang University
East Beijing Road 339
Jiangxi Nanchang **China**

Tel: +86-791/830-4504

Southeast University
Department of Architecture
Sipailou
210096 Nanjing **China**

Tel: +86-25/379-2464
Fax: +86-25/771-2719

Architectural & Engineering Institute Nanjing
North Zhongshan Road
Jiangsu Nanjing **China**

Qingdao Architectural & Engineering Institute
11 Fushan Road
Shandong Qingdao **China**

Huaqiao University
Department of Architecture
Fujian Province
362011 Quanzhou **China**

Tel: +86-595/268-1545

Overseas Chinese University
Department of Architecture
Fujian Quanzhou **China**

Tel: +86/269-1545

Shanghai Institute of Urban Construction
Chifong Road
Shanghai **China**

Tung Chi University
Department of Civil Engineering and Architecture
Kiangsu
Shanghai **China**

Tongji University
School of Architecture and Urban Planning
Siping Road
200092 Shanghai **China**

Tel: +86-21/6502-0707
Fax: +86-21/6515-3065

Shenyang Architectural & Civil Engineering
Institute
No. 19 Wenyi Road
Shenhe District
Liaoning 110015 Shenyang **China**

Shenzhen University
Department of Architecture
Nantouqu
518060 Shenzhen **China**

Tel: +86-755/666-9643
Fax: +86-755/666-0674

Suzhou Inst. of Urban Construction &
Environmental Protection
Fengqiaoyuan
Hanshansi
Jiangsu Suzhou **China**

Tayuan Polyetchnical University
West Yinzhe Avenue
Shanxi Tayuan **China**

Hebei Institute of Technology
Dept. of Civil Engineering & Architecture
Dingzigu, Hongqiao District
Tianjin **China**

Tianjin Institute of Urban Construction
Wangquanchang
Hedong District
Tianjin **China**

Tianjin University
Department of Architecture
Weijin Road, Qilitai
300074 Tianjin **China**

Tel: +86-22/335-8116 ext.2492
Fax: +86-22/335-8329

Tientsin University
Dept. of Civil Engineering & Architecture
Tientsin **China**

Huazhong University of Science and Technology
Department of Architecture
Hubei 430074 Wuhan **China**

Wuhan Polytechnical University
Mafangshan
Hubei Wuhan **China**

Wuhan Urban Construction Institute
Department of Architecture
430074 Wuhan **China**

Xiamen University
Department of Architecture
Fujian Xiamen **China**

Xian University of Building Science and Technology
Department of Architecture
Yantalu
710055 Xian **China**

Tel: +86-29/552-7821
Fax: +86-29/721-5422

Northwestern Architectural Engineering Institute
Ziaozhai
Shanxi Xian **China**

Northwestern Polytechnic Institute
Department of Architecture
West Youyi Road
Shanxi Xian **China**

Xian Jiaotong University
Department of Architecture
Xianning Road
Shanxi Xian **China**

Xian Metallurgical and Architectural Institute
Lijiacun
Shanxi Xian **China**

China University of Mining & Technology
Department of Architecture
Jiangsu 221008 Xuzhou **China**

Yantai University
Department of Architecture
Shandong Yantai **China**

Yellow River University
Department of Architecture
Henan Zhenzhou **China**

Zhenzhou Institute of Technology
Department of Architecture
Wenhua Road
Henan 450002 Zhenzhou **China**

Fiji Institute of Technology
School of Building and Civil Engineering
PO Box 3722
Samabula **Fiji**

Sushant School of Art & Architecture
Sushant Lok
Gurgaonaon
Haryana 122 001 **India**

Tel: +91-124/385-896

D.C. Patel School of Architecture
Institute of Environmental Design
Near B.V.M. New Hostel, Vallabh Vidyanagar
Gujarat 388 120 **India**

Bangalore University
Faculty of Engineering, Civil Engineering
Jnana Bharathi, Bangalore
Karnataka State 560056 **India**

Centre for Envrionmental Planning & Technology (CEPT)
School of Architecture, Kasturbhai Lalbhai
CEPT Campus, Navrangpura
380 009 Ahmedabad **India**

Tel: +91-79/644-2470

Guru Nanak Dev University
Faculty of Fine Arts & Architecture
Amritsar **India**

Sri Venkateswara University
Faculty of Engineering, Dept. of Civil Engineering
Tirupati, District Chittoor
517502 Andhra Pradesh **India**

College of Engineering
Department of Architecture
Visveswaraya
Bangalore 1 **India**

The Maharaja Sayajirao University of Baroda
Department of Architecure
380009 Baroda **India**

Maulana Azad College of Tecnology
Department of Architecture
462007 Bhopal **India**

Jadavpur University
Department of Architecture
700 032 Calcutta **India**

Chandigarh College of Architecture
Sector 12
160 012 Chandigarh **India**

Bengal Engineering College
Dept. of Architecture, Town and Regional Planning
711 103 Howrah **India**

Jawaharlal Nehru Technological University
School of Planning and Architecture
Hyderabad 28 **India**

Indian Institute of Technology, Kanpur
Department of Civil Engineering
208016 UP IITPO Kanpur **India**

University of Jodhpur
Faculty of Engineering
Civil & Structural Engineering
Rajasthan Jodhpur **India**

Manipal Institute of Technology
Department of Architecture
Manipal 576 119
Karnataka **India**

Tel: +91-82/527-1061

A:C. College of Technology
Department of Architecture
Guindy
600 025 Madras **India**

Indian Institute of Technology, Madras
Department of Civil Engineering
600036 Madras **India**

The Madras University
Architecture Section, University Building
Chepauk
Madras 5 **India**

Indian Institute of Technology, Bombay
Department of Civil Engineering
Powai, Mumbai 400076
Maharashtra State **India**

Sir J.J. College of Architecture
Dr. Dadabhai Naoroji Road Fort
400 001 Mumbai **India**

University of Bombay
Faculty of Arts, Planning and Development
University Road, Fort
400032 Mumbai **India**

Academy of Architecture
Municipal School Building,
Sakubai-Mohite Marg
Off N.M. Joshi Marg (near Police Station)
Mumbai 13 **India**

Academy of Architecture
Next to Tyresoles Co. Pvt. Ltd., Behind
Ravindra Natya Mandir
Off Sayani Road, Cross Lane, Prahbadevi
Maharashtra Mumbai 25 **India**

L.S. School of Architecture
Architecture Section
Saint Martin's Road, Bandra
Mumbai 50 **India**

Visvesvaraya Regional College of Engineering
Department of Architecture
440 001 Nagpur **India**

University of Science and Technology
Faculty of Engineering and Technology,
Architecture, Civil Engineering
Rabindranath Tagore Marg.
Maharashtra Nagpur 440001 **India**

School of Planning and Architecture
4, Block-B, Indraprastha Estate
110002 New Delhi **India**

Tel: +91-11/331-7390 or 8387

Birla Institute of Technology and Science
Department of Civil Engineering
Rajasthan 333031 Pilani **India**

BKPS College of Architecture
2043 Sadashiv Peth
Tilak Road
411 030 Pune 30 **India**

University of Roorkee
Department of Architecture and Planning
247 667 Roorkee **India**

Tel: +91-1332/73560-5214

South Gujarat University
Faculty of Engineering, Dept. of Civil Engineering
P.B. 49
Gujarat Surat 395007 **India**

College of Engineering
Department of Architecture
695016 Trivandrum **India**

Indian Institute of Technology
Dept. of Architecture and Planning
Kharagppur PIN 721 302
West Bengal **India**

Tel: +91/3222-55221 or 55222

Parahyangan Catholic University
Department of Architecture
Jalan Ciumbuleuit 94
40141 Bandung **Indonesia**

Tel: +62-22/233-691

Gadjah Mada University
Faculty of Engineering, Dept. of Architecture
Jalan Teknika Utara Mo. 1
Yogyakarta 55281 Barek **Indonesia**

University Tarumanagara
Department of Architecture
Lef. Jen. S. Parman No. 1
11440 Jakarta **Indonesia**

Universitas Syiah Kuala
Faculty of Engineering
Banda Aceh Jalan Darusalam **Indonesia**

Institut Teknologi Bandung
Faculty of Civil Engineering & Planning
Department of Architecture
Bandung 40132 Jalan Ganesha 10 **Indonesia**

Tel: +62-22/250-4962

Lampung University
Faculty of Civil Engineering
Telukbetung Jl. Hasanudin 34 **Indonesia**

Universitas Kristen Satya Wacana
Faculty of Technology, Planning, Development
& Relations
Jalan Diponegoro 54-58
Central Java Salatiga **Indonesia**

Universitas Diponegoro
Fakultas Teknik, Jurusan Teknik Sipil
Jalan Iman Barjo. S.H. 1-3
50241 Semarang **Indonesia**

Tel: +62-24/312-417

Institute of Technology Sepuluh
Faculty of Architecture, Dept. of Architecture
Nopember (ITS)
Surabaya 60111 Sukolilo **Indonesia**

Petra Christian University
Faculty of Engineering, Dept. of Architecture
Jalan Siwalnkerto 121-131
60019 Surabaya **Indonesia**

Tel: +62-31/843-9040

Surabaya Institute of Technology
Faculty of Architecture
Jalan Cokroaminoto 12A
Surabaya **Indonesia**

Jundi Shapur University
Faculty of Architecture and Civil Engineering
Khuzestan Ahwas **Iran**

Universite de Chiraz
Faculte d'Architecture
Chiraz **Iran**

Shahid Beheshti University
School of Architecture and Urban Planning
Teheran 19834 Eveen **Iran**

Tel: +98-21/204-0440

Iran University of Science and Technology
College of Architecture and Urban Planning
Tehran 16844 Narmak **Iran**

Tel: +98-21/745-4052

University of Art
Faculty of Architecture and
Environmental Planning
Pardis College - Isfahan, P.O. Box 14155-6434
Teheran **Iran**

Tel: +98-21/886-4606 or 4607

Nafisi Technicom Institute
Building & Civil Engineering
Baharestan St.
Tehran **Iran**

Buluchistan University
Faculty of Civil Engineering
Zahedan **Iran**

College of Engineering
Department of Architecture
Bab-Al-Muatham
Baghdad **Iraq**

University of Baghdad
College of Engineering
Department of Architecture
Baghdad **Iraq**

University of Technology
Department of Architecture & Planning
Tel Mohomad, P.O. Box 745
Baghdad **Iraq**

University of Mosul
College of Engineering
Department of Architecture
Mosul **Iraq**

Technion - Israel Institute of Technology
Faculty of Architecture and Town Planning
32000 Haifa **Israel**

Tel: +972-4/829-4001

Bezalel Academy of Arts and Design
Course in Environmental Design
10 Shmuel Hanagid St., P.O. Box 24046
Jerusalem **Israel**

Tel: +972-2/589-3201

University of Ryukyus
Department of Civil Engineering and
Architecture, Faculty of Engineering
1, Senbaru, Nishirara-cho
903-01 Okinawa **Japan**

Tel: +81-98/895-2221
Fax: +81-98/895-6434

Aichi Sangyo University
Department of Architecture,
Faculty of Design and Architecture
12-5, Harayama, Okamachi, Okazaki-shi
00444 Aichi **Japan**

Tel: +81-56/448-4511
Fax: +81-56/448-4940

Chubu University
Department of Architecture, Faculty of Engineering
1200, Matsumoto-cho, Kasugai-shi
00487 Aichi **Japan**

Tel: +81-56/851-1111
Fax: +81-56/852-0134

Toyohashi University of Technology
Department of Architecture and
Civil Engineering
1-1, Hibarigaoka, Tenpaku-cho, Toyohashi-shi
00440 Aichi **Japan**

Tel: +81-53/247-0111
Fax: +81-53/244-6831
Web: www.tutrp.tut.ac.jp

Nagoya University of Arts
Space Design Course
65, Nishinuma, Tokushige, Nishiharu-cho,
Nishi-Kasugai-gun
00481 Aichi **Japan**

Tel: +81-56/824-0325
Fax: +81-56/824-0326

Toyota National College of Technology
Department of Architecture
2-1, Eisei-cho, Toyota-shi
00471 Aichi **Japan**

Tel: +81-56/532-8811
Fax: +81-56/535-0291

Konan Women's Junior College
Course of Interior Design, Department of Living Science
172, Omatsubara, Takaya-cho, Konan-shi
00483 Aichi **Japan**

Tel: +81-58/755-6165
Fax: +81-58/755-6167

Akita Polytechnic College
Housing Environment Department
6-1, Michishita, Ogida, Odate-shi
00017 Akita **Japan**

Tel: +81-18/642-5700
Fax: +81-18/642-5719

Hochinohe Institute of Technology
Department of Architectural Engineering,
Faculty of Engineering
88-1, Daikai, Myo, Hochinohe-shi
00031 Aomori **Japan**

Tel: +81-17/825-3111
Fax: +81-17/825-5018

Chiba University
Department of Environmental Science and
Landscape Architecture, School of Horticulture
648, Matsudo, Matsudo-shi
00271 Chiba **Japan**

Tel: +81-47/363-1221
Fax: +81-47/366-2234

Chiba University
Department of Architecture, Faculty of Engineering
1-33, Yayoi-cho, Inage-ku
00263 Chiba **Japan**

Tel: +81-43/251-1111
Fax: +81-43/290-3039

Chiba Institute of Technology
Department of Architecture, Faculty of Engineering
2-17-1, Tsudanuma, Narashino-shi
00275 Chiba **Japan**

Tel: +81-47/478-0475
Fax: +81-47/478-0499

Chiba Institute of Technology
Department of Industrial Design, Faculty of Engineering
2-17-1, Tsudanuma, Narashino-shi
00275 Chiba **Japan**

Tel: +81-47/478-0550
Fax: +81-47/478-0569

Science University of Tokyo
Department of Architecture,
Faculty of Science and Technology
2641, Yamazaki, Noda-shi
00278 Chiba **Japan**

Tel: +81-47/124-1501
Fax: +81-47/125-7533

Science University of Tokyo
Center for Fire Science and Technology
2641, Yamazaki, Noda-shi
00278 Chiba **Japan**

Tel: +81-47/124-1501
Fax: +81-47/123-9763

Nihon University
Department of Architecture and Architectural
Engineering, College of Industrial Technology
1-2-1, Izumi-cho, Narashino-shi
00275 Chiba **Japan**

Tel: +81-47/474-2480
Fax: +81-47/474-2499
Web: www.arch.cit.nihon-u.ac.jp/arch_j.htm

Nihon University
Department of Mathematics Engineering,
College of Industrial Technology
1-2-1, Izumi-cho, Narashino-shi
00275 Chiba **Japan**

Tel: +81-47/474-2650
Fax: +81-47/474-2669

Nihon University
Course of Architecture,
Junior College of Technology
7-24-1, Narashinodai, Funabashi-shi
00274 Chiba **Japan**

Tel: +81-47/469-5287
Fax: +81-47/469-5287

Chiba Polytechnic College
Architectural Tectonics on Environment,
System of Dwelling and Architecture
2-25, Tonya-cho, Chuo-ku
00260 Chiba **Japan**

Tel: +81-43/242-4166
Fax: +81-43/248-5072

Nihon University
Department of Oceanic Architecture and
Engineering, College of Science and Technology
7-24-1, Narashinodai, Funabashi-shi
00274 Chiba **Japan**

Tel: +81-47/469-5420
Fax: +81-47/467-9446

Fukui University
Department of Architecture and Civil
Engineering, Faculty of Engineering
3-9-1, Bunkyo
00910 Fukui **Japan**

Tel: +81-77/623-0500
Fax: +81-77/627-8746

Fukui University of Technology
Architecture Major, Department of
Architecture and Civil Engineering,
Faculty of Engineering
3-6-1, Gakuen
00910 Fukui **Japan**

Tel: +81-77/622-8111
Fax: +81-77/622-7891

Kyushu University
Department of Architecture, Faculty of Engineering
6-10-1, Hakozaki, Higashi-ku
00812 Fukuoka **Japan**

Tel: +81-92/642-3361
Fax: +81-92/642-3363

Kyushu University
Specializing in Thermal Energy System,
Interdisciplinary Graduate School of
Engineering Sciences
6-1, Kasugakoen, Kasuga-shi
00816 Fukuoka **Japan**

Tel: +81-92/583-7555
Fax: +81-92/592-0211

Kyushu Institute of Design
Department of Environmental Design,
Faculty of Design
4-9-1, Shiobara, Minami-ku
00815 Fukuoka **Japan**

Tel: +81-92/553-4470
Fax: +81-92/553-4598

Kyushu Sangyo University
Department of Architecture,
Faculty of Engineering
2-3-1, Matsukadai, Higashi-ku
00813 Fukuoka **Japan**

Tel: +81-92/673-5050
Fax: +81-92/673-5699

Kinki University
Department of Architecture,
Kyushu Faculty of Engineering
11-6, Kayanomori, Iizuka-shi
00820 Fukuoka **Japan**

Tel: +81-94/822-5655
Fax: +81-94/823-0536

Kurume Institute of Technology
Department of Architectural Equipment
Engineering, Faculty of Engineering
2228, Kamitsu, Kurume-shi
00830 Fukuoka **Japan**

Tel: +81-94/222-2345
Fax: +81-94/222-7119

Towa University
Department of Architecture and Building
Science, Faculty of Engineering
1-1-1, Chikushioka, Minami-ku
00815 Fukuoka **Japan**

Tel: +81-92/541-9710
Fax: +81-92/552-2707

Nishinippon Institute of Technology
Department of Architecture
1633, Aratsu, Kanda-machi, Miyako-gun
800-03 Fukuoka **Japan**

Tel: +81-93/023-1491
Fax: +81-93/024-7900

Fukuoka University
Department of Architecture, Faculty of Engineering
8-19-1, Nanakuma, Jonan-ku
814-80 Fukuoka **Japan**

Tel: +81-92/871-6631
Fax: +81-92/865-6031

Ariake National College of Technology
Department of Architecture
150, Higashi-Hagio, Omuta-shi
00836 Fukuoka **Japan**

Tel: +81-94/453-1011
Fax: +81-94/453-8871

Kinki University
Department of Industrial Design, Kyushu
Faculty of Engineering
11-6, Kayanomori, Iizuka-shi
00820 Fukuoka **Japan**

Tel: +81-94/822-5655
Fax: +81-94/823-0536

Kinki University
Division of Systematic Design,
Graduate School of Advanced Technology
11-6, Kayanomori, Iizuka-shi
00820 Fukuoka **Japan**

Tel: +81-948-22-5655
Fax: +81-948-23-0536

Koriyama Women's University
Department of Human Life,
Faculty of Home Economics
3-25-2, Kaisei, Koriyama-shi
00963 Fukushima **Japan**

Tel: +81-24/932-4848
Fax: +81-24/933-6748

Nihon University
Department of Architecture,
College of Engineering
1, Nakagawara, Tokusada, Tamura-machi,
Koriyama-shi
00963 Fusushima **Japan**

Tel: +81-24/956-8600
Fax: +81-24/956-8859

Gifu Women's University
Department of Housing and Design,
Faculty of Home Economics
80, Taromaru
501-25 Gifu **Japan**

Tel: +81-58/229-2211
Fax: +81-58/229-2222

Gifu National College of Technology
Department of Architecture
Shinsei-cho, Motosu-gun
501-04 Gifu **Japan**

Tel: +81-58/320-1211
Fax: +81-58/320-1429

Maebashi City College of Technology
Department of Architecture
460, Kamisadori-machi, Maebashi-shi
00371 Gunma **Japan**

Tel: +81-27/265-0111
Fax: +81-27/265-3837

Kinki University
Department of Architecture, Faculty of Engineering
1, Takaya-Umenobe, Higashihiroshima-shi
729-17 Hiroshima **Japan**

Tel: +81-82/434-7000
Fax: +81-82/434-7011

Hiroshima University
Course of Architectural Engineering, Course of
Architecture and Building Science and Course
of Environmental Planning, Cluster IV, Faculty
of Engineering
1-4-1, Kagamiyama, Higashihiroshima-shi
00724 Hiroshima **Japan**

Tel: +81-82/422-7111
Fax: +81-82/422-7194

Hiroshima Institute of Technology
Department of Environmental Design,
Faculty of Environmental Studies
2-1-1, Miyake, Saeki-ku
731-51 Hiroshima **Japan**

Tel: +81-82/921-3121
Fax: +81-82/923-4163

Hiroshima Institute of Technology
Architectural Engineering Course, Department
of Civil Engineering, Faculty of Engineering
2-1-1, Miyake, Saeki-ku
731-51 Hiroshima **Japan**

Tel: +81-82/921-3121
Fax: +81-82/923-7083

Fukuyama University
Department of Architecture, Faculty of Engineering
Sanzo, Ichibanchi, Gakuen-machi, Fukuyamashi
729-02 Hiroshima **Japan**

Tel: +81-84/936-2111
Fax: +81-84/936-2023

Fukuyama Polytechnic College
Department of Interior Design
4-8-48, Kitahonjo, Fukuyama-shi
00720 Hiroshima **Japan**

Tel: +81-84/923-6413
Fax: +81-84/921-7038

Kure National College of Technology
Department of Architecture and
Structural Engineering
2-2-11, Aga-Minami, Kure-shi
00737 Hiroshima **Japan**

Tel: +81-82/373-8495
Fax: +81-82/373-8496

Dohto University
Department of Architecture,
Faculty of Fine Arts
149, Nakanosawa, Kitahiroshima-shi
061-11 Hokkaido **Japan**

Tel: +81-11/372-3111
Fax: +81-11/372-2580

Dohto University
Institute of International Architecture
149, Nakanosawa, Kitahiroshima-shi
061-11 Hokkaido **Japan**

Tel: +81-11/372-3111
Fax: +81-11/372-2580

Hokkaido Tokai University
Department of Architecture,
School of Art and Technology
224, Kamui-cho, Asahikawa-shi
00070 Hokkaido **Japan**

Tel: +81-16/661-5111
Fax: +81-16/662-8180
Web: www.htokai.ac.jp

Muroran Institute of Technology
Department of Civil Engineering and
Architecture, Faculty of Engineering
27-1, Mizumoto-cho, Muroran-shi
00050 Hokkaido **Japan**

Tel: +81-14/344-4181
Fax: +81-14/347-3127

Dohoto University Junior College Division
Architecture Major, Department of Construction
149, Nakanosawa, Hiroshima-cho, Sapporogun
061-11 Hokkaido **Japan**

Tel: +81-11/372-3111
Fax: +81-11/372-2580

Hokkaido Polytechnic College
Department of Architectural Technology
3-190, Zenibako, Otaru-shi,
047-02 Hokkaido **Japan**

Tel: +81-13/462-3553
Fax: +81-13/462-2154

Kushiro National College of Technology
Department of Architecture
2-32-1, Otanoshike-Nishi, Kushiro-shi,
00085 Hokkaido **Japan**

Tel: +81-15/457-8041
Fax: +81-15/457-5360

Akashi College of Technology
Department of Architecture
679-3, Nishioka, Uozumi-cho, Akashi-shi
00674 Hyogo **Japan**

Tel: +81-78/946-6234
Fax: +81-78/946-6235

University of Tsukuba
School of Art and Design
1-1-1, Tennodai, Tsukuba-shi,
00305 Ibaraki **Japan**

Tel: +81-29/853-2111

University of Tsukuba
Engineering Mechanics, College of Engineering
and Science, Third Cluster of Colleges
1-1-1, Tennodai, Tsukuba-shi
00305 Ibaraki **Japan**

Tel: +81-29/853-5203
Fax: +81-29/853-5207

University of Tsukuba
Department of City Planning,
Institute of Socio-economic Planning
1-1-1, Tennodai, Tsukuba-shi
00305 Ibaraki **Japan**

Tel: +81-29/853-5170
Fax: +81-29/855-3849

Tsukuba College of Technology
Department of Architectural Engineering
4-3-15, Amakuho, Tsukuba-shi
00305 Ibaraki **Japan**

Tel: +81-29/858-9383
Fax: +81-29/858-9383

Kanazawa Institute of Technology
Department of Architecture, Faculty of Engineering
7-1, Ogigaoka, Nonoichi-machi, Ishikawa-gun
00921 Ishikawa **Japan**

Tel: +81-76/294-6714
Fax: +81-76/294-6707

Kanazawa Institute of Technology
Urban Planning Laboratory
7-1, Ogigaoka, Nonoichi-machi, Ishikawa-gun
00921 Ishikawa **Japan**

Tel: +81-76/294-6714
Fax: +81-76/294-6707

Ishikawa National College of Technology
Department of Architecture
Kitatyujo, Tsubata-machi, Kahoku-gun
929-03 Ishikawa **Japan**

Tel: +81-76/288-8000
Fax: +81-76/288-8191

Kanazawa University
Department of Civil Engineering,
Faculty of Engineering
2-4-20, Kodatsuno, Kanazawa-shi
00920 Ishikawa **Japan**

Tel: +81-76/234-4560
Fax: +81-76/234-4644

Kanazawa University
Center for Cooperative Research
2-4-20, Kodatsuno, Kanazawa-shi
00920 Ishikawa **Japan**

Tel: +81-76/234-4571
Fax: +81-76/234-4575

Kagawa Polytechnic College
Housing Environment Department,
Housing System Department
3202, Gunge-cho, Marugame-shi
00763 Kagawa **Japan**

Tel: +81-87/724-6290
Fax: +81-87/724-6291

Kagoshima University
Department of Architecture,
Faculty of Engineering
1-21-40, Koorimoto
00890 Kagoshima **Japan**

Tel: +81-99/285-8300
Fax: +81-99/285-8301

Daiichi University
Department of Architecture,
College of Technology
1-10-2, Chuo, Kokubu-shi
899-43 Kagoshima **Japan**

Tel: +81-99/545-1640
Fax: +81-99/547-2083

Tokai University
Department of Architecture and Building
Engineering, School of Engineering
1117, Kitakaname, Hiratsukashi
259-12 Kanagawa **Japan**

Tel: +81-46/358-1211
Fax: +81-46/350-2024

Tokyo Institute of Polytechnics
Department of Architecture,
Faculty of Engineering
1583, Iiyama, Atsugi-shi,
243-01 Kanagawa **Japan**

Tel: +81-46/241-0454
Fax: +81-46/242-3000

Nihon University
Department of Bioenvironment and Agriculture
Engineering, College of Bioresources
1866, Kameino, Fujisawa-shi
00252 Kanagawa **Japan**

Tel: +81-46/681-6241
Fax: +81-46/680-1105

Polytechnic University
Department of Architectural Engineering
4-1-1, Hashimotodai, Sagamihara-shi
00229 Kanagawa **Japan**

Tel: +81-42/763-9203
Fax: +81-42/763-9204

Keio University
Graduate School of Media and Governance
5322, Enodo, Fujisawa, Kanazawa-shi
00252 Kanagawa **Japan**

Tel: +81-46/647-5111
Fax: +81-46/647-5011
Web: www.keio.ac.jp

Nihon University
Department of Forest Science and Resources,
College of Bioresource Sciences
1866, Kameino, Fujisawa-shi
00252 Kanagawa **Japan**

Tel: +81-46/681-6241
Fax: +81-46/680-1135

Meij University
Department of Architecture,
School of Science and Technology
1-1-1, Higashimita, Tamagawa-ku
00214 Kawasaki **Japan**

Tel: +81-44/934-7171
Fax: +81-44/934-7910

Kyushu Kyoritsu University
Department of Architecture,
Faculty of Engineering
1-8, Jiyugaoka, Yahatanishi-ku
00807 Kitakyushu **Japan**

Tel: +81-93/691-3331
Fax: +81-93/603-8186

Kobe University
Department of Architecture and Civil
Engineering, Faculty of Engineering
Rokkodai-cho, Nada-ku
00657 Kobe **Japan**

Tel: +81-78/881-1212
Fax: +81-78/881-3921

Kobe Design University
Department of Environmental Design,
Faculty of Design
8-1-1, Gakuennishi-machi, Nishi-ku
651-21 Kobe **Japan**

Tel: +81-78/794-5031
Fax: +81-78/794-5032

Kyushu Tokai University
Department of Architecture,
School of Engineering
9-1-1, Toroku
00860 Kumamoto **Japan**

Tel: +81-96/382-1141
Fax: +81-96/381-7956

Kumamoto University
Department of Architecture and Civil
Engineering, Faculty of Engineering
2-39-1, Kurokami
00860 Kumamoto **Japan**

Tel: +81-96/344-2111
Fax: +81-96/342-3569

Kumamoto Institute of Technology
Department of Architecture, Faculty of Engineering
4-22-1, Ikeda
00860 Kumamoto **Japan**

Tel: +81-96/326-3111
Fax: +81-96/326-3000

Yatsushiro National College of Technology
Department of Civil and Architectural Engineering
2627, Hirayama-Shinmachi, Yatsushiro-shi
00866 Kumamoto **Japan**

Tel: +81-96/535-1161
Fax: +81-96/533-0616

Kumamoto Institute of Technology
Department of Structural Engineering,
Faculty of Engineering
4-22-1, Ikeda
00860 Kumamoto **Japan**

Tel: +81-96/326-3111
Fax: +81-96/326-3000

Kyoto University
School of Architecture, Faculty of Engineering
Yoshida-Honmachi, Sakyo-ku
606-01 Kyoto **Japan**

Tel: +81-75/753-5720
Fax: +81-75/753-5748
Web: www.archi.kyoto-u.ac.jp

Kyoto University
Division of Global Environment Engineering,
Graduate School of Engineering
Yoshida-Honmachi, Sakyo-ku
606-01 Kyoto **Japan**

Tel: +81-75/753-5111
Fax: +81-75/753-5748

Kyoto University
Department of Human and Environmental
Studies, Department of Cultural and Regional
Studies, Graduate School of Human and
Environmental Studies
Yoshida-Konoe-cho, Sakyo-ku
606-01 Kyoto **Japan**

Tel: +81-75/753-2951
Fax: +81-75/753-2999

Kyoto University
Disaster Prevention Research Institute
Gokasho, Uji-shi,
00611 Kyoto **Japan**

Tel: +81-77/432-3111
Fax: +81-77/432-4115

Kyoto Institute of Technology
Department of Architecture and Design,
Faculty of Engineering and Design
Gosho-Kaido-cho, Matsugasaki, Sakyo-ku
00606 Kyoto **Japan**

Tel: +81-75/724-7606
Fax: +81-75/724-7605

Kyoto Seika University
Department of Architecture, Faculty of Art
137, Iwakura-Kino-cho, Sakyo-ku
00606 Kyoto **Japan**

Tel: +81-75/702-5200
Fax: +81-75/722-0838

Kyoto Prefectural University
Department of Housing and Environmental
Design, Faculty of Living Science
1-5, Shimogamo-Hangi-cho, Sakyo-ku
00606 Kyoto **Japan**

Tel: +81-75/781-3131
Fax: +81-75/781-1841

Kyoto University
Department of Architecture and Environmental
Design, Graduate School of Engineering
Yoshida-Honmachi, Sakyo-ku
606-01 Kyoto **Japan**

Tel: +81-75/753-5720
Fax: +81-75/753-5760

Mie University
Department of Architecture,
Faculty of Engineering
1515, Kamihama-cho, Tsu-shi
00514 Mie **Japan**

Tel: +81-59/232-1211
Fax: +81-59/231-9452
Web: www.arch.mie-u.ac.jp

Mie University
Cooperative Research Center
1515, Kamihama-cho, Tsu-shi
00514 Mie **Japan**

Tel: +81-59/232-1211
Fax: +81-59/231-9047

Miyagi Polytechnic College
Department of Housing Environment
26, Hagisawa-Dobashi, Tsukidate-cho,
Kurihara-gun
987-22 Miyagi **Japan**

Tel: +81-22/822-2081
Fax: +81-22/822-2432

Miyagi National College of Technology
Department of Architecture
48, Nodayama, Medeshima-Shiote, Natori-shi
981-12 Miyagi **Japan**

Tel: +81-22/384-2171
Fax: +81-22/384-3679

Miyakonojo National College of Technology
Department of Architecture
473-1, Yoshio-cho, Miyakonojo-shi
00885 Miyazaki **Japan**

Tel: +81-98/638-1010
Fax: +81-98/638-1508

Shinshu University
Department of Architecture and Civil
Engineering, Faculty of Engineering
500, Wakasato
00380 Nagano **Japan**

Tel: +81-26/226-4101
Fax: +81-26/223-5105

Nagasaki University
Department of Structural Engineering,
Faculty of Engineering
1-14, Bunkyo-cho
00852 Nagasaki **Japan**

Tel: +81-95/847-1111
Fax: +81-95/843-7464

Nagasaki Institute of Applied Science
Department of Architecture,
Faculty of Engineering
536, Aba-machi
851-01 Nagasaki **Japan**

Tel: +81-95/839-3111
Fax: +81-95/830-1281

Sugiyama Jogakuen University
Environmental Planning and Design Division,
Department of Human Environment,
Faculty of Life Studies
17-3, Hoshigaoka-Motomachi, Chikusa-ku
00464 Nagoya **Japan**

Tel: +81-52/781-1186
Fax: +81-52/782-7265

Daido Institute of Techonology
Department of Architecture and Construction
Engineering, Faculty of Engineering
2-21, Daido-cho, Minami-ku
00457 Nagoya **Japan**

Tel: +81-52/612-5571
Fax: +81-52/612-5953

Nagoya University
Department of Architecture,
Graduate School of Engineering
Furo-cho, Chikusa-ku
00464 Nagoya **Japan**

Tel: +81-52/789-3587
Fax: +81-52/789-3773

Nagoya Institute of Technology
Department of Architecture and Civil
Engineering, Faculty of Engineering
Gokiso-cho, Showa-ku
00466 Nagoya **Japan**

Tel: +81-52/735-5521
Fax: +81-52/735-5522
Web: http://archi.ace.nitech.ac.jp/

Meijo University
Department of Architecture,
Faculty of Science and Engineering
1-501, Shiogawaguchi, Tenpaku-ku
00468 Nagoya **Japan**

Tel: +81-52/832-1151
Fax: +81-52/832-1179

Nagoya Feminine Culture Junior College
Interior Course
1-17-8, Aoi, Higashi-ku
00461 Nagoya **Japan**

Tel: +81-52/931-7112
Fax: +81-52/931-7117

Nagoya City University
Department of Visual and Urban Design,
School of Design and Architecture
2-1-10, Kita-Chikusa, Chikusa-ku
00460 Nagoya **Japan**

Tel: +81-52/721-1225
Fax: +81-52/721-3110

Nara Women's University
Department of Residential Environment and
Design, Division of Human Environment,
Faculty of Human Life and Environment
Kita-Uoya-Nishimachi
00630 Nara **Japan**

Tel: +81-74/220-3498
Fax: +81-74/220-3499

Nagaoka University of Technology
Department of Architecture and
Civil Engineering
1603-1, Kamitomioka-machi, Nagaoka-shi
940-21 Niigata **Japan**

Tel: +81-25/846-6000
Fax: +81-25/847-0019

University of Niigata
Department of Civil Engineering and
Architecture, Faculty of Engineering
8050, Ikarashi-Nino-cho
950-21 Niigata **Japan**

Tel: +81-25/262-7204
Fax: +81-25/263-3174

Niigata Institute of Technology
Department of Architecture and Building
Engineering, Faculty of Engineering
1719, Fujihashi, Kashiwazaki-shi
945-11 Niigata **Japan**

Tel: +81-25/722-8166
Fax: +81-25/722-8167

Oita University
Department of Architectural Engineering,
Faculty of Engineering
700, Dannoharu
870-11 Oita **Japan**

Tel: +81-97/569-3311
Fax: +81-97/554-7938
Web: www.arch.oita-u.ac.jp/index.html
Nippon Bunri University
Department of Architecture,
Faculty of Engineering
1727-162, Ichigi
870-03 Oita **Japan**

Tel: +81-97/592-1600
Fax: +81-97/593-2071

Sanyo Gakuen College
Department of Living Design
1-14-1, Hirai
00703 Okayama **Japan**

Tel: +81-86/272-6254
Fax: +81-86/273-3226

Okinawa Prefectural University of Arts
Product Course for Design Majors, Design
and Crafts, Department of Arts and Crafts
1-4, Shuri-Tonokura-cho, Naha-shi
00903 Okinawa **Japan**

Tel: +81-98/831-5000
Fax: +81-98/831-5033

Osaka University
Department of Architectural Engineering,
Faculty of Engineering
2-1, Yamadagaoka, Suita-shi
00565 Osaka **Japan**

Tel: +81-68/77-5111
Fax: +81-68/79-7629
Web: www.arch.eng.osaka-u.ac.jp/index.html

Osaka University
Department of Environmental Engineering,
Faculty of Engineering
2-1, Yamadagaoka, Suita-shi
00565 Osaka **Japan**

Tel: +81-6/879-7683
Fax: +81-6/877-8497
Web: www.env.eng.osaka-u.ac.jp

Osaka City University
Department of Architecture and Building
Engineering, Faculty of Engineering
3-3-138, Sugimoto, Sumiyoshi-ku
00558 Osaka **Japan**

Tel: +81-6/605-2121
Fax: +81-6/605-2769

Osaka City University
Department of Environmental Design,
Faculty of Human Life Science
3-3-138, Sugimoto, Sumiyoshi-ku
00558 Osaka **Japan**

Tel: +81-6/605-2801
Fax: +81-6/605-3086

Osaka University of Arts
Department of Architecture
469, Higashiyama, Kanan-cho,
Minami-Kawachi-gun
00585 Osaka **Japan**

Tel: +81-72/193-3781
Fax: +81-72/193-5587
Osaka University of Arts
Department of Environmental Design
469, Higashiyama, Kanan-cho,
Minami-Kawachi-gun
00585 Osaka **Japan**

Tel: +81-72/193-3781
Fax: +81-72/193-5380

Osaka Institute of Technology
Department of Architecture,
Faculty of Engineering
5-16-1, Omiya, Asahi-ku
00535 Osaka **Japan**

Tel: +81-6/954-4206
Fax: +81-6/957-2132

Osaka Sangyo University
Department of Environmental Design
3-1-1, Nakagaito, Daito-shi
00574 Osaka **Japan**

Tel: +81-72/075-3001
Fax: +81-72/070-7857

Kansai University
Department of Architecture,
Faculty of Engineering
3-3-35, Yamate-cho, Suita-shi
00564 Osaka **Japan**

Tel: +81-6/388-1121
Fax: +81-6/330-3770

Kinki University
Department of Architecture,
Faculty of Science and Engineering
3-4-1, Kowakae, Higashiosaka-shi,
00577 Osaka **Japan**

Tel: +81-6/721-2332
Fax: +81-6/730-1320

Setsunan University
Department of Architecture,
Faculty of Engineering
17-8, Ikeda-Naka-machi, Neyagawa-shi
00572 Osaka **Japan**

Tel: +81-72/039-9128
Fax: +81-72/038-6599

Osaka Institute of Technology Junior College
Department of Architecture
5-16-1, Omiya, Asahi-ku
00572 Osaka **Japan**

Tel: +81-6/952-3131
Fax: +81-6/955-6265

Heian Jogakuin (St.Agnes') College
Division of Housing and Environmental
Design, Department of Human Life Science
5-81-1, Nanpeidai, Takatsuki-shi
00569 Osaka **Japan**

Tel: +81-72/696-4934
Fax: +81-72/696-4919

Saga University
Department of Civil Engineering,
Faculty of Science and Engineering
1, Honjo-machi,
00840 Saga **Japan**

Tel: +81-95/228-8583
Fax: +81-95/228-8190

SCHOOLS OF ARCHITECTURE WORLDWIDE

Shibaura Institute of Technology
Department of Architecture and Environment
System, Faculty of System Engineering
307, Fukasaku, Omiya-shi
00330 Saitama **Japan**

Tel: +81-48/683-2020
Fax: +81-48/687-5199

Toyo University
Department of Architecture,
Faculty of Engineering
2100, Kujirai, Kawagoe-shi,
00350 Saitama **Japan**

Tel: +81-49/239-1411
Fax: +81-49/231-1400

Nippon Institute of Technology
Department of Architecture,
Faculty of Engineering
4-1, Gakuendai, Miyashiro-machi,
Minami-Saitama-gun
00345 Saitama **Japan**

Tel: +81-48/034-4111
Fax: +81-48/433-7715

Nippon Institute of Technology
Building Engineering Center
4-1, Gakuendai, Miyashiro-machi,
Minami-Saitama-gun
00345 Saitama **Japan**

Tel: +81-48/034-4111
Fax: +81-48/433-7568

Kyoei Gakuen Junior College
Housing Studies Department
4158, Uchimaki, Kasukabe-shi
00344 Saitama **Japan**

Tel: +81-48/761-5801
Fax: +81-48/761-0569

Hokkai-Gakuen University
Department of Architecture,
Faculty of Engineering
1-1, Nishi 11-chome, Minami 26-jo, Chuo-ku
00064 Sapporo **Japan**

Tel: +81-11/841-1161
Fax: +81-11/551-2951

Hokkaido University
Department of Architecture,
Faculty of Engineering
Nishi 8-chome, Kita 13-jo, Kita-ku
00060 Sapporo **Japan**

Tel: +81-11/716-2111
Fax: +81-11/706-6255

Hokkaido University
Department of Sanitary Engineering,
Faculty of Engineering
Nishi 8-chome, Kita 13-jo, Kita-ku
00060 Sapporo **Japan**

Tel: +81-11/716-2111
Fax: +81-11/706-7890

Hokkaido Institute of Technology
Department of Architecture,
Faculty of Engineering
15-4-1, Maeda 7-jo, Teine-ku
00006 Sapporo **Japan**

Tel: +81-11/681-2161
Fax: +81-11/681-3622

Hokkaido Tokai University
Course of Comparative Culture, Department
of International Cultural Relations, School
of International Relations
1-1-1, Minamisawa 5-jo, Minami-ku
00005 Sapporo **Japan**

Tel: +81-11/571-5111
Fax: +81-11/571-7879

Sapporo School of the Arts
Department of Design
1, Geijutunomori, Minami-ku
00005 Sapporo **Japan**

Tel: +81-11/592-5400
Fax: +81-11/592-5377

Tohoku University
Department of Architecture, Urban Planning
and Building Engineering, Division of
Engineering, Graduate School
Aza Aoba, Aramaki, Aoba-ku,
980-77 Sendai **Japan**

Tel: +81-22/217-7890
Fax: +81-22/217-7895

Tohoku University
Disaster Control Research Center,
Faculty of Engineering
Aza Aoba, Aramaki, Aoba-ku
980-77 Sendai **Japan**

Tel: +81-22/217-7854
Fax: +81-22/217-7854

Tohoku Institute of Technology
Department of Architecture,
Faculty of Engineering
35-1, Yagiyama-Kasumi-cho, Taihaku-ku
00952 Sendai **Japan**

Tel: +81-22/229-1151
Fax: +81-22/229-8279

Tohoku Institute of Technology
Department of Industrial Design,
Faculty of Engineering
35-1, Yagiyama-Kasumi-cho, Taihaku-ku
00952 Sendai **Japan**

Tel: +81-22/229-1151
Fax: +81-22/229-1545
College of Science and Technology, Tohoku
Department of Environmental Engineering
of Architecture
6-45-16, Kunimi, Aoba-ku
00981 Sendai **Japan**

Tel: +81-22/233-3310
Fax: +81-22/233-7941

Shiga Polytechnic College
Department of Architecture
1414, Furukawa-cho, Omihachiman-shi
00523 Shiga **Japan**

Tel: +81-74/831-2250
Fax: +81-74/831-2255

The University of Shiga Prefecture
Department of Environmental Planning,
School of Environmental Science
2500, Hassaka-cho, Hikone-shi
00522 Shiga **Japan**

Tel: +81-74/928-8301
Fax: +81-74/928-8477

Ashikaga Institute of Technology
Department of Architecture,
Faculty of Engineering
268-1, Omaemachi, Ashikaga-shi,
00326 Tochigi **Japan**

Tel: +81-28/462-0605
Fax: +81-28/462-4235

Oyama National College of Technology
Department of Architecture
771, Nakakuki, Oyama-shi
00323 Tochigi **Japan**

Tel: +81-285-22-3344
Fax: +81-285-21-0399

Ochanomizu University
Division of Human Science and Technology,
Department of Human Environmental Engineering
2-1-1, Otsuka, Bunkyo-ku
00112 Tokyo **Japan**

Tel: +81-3/5978-5738
Fax: +81-3/5978-5737

Kyorits Women's University
Department of Living Arts,
College of Home Economics
2-2-1, Hitotsubashi, Chiyoda-ku
00101 Tokyo **Japan**

Tel: +81-3/3237-2656
Fax: +81-3/3237-2656

Kogakuin University
Architecture Course, Urban Architectural
Design Course, Department of Architecture,
Faculty of Engineering
1-24-2, Nishi-shinjuku, Shinjuku-ku
163-91 Tokyo **Japan**

Tel: +81-3/3342-1211
Fax: +81-3/3340-0149

Kokushikan University
Department of Architecture, Faculty of Engineering
4-28-1, Setagaya, Setagaya-ku
00154 Tokyo **Japan**

Tel: +81-3/5481-3290
Fax: +81-3/5481-3253

Shibaura Institute of Technology
Department of Architecture,
Faculty of Engineering
3-9-14, Shibaura, Minato-ku
00108 Tokyo **Japan**

Tel: +81-3/5476-3059
Fax: +81-3/5476-3167

Shibaura Institute of Technology
Department of Architecture and Building
Engineering, Faculty of Engineering
3-9-14, Shibaura, Minato-ku
00108 Tokyo **Japan**

Tel: +81-3/5476-3080
Fax: +81-3/5476-3168

Showa Women's University
Department of Human Environmental Science
and Design, Faculty of Practical Arts and Science
1-7, Taishido, Setagaya-ku
00154 Tokyo **Japan**

Tel: +81-3/3411-5111
Fax: +81-3/3795-5757

Tama Art University
Architecture Department, Faculty of Art and Design
1723, Yarimizu, Hachioji-shi
192-03 Tokyo **Japan**

Tel: +81-42/676-8611
Fax: +81-42/676-2935

Tokai University
Course of Architectural Engineering,
Department of Construction Engineering,
School of Engineering II (Evening Session)
2-28-4, Tomigaya, Shibuya-ku
00151 Tokyo **Japan**

Tel: +81-3/3467-2211
Fax: +81-3/3485-4970

University of Tokyo
Department of Architecture,
Faculty of Engineering
7-3-1, Hongo, Bunkyo-ku
00113 Tokyo **Japan**

Tel: +81-3/3812-2111
Fax: +81-3/5689-4653
Web: www.arch.t.u-tokyo.ac.jp

University of Tokyo
Department of Urban Engineering,
School of Engineering
7-3-1, Hongo, Bunkyo-ku
00113 Tokyo **Japan**

Tel: +81-3/3812-2111
Fax: +81-3/3818-5946
Web: http://up.t.u-tokyo.ac.jp/ue/index.html

University of Tokyo
Institute of Industrial Science
7-22-1, Roppongi, Minato-ku
00106 Tokyo **Japan**

Tel: +81-3/3402-6231
Web: www.iis.u-tokyo.ac.jp

University of Tokyo
Architectural Engineering Section, Engineering
Research Institute, School of Engineering
2-11-16, Yayoi, Bunkyo-ku, Tokyo
00113 Tokyo **Japan**

Tel: +81-3/3812-2111
Fax: +81-3/5800-6826

University of Tokyo
Earthquake Research Institute
1-1-1, Yayoi, Bunkyo-ku
00113 Tokyo **Japan**

Tel: +81-3/3812-2111
Fax: +81-3/5689-7265
Web: www.eri.u-tokyo.ac.jp/Jhome.html

Tokyo Kasei Gakuin University
Department of Housing and Planning,
Faculty of Home Economics
2600, Aihara-machi, Machida-shi
194-02 Tokyo **Japan**

Tel: +81-42/782-9811
Fax: +81-42/782-9880

Tokyo National University of Fine Arts and Music
Department of Architecture
12-8, Uenokoen, Taito-ku
00110 Tokyo **Japan**

Tel: +81-3/5685-7618
Fax: +81-3/5685-7775

Tokyo Institute of Technology
Department of Architecture and Building
Engineering, Faculty of Engineering
2-12-1, Oookayama, Meguro-ku
00152 Tokyo **Japan**

Tel: +81-3/3726-1111
Fax: +81-3/3729-0990

Tokyo Institute of Technology
Department of Social Engineering,
Faculty of Engineering
2-12-1, Oookayama, Meguro-ku
00152 Tokyo **Japan**

Tel: +81-3/726-1111
Fax: +81-3/5734-2926

Tokyo Institute of Technology
Research and Development Center for
Education Facilities
2-12-1, Oookayama, Meguro-ku
00152 Tokyo **Japan**

Tel: +81-3/3726-1111
Fax: +81-3/5734-2999

Tokyo Zokei University
Environmental Planning,
Department of Design, Faculty of Art
1556, Utsunuki-machi, Hachioji-shi
00192 Tokyo **Japan**

Tel: +81-42/637-8111
Fax: +81-42/637-8110

Tokyo Denki University
Department of Architecture,
Faculty of Engineering
2-2, Kanda-Nishiki-cho, Chiyoda-ku
00101 Tokyo **Japan**

Tel: +81-3/5280-3425
Fax: +81-3/5280-3572

Tokyo Metropolitan University
Department of Architecture,
Faculty of Engineering
1-1, Minami-Osawa, Hachioji-shi
192-03 Tokyo **Japan**

Tel: +81-42/677-1111
Fax: +81-42/677-2793

Tokyo University of Agriculture
Department of Landscape Architecture,
Faculty of Agriculture
1-1-1, Sakuragaoka, Setagaya-ku
00156 Tokyo **Japan**

Tel: +81-3/5477-2422
Fax: +81-3/5477-2625

Science University of Tokyo
Department of Architecture,
Faculty of Engineering
1-3, Kagurazaka, Shinjuku-ku
00162 Tokyo **Japan**

Tel: +81-3/3260-4271
Fax: +81-3/3235-6897

Nihon University
Architectural Design Course,
Department of Design, College of Arts
2-42-1, Asahigaoka, Nerima-ku
00176 Tokyo **Japan**

Tel: +81-3/5995-8231
Fax: +81-3/5995-8691

Nihon University
Department of Architecture,
College of Science and Technology
1-8-14, Kanda-Surugadai, Chiyoda-ku,
00101 Tokyo **Japan**

Tel: +81-3/3259-0724
Fax: +81-3/3293-8253

Japan Women's University
Department of Housing,
Faculty of Home Economics
2-8-1, Mejirodai, Bunkyo-ku
00112 Tokyo **Japan**

Tel: +81-3/3943-3131
Fax: +81-3/3942-6113

Hosei University
Department of Architecture,
College of Engineering
3-7-2, Kajino-cho, Koganei-shi
00184 Tokyo **Japan**

Tel: +81-42/387-6115
Fax: +81-42/387-6125

Musashi Institute of Technology
Department of Architecture,
Faculty of Engineering
1-28-1, Tamatsutsumi, Setagaya-ku
00158 Tokyo **Japan**

Tel: +81-3/3703-3111
Fax: +81-3/3703-1999

Musashino Art University
Department of Architecture,
College of Art and Design
1-736, Ogawa-cho, Kodaira-shi
00187 Tokyo **Japan**

Tel: +81-42/342-6067
Fax: +81-42/344-1599

Waseda University
Department of Architecture,
Faculty of Science and Engineering
3-4-1, Okubo, Shinjuku-ku
00169 Tokyo **Japan**

Tel: +81-3/3203-4141
Fax: +81-3/3200-2567

Waseda University
Advanced Research Center for Science
and Engineering
3-4-1, Okubo, Shinjuku-ku
00169 Tokyo **Japan**

Tel: +81-3/3203-4141
Fax: +81-3/3200-9886

Atomi Gakuen Junior College
Department of Home Economics
1-5-2, Otsuka, Bunkyo-ku
00112 Tokyo **Japan**

Tel: +81-3/3941-8161
Fax: +81-3/3945-1836

Tokyo Polytechnic College
Department of Architecture
2-32-1, Ogawanishi-machi, Kodaira-shi
00187 Tokyo **Japan**

Tel: +81-42/341-3331
Fax: +81-42/344-5609

Shibaura Institute of Technology
Department of Electrical Systems for Urban
Engineering, Faculty of Engineering
3-9-14, Shibaura, Minato-ku
00108 Tokyo **Japan**

Tel: +81-3/3452-3201
Fax: +81-3/5476-3068

Tokyo Metropolitan University
Graduate School of Urban Science
1-1, Minami-Osawa, Hachioji-shi
192-03 Tokyo **Japan**

Tel: +81-42/677-2351
Fax: +81-42/677-2352

Yonago National College of Technology
Department of Architecture
4448, Hokona-cho, Yonago-shi
00683 Tottori **Japan**

Tel: +81-85/925-5000
Fax: +81-85/924-5009

Aichi Institute of Technology
Department of Architecture,
Faculty of Engineering
1248, Yachigusa, Yakusa-cho
470-03 Toyota **Japan**

Tel: +81-56/548-8121
Fax: +81-56/548-0030

Aichi Institute of Technology
Department of Architecture and Building
Engineering, Faculty of Engineering
1248, Yachigusa, Yakusa-cho
470-03 Toyota **Japan**

Tel: +81-56/548-8121
Fax: +81-56/548-0222

Utsunomiya University
Department of Architecture,
Faculty of Engineering
2753, Ishii-machi
00321 Utsunomiya **Japan**

Tel: +81-28/636-1515
Fax: +81-28/689-6198

Wakayama University
Department of Environmental Systems,
Faculty of System Engineering
930, Sakaedani,
00640 Wakayam **Japan**

Tel: +81-73/454-0361
Fax: +81-73/454-0134

Tohoku University of Art and Design
Department of Environmental Design,
Faculty of Design
Kamisakurada, Yamagata-shi
00990 Yamagata **Japan**

Tel: +81-23/627-2000
Fax: +81-23/627-2081

Tokuyama College of Technology
Department of Civil Engineering
and Architecture
3538, Takashiro, Kume, Tokuyama-shi,
00745 Yamaguchi **Japan**

Tel: +81-83/428-3766
Fax: +81-83/428-9813

Tokyo Institute of Technology
Department of Built Environment,
Graduate School at Nagatusta
4259, Nagatsuta-cho, Midori-ku
00227 Yokohama **Japan**

Tel: +81-45/922-1111
Fax: +81-45/922-3840
Web: www.enveng.titech.ac.jp

Tokyo Institute of Technology
Department of Environmental Physics and
Engineering, Interdisciplinary Graduate School
of Science and Engineering
4259, Nagatsuta-cho, Midori-ku
00227 Yokohama **Japan**

Tel: +81-45/922-1111
Fax: +81-45/924-5519

Kanagawa University
Department of Architecture,
Faculty of Engineering
3-27-1, Rokkakubashi, Kanagawa-ku
00221 Yokohama **Japan**

Tel: +81-45/481-5661
Fax: +81-45/491-7915

Kanto Gakuin University
Department of Architecture,
College of Engineering
4834, Mutsura-cho, Kanazawa-ku
00236 Yokohama **Japan**

Tel: +81-45/781-2001
Fax: +81-45/786-7743

Kanto Gakuin University
Department of Environmental Engineering of
Architecture, College of Engineering
4834, Mutsura-cho, Kanazawa-ku
00236 Yokohama **Japan**

Tel: +81-45/781-2001
Fax: +81-45/786-7219

Kanto Gakuin University
Osawa Memorial Institute of Architectural
Environmental Engineering
4834, Mutsura-cho, Kanazawa-ku
00236 Yokohama **Japan**

Tel: +81-45/781-2001
Fax: +81-45/786-7219

Yokohama National University
Department of Architecture and Building
Science, Faculty of Engineering
156, Tokiwadai, Hodogaya-ku
00240 Yokohama **Japan**

Tel: +81-45/335-1451
Fax: +81-45/331-1730

Tokyo Institute of Technology
Structural Engineering Research Center
4259, Nagatsuda-cho, Midori-ku
00226 Yokohama **Japan**

Tel: +81-45/924-5360
Fax: +81-45/924-5360
Web: www.serc.titech.ac.jp

Tselinograd Agricultural Institute
Victory Square, 116
Tselinograd 473012 **Kazakhstan**

Ust-Kamenogorsk Civil and Highway Institute
Faculty of Architecture
Ust-Kamenogorsk 492043 **Kazakhstan**

Université Agraire d'Akmola
Section d'architecture
116, avenue Pobeda
47 3012 Akmola **Kazakhstan**

Tel: +7-317/275-2329

Ecole Polytechnique de Kazakhie
22 rue Oouniveritetskaia
Alma-Ata **Kazakhstan**

Académie d'architecture et de Construction
28, rue Obroutcheva
Almaty **Kazakhstan**

Tel: +7-327/220-1450

Université Technique d'Est du Kazakstan
Faculté d'Architecture
19, rue Lougovaya
Oust Kamenogorsk **Kazakhstan**

Tel: +7-323/244-6221
Fax: +7-323/244-6920

Kuwait University
Faculty of Engineering and Petroleum,
Dept. of Architecture
P.O.B. 5969
13060 **Kuwait**

Tel: +965/481-7240

Kirgizski Architectural & Building Institute
Moldybaeva Str.,34-B
720020 Bishkek **Kyrgyzstan**

Tel: +996-331/244-0778

Lebanese University
Institute of Fine Arts (Central Administration)
El Mathaf Street/ PO BOX 14-6573
Beyrouth **Lebanon**

Tel: +961-1/807-608

Lebanese Academie of Fine Arts
Sin El Fil
POB 55251
Beyrouth **Lebanon**

Tel: +961-1/502-370-1
Fax: +961-1/502-370

Lebanese American University
(formerly Beirut University College)
Madame Curie Street / P.O. Box 13-5053
Beyrouth **Lebanon**

Tel: +961-1/811-964
Fax: +961-1/867-098

Beirut Arab University
Faculty of Architecture
Sleiman Al Bustani Str./ P.O. Box 115020
Beyrouth **Lebanon**

Tel: +961-1/300-110
Fax: +961-1/818-402

American University of Beirut
Faculty of Engineering and Architecture
P.O.B. 11-023
Beyrouth **Lebanon**

Tel: +961-1/865-255
Fax: +961-1/212-4782

Saint Joseph University
Higher Institute of Engineering
B.P. 1514
El Mansourieh Mar Roukouz **Lebanon**

Tel: +961-1/201-236/7
Fax: +961-1/500-981
E-mail: admesib@inco.com.lb

Université Saint-Esprit -USEK
Faculty of Architecture
PO BOX 446
Kaslik-Jounieh **Lebanon**

Tel: +961-9/912-019
Fax: +961-9/914-941

Notre Dame University
Faculty of Architecture
PO BOX 72 Zouk Mikael
Zouk Mosbeh **Lebanon**

Tel: +961-9/218-950
Fax: +961-9/218-771

Universiti Malaya
Faculty of Engineering
Built Environment Programme
Kuala Lumpur 50603 **Malaysia**

Tel: +60-3/759-5420

Universiti Teknologi Malaysia
Faculty of Built Environment
Locked Bag 791
Johor 80990 **Malaysia**

Tel: +60-7/550-2613

Ungku Omar Polytechnic
Department of Civil Engineering
Dairy Road
Perak 31400 Ipoh **Malaysia**

Tel: +60-5/545-7622

University of Technology Malaysia
Faculty of Built Environment
Karung Berkunci 791Skudai/ Johor
Kuala Lumpur **Malaysia**

Institute of Technology Mara
Department of Architecture, Planning & Surveying
Shah Alam
Mara **Malaysia**

University of Science Malaysia
School of Housing, Building & Planning
11800 Pulau Pinang **Malaysia**

University of Auckland
Department of Architecture
Private Bag 92019
Auckland **New Zealand**

Tel: +64-9/373-7599

University of Canterbury
Faculty of Engineering
Dept. of Civil Engineering
Christchurch 1 **New Zealand**

Victoria University of Wellington
School of Architecture
P.O. Box 600
Wellington **New Zealand**

Tel: +64-4/802-6200

Hamhung Civil Engineering School
Hamhung
Bonryong District **North Korea**

Bontonggang Civil Engineering School
Pyongyang
Bontonggang District **North Korea**

Donggaewon Sr Civil Engineeing School
Pyongyang
Donggaewon District **North Korea**

Wonsan Civil Engineering School
Wonsan
Kangwon Province **North Korea**

Sariwon Civil Engineering School
Sariwon
North Hwanghai Province **North Korea**

University of Construction and Building Materials
Taedonggang District
Pyongyang **North Korea**

Chungjin Civil Engineering School
Chungjin
Runam District **North Korea**

University of Engineering & Technology, Lahore
Department of Architecture
Grand Trunk Road
Lahore 54890 **Pakistan**

Tel: +92-42/339-292

Mehran University of Engineering & Technology
Department of Architecture
Jamshoro **Pakistan**

Dawood College of Engineering & Technology
Department of Architecture
M.A. Jinnah Road
Karachi 5 **Pakistan**

National College of Arts
Department of Architecture
4-Shahra-E Quaid-E-Azam
54000 Lahore **Pakistan**

University of Peshawar
Faculty of Engineering
Civil Engineering
N.W.F.P. Peshawar **Pakistan**

Papua New Guinea University of Technology
Dept. of Architecture and Building
Private Mail Bag
Lae Papua **New Guinea**

Tel: +675/473-4501

La Consolacion College
College of Architecture & Fine Arts
05000 Bacolod City **Philippines**

Don Honorio Ventura College of Arts & Trades,
Architecture and Engineering Department
Pampanga 2001 Bacolor **Philippines**

Baguio Colleges Foundation
Architecture Department
Gov. Pack Road
02600 Baguio City **Philippines**

Saint Louis University
Department of Architecture
P.O. Box 71
02600 Baguio City **Philippines**

Western Mindanao State University
College of Architecture
Normal Road
Zamboanga City 7000 Baliwasan **Philippines**

Pamantasan NG Araullo
Dept. of Architecture
Cabanatuan City 3100 Bitas **Philippines**

Saint Joseph Institute of Technology
Montilla Blvd. Cor. Rosales St.
08600 Bututan **Philippines**

Cagayan de Oro College
Arch. Dept., Max Suniel St.
Cagayan de Oro City 9000 Carmen
Philippines

Cebu Institute of Technology
Architecture Dept.
06000 Cebu City **Philippines**

University of the Visayas
Dept. of Architecture
Colon St.
06000 Cebu City **Philippines**

Luzon Colleges
Dept. of Architecture
Perez Blvd.
Dagupan City **Philippines**

University of Pangasinan
College of Architecture
Arellano St.
02400 Dagupan City **Philippines**

Adamson University
900 San Marcelino St.
Manila 1000 Ermita **Philippines**

University of St. Tomas
College of Architecture and Fine Arts
Manila 1008 Espana **Philippines**

University of San Agustin
Dept. of Architecture
05000 Iloilo City **Philippines**

Mapua Institute of Science and Technology
Muralla Str.
Manila 1002 Intramuros **Philippines**

Pamantasan NG Lungsod NG Maynila
Manila 1002 Intramuros **Philippines**

Aquinas University
College of Architecure & Fine Arts
04500 Legaspi City **Philippines**

Bicol University
Dept. of Architecture
04500 Legaspi City **Philippines**

Manuel S. Enverga University Foundation
University Site
04301 Lucena City **Philippines**

Bulacan College of Arts & Trades
School of Engineering & Architecture
Bulacan 3000 Malolos **Philippines**

Rizal Technological Colleges
Boni Av.
Metro Manila Mandaluyong City **Philippines**

Feati University
1003 Sta Cruz Str.
Manila **Philippines**

Technological University of the Philippines
Dept. of Architecture & Fine Arts
Ayala Blvd.
Manila **Philippines**

Far Eastern University
Institute of Architecture and Fine Arts
Manila Morayata **Philippines**

Central Colleges of the Philippines
College of Architecture
52, Aurora Blvd.
Manila Quezon City **Philippines**

Technological Institute of the Philippines - QC
20th Ave.
Cubao MM Quezon City **Philippines**

University of the Philippines
Diliman 1101 Quezon City **Philippines**

Manuel L. Quezon University
College of Architecture
916 R. Hidalgo Str.
Manila 1001 Quiapo **Philippines**

Technological Institute of the Philippines - MLA
College of Engineering & Architecture
888 Gonzalo Puyat St.
Metro Manila Quiapo **Philippines**

Eulogio "Amang" Rodriguez Institute of
Science & Technology
Dept. of Technology & Architecture
Nagtahan St.
Manila 1008 Sampaloc **Philippines**

National University
School of Architecture & Fine Arts
MF Jhocson Str.
Manila 1008 Sampaloc **Philippines**

University of the Assumption
College of Architecture
Pampanga 2000 San Fernando **Philippines**

University of Northeastern Philippines
Iriga City 4431 San Roque **Philippines**

Polytechnic University of the Philippines
Dept. of Architecture
Hippodromo Str.
Manila 1016 Santa Mesa **Philippines**

Leyte Institute of Technology
Architecture Department
Salazar St.
Tacloban City 6500 **Philippines**

University of Bohol
College of Architecture
06300 Tagbilaran **Philippines**

University of San Carlos
College of Art & Fine Arts
Talamban Campus
Cebu City 6000 Talamban **Philippines**

Tarlac State University
Romulo Blvd
Tarlac 2300 Tarlac **Philippines**

St. Louis College of Tuguerao
Mabini Str.
Cagayan 3500 Tuguegarao **Philippines**

University of Northern Philippines
Tamag
Ilocos Sur 2700 Vigan **Philippines**

King Faisal University
College of Architecture and Planning
P.O. Box 2397
31451 Damman **Saudi Arabia**

Tel: +966-3/857-8206

King Fahd University of Petroleum and Minerals
College of Environmental Design
31261 Dhahran **Saudi Arabia**

King Abdul Aziz University
College of Engineering, Dept. of Architecture
P.O. Box 9027
21413 Jeddah **Saudi Arabia**

National University of Singapore
School of Architecture
10 Kent Ridge Crescent
119260 Singapore **Singapore**

Tel: +65/772-3452

Temasek Polytechnic
School of Interior Architecture and Design
20, Tampines Avenue 1
529757 Singapore **Singapore**

Ajou University
College of Engineering -
Department of Architectural Engineering
San 5, Wonchon-dong, Kwonsun-gu,
Suwon-shi, Kyonggi-do
Ajou **South Korea**

Tel: +82-331/219-2491
Fax: +82-331/213-5158

Chonbuk Sanup University
College of Engineering -
Department of Architectural Engineering
663, Soryong-dong,
Kwqngju-shi
Chonbuk **South Korea**

Tel: +82-65/460-3309
Fax: +82-65/460-3253

Chonbuk National University
College of Engineering -
Department of Architectural Engineering
664-14, Dukjindong 1-ga, Dukjin-gu,
Jeonju-shi
Chonbuk **South Korea**

Tel: +82-65/270-2276
Fax: +82-65/270-2263

Chongju University
College of Natural Science & Engineering -
Department of Architectural Engineering
36, Naedeok-dong, Chongju-shi,
Chungchongbuk-do
Chongju **South Korea**

Tel: +82-43/1229-8375
Fax: +82-43/1229-8375

Chonnam National University
College of Engineering -
Department of Architectural Engineering
300, Yongbong-dong, Kwangju-shi
Chonnam **South Korea**

Tel: +82-62/520-6320
Fax: +82-62/511-7223

Chosun University
College of Engineering -
Department of Architectural Engineering
375, Sesuk-dong, Tong-gu, Kwangju-shi
Chosun **South Korea**

Tel: +82-62/230-7114

Chungang University
College of Engineering -
Department of Architectural Engineering
San 40-1, Ne-ri, Daeduok-myen, Ansung-gun,
Kyonggi-do
Chungang **South Korea**

Tel: +82-33/470-3342
Fax: +82-33/4675-1387

Chungbuk National University
College of Engineering -
Department of Architectural Engineering
San 48, Gaeshin-dong, Chongju-shi,
Chungchongbuk-do
Chungbuk **South Korea**

Tel: +82-43/161-2427
Fax: +82-43/163-2635

Chungnam National University
College of Engineering -
Department of Architectural Engineering
220, Gung-dong, Yoosung-gu, Taejon-shi
Chungnam **South Korea**

Tel: +82-42/821-5621
Fax: +82-42/823-9467

Dong-A University
College of Engineering -
Department of Architectural Engineering
840, Hadun-dong, Saha-gu, Pusan-shi
Dong-A **South Korea**

Tel: +82-51/200-7606
Fax: +82-51/200-7616

Dongeui University
College of Engineering -
Department of Architectural Engineering
San 24, Gaya 2-dong, Pusanjin-gu, Pusan-shi
Dongeui **South Korea**

Tel: +82-51/890-1620
Fax: +82-51/898-3462

Gyeongsang National University
College of Engineering -
Department of Architectural Engineering
900, Kazoa-dong, Jinju-Shi, Kyongsangnam-do
Gyeongsang **South Korea**

Tel: +82-591/751-5284
Fax: +82-591/751-5284
Email: archit@nongae.gsnu.ac.kr
Web: www.gsnu.ac.kr

Honam University
Department of Architecture
59-1, Seobong-dong, Kwangsan-gu, Kwangju-shi
Honam **South Korea**

Tel: +82-62/940-5450
Fax: +82-62/940-5005

Inha University
College of Engineering -
Department of Architectural Engineering
253, Yonghyun-dong, Nam-gu, Inchon-shi
Inha **South Korea**

Tel: +82-32/860-7580
Fax: +82-32/866-4624

Kangwon National University
College of Engineering -
Department of Architectural Engineering
192-1, Hyoja 2-dong, Chunchon-shi,
Kangwon-do
Kangwon **South Korea**

Tel: +82-36/150-6210
Fax: +82-36/156-3566
Web: www.kangwon.ac.kr

Keimyung University
College of Engineering -
Department of Architectural Engineering
1000, Shindang-dong, Dalsu-gu, Taegu-shi
Keimyung **South Korea**

Tel: +82-53/580-5047
Fax: +82-53/580-5165
Web: www.keimyung.ac.kr

Kwangju University
College of Engineering -
Department of Architectural Engineering
Kwangju **South Korea**

Tel: +82-62/670-2371
Fax: +82-62/670-2188
Email: yunjahee@hosim.kwangju.ac.kr
Web: www.kwangju.ac.kr

Kwangju University
College of Engineering -
Department of Architectural Engineering
592, Jinwol-dong, Seo-gu, Kwangju-shi
Kwangju **South Korea**

Tel: +82-62/670-2371
Fax: +82-62/676-7776

Kyunghee University
College of Engineering -
Department of Architectural Engineering
Sochun 1-ri, Giheung-eup, Yongin-gun,
Kyunggi-do
Kyunghee **South Korea**

Tel: +82-331/280-2536
Fax: +82-331/283-1354

Kyungil University
Department of Architectural Engineering
33, Puho-ri, Hayang-eup, Kyongsan-gun,
Kyongsangbuk-do
Kyungil **South Korea**

Tel: +82-53/853-7240
Fax: +82-53/850-7607
Email: ycchung@bear.kyungil.ac.kr
Web: www.kyungil.ac.kr

Kyungnam University
College of Engineering -
Department of Architectural Engineering
449, Wolyong-dong, Masan-shi,
Kyungsangnam-do
Kyungnam **South Korea**

Tel: +82-55/149-2674
Fax: +82-55/149-2674

Kyungpook National University
College of Engineering -
Department of Architectural Engineering
1370, Sanguk-dong, Buk-gu, Taegu-shi
Kyungpook **South Korea**

Tel: +82-53/950-5590
Fax: +82-53/950-6590

Kyungwon University
College of Engineering -
Department of Architectural Engineering
San 65, Pokjong-dong, Sungnam-shi,
Kyunggi-do
Kyungwon **South Korea**

Tel: +82-342/750-5304
Fax: +82-342/750-5304

Miryang National University
Department of Architectural Engineering
1025-1, Nae 2-dong, Miryang-shi,
Kyongsangnam-do
Miryang **South Korea**

Tel: +82-52/750-5340
Fax: +82-52/750-5343
Email: samlih@arang.miryang.ac.kr

Mokwon University
Department of Architecture
24, Mok-dong, Chung-gu, Taejon-shi
Mokwon **South Korea**

Tel: +82-42/220-6231
Fax: +82-42/254-5268

Myongji University
College of Engineering -
Department of Architectural Engineering
San 38-2, Nam-ri, Yongin-eup, Yongin-shi,
Kyunggi-do
Myongji **South Korea**

Tel: +82-33/530-6394
Fax: +82-33/530-6394

Wonkwang University
College of Engineering -
Department of Architectural Engineering
344, Shinyong-dong, Iri-shi, Junrabuk-do
Myongji **South Korea**

Tel: +82-65/350-6704
Fax: +82-65/384-30782

Pukyong National University
College of Engineering -
Department of Architectural Engineering
San 100, Yongdang-dong, Nam-gu, Pusan-shi
Pukyong **South Korea**

Tel: +82-51/620-1390
Fax: +82-51/622-8340

Pusan National University
College of Engineering -
Department of Architectural Engineering
San 30, Changjon-dong, Kumjong-gu, Pusan-shi
Pusan **South Korea**

Tel: +82-51/512-0311
Fax: +82-51/514-2230

Konkuk University
College of Engineering -
Department of Architectural Engineering
93-1, Mojin-dong, Kwangjin-gu
Seoul **South Korea**

Tel: +82-2/450-3446
Fax: +82-2/454-0428

Kyonggi University
College of Engineering -
Department of Architectural Engineering
71, Chungjongno 2-ga, Sedaemun-gu
Seoul **South Korea**

Tel: +82-2/390-5154
Fax: +82-2/392-7664

Hongik University
Department of Architecture
72-1, Sangsu-dong, Mapo-gu
Seoul **South Korea**

Tel: +82-2/320-1106
Fax: +82-2/320-1106
Web: www.hongik.ac.kr

Seoul National University
College of Engineering -
Department of Architectural Engineering
San 56-1, Shinlim-dong, Kwanak-gu
Seoul **South Korea**

Tel: +82-2/880-7051
Fax: +82-2/871-5518

Kookmin Universty
College of Engineering -
Department of Architectural Engineering
861-1, Joungnung-dong, Songbuk-gu
Seoul **South Korea**

Tel: +82-2/910-4590
Fax: +82-2/918-7079

Yonsei University
College of Engineering -
Department of Architectural Engineering
134, Shinchon-dong, Seodaimun-gu
Seoul **South Korea**

Tel: +82-2/361-2780
Fax: +82-2/365-4668

Korea University
College of Engineering -
Department of Architectural Engineering
1, Anamdong 5-ga, Songbuk-gu
Seoul **South Korea**

Tel: +82-2/920-1504
Fax: +82-2/921-7947

Seoul National Polytechnic University
Department of Architectural Engineering
172, Kongnung 2-dong, Nowon-gu
Seoul **South Korea**

Tel: +82-2/974-1480
Fax: +82-2/970-6551

Hanyang University
College of Engineering -
Department of Architectural Engineering
San 17, Haengdang-dong, Songdong-gu
Seoul **South Korea**

Tel: +82-2/290-0300
Fax: +82-2/281-2810

Seoul City University
College of Engineering -
Department of Architectural Engineering
San 90, Chonnong-dong, Tongdaemun-gu
Seoul **South Korea**

Tel: +82-2/210-2252
Fax: +82-2/248-0382

Dankook University
College of Engineering -
Department of Architectural Engineering
San 8, Hannam-dong, Yongsan-gu
Seoul **South Korea**

Tel: +82-2/709-2536
Fax: +82-2/709-2536

Sungkyunkwan University
College of Engineering -
Department of Architectural Engineering
300, Chonchon-dong, Jangan-gu, Suwon-shi,
Kyunggi-do
Sungkyunkwan **South Korea**

Tel: +82-331/290-7550
Fax: +82-331/290-7570

Suwon University
College of Engineering -
Department of Architectural Engineering
San 2-2, Wan-ri, Bongdam-Myon,
Whasung-gun, Kyunggi-do
Suwon **South Korea**

Tel: +82-331/222-2523
Fax: +82-331/220-2115

Taegu University
College of Engineering -
Department of Architectural Engineering
San 23-1, Naeri-dong, Jinlyang-myen,
Kyongsan-gun, Kyongsangbuk-do
Taegu **South Korea**

Tel: +82-541/850-6514

Taejon National University of Technology
College of Engineering -Department of
Architectural Engineering
San 16-1, Dukmyung-dong, Yoosung-gu,
Taejon-shi
Taejon **South Korea**

Tel: +82-42/821-1116

Taejon University
College of Engineering -
Department of Architectural Engineering
96-3, Yongun-dong, Tong-gu, Taejon-shi
Taejon **South Korea**

Tel: +82-42/280-2510
Fax: +82-42/284-0109
University of Ulsan
College of Engineering -
Department of Architectural Engineering
San 29, Muge-dong, Nam-gu, Ulsan-shi
Ulsan **South Korea**

Tel: +82-522/259-2272
Fax: +82-522/259-2865

Yeungnam University
College of Engineering -
Department of Architectural Engineering
214-1, Dai-dong, Kyungsan-shi,
Kyungsangbuk-do
Yeungnam **South Korea**

Tel: +82-53/810-2420
Fax: +82-53/816-3460

University of Moratuwa
Department of Architecture
Moratuwa **Sri Lanka**

Tel: +94/645-216
Fax: +94/245-216

University of Peradeniya
Faculty of Engineering
Civil Engineering
Peradeniya University Park
Sri Lanka

Aleppo University
Aleppo **Syria**

Tel: +963-21/670-300
Fax: +963-21/229-184

Damascus University
Damascus **Syria**

Tel: +963-11/212-4051
Fax: +963-11/211-9842

Alba'ath University
Homs **Syria**

Tel: +963-31/426-701
Fax: +963-31/426-716

Tishreen University
Lattakia **Syria**

Tel: +963-41/437-840
Fax: +963-41/418-504

Taadjik Polytechnical Institute
Architectural Faculty
Kulbishev Str., 10-A
734042 Dushanbe **Tadjikistan**

Tel: +7-3772/23511

National Central University
College of Engineering
Dept. of Civil Engineering
Chung-li **Taiwan**

National Chiao Tung University
College of Engineering,
Dept. of Civil Engineering
45 Po Ai Street
Hsinchu **Taiwan**

Kaohsiung Institute of Technology
Department of Civil Engineering
149 Chien-Kung Street
Kaohsiung **Taiwan**

Feng Chia College of Engineering and Business
100 Wenhwa Road, Seatwen
Taichung **Taiwan**

Tunghai University
College of Engineering
Taichung **Taiwan**

National Cheng Kung University
1 Tah-Hsueh Road
Tainan **Taiwan**

National Taiwan University
Graduate Inst. Of Civil Engineering
1 Roosevelt Road 4
Taipei **Taiwan**

Tel: +886-2/362-3356

University of Chinese Culture
Hwa Kang
Yang Min Shan **Taiwan**

Silpakorn University
Faculty of Architecture
Naphralan Road
10200 Bangkok **Thailand**

Tel: +66-2/221-3850
Fax: +66-2/221-8837

Chulanlongkorn University
Faculty of Architecture
Phyathai Road
00010 Bangkok **Thailand**

Tel: +66-2/218-43016
Fax: +66-2/251-8862

King Mongkut's Institute of Technology
Faculty of Architecture
3, Chalongskrung Road
10520 Ladkrabang District
Bangkok **Thailand**

Tel: +66-2/326-9971
Fax: +66-2/326-9156

King Mongkut's Institute of Technology
School of Architecture
Sukawat Road 48
Ratburana 10140
Bangkok **Thailand**

Tel: +66-2/427-0058
Fax: +66-2/428-4023

Kasem Bundit University
Faculty of Architecture
99/101 Soi Arkanay, Pattanakam Road
10250 Bangkok **Thailand**

Tel: +66-2/321-69308 ext.208
Fax: +66-2/321-4444

Kasetsart University, Faculty of Architecture
Department of Architecture
50 Phaholyoyhin Road
10900 Bangkok **Thailand**

Tel: +66-2/561-4121 ext.352
Fax: +66-2/579-0730

Sripatum University
Faculty of Architecture
61 Phaholyothin Road
Jatujak 10900
Bangkok **Thailand**

Tel: +66-2/579-9120 or 39
Fax: +66-2/561-1721

Chiangmai University, Faculty of Fine Arts
Department of Architecture
50200 Chiangmai **Thailand**

Tel: +66-5/322-1699
Fax: +66-5/321-1724

Khonkaen University
Faculty of Architecture
00040 Khonkaen **Thailand**

Tel: +66-4/324-2389
Fax: +66-4/324-2389

Vongchavalitkul University
Faculty of Architecture,
Department of Architecture
30000 Korat **Thailand**

Tel: +66-4/427-1317
Fax: +66-4/427-1318

Rangsit University
Faculty of Architecture
52/347 Muang-Ake/ Phaholyothin Road
00120 Pathumthani **Thailand**

Tel: +66-2/533-9020
Fax: +66-2/500-0470

Turkmenski Polytechnical Institute
Department of Architecture
Kotovski St.
Ashkhabad 744011
Turkmenistan

Samarkand Architectural & Building Institute
Lalazar St., 70
703047 Samarkand
Uzbekistan

Tel: +7-2/320-250

Architectural & Building Institute
Navoi St., 13
700011 Tashkent
Uzbekistan

Tel: +7-2/411-312

University of Fine Arts
Ho Chi Minh City, 5 Phan Dang Luu Street
Binh Thanh District
Gia Dinh **Vietnam**

Dong Do University of Science and Technology
Faculty of Architecture
55 Quan Thanh Str.
Hanoi **Vietnam**

Tel: +84-4/843-3268
Fax: +84-4/826-9306

Hanoi Architectural University
Km10, Nguyen Trai
Hanoi **Vietnam**

Tel: +84-4/854-4346
Fax: +84-4/854-1616

Hanoi University of Civil Engineering
Faculty of Architecture
5 Giai Phong St.
Hanoi **Vietnam**

Tel: +84-4/869-6765
Email: nkthai@netnam.org.vn

Universite d'Architecture de Ho Chi Minh Ville
196, rue Pasteur, 3 Arrond.
Ho Chi Minh City **Vietnam**

Tel: +84-8/822-2748
Fax: +84-8/244-678

Universite of Ho Chi Minh City
Department d'Architecture
3 Cong-Truong Chien-Si
Ho Chi Minh City **Vietnam**

Institut de Construction
Faculte d'Architecture
(Huong-Canh)
Vinh Phu **Vietnam**

EUROPE

Erevan Architectural & Building Institute
Terjan Str.105
375009 Erevan **Armenia**

Tel: +374-2/565-390

Technsiche Hochschule Wien
Fakultat fur Bauingenieurwesen un Architektur
Karlsplatz, 3
Wien 01040 **Austria**

Leopold Franzens Universitat
Faculty of Civil Engineering and Architecture
Technikerstrasse. 13
Innsbruck 06020 **Austria**

Technische Universität Graz
Fakultät für Architektur
Rechbauerstrasse, 12
A-8010 Graz **Austria**

Tel: +43-316/8730
Fax: +43-316/827-679

Universität Innsbruck
Innrain, 52
A-6020 Innsbruck **Austria**

Tel: +43-512/5070
Fax: +43-512/507-2800

Hochschule für Kunstlerische und Industrielle
Gestaltung in Linz
Hauptplatz, 8
A-4020 Linz **Austria**

Tel: +43-732/785-173
Fax: +43-732/783-508

Technische Universität Wien
Karlsplatz, 13
A-1040 Wien **Austria**

Tel: +43-1/588-010
Fax: +43-1/505-5856

Akademie der Bildenden Künste in Wien
Schillerplatz, 3
A-1010 Wien **Austria**

Tel: +43-1/588-160
Fax: +43-1/5881-6137

Hochschule für angewandte Kunst in Wien
Oskar Kokoska Platz, 2
A-1010 Wien **Austria**

Tel: +43-1/711-330
Fax: +43-1/7113-3222

Ecole Polytechnique d'Azerbaidjan
25 Prospekt Narimanova
Baku **Azerbaijan**

University of Civil Engineering
Faculty of Architecture
Sultanova Street, 5
370 073 Baku **Azerbaijan**

Tel: +994-12/391-015

Belorussian Polytechnical Academy
Skoriny, 150
220045 Minsk **Belarus**

Tel: +375-172/649-859
Fax: +375-172/649-859

Institut Superieur d'Architecture Saint-Luc
21, rue des Anglais
Liege 04000 **Belgium**

Universite de Liege
Section d'Architecture
7, place du Vingt Aout
Liege 04000 **Belgium**

Academie Royale des Beaux Arts de Mons
Section d'Architecture
106, rue de Nimy
Mons 07000 **Belgium**

Hogeschool Gent
Departement Architectuur
J. Kluyskensstraat 2
Gent 09000 **Belgium**

Tel: +32-9/266-0800

Instituut Henry Van de Velde
Mutsaertstraat 31
02000 Antwerp **Belgium**

Tel: +32-3/231-7084
Fax: +32-3/226-0411

Institut Superieur d'Architecture La Cambre
Place Eugène Flagey 19
01000 Brussels **Belgium**

Tel: +32-2/640-9696
Fax: +32-2/647-4655

Institut Superieur d'Architecture Victor Horta
U.L.B. Campus de la Plaine Bd. du
Triomphe/CP 248
01050 Brussels **Belgium**

Tel: +32-2/650-5095
Fax: +32-2/650-5093

Institut Superieur d'Architecture Saint Luc
Rue d'Irlande 57
01060 Brussels **Belgium**

Tel: +32-2/537-3419
Fax: +32-2/537-0063

Instituut Sint-Luc
Paleizenstraat 65-67
01210 Brussels **Belgium**

Tel: +32-4/123-3810
Fax: +32-4/123-6015

Vrije Universiteit van Brussel (V.U.B.)
Faculteit der Toegpaste Wetenschappen
Afdeling Architectuur
Pleinlaan, 2
01050 Brussels **Belgium**

Tel: +32-2/629-2840
Fax: +32-2/629-2841

Provinciaale Hogeschool Limburg
Departement Architectuur
Universitaire Campus, Blok E
03590 Diepenbeek **Belgium**

Tel: +32-11/269-011
Fax: +32-11/269-019

Department Architectuur Instituut Sint-Lucas
Gent
Zwarte Zustersstraat, 34/Campus Gent
09000 Gent **Belgium**

Tel: +32-9/225-4290
Fax: +32-9/223-4636

Uiniversiteit Gent
Faculteit der Toegepaste Wetenschappen
Afdeling Architectuur
J. Plateaustraat, 22
09000 Gent **Belgium**

Tel: +32-9/264-3742
Fax: +32-9/264-4185

Katholieke Universiteit te Lewven K.U.L.
Faculteit der Toegepaste Weterschappen
Afdeling Architectuur
Kasteel Arenberg
03001 Heverlee **Belgium**

Tel: +32-16/321-361
Fax: +32-16/321-984

Université Catholique de Louvain U.C.L.
Faculté des Sciences Appliquées
Unité d'Architecture
Place du Levant, 1
01348 Louvain-la-Neuve **Belgium**

Tel: +32-10/47-2341
Fax: +32-10/47-4544

Institut Supérieur d'architecture Lambert
Lombard
Rue Saint-Gilles, 33
04000 Liege **Belgium**

Tel: +32-4/121-7900
Fax: +32-4/121-7925
Université de Liège Faculté des Sciences
Appliquées
Chaire d'Architecture
6, Quai Banning
04000 Liege **Belgium**

Tel: +32-4/166-9242
Fax: +32-4/166-9531

Institut Supérieur d'Architecture Saint Luc de Wallonie
Rue Sainte Marie, 30
04000 Liege **Belgium**

Tel: +32-4/123-3810
Fax: +32-4/123-6015

Faculté Polytechnique de Mons
Unité d'Architecture
Rue du Joncquois, 53
07000 Mons **Belgium**

Tel: +32-65/374-570
Fax: +32-65/374-600

Institut Supérieur d'Architecture de Mons
Rue d'Havré, 88
07000 Mons **Belgium**

Tel: +32-65/314-620
Fax: +32-65/364-661

Institut Superieur d'Architecture Saint-Luc de Wallonie
Chaussée de Tournai, 50
07520 Ramegnies **Belgium**

Tel: +32-69/227-202
Fax: +32-69/224-900
Arhitektonski Fakultet
30, Patriotske lige
71000 Sarajevo **Bosnia**

Tel: +387-71/663-390
Fax: +387-71/663-390

Université d'Architecture, Génie Civil et Géodesie
Faculté d'Architecture
1, Boul.Christo Smirnenski
01421 Sofia **Bulgaria**

Tel: +359-2/63321
Fax: +359-2/656863
Email: aceadm@bgace5.uacg.acad.bg
Web: www.uacg.acad.bg

University of Zagreb
Faculty of Architecture
Kaciceva, 26
10000 Zagreb **Croatia**

Tel: +385-1/456-1222
Fax: +385-1/440-839
Email: dekan@arhitekt.hr
Web: www.arhitekt.hr

Higher Technical Institute
Course in Civil Engineering
P.O.B. 2423
Nicosia **Cyprus**

Technical University Brno
Faculty of Architecture
Porici 5
66283 Brno
Czech Republic

Tel: +420-5/4214-2123
Fax: +420-5/4214-2125
Email: novy@palladio.fa.vutbr.cz

Technical University Liberec
Faculty of Architecture
Halkova, 6
46117 Liberec
Czech Republic

Tel: +420-48/29553
Fax: +420-48/23317
Email: jiri.suchomel@vslib.cz

The Academy of Arts, Architecture and Design
Namesti Jana Palacha
11000 Prague 1
Czech Republic

Tel: +420-2/2481-1172
Fax: +420-2/232-6884

Czech Technical University in Prague
Faculty of Architecture
Thakurova 7
16000 Prague 6
Czech Republic

Tel: +420-2/2431-1086
Fax: +420-2/2431-0573
Email: zatkova@fanet.fa.cvut.cz

Academy of Fine Arts in Prague
School of Architecture
U Akademie 2
17000 Prague 7
Czech Republic

Tel: +420-2/373-641
Fax: +420-2/375-781
Email: arch@avu.cz
Web: www.avu.cz
Arkitektskolen i Aarhus
(The School of Architecture)
Noerreport, 20
8000-C Aarhus **Denmark**

Tel: +45-8/936-0000
Fax: +45-8/613-0645
Email: aaa@a-aarhus.dk
Web: www.a-aarhus.dk

Kunstakademiets Arkitektskole
(The Royal Academy of Fine Arts)
Philip de Langes Allé 10
1435-DK Copenhagen **Denmark**

Tel: +45-3/268-6000
Fax: +45-3/268-6111
Web: www.karch.dk

Tallin Art University
School of Architecture
Tartu Mnt.1
EE 0001 Tallinn **Estonia**

Tel: +372-2/421-481
Fax: +372-2/432-659

Lahti Institute of Technology
Faculty of Architecture
Stahlberginkatu 10
15110 Lahti 11 **Finland**

Tampere University of Technology
Department of Architecture
Korkeakoulunkatu 3
33101 Tampere **Finland**

Tel: +358-3/365-3234

University of Oulu
Department of Architecture
Aleksanterinkatu 6
90100 Oulu **Finland**

Tel: +358-8/553-4910

Helsinki University of Technology
Faculty of Architecture
Otakaari 1 X
FIN-02150 Espoo **Finland**

Tel: +358-0/685-4473

Ecole Nationale d'Art Decoratif
20, avenue Stephen Liegard
06000 Nice **France**

Regional de l'Universite d'Aix-Marseille
Institut d'Amenagement
3, avenue Robert Schuman
13100 Aix-en-Provence **France**

Ecole Nationale des Beaux Arts et Arts
Appliques a l'Industrie
1, rue des Beaux Arts
18000 Bourges **France**

Ecole Nationale des Beaux Arts
3, rue Michelet
21000 Dijon **France**

Ecole National d'Art Decoratif
Place Villeneuve
23200 Aubusson **France**

Universite de Tours
Centre d'Etudes Superieures de
l'Amenagement du Territoire
Avenue Monge, Parc Grandmont
37000 Tours **France**

Ecole Nationale des Beaux Arts et Arts
Appliques
1, avenue Boffrand
54000 Nancy **France**

Ecole Nationale des Ponts et Chaussees
Seminaire d'Ameneagement,
Urbain et Regional
28, rue des Saints Peres
75005 Paris **France**

Ecole Nationale Superieure des Arts
Decoratifs
31, rue d'Ulm
75005 Paris **France**

Universite de Paris VII
Departement de l'Environnement
2, place Jussieu, Tour 24-34,
3eme Tage, P. 06
75005 Paris **France**

Unite Pedagogique d'Architecture no. 2
1, rue Jacques Callot
75006 Paris **France**

Unite Pedagogique d'Architecture no. 8
69-71, rue de Chevaleret
75013 Paris **France**

Centre de Recherche d'Urbanisme (CRU)
4, avenue du Recteur Poincare
75016 Paris **France**

Ecole Nationale d'Art Decoratif
8, place Winston Churchill
87000 Limoges **France**

Institut d'Urbanisme de Paris
Avenue du General de Gaulle
94000 Creteil **France**

Ecole d'Architecture de Paris-Val de Marne
11, rue du Séminaire de Conflans
94220 Charenton **France**

Tel: +33-143/536-060
Fax: +33-143/536-070

Ecole d'Architecture de Clermont-Ferrand
71, Bd Côte Blatin
63000 Clermont Ferrand **France**

Tel: +33-473/347-150
Fax: +33-473/347-169

Ecole d'Architecture de Grenoble
60, av. Constantine/ BP 2636
38036 Cedex 2 Grenoble **France**

Tel: +33-476/698-300
Fax: +33-476/698-338
Email: info@grenoble.archi.fr

Ecole d'Architecture de Marseille-Luminy
184, rue de Luminy/Case 912
13288 Cedex 09 Marseille **France**

Tel: +33-491/827-100
Fax: +33-491/827-180

Ecole d'Architecture du Languedoc-Roussillon
179, rue de l'Espérou
34093 Cedex 5 Montpellier **France**

Tel: +33-467/633-430
Fax: +33-467/413-507

Ecole d'Architecture de Nancy
2, rue Bastien Lepage/BP 435
54001 Cedex Nancy **France**

Tel: +33-383/308-100
Fax: +33-383/308-130

Ecole d'Architecture de Paris-La Défense
41, allée Le Corbusier
92023 Cedex Nanterre **France**

Tel: +33-147/760-105
Fax: +33-147/780-807

Ecole d'Architecture de Nantes
La Mulotière, rue Massenet
44300 Nantes **France**

Tel: +33-240/160-121
Fax: +33-240/591-670

Ecole d'Architecture de Paris-Belleville
78/80, rue Rebeval
75019 Paris **France**

Tel: +33-1/5338-5000
Fax: +33-1/5338-5001

Ecole d'Architecture de Paris-Tolbiac
5 rue du Javelot
75645 Cedex 13 Paris **France**

Tel: +33-1/4406-8510
Fax: +33-1/4584-5373

Ecole d'Architecture de Paris-La Seine
14, rue Bonaparte
75006 Paris **France**

Tel: +33-1/4450-5600
Fax: +33-1/4450-5621

Ecole d'Architecture de Paris-Villemin
11, Quai Malaquais
75272 Cedex 06 Paris **France**

Tel: +33-1/4703-5000
Fax: +33-1/4927-9954

Ecole d'Architecture de Paris-La Villette
144 rue de Flandre
75019 Paris **France**

Tel: +33-1/4465-2300
Fax: +33-1/4465-2301

Ecole Spéciale d'Architecture (ESA)
254 Boulevard Raspail
75014 Paris **France**

Tel: +33-1/4047-4047
Fax: +33-1/4322-8116

Ecole d'Architecure de Bretagne
44, Bd. de Chézy
35000 Rennes **France**

Tel: +33-299/296-800
Fax: +33-299/304-249

Ecole d'Architecture de Saint Etienne
1 rue Buisson
42000 Saint Etienne **France**

Tel: +33-477/423-542
Fax: +33-477/423-540

Ecole d'Architecture de Strasbourg
8, Bd. Wilson/ BP 37
67068 Strasbourg **France**

Tel: +33-388/322-535
Fax: +33-388/328-241

Ecole Nationale Supérieure des Arts et
Industries de Strasbourg (ENSAIS)
24, Bd de la Victoire
67084 Strasbourg **France**

Tel: +33-388/144-700
Fax: +33-388/241-490

Ecole d'Architecture de Bordeaux
Domaine de Raba
33405 Talence **France**

Tel: +33-557/350-000
Fax: +33-556/370-323

Ecole d'Architecture de Toulouse
83, rue Aristide Maillol/BP 1329
31106 Toulouse **France**

Tel: +33-562/115-050
Fax: +33-562/115-099

Ecole d'Architecture de Lyon
3, rue Maurice Audin/BP 170
69120 Cedex 9 Vaulx-en-Velin **France**

Tel: +33-478/795-050
Fax: +33-478/804-068

Ecole d'Architecture de Versailles
2, avenue de Paris/BP 674
78000 Versailles **France**

Tel: +33-239/515-251
Fax: +33-239/500-851

Ecole d'Architecture de Lille et Régions Nord
Quartier de l'Hôtel de Ville
59650 Villeneuve d'Asq **France**

Tel: +33-320/619-550
Fax: +33-320/619-551

Ecole d'Architecture de Normandie
27, rue Lucien Fromage
76160 Darnetal **France**

Tel: +33-232/832-200
Fax: +33-232/834-210

Georgian Technical University
Architectural Institute
77, Costava Str.
380015 Tbilisi **Georgia**

Tel: +995-32/367-163

Tbilis State Academy of Art
Faculty of Architecture, History and Theory
of Art, Monumental and Decorative Art
22, Griboedov Str.
380008 Tbilisi **Georgia**

Tel: +995-32/936-951
Fax: +995-32/936-959

Wirtschaft u
Hochschule für Technik,nd Kultur Leipzig (FH)
Fachbereich Bauwesen/Lehrbereich Archtektur
Postfach 66
Leipzig 04251 **Germany**

Tel: +49-341/307-6207
Fax: +49-341/307-6252

Hochschule Bremen
Fachberiech Architektur
Neustadtswall 30
Bremen 28799 **Germany**

Fachhochschule Hildesheim
Fachbereiche Architektur und
Bauingenieurwesen
Harmannplatz 3
Holzminden 37603 **Germany**

Tel: +49-55/311-260

Staatliche Werkkunstschule Berlin
Architekturabteilung
Strasse der 17 Juni 118
1000 Berlin 12 **Germany**

Fachhochschule Hildesheim, Iholz Minden
Fachbereich Produktgestaltung, Studeinegang
Innenarchitektur
Am. Marienfriedhof 1
32 Hildesheim **Germany**

Fachhochschule Essen
Schutzenbahn 70
43 Essen **Germany**

Staatliche Ingenieurschule
Fachrichtung Hochbau
Robert Schmidt Strasse 1
43 Essen **Germany**

Werkkunstschule der Stadt Essen
Folkwangschule fur Gestaltung
Abtei 43 Essen-Werden **Germany**

Werkschule Munster
Architekturabteilung
Sentmaringe, Weg 53
44 Munster **Germany**

Gesamthochschule Paderborn
Fachberieich Architektur
Warbergerstr. 100
479 Paderborn **Germany**

Kolner Werkschulen
Ubierring 40
5 Koln **Germany**

Staatiche Ingenieurschule fur Bauwesen
Bayernallee 9
Ecke Raerenerstrasse
51 Aachen **Germany**

Staatliche Ingenieurschule
Fachrichtung Hochbau
54 Koblenz-Karthause **Germany**

Gesamthochschule Wuppertal
Hofkamp 86
56 Wuppertal-Elberfeld **Germany**

Fachhochschule Hagen
Haldenerstrasse 182
5800 Hagen **Germany**

Gesamthochschule Siegen-Gummersbach
Paul-Bonatz Strasse 9
593 Huttental-Weidenau **Germany**

Staatliche Hochschule fur Bildende Kunste
Stadelschule, Durerstrasse 10
6 Frankfurt-Am-Main **Germany**

Staatsbauschule Darmstadt
Havelstrasse
61 Darmstadt **Germany**

Werkkunstschule Darmstadt
Architekturabteilung
Olbrichweg 10
61 Darmstadt **Germany**

Fachhochschule fur Technik
Willi-Bleicher Strasse 29
7000 Stuttgart **Germany**

Fachhochschule Munchen
Lothstrasse 34
8000 Munchen **Germany**

Akademie der Bildenden Kunste
Aufbaustudium Architektur
Akademiestr. 2
8000 Munchen 40 **Germany**

Fachhochschule Rosenheim
Marienberger Strasse 26
82 Rosenheim **Germany**

Akademie der Bildenden Kunste
Bingstrasse 60
85 Nurnberg **Germany**

Fachhochschule Wurzburg-Schweinfurt
Munzstrasse 12
8700 Wurzburg **Germany**

Technische Universität Dresden
Fakultät Architektur
Mommsenstr. 13
Dresden D-01062 **Germany**

Tel: +49-351/463-4197
Fax: +49-351/463-7103

Hochschule für Technik und Wirtsschaft (FH)
Fachbereich Architektur
Friedrich-List-Platz 1
Dresden D-01069 **Germany**

Tel: +49-351/462-3401
Fax: +49-351/462-2186
Web: www.htw-dresden.de

Hochschule für Technik,
Wirtschaft und Sozialwesen (FH)
Fachbereich Architektur
Theodor-Körner-Allee 16
Zittau D-02763 **Germany**

Fax: +49-358/361-1254
Email: postmaster@htw-zittau.de
Web: www.htw-zittau.de

Westsächsische Hochschule Zwickau (FH)
Hochschulteil Reichenbach/ Fachbereich
Architektur
Klinkhardt-Str. 30
Reichenbach D-087468 **Germany**

Tel: +49-376/555-5210
Fax: +49-376/555-2142

Hochschule der Künste Berlin
Fachbereich 2 - Architektur
Hardenbergstr. 33
Berlin D-10623 **Germany**

Tel: +49-30/3185-2209
Fax: +49-30/3185-2682

Technische Fachhochschule
Fachbereich 4 - Architektur
Luxemburger Str. 10
Berlin D-12253 **Germany**

Tel: +49-30/4504-2577
Fax: +49-30/4504-2015

Kunsthochschule Berlin-Weissensee
Str. 203, Nr. 20
Berlin D-13086 **Germany**

Tel: +49-30/471-4061
Fax: +49-30/471-5082

Technische Universität Berlin
Fachbereich 8 - Architektur
Rohrdamm 22
Berlin D-13629 **Germany**

Tel: +49-30/3800-6175/176
Fax: +49-30/3800-6198

Fachhochschule Nordost-Niedersachsen
Fachbereich Architektur
Harburger Str. 6
Buxtehude D-21614 **Germany**

Tel: +49-41/616-0080
Fax: +49-41/616-00866

Hochschule für Bildende Künste
Hamburg - Fachbereich Architektur
Lerchenfeld 2
Hamburg D-22081 **Germany**

Fachhochschule Hamburg
Fachbereich Architektur
Hebebrandstr. 1
Hamburg D-22297 **Germany**

Tel: +49-40/4667-3745
Fax: +49-40/4667-3809

Fachhochschule Lübeck
Fachbereich Architektur und
Bauingenieurwesen
Stephensonstr. 1
Lübeck D-23 562 **Germany**

Tel: +49-451/500-5159
Fax: +49-451/500-5079

Muthesius-Hochschule
Fachhochschule für Kunst und Gestaltung
Lorentzendamm 6-8
Kiel D-24103 **Germany**

Tel: +49-431/519-8400
Fax: +49-431/519-8408

Fachhochschule Kiel
Fachbereich Bauwesen/ Fachgebiet
Architektur
Lorenz-v.Stein.Ring 1-5
Eckernförde D-24340 **Germany**

Tel: +49-435/14730
Fax: +49-435/147314
Email: bauwesen.verwaltung@fh-kiel.de

Fachhochschule Oldenburg
Fachbereich Architektur, Bauingenieur,
Vermessungswesen und Seefahrt
Ofener Str. 16-19
Oldenburg D-26121 **Germany**

Tel: +49-441/77080
Fax: +49-441/770-8100
Web: www.fh-wilhelmshaven.de

Hochschule für Technik
Fachbereich Architektur
Langemarckstr. 116
Bremen D-28199 **Germany**

Tel: +49-421/59051
Fax: +49-421/590-5292

Universität Hannover
Fachbereich Architektur
Schloßwender Str. 1
Hannover D-30159 **Germany**

Tel: +49-511/762-4276
Fax: +49-511/762.-2115

Fachhochschule Hildesheim/Holzminden
Fachbereich Architektur
Hohnsen 2
Hildesheim D-31134 **Germany**

Tel: +49-512/188-1201
Fax: +49-512/188-1125

Fachhochschule Hannover
Fachbereich Architektur und
Bauingenieurwesen
Bürgermeister-Stahn-Wall 9
Nienburg D-31582 **Germany**

Tel: +49-502/16080
Fax: +49-502/160-8100

Fachhochschule Bielefeld/Bteilung Minden
Fachbereich Architektur
Artilleriestr. 9
Minden D-32427 **Germany**

Tel: +49-571/83850
Fax: +49-571/838-5250

Fachhochschule Lippe Abtl. Detmold
FB Architektur/Innenarchitektur
Bielefelderstr. 66
Detmold D-32756 **Germany**

Tel: +49-523/191-260
Fax: +49-523/163-787

Gesamthochschule Kassel
Fachbereich 12 - Architektur
Mönchebergstr. 19
Kassel D-34125 **Germany**

Tel: +49-561/8040
Fax: +49-561/2330

Universität/Gesamthochschule Paderborn
Abteilung Höxter, Fachbereich,
Landschaftsarchitektur und Umweltplanung
An der Wilhelmshöhe 44
Höxter 1 D-37671 **Germany**

Tel: +49-527/168-7106 or 7102
Fax: +49-527/168-7200

Technische Universität Braunschweig
Fachbereich Architektur
Mühlenpfordtstr. 22/23
Braunschweig D-38106 **Germany**

Tel: +49-531/391-5938 or 5939
Fax: +49-531/391-5937

Fachhochschule Düsseldorf
Fachbereich Architektur
Georg-Glock-Str. 15
Düsseldorf D-40474 **Germany**

Tel: +49-211/435-1101 or 1110
Fax: +49-211/435-1509

Bergische Universität
Gesamthochschule Wuppertal/Fachbereich 10
- Architektur
Pauluskirchstr. 7
Wuppertal D-42097 **Germany**

Tel: +49-202/439-3075
Fax: +49-202/439-3130

Fachhochschule Dortmund
Fachbereich Architektur
Postfach 105018
Dortmund D-44047 **Germany**

Tel: +49-231/755-4431
Fax: +49-231/755-4466

Universität Dortmund
Fakultät BauwesenLehrstuhl Baubetrieb
August-Schmidt-Str. 8
Dortmund D-44221 **Germany**

Tel: +49-231/755-2073
Fax: +49-231/755-4465
Web: www.uni-dortmund.de

Fachhochschule Bochum
Fachbereich 1 - Architektur
Lennershofstr. 140
Bochum D-44801 **Germany**

Tel: +49-234/700-7132
Fax: +49-234/709-4218

Fachhochschule Münster
Fachbereich Architektur
Gievenbecker Weg 65
Münster D-48149 **Germany**

Tel: +49-251/834-389
Fax: +49-251/839-739

Fachhochschule Koln
Fachberich Architektur
Reitweg 1
Koln 21 D-5000 **Germany**

Fachhochschule Köln
Fachbereich Architektur
Betzdorfer Str. 2
Köln D-50679 **Germany**

Tel: +49-221/8275-2811 or 2812
Fax: +49-221/8275-2815

Rheinisch-Westfälische Technische
Hochschule Aachen
Fakultät für Architektur
Schinkelstr. 1
Aachen D-52062 **Germany**

Tel: +49-241/805-000
Fax: +49-241/48291

Fachhochschule Aachen
Fakultät für Architektur
Bayernallee 9
Aachen D-52066 **Germany**

Tel: +49-241/1110
Fax: +49-241/1480

Fachhochschule des Landes Rheinland-
Pfalz/Abteilung Trier
Fachbereich Architektur
Schneidershof
Trier D-54293 **Germany**

Tel: +49-651/810-3300
Fax: +49-651/810-3333

Fachhochschule Mainz
Fachbereich Architektur
Holzstr. 36
Mainz D-55116 **Germany**

Fachhochschule Koblenz
Fachbereich Architektur und Stadtplanung
Zwickauerstr. 23
Koblenz D-56075 **Germany**

Tel: +49-261/952-8198
Fax: +49-261/53151

Universität - Gesamthochschule Siegen
FB Architektur und Städtebau
Paul-Bonatz-Str. 9-11
Siegen D-57068 **Germany**

Tel: +49-271/740-2112
Fax: +49-271/740-2510

Fachhochschule Frankfurt
Fachbereich Architektur
Nibelungenplatz 1
Frankfurt-am-Main D-60318 **Germany**

Tel: +49-69/1533-2741
Fax: +49-69/1533-2761

Technische Hochschule Darmstadt
Fachbereich 15 - Architektur
El-Lissitzky-Str. 1
Darmstadt D-64287 **Germany**

Tel: +49-615/116-2101
Fax: +49-615/116-6915

Fachhochschule Darmstadt
Fachbereich Architektur
Schöfferstr. 1
Darmstadt D-64295 **Germany**

Tel: +49-615/116-1801
Fax: +49-615/116-8960
Web: www.fba.fh-darmstadt.de

Fachhochschule Wiesbaden
Fachbereich Architektur
Kurt-Schumacher-Ring 18
Wiesbaden D-65197 **Germany**

Tel: +49-611/949-5401
Fax: +49-611/949-5422

Hochschule für Technik u. Wirtschaft
Fachbereich Architektur
Waldhausweg 14
Saarbrücken D-66123 **Germany**

Tel: +49-681/58670
Fax: +49-681/30775

Universität Kaiserslautern
Fachbereich Architektur, Raum- und
Umweltplanung
Pfaffenbergstr. 95
Kaiserslautern D-67663 **Germany**

Tel: +49-631/205-2291
Fax: +49-631/205-2430
Email: dekarubi@rhrk.uni-kl.de

Fachhochschule Kaiserslautern
Fachbereich Architektur/ Abteilung
Kaiserslautern
Schoenstr. 6
Kaiserslautern D-67663 **Germany**

Tel: +49-631/372-4401
Fax: +49-631/372-4444

Fachhochschule Heidelberg
Staatl. anerk. Fachhochschule der SRHGruppe
Fachbereich Architektur
Maaßstr. 32
Heidelberg D-69123 **Germany**

Tel: +49-622/188-2225
Fax: +49-622/188-2090
Email: methner@pico.fh-heidelberg.de

Universität Stuttgart
Fakultät 1/Architektur und Stadtplanung
Keplerstr. 11
Stuttgart D-70174 **Germany**

Tel: +49-711/121-3223 or 3224
Fax: +49-711/121-2788

Fachhochschule Stuttgart
Hochschule für Technik/ Fachbereich
Architektur
Schellingstr. 24
Stuttgart D-70174 **Germany**

Tel: +49-711/121-2590
Fax: +49-711/121-2594
Web: www.fht-stuttgart.de
Email: sekretariat.fba@fht-stuttgart.de

Staatliche Akademie der Bildenden Kunste
Stuttgart
Fachgruppe Architektur und Design
Am Weissenhof 1
Stuttgart 1 D-70191 **Germany**

Universität Karlsruhe
Fakultät für Architektur
Englerstr. 7
Karlsruhe D-76131 **Germany**

Tel: +49-721/608-2156
Fax: +49-721/608-6090
Web: www.architektur.uni-karlsruhe.de

Fachhochschule Karlsruhe
Fachbereich Architektur
Moltkestr. 4
Karlsruhe D-76133 **Germany**

Tel: +49-721/169-420
Fax: +49-721/169-420

Fachhochschule Konstanz
Fachbereich Architektur
Brauneggerstr. 55
Konstanz D-78462 **Germany**

Tel: +49-753/120-6192
Fax: +49-753/120-6193
Web: www.fh-konstanz.de

Fachhochschule München
Fachbereich Architektur
Karlstr. 6
München D-80333 **Germany**

Tel: +49-89/1265-2625
Fax: +49-89/1265-2630

Technische Universität München
Fakultät für Architektur
Arcisstrasse 21
München D-80333 **Germany**

Tel: +49-89/2892-2460
Fax: +49-89/2892-5326

Fachhochschule Augsburg
Hochschule für Technik,
Wirtschaft und Gestaltung
Baumgartnerstr. 16
Augsburg D-86161 **Germany**

Tel: +49-821/55860
Fax: +49-821/558-6222
Web: www.fh-augsburg.de

Fachhochschule Biberach
Fachbereich Architektur
Karlstr. 9 - 11
Biberach D-88400 **Germany**

Tel: +49-735/158-221
Fax: +49-735/158-249

Fachhochschule Nürnberg
Fachbereich Architektur
Kesslerplatz 12
Nürnberg D-90589 **Germany**

Tel: +49-911/58800
Fax: +49-911/588-0309

Fachhochschule Regensburg
Fachbereich Architektur
Prüfeninger Str. 58
Regensburg D-93049 **Germany**

Tel: +49-941/23091
Fax: +49-941/21009

Fachhochschule Coburg
Fachbereich Architektur/ Innenarchitektur
Friedrich-Streib-Str. 2
Coburg D-96450 **Germany**

Tel: +49-956/131-7234
Fax: +49-956/131-7273

Fachhochschule Würzburg-Schweinfurt-
Aschaffenburg
FB Architektur und Bauingenieurwesen
Röntgenring 8
Würzburg D-97070 **Germany**

Tel: +49-931/304-262
Fax: +49-931/304-263

SCHOOLS OF ARCHITECTURE WORLDWIDE

Bauhaus-Universität Weimar
Fakultät Architektur, Stadt-und
Regionalplanung
Berkaer Str. 9
Weimarok infos de 7.99 D-99421
Germany

Tel: +49-364/358-3181
Fax: +49-364/358-3234

National Technical University
Faculty of Architecture
University Campus
15780 Zografou Athenes
Greece

Tel: +30-1/772-1943
Fax: +30-1/772-2042
Web: www.tech.admin.ntua.gr

Aristotle University of Thessaloniki
Faculty of Architecture, School of Technology
University Campus
54006 Thessalonique
Greece

Tel: +30-31/995-595
Fax: +30-31/995-597

Budapest College University of Applied Arts
Faculty of Architecture
Zugligeti ut 9-15
H-1121 Budapest **Hungary**

Tel: +36-1/176-1722
Fax: +36-1/176-7488

Budapest Technical University
Faculty of Architecture
Müegyetem Rakpart 3
H-1111 Budapest **Hungary**

Tel: +36-1/463-3521
Fax: +36-1/463-3520

Ybl Miklos Technical College
Faculty of Architecture
Tkököly ut 74
H-1146 Budapest **Hungary**

Tel: +36-1/322-8693
Fax: +36-1/322-9602

Ybl Miklos Technical College
Faculty of Architecture
Otemetö utca 2-4
H-4028 Debrecen **Hungary**

Tel: +36-52/415-155
Fax: +36-52/415-643

Széchenyi Istvan Technical College
Faculty of Architecture
Hédervari ut3
H-9026 Gyor **Hungary**

Tel: +36-96/429-722
Fax: +36-96/329-263

Pollak Mihaly Technical College
Faculty of Architecture
Boszorkany ut 2
H-7624 Pecs **Hungary**

Tel: +36-72/211-968
Fax: +36-72/211-036

University College Dublin
School of Architecture
Richview/ Clonskeagh
00014 Dublin **Ireland**

Tel: +353-1/269-3244
Fax: +353-1/283 7778

College of Technology
Department of Architecture
Bolton Street
1 Dublin **Ireland**

Tel: +353-1/402-3690
Fax: +353-1/872-7879

Università di Roma La Sapienza
Facoltà di Architettura
Via Gramsci, 53
Roma 00197 **Italy**

Tel: +39-6/4991-9139 to 44
Fax: +39-6/4991-9138
Web: www.uniroma1.it
Politecnico di Torino
Facoltà di Architettura
Castello del Valentino/Viale Mattioli 39
Torino 10125 **Italy**

Tel: +39-11/564-6329
Fax: +39-11/564 6379

Università di Genova
Facoltà di Architettura
Stradone S. Agostino, 37
Genova 16123 **Italy**

Tel: +39-10/209-5877
Fax: +39-10/209-5905
Web: www.unige.it

Politecnico di Milano
Facoltà di Architettura
Via Bonardi, 3
Milano 20133 **Italy**

Tel: +39-2/2399-2615
Fax: +39-2/2399-2610
Web: www.arch.polimi.it

Istituto Universitario di Architettura
S. Croce Tolentini 197
Venezia 30122 **Italy**

Tel: +39-41/522-8185
Fax: +39-41/257-1760
Web: www.iuav.unive.it

Universita di Ferrara
Facoltà di Architettura
Via Quartieri, 8
44100 **Italy**

Tel: +39-53/229-3600
Fax: +39-53/276-3146
Web: www.unife.it

Università di Firenze
Facoltà di Architettura
Via Micheli, 2
Firenze 50121 **Italy**

Tel: +39-55/570-050
Fax: +39-55/575-904
Web: www.unifi.it

Universita di Camerino
Facoltà di Architettura
Viale della Rimembranza/Lungo Castellana
Sisto V, 36
Ascoli Piceno 63100 **Italy**

Tel: +39-73/627-6218
Fax: +39-73/627-6214
Web: www.unicam.it

Universita di Chieti
Facoltà di Architettura
Viale Pindaro, 42
Pescara 65127 **Italy**

Tel: +39-85/453-7381
Fax: +39-85/453-7385
Web: www.unich.it

Politécnico di Bari
Facoltà di Architettura
Via E. Orabona, 4/10
Bari 70125 **Italy**

Tel: +39-80/546-0810 or 0811
Fax: +39-80/544-3510
Web: www.poliba.it

Università di Napoli Federico II
Facoltà di Architettura
Via Monteoliveto, 3
Napoli 80134 **Italy**

Tel: +39-81/552-8185
Fax: +39-81/552-1401

Università di Napoli II
Facoltà di Architettura
Via S. Lorenzo ad Septimium
Aversa (Napoli) 81031 **Italy**

Tel: +39-81/814-2166
Fax: +39-81/814-8626

Università di Reggio Calabria
Instituto Universitario de Architettura
Salita Melissari - Feo di Vito
Reggio Calabria 89124 **Italy**

Tel: +39-965/33880
Fax: +39-965/330-981
Web: www.unic.it

Università di Palermo
Facoltà di Architettura
Via Maqueda, 175
Palermo 90133 **Italy**

Tel: +39-91/616-8425
Fax: +39-91/616-8136
Web: www.archlab.unipa.it

Riga Technical University
Faculty of Architecture
Azenes iela 16
LV-1048 Riga **Latvia**

Tel: +371-2/761-1969
Fax: +371-2/761-1969

VAA Kaunas Art Institute
Department of Architecture
Muitines Str.4
LT-3000 Kaunas **Lithuania**

Tel: +370-7/222-577
Fax: +370-7/222-693

Kaunas Technology University,
Faculty of Structure and Architecture
Department of Environment Design
and Architecture
Studenttu Str.48
03031 Kaunas **Lithuania**

Tel: +370-7/761-471
Fax: +370-7/765-960

Vilnius Academy of Arts
Department of Architecture
Maironio Str.6
02600 Vilnius **Lithuania**

Tel: +370-2/619-944

Vilnius Gedimino Technical University
Faculty of Architecture
Sauletekio, 11
02040 Vilnius **Lithuania**

Tel: +370-2/700-492
Fax: +370-2/700-498

University SS Kiril and Metodij
Faculty of Architecture
Bul. Partizanski Odredi, b.b.
91000 Skopje **Macedonia**

Tel: +389-9/111-6367
Fax: +389-9/111-6328

University of Malta
Faculty of Architecture & Civil Engineering
Msida **Malta**

Technical University of Moldova
Faculty of Urban Architecture
39 Bd. Dacia, Chisinau
MD-2060 **Moldova**

Amsterdamse Hogeschool voor de Kunsten
Academie van Bouwkunst
Waterlooplein 211
1011 PB Amsterdam **The Netherlands**

Tel: +31-20/622-0188
Fax: +31-20/623-2519

Academie van Bouwkunst
Onderlangs, 9
6812 CE Arnhem **The Netherlands**

Tel: +31-26/353-5604
Fax: +31-26/353-5677

Technische Universiteit Delft
Studierichting der Bowkunst
Postbus 5
2600 AA Delft **The Netherlands**

Tel: +31-15/278-4184
Fax: +31-15/278-4727

Technische Universiteit Eindhoven
Studierichting der Bouwkunst
Postbus 513
5600 MB Eindhoven **The Netherlands**

Tel: +31-40/247-9111
Fax: +31-40/245-2432

Academie van Bouwkunst
Ubbo Emmiusstraat, 30 A
9711 CC Groningen **The Netherlands**

Tel: +31-50/313-8047
Fax: +31-50/318-6083

Academie van Bouwkunst
Tongerstraat 49 A
6211 LM Maastricht **The Netherlands**

Tel: +31-43/321-9645
Fax: +31-43/325-2493

Hogeschool Rotterdam & Omstreken
Academie van Bouwkunst
Overblaak, 85
3001 MH Rotterdam **The Netherlands**

Tel: +31-10/413-0554
Fax: +31-10/433-1856

Hogeschool Katholieke Leergangen Tilburg
Academie van Bouwkunst
Prof. Cobbenhagenlaan, 205
5037 DB Tilburb **The Netherlands**

Tel: +31-13/535-5835
Fax: +31-13/463-8271

Bergen School of Architecture-BAS
Sandviksboder 59-61
N-5035 Bergen **Norway**

Tel: +47-5/531-4692
Fax: +47-5/531-9105
Email: bas@bgnett.no

The School of Architecture in Oslo-AHO
St. Olavsgt., 4 Box 6768-St. Olavs Pl.
N-0130 Oslo **Norway**

Tel: +47-22/997-000
Fax: +47-22/997-190
Web: www.aho.no

NTNU - Norwegian University of Science
and Technology
Fakultet for Arkitektur, Plan og Kunst
Gloshaugen
N-7034 Trondheim **Norway**

Tel: +47-73/595-000
Fax: +47-73/595-094

Akademia Sztuk Peiknych
Wydzial Architektury I Wzornictwa
Targ Weglowy 6
Gdansk 80-836 **Poland**

Academy of Fine Arts
Department of Interior Design
Ul. Humberta 3
Krakow 31-121 **Poland**

Technical University
Institute of Architecture and Town Planning
Aleja Politechniki 6
Lodz 93-590 **Poland**

Wydzial Projektowania Plastycznego
Panstowowa Wyzsza Szkola Sztuk Pieknych
Ul. Marcinkowskiego 29
Poznan 61-745 **Poland**

Wydzial Projektowania Plastycznego
Akademia Sztuk Pieknych
Krakowskie Przedmiescie 5
Warszawa 00-068 **Poland**

Politechniki Bialostockiej
Wydzial Architektury
Ul. Krakowska, 9
15 375 Bialystok **Poland**

Tel: +48-85/422-929
Fax: +48-85/422-929

Politechniki Gdanskiej
Wydzial Architektury
Ul. Narutowicza11/12
80 952 Gdansk **Poland**

Tel: +48-58/472-202
Fax: +48-58/472-223

Politechniki Slaskiej
Wyzdzial Architektury
Ul. Akademicka, 7
00044 Gliwice **Poland**

Tel: +48-32/371-210
Fax: +48-32/372-491

Politechniki Krakowskiej
Wydzial Architektury
Ul. Warszawska, 24
31 155 Krakow **Poland**

Tel: +48-12/335-453
Fax: +48-12/335-453

Politechniki Lodzkiej
Wydzial Budownictwa, Architektury i Inzynierii
Srodowiska
Al. Politechniki, 6
93 590 Lodz **Poland**

Tel: +48-42/368-664
Fax: +48-42/313-502

Politechniki Poznanskiej
Wydzial Budownictwa i Architektury
Piotrovo, 5
00061 Poznan **Poland**

Tel: +48-61/782-413
Fax: +48-61/782-444

Politechniki Szozecinskiej
Wydzial Budownictwa i Architektury
Al. Piastow, 50
70 311 Szczecin **Poland**

Tel: +48-91/494-865
Fax: +48-91/233-8642

Politechniki Warszawskiej
Wydzial Architektury
Ul. Koszykowa, 55
00 659 Warszawa **Poland**

Tel: +48-22/628-2887
Fax: +48-22/628-3236

Politechniki Wroclawskiej
Wydzial Architektury
Ul. B. Prusa, 53/55
50 317 Wroclaw **Poland**

Tel: +48-71/206-230
Fax: +48-71/212-448

Universidade de Coimbra - Faculdade de
Ciências e Tecnologias
Departamento de Arquitectura
03000 Coimbra **Portugal**

Tel: +351-39/29220
Fax: +351-39/29817

Faculdade de Arquitectura
Rua Professor Cid dos Santos
01300 Lisboa **Portugal**

Tel: +351-1/362-5128
Fax: +351-1/362-5138

Universidade Lusiada
Departamento de Arquitectura
R. da Junqueira, 190/198
01300 Lisboa **Portugal**

Tel: +351-1/363-9944
Fax: +351-1/363-8307

Faculdade de Arquitectura do Porto
Rua do Golgota, 215
03100 Porto **Portugal**

Tel: +351-2/600-2968
Fax: +351-2/600-2209

Escola Superioir Artística do Porto
Departamento de Arquitectura
Largo de S. Domingos, 63,2
04000 Porto **Portugal**

Tel: +351-2/200-1104
Fax: +351-2/208-6914

Escola de Arquitectura
Rua Lopo de Carvalho
04300 Porto **Portugal**

Tel: +351-2/483-384
Fax: +351-2/487-972

Escola de Arquitectura
Edifício Lapa
04760 Vila Nova de Famalicao **Portugal**

Tel: +351-52/312-867
Fax: +351-52/276-363

Grupal Scolar Industrial
Constructii Montaj Baia Mare
Strada Progresului No. 43
4800 Baia Mare **Romania**

Liceul Industrial 22
Str. Occidentului Nr. 12, Sector 1
Bucarest **Romania**

Scoala medie de Arhitectura
Strada Occidentului No. 10
Raion 30 Decembria Bucarest **Romania**

Centrul scolar de constructii
Strada Armata Rosio No. 74
Reguinea Cluj Cluj. **Romania**

Centrul scolar de constructii
Strada Dr. Victor Babes nr 11 Tg.
Mures, Reguinea Mures
Maghiara Autonmoa **Romania**

Centrul scolar de constructii
Strada Peltinisului nr 1
Reguinea Crisana Oradea **Romania**

Institutul de Arhitectura si Urbanism
Facultea de Arhitectura
Academiei Str. 18-20Sector 1
70109 Bucarest **Romania**

Tel: +40-1/615-5482
Fax: +40-1/312-3954

Universitatea Tehnica din Cluj
Facultea de Arhitectura din Cluj
Observatorului, 72-76
03400 Cluj-Napoca **Romania**

Tel: +40-64/191-812

Universitatea Tehnica "Gh.Asachi" Iasi
Facultea de Constructii si Arhitectura Sectia
de Arhitectura "G.M. Cantacuzino"
Bd. Mageron, 43
06600 Iasi **Romania**

Tel: +40-32/137-838
Fax: +40-32/211-667

Universitatea Politehnica din Timisoara
Facultea de Constructii Departamentul de Arhitectura
Traian Lalescu Str.,2A
01900 Timisoara **Romania**

Tel: +40-56/203-125
Fax: +40-56/193-110

Université Technique d'Altaï
Lénine 46
Barnaoul **Russia**

Belgorod State Technological Academy of
Build Materials
Kostynkov Str.46
308012 Belgorod **Russia**

Irkutsk State Polytechnical University
Lermontov Str. 83
664074 Irkoutsk **Russia**

Ivanovo Engineering-Construction Institute
8, Marta Str.20
153037 Ivanovo **Russia**

Kazan State Architectural Construction
Academy
Zelenaya Str., 1
420043 Kazan **Russia**
Khabarosk State Technical University
Tikhookeankoye sh., 136
680035 Khabarovsk **Russia**

Kostroma State Rural Institute
157930 Kostroma P/O Karavayevo **Russia**

Krasnojersk Engineering Construction Academy
Svobodniy pr. 82
660062 Krasnojarsk **Russia**

Académie de Métallurgie de Montagne de Magnitogorsk
Lénine, 38
455000 Magnitogorsk **Russia**

Moscow Architectural Institute
Rozhdestvenka Str. 11
103754 Moscow Russia
State University on Land use
Kasakov Str., 15
103064 Moscow **Russia**

Académie de Restauration
Gorodok Baoumana, 3-4
105037 Moscow **Russia**

Nizhegorodskaya Architectural Construction Academy
Ilyinskaya Str. 65
603600 Nizhniy Nougorod **Russia**

Nogorod State University
Bolshaya Petersburgkaya Str. 41
173610 Nougorod **Russia**

Novosibirsk Architectural Arts Academy
Krasniy pr. 38
630099 Novossibirsk **Russia**

Institut de l'Industrie d'Oukhta
Pervomayysk, 13
169400 (République de Comie) Oukhta
Russia

Penza State Architectural Construction Institute
Titov Str., 28
440028 Penza **Russia**

Rostov Architectural Institute
Budennovskiy Prosp., 39
344700/082 Rostov on don **Russia**

Samara Architectural Construction Academy
Molodogvardeiskaya Str. 19
443644 Samara **Russia**

Saratov State Technical University
Politechnical Str., 77
410016 Saratov **Russia**

Repin's Institute of Arts, Sculpture
and Architecture
Universitetskaya nab. 17
99034 St. Petersburg **Russia**

Petersburg State Architectural-Construction University
2-ya Krasnoarmeiskaya Str. 4
198005 St. Petersburg **Russia**

Université Technique de Tambov
Sovetskaya, 106
392620 Tambov **Russia**

Tchelyabinsk State Technical University
Lenin pr. 76
454044 Tchelyabinsk **Russia**

Tomsk Civil Architectural Construction
Academy
Solyanaya Sq., 2
634003 Tomsk **Russia**

Académie d'architecture et de construction
de Tumene
Lounatcharskogo, 2
625001 Tumene **Russia**

Ufa State Oil Technical University
Komarov Str., 1
450082 Ufa **Russia**

Ulianovsk State Technical University
Severniy Venetz, 32
432700 Ulianovsk **Russia**

Université Technologique de Caucasie
de Nord
Nicolaeva, 44
362021 Vladicaucasie **Russia**

Vladimirstate Technical University
Gorky Str.87
600026 Vladimir **Russia**

Dalnevostochniy Far East State Technical
University
Poushkin Str., 10
690600 Vladivostok **Russia**

Volgograd State Architectural Construction
Academy
Akadémitcheskaja Str., 1
400074 Volgograd **Russia**

Vologda Polytechnical Institute
Leninstr. 15
160008 Vologda **Russia**

Voronej Architectural Construction Academy
20-letiyae Oktjabrja, 84
394680 Voronezh **Russia**

Yaroslavl State Technical University
Moskovskiy pr.88
150053 Yaroslavl **Russia**

Ural Architectutral-Arts Academy
K. Liebknecht Str. 23
620219 GSP-1089 Yekaterinburg **Russia**

Slovenska Technika Univerzita
Fakulta Architektury
Námestie slobody, 19
81245 Bratislava **Slovak Republic**

Tel: +421-7/5727-6214 or 215
Fax: +421-7/5292-1533
Email: dekan@fa.stuba.sk
Web: www.fa.stuba.sk

Slovenska Technika Univerzita
Stavebna Fakulta
Radlinskeho, 11
81368 Bratislava **Slovak Republic**

Tel: +421-7/363-151
Fax: +421-7/367-027
Vysoka Skola Vytvarnych Umeni
Hviezdoslavovo nam.18
81437 Bratislava **Slovak Republic**

Tel: +421-7/533-2431
Fax: +421-7/533-2340
Email: slachta@vsvu.sanet.sk

Technika Univerzita
Stavebna Fakulta
Vysokoskolska, 4
04200 Kosice **Slovak Republic**

Tel: +421-95/632-2473
Fax: +421-95/623-3219

University of Ljubljana
Faculty for Architecture
Zoisova 12
01000 Ljubljana **Slovenia**

Tel: +386-61/126-4319
Fax: +386-61/125-7414
Email: dekanat@arh.uni-lj.si

Universidad de la Laguna
Escuela de Arquitectura
Av. De la Universidad s/n La Laguna
Gran Canaria **Spain**

Univ. de Santiago de Compostela
Escuela Tecnica Superior de Arquitectura
Plaza del Obradoiro, Palacio de San
Geronimo, s/n
Santiago de Compostela **Spain**

Escuela Técnica Superior de Arquitectura
Avenida Reina Mercedes s/n
41012 Sevilla **Spain**

Tel: +34-5/461-0878
Fax: +34-5/455-6534

Universidad Politecnica de Cataluna
Escuela Técnica Superior de Arquitectura
del Vallés
C/ Sitges s/n
08190San Cugat del Vallés Barcelona **Spain**

Tel: +34-3/401-7900
Fax: +34-3/401-7901

Escola Técnica Superior de Arquitectura
Diagonal 649
08028 Barcelona **Spain**

Tel: +34-3/401-6341
Fax: +34-3/334-3783
Web: www.upc.es

Escuela Técnica Superior de Arquitectura
C/ Rector Lopez Arguetta s/n
18001 Granada **Spain**

Tel: +34-58/244-345
Fax: +34-58/244-148

Escuela Técnica Superior de Arquitectura
Castro de Elvina s/n
15192 La Coruna **Spain**

Tel: +34-81/280-788
Fax: +34-81/295-965

Escuela Técnica Superior de Arquitectura
Campus Universitario de Tarifa
35017 Las Palmas de Gran Canaria **Spain**

Tel: +34-28/451-300
Fax: +34-28/451-378
Web: www.cda.ulpgc.es

Escuela Técnica Superior de Arquitectura
Avda. Juan de Herrera n 4
28040 Madrid **Spain**

Tel: +34-1/336-6550
Fax: +34-1/544-2481
Web: www.upm.es

Universidad de Navarra
Escuela Técnica Superior de Arquitectura
Campus Universitario
31080 Pamplona **Spain**

Tel: +34-48/425-600
Fax: +34-48/425-629

Universidad del Pais Vasco
Escuela Técnica Superior de Arquitectura
P de Onate, 2
20009 San Sebastian **Spain**

Tel: +34-43/218-466
Fax: +34-43/219-727
Web: www.sc.ehu.es

Escuela Técnica Superior de Arquitectura
Camino de Vera s/n
46022 Valencia **Spain**

Tel: +34-6/387-7110
Fax: +34-6/387-7119
Web: www.upv.es

Escuela Técnica Superior de Arquitectura
Carretera de Salamanca S/n
47014 Valladolid **Spain**

Tel: +34-83/423-428
Fax: +34-83/423-425
Web: www.uva.es

National Swedish Institute for
Building Research
Box 27163
Stockholm 27 10252 **Sweden**

Chalmers Tekniska Högskola
Arkitektursektionen
Sven Hultins Gata 6
S-412 96 Goteborg **Sweden**

Tel: +46-31/772-1000
Fax: +46-31/772-2485

Tekniska Högskola n i Lund
Arkitektursektionen
Sölvegatan, 24/ BOX 118
S-221 00 Lund **Sweden**

Tel: +46-46/222-0000
Fax: +46-46/222-3405

Kungliga Tekniska Högskolan (KTH)
Arkitekturskolan KTH
Ostermalmsgatan, 26
S-100 44 Stockholm **Sweden**

Tel: +46-8/790-8542
Fax: +46-8.790-8539
Email: school@arch.kth.se

Ecoles d'Ingenieurs de Bienne
Rockhall 1
Fauborg du Lac 103
2502 Bienne **Switzerland**

Ingenieurschule Burgdorf
Pestalozzistrasse, 20
3400 Burgdorf **Switzerland**

Scuola Tecnica Superiore (STS)
de Cantone Ticino
6952 Canobbio Lugano-Trevano **Switzerland**

Ingenieurschule Bern HTL
Höher Technische Lehranstalt
Morgartenstrasse, 2
Bern 3014 **Switzerland**

Tel: +41-31/335-5111
Fax: +41-31/333-0625

Ingenieurschule Biel (Ecoles d'Ingénieurs de Bienne)
Rockhall 1-Seevorstadt 103
Biel 2502 **Switzerland**

Tel: +41-32/273-111
Fax: +41-32/233-352

Ingenieurschule Burgdorf
Pestalozzistrasse, 20
Burgdorf 3400 **Switzerland**

Tel: +41-34/214-141
Fax: +41-34/231-513

Universita della Svizzera Italiana
Accademia di architettura
Villa Argentina, Largo Bernasconi 2
Mendrisio CH-6850 **Switzerland**

Abendtechnikum Chur
Ringstrasse 18
Chur 7000 **Switzerland**

Tel: +41-81/225-848

Ecole l'Ingénieurs de Fribourg
Ecole Technique Supérieure
4, Chemin du Musée
Fribourg 1700 **Switzerland**

Tel: +41-37/824-141

Ecole d'Ingénieurs de Genève
Ecole Technique Supérieure du soir
4, rue de la Prairie
Geneve 1202 **Switzerland**

Tel: +41-22/447-750

Université de Genève (EAUG)
Ecole d'Architecture
9 Boulevard Helvétique
Geneve 1205 **Switzerland**

Tel: +41-22/705-7144

Abendtechnikum der Innerschweiss-ATIS
Ingenieurschule HTL
Technikumstrasse, 6
Horw/ lu 6048 **Switzerland**

Tel: +41-41/340-1616
Fax: +41-41/340-7616

Zentralschweiss. Technicum Luzern
Ingenieurschule HTL
Technikumstrasse, 6
Horw/ lu 6048 **Switzerland**

Tel: +41-41/349-3311
Fax: +41-41/349-3960

Ecole Polytechnique Fédérale de Lausanne (EPFL)
Département d'Architecture
Dorigny
Lausanne 1015 **Switzerland**

Tel: +41-21/693-1111
Fax: +41-21/693-3229

Ingenieurschule Beider Basel (HTL)
Gründenstrasse, 40
Muttenz 4132 **Switzerland**

Tel: +41-61/467-4242
Fax: +41-61/467-4460

Ingenieurschule St. Gallen
Tellstrasse 2
St. Gallen 9000 **Switzerland**

Tel: +41-71/233-853

Ingenieurschule Brugg-Windish
Windish 5200 **Switzerland**

Tel: +41-56/416-363

Technikum Winterthur Ingenieurschule
Technikumstrasse 9
Winterthur 8401 **Switzerland**

Tel: +41-52/267-7171
Fax: +41-52/267-7231

Ingenieurschule Zürich HTL
Lagerstrasse 45 (Postadress: Postafacch
183, 8021 ZURICH)
Zurich 8004 **Switzerland**

Tel: +41-1/298-2522

Ecole Polytechnique Fédérale de Zürich (ETHZ)
Département d'Architecture
Hönggerberg
Zurich 8093 **Switzerland**

Tel: +41-1/633-1111

Trakya Universitesi
Faculty of Architecture
Edirne 21280 **Turkey**

Istanbul Technical University
Faculty of Architecture
Taskisla, Taksim
Istanbul 80191 **Turkey**

Yildiz Technical University
Faculty of Architecture
Istanbul Besiktas 80750
Turkey

Mimar Sinan Universitesi
Faculty of Architecture
Istanbul 80040 Findiliki
Turkey

Cukurova University
Faculty of Engineering & Architecture
Dept. of Architecture
Adana 01330 **Turkey**

Tel: +90-71/322-338-6084

Orta Dogu Teknik Universitesi
Faculty of Architecture
Ankara 06531 **Turkey**

Tel: +90-4/312-210-2203

Gazi Universitesi
Faculty of Engineering and Architecture
Ankara 06570 **Turkey**

Anadolu Universitesi
Faculty of Architecture
Eskisehir 26470 **Turkey**

Selcuk Universitesi
Faculty of Architecture
Konya 420580 **Turkey**

Ege Universitesi
Faculty of Engineering and Architecture
Dept. of Civil Engineering
Izmir Buca Cami Sokak 2 **Turkey**

Dokuz Eylul Universitesi
Sehitlor Cad. No. 12
35230 Alsancak
Izmir **Turkey**

Tel: +90-51/232-464-0500

S.U. Muhendisklik
Mimarlik Fakultesi
Konya **Turkey**

Ankara Devlet Muhendislik ve Mimarlik
Akademisi
Mimarlik Fakultesi
Ankara Maltepe **Turkey**

Balck Sea Technical University
Faculty of Civil Engineering and Architecture
61080 Trabzon **Turkey**

Pridniprovska State Academy of Building
and Architecture
Chernyshevsky Str. 24-A
320631 Dnipropetrovsk **Ukraine**

Tel: +380-562/452-372
Fax: +380-562/470-788

Kharkiv State Academy of Municipal Economy
Revolution Str. 12
310000 Kharkiv **Ukraine**

Tel: +380-572/422-162

Kharkiv State Technical University of Building
and Architecture
Sumska Str., 40
3100022 Kharkiv **Ukraine**

Tel: +380-572/433-812
Fax: +380-572/432-017

Kiev Academy of Arts
Smirnov-Lastochkina Str., 20
253053 Kiev **Ukraine**

Tel: +380-44/212-1540
Fax: +380-44/212-1948

Kiev State Technical University of Building
and Architecture
Povltroflotsky av., 31
252037 Kiev **Ukraine**

Tel: +380-44/276-5330

Lviv State University "Lviv's Politechnics"
Faculty of Landscape Architecture
121, S. Bandera Str.
290012 Lviv 13 **Ukraine**

Tel: +380-322/726-565
Fax: +380-322/724-733

Lviv Forestly Technical University
Faculty of Landscape Architecture
103, Pushkin Str.
290013 Lviv 13 **Ukraine**

Tel: +380-322/352-411

Donbass State Academy of Building
and Architecture 1, Derjavina Str.
339123 Makeevka 23 **Ukraine**

Tel: +380-623/290-2938

Odessa State Academy Building and Architecture
Ditrikhson Str., 4
270029 Odessa **Ukraine**

Poltava State Technical University
Pervomaysky Str., 24
314011 Poltava **Ukraine**

Tel: +380-532/273-327
Fax: +380-532/222-850

Crimea Institute of Environment and
Recreation Building
Faculty of Landascape Architecture
181, Kiev Str.
333000 The Cremia Symferopol **Ukraine**

Tel: +380-532/222-2459

Birmingham School of Architecture
Art & Design Centre, Corporation Street
B4 7BX Birmingham **United Kingdom**

College of Technology
Faculty of Engineering and Construction
Bell Street
DD1 4HT Dundee Scotland **United Kingdom**

Humberside College of Higher Education
School of Architecture
Strand Close
HU2 9BT Kingston Upon Hull **United Kingdom**

University of Humberside
School of Art, Architecture and Design
Queens Gardens
HU1 3DQ Hull **United Kingdom**

University of York
Institute of Advanced Architectural Studies
The King's Manor
YO1 2EP York **United Kingdom**

Robert Gordon University, Faculty of Design
Scott Sutherland School of Architecture
Garthdee Road
AB9 2QB Aberdeen Scotland **United Kingdom**

Tel: +44-1224/263-500
University of Bath
School of Architecture and Civil Engineering
BA2 7AY Bath **United Kingdom**

Tel: +44-1225/826-826

The Queen's University of Belfast
Department of Architecture & Planning
BT7 1NN Belfast **United Kingdom**

Tel: +44-1232/245-133

University of Central England in Birmingham,
Faculty of the Built Environment
Birmingham School of Architecture
Perry Barr
B42 2SU Birmingham **United Kingdom**

Tel: +44-121/331-5130

University of Brighton
School of Architecture and Interior Design
Mithras House-Lewes Road
BN2 4AT Brighton East Sussex
United Kingdom

Tel: +44-1273/642-349

University of Cambridge
Dept of Architecture
1 Scroope Terrace/Trumpington Street
CB2 1PX Cambridge **United Kingdom**

Tel: +44-1223/332-950

Kent Institute of Art & Design
Canterbury School of Architecture
New Dover Road
CT1 3AN Canterbury Kent **United Kingdom**

Tel: +44-1227/769-371

University of Wales, College of Cardiff
The Welsh School of Architecture
Bute Building - King Edward VII Avenue
CF1 3AP Cardiff **United Kingdom**

Tel: +44-1222/874-438

University of Greenwich
School of Architecture and Landscape
Dartford Campus - Oakfield Lane
DA1 2SZ Dartford Kent **United Kingdom**

Tel: +44-208/316-9100

SCHOOLS OF ARCHITECTURE WORLDWIDE

University of Dundee, Faculty of Duncan
of Jordanstone College
School of Architecture
13, Perth Road
DD1 4HT Dundee Scotland **United Kingdom**

Tel: +44-1382/345-315

University of Edinburgh
Dept of Architecture
20 Chambers Street
EH1 1JZ Edinburgh Scotland **United Kingdom**

Tel: +44-131/650-2306
Heriot-Watt University, Edinburgh College of Art
School of Architecture
Lauriston Place
EH3 9DF Edinburgh Scotland **United Kingdom**

Tel: +44-131/221-6071

University of Strathclyde
Dept of Architecture & Building Science
131 Rottenrow
G4 0NG Glasgow Scotland **United Kingdom**

Tel: +44-141/552-4400 ext.3023

University of Glasgow/The Glasgow School of Art
Department of ArchitectureThe Mackintosh School
167 Renfrew Street
G3 6RQ Glasgow Scotland **United Kingdom**

Tel: +44-141/353-4686

The University of Huddersfield Polytechnic
The Scool of Design Technology -
Dept of Architecture
Queensgate
HD1 3DH Huddersfield **United Kingdom**

Tel: +44-1484/472-289
University of Lincolnshire and Humberside
The Hull School of Architecture
Georges Street
HU1 38B Hull **United Kingdom**

Tel: +44-1482/440-550

School of Architecture
Knights Park
Surrey KT1 2QJ
Kingston University Kingston Upon Thames
United Kingdom

Tel: +44-181/547-2000

Leeds Metropolitan University
Faculty of Design and Built Environment
Brunswick Terrace
LS2 8BU Leeds Yorkshire **United Kingdom**

Tel: +44-113/283-2600 ext.4070

The Monfort University
School of Built Environment - Dept of Architecture
The Gateway
LE1 9BH Leicester **United Kingdom**

Tel: +44-116/257-7415

University of Liverpool
Liverpool School of Architecture & Building Enginering
Leverthulme Building-Abercrombie Square
L69 3BX Liverpool **United Kingdom**

Tel: +44-151/794-2604

Liverpool John Moores University
School of the Built Environment-Center for Architecture
98, Mount Pleasant
L3 5UZ Liverpool **United Kingdom**

Tel: +44-151/231-3704

Architectural Association
School of Architecture
34-36 Bedford Square
WC1B 3ES London **United Kingdom**

Tel: +44-207/636-0974

University of North London
School of Architecture and Interior Design
166-220 Holloway
N7 8DB London **United Kingdom**

Tel: +44-207/753-5042

South Bank University
School of Architecture and Civil Engineering
Wandsworth Road
SW8 2JZ London **United Kingdom**

Tel: +44-207/815-7102

University of East London,
Faculty of Design and Built Environment
School of Architecture
Holbrook Road
E15 3EA London **United Kingdom**

Tel: +44-208/590-7722
Royal College of Art
School of Architecture & Interior Design
Kensington Gore
SW7 2EU London **United Kingdom**

Tel: +44-207/584-5020

University College London
The Bartlett School of Architecture, Building,
Environmental Design and Planning
Wates House - 22 Gordon Street
WC1H 0QB London **United Kingdom**

Tel: +44-207/387-7050

The Prince of Wales's Institute of Architecture
14-15 Gloucester Gate, Regents Park
NW1 4HG London **United Kingdom**

Tel: +44-207/916-7380

The University of Westminster,
Faculty of the Environment
School of Architecture & Engineering
35 Marylebone Road
NW1 5LS London **United Kingdom**

Tel: +44-207/911-5000

The University of Luton,
Faculty of Design and Technology
Department of Built Environment
Park Square
LU1 3JU Luton **United Kingdom**

Tel: +44-158/234-111

University of Manchester
Schol of Architecture
M13 9PL Manchester **United Kingdom**

Tel: +44-161/275-9634

The Manchester Metropolitan University
Dept of Architecture
Loxford Tower
M15 6HA Manchester **United Kingdom**

Tel: +44-161/247-1103

University of Newcastle
Dept of Architecture
NE1 7RU Newcastle Upon Tyne
United Kingdom

Tel: +44-191/222-6000

University of Nottingham
The Nottingham School of Architecture
University Park
NG7 7RD Nottingham **United Kingdom**

Tel: +44-115/951-3155

Oxford Brookes University
School of Architecture
Gipsy Lane Campus - Headington
OX3 0BP Oxford **United Kingdom**

Tel: +44-1865/483-200

University of Plymouth
Plymouth School of Architecture
The Hoe Centre/ Notte Street
PL1 2AR Plymouth **United Kingdom**

Tel: +44-1752/233-600

University of Portsmouth
School of Architecture
King Henry I Street
PO1 2DY Portsmouth **United Kingdom**

Tel: +44-1705/842-083

University of Sheffield
School of Architecture
S10 2TN Sheffield **United Kingdom**

Tel: +44-114/276-8555

CARIBBEAN, MEXICO, CENTRAL & SOUTH AMERICA

Universidad de Buenos Aires
Facultad de Arquitectura y Urbanismo
Pabellon 3, Piso 3, Ciudad Universitaria
1428 Buenos Aires **Argentina**

Universidad de Palermo
Facultad de Arquitectura y Urbanismo
Soler 3686
1425 Buenos Aires **Argentina**

Universidad Argentina "John F. Kennedy"
Facultad de Arquitectura y Urbanismo
Zabala 1837/51
1037 Capital Federal **Argentina**

Universidad de Belgrano
Facultad de Arquitectura y Urbanismo
Zabala 1837 (1426)
Capital Federal **Argentina**
Universidad de Concepcion del Uruguay
Facultad de Arquitectura y Urbanismo
8 de Junio 522
(Entre Rios) 3260 Concepcion del Uruguay
Argentina

Universidad Catolica de Cordoba
Facultad de Arquitectura
Obispo Trejo 323
5000 Cordoba **Argentina**

Universidad Nacional de Cordoba
Facultad de Arquitectura y Urbanismo
Avenida Velez Sarsfield 264
5000 Cordoba **Argentina**

Universidad Nacional del Nordeste
Facultad de Arquitectura
25 de Mayo 868
3400 Corrientes **Argentina**

Universidad Catolica de La Plata
Facultad de Arquitectura
Diag. 73, Esq. 47
(Buenos Aires) 1900 La Plata **Argentina**

Universidad Nacional de La Plata
Facultad de Arquitectura y Urbanismo
Calle 47 y 117, Paseo del Bosque
(Buenos Aires) 1900 La Plata **Argentina**

Universidad Nacional de Mar del Plata
Facultad de Arquitectura y Urbanismo
Boulevard Juan B. Alberdi 2695, Funes 3250
(Buenos Aires) 7600 Mar del Plata
Argentina

Universidad de Mendoza
Facultad de Arquitectura y Urbanismo
Hammarskjold 750
5500 Mendoza **Argentina**

Universidad de Moron
Facultad de Arquitectura
Cabildo 134
(Buenos Aires) 1708 Moron **Argentina**

Universidad Nacional del Noredeste
Facultad de Arquitectura y Urbanismo
Avenida Las Heras 727
3500 Resistencia **Argentina**

Escuela de Arquitectura y Planeamiente
de Rosario
Avenida Pellegrini 250
(Santa Fe) Rosario **Argentina**

Universidad Nacional de Rosario
Facultad de Arquitectura,
Planeamiento y Diseno
Riobamba 220 bis
(Santa Fe) 2000 Rosario **Argentina**

Universidad Catolica de Salta
Facultad de Arquitectura y Urbanismo
Ciudad Univ. Campo Castanares
4400 Salta **Argentina**

Escuela de Arquitectura de San Juan
Jufre, Parque de Mayo
San Juan **Argentina**

Universidad Nacional de San Juan
Facultad de Arquitectura, Campo Universitario
Islas Malvinas
Av. Ignacio de la Roza 590, Rivadavia
5400 San Juan **Argentina**

Universidad Nacional de Tucuman
Facultad de Arquitectura y Urbanismo
c/c. 143
4000 San Miguel de Tucuman **Argentina**

Universidad Catolica de Santa Fe
Facultad de Arquitectura
Echague 7151
3000 Santa Fe **Argentina**

Universidad Nacional del Litoral
Facultad de Arquitectura, Diseno y Urbanismo
Boulevard Pellegrini 2947
3000 Santa Fe **Argentina**

Universidad Mayor de San Simon
Facultad de Arquitectura y Urbanismo
Calama Final Este, Casilla No. 992
Cochabamba **Bolivia**

Universidad Mayor de San Andres
Facultad de Arquitectura y Artes
Calle Heroes del Acre No. 1850,
Cajon Postal No. 1943
La Paz **Bolivia**

Universidad Privada de Santa Cruz de la Sierra
Facultad de Arquitectura y Urbanismo
Av. Paragua, 4to. Anillo, Casilla 2944
Santa Cruz de la Sierra **Bolivia**

Universidade de Alfenas
Rodovia MG 179 KMO Caixa Postal 23
37130-000 Alfenas **Brazil**

Tel: +55-35/922-2910
Fax: +55-35/921-4403

Universidade da Região da Campanha-URCAMP
Rua Tupy Silveira, 2099 Caixa Postal
141/Centro
96400-110 Bage **Brazil**

Tel: +55-532/422-244
Fax: +55-532/422-898

Faculdade de Arquitetura de Barra do Pirai
Km. 11, Rodovia Benjamin Ielpo/Caixa
Postal 82-828
27101-970 Barra do Pirai **Brazil**

Tel: +55-244/421-243

Faculdade de arquitetura, Artes e
Comunicação-UNESP
Av. Luis Edmundo Carrijo Coube s/n
17033-360 Bauru **Brazil**

Universidade Federal de Minas Gerais-UFMG
Escola de Arquitetura
Av.Antonio Carlos, 6627 Pampulha Campus
Universitario - Caixa Postal 1621
31270-900 Belo Horizonte **Brazil**

Tel: +55-31/441-1790
Fax: +55-31/491-1056
Faculdades Metodistas Integradas Izabela
Hendrix-FAMIH
Escola de Arquitetura
Rua da Bahia, 2020
30160-012 Belo Horizonte **Brazil**

Tel: +55-31/344-0977
Fax: +55-31/344-0467

Pontificia Universidade Catolica de Minas
Gerais-PUC/M
Escola de Arquitetura
Av.Dom Gaspar, 500 Caixa Postal 2686-
Coração Eucaristico
31270-900 Belo Horizonte **Brazil**

Tel: +55-31/319-1120
Fax: +55-31/319-1225

Universidade Federal do Para-UFPA
Departamento de Arquitetura
Rua Augusto Correia s/n Caixa Postal 459/
Guama
66075-110 Belem **Brazil**

Tel: +55-91/229-1108
Fax: +55-91/229-9677

União das Escolas Superiores
Departamento de Arquitetura
Av. Alcindo Cacela, 287/ Umarizal
66060-000 Belem **Brazil**

Universidade Regional de Blumenau
Rua António Veiga, 140 Caixa Postal
1507/ Vila Nova
89010-971 Blumenau **Brazil**

Tel: +55-47/322-8288
Fax: +55-47/322-8818

Universidade de Brasilia-UNB
Instituto de Arquitetura e Urbanismo
Campus Universitario-Asa Norte Caixa
Postal 15299
70910-900 Brasilia **Brazil**

Tel: +55-61/348-2200
Fax: +55-61/272-0003

Centro de Ensino Superior Prof. Plinio M. dos
Santos-CESUP
Rua Ceara 333Miguel Couto
79003-010 Campo Grande **Brazil**

Tel: +55-67/382-7660

Pontificia Universidade Catolica de Campinas-
PUCCAMP
Rodovia Dom Pedro I, KM 136 Caixa Postal 3217
13089-500 Campinas **Brazil**

Tel: +55-19/252-1995
Fax: +55-19/252-8477

Universidade Luterana do Brasil
Rua Miguel Tostes, 101 Caixa Postal
124/S.Luis
92420-280 Canoas **Brazil**

Tel: +55-51/472-5599
Fax: +55-51/476-5205
Universidade Federal do Parana-UFPR
Departmento de Arquitetura
Rua 15 Novembro, 1299 Caixa Postal
441/Centro
80060-000 Curitiba **Brazil**

Tel: +55-41/264-3571
Fax: +55-41/264-2243

Pontificia Universidade Catolica do
Parana-OUC/PR
Rue Imaculada Conceiçao 1155 Caixa
Postal 670/Prado Velho
80.000 PR - Prado Velho Curitiba **Brazil**

Tel: +55-41/322-1515
Fax: +55-41/226-1826

Universidade Federal do Ceara-UFC
Curso de Arquitetura e Urbanismo
Avenida da Universidade 2853 Caixa Postal
2600/Benfica Benfica
60000 Ce Fortaleza **Brazil**

Tel: +55-85/281-3011
Fax: +55-85/243-4746

Universidade Federal de Santa Catarina-UFSC
Curso de Arquitectura e Urbanismo
Campus Universitario Caixa Postal
476/Trindade
88040-900 Florianopolis **Brazil**

Tel: +55-48/231-9320
Fax: +55-48/234-4069

União das Faculdades Francanas-UNIFRAN
Anel Viario KM3-Campus Universitario Caixa
Postal 082
14400-000 Franca **Brazil**

Tel: +55-16/724-2211

Universidade Catolica de Goias-UCG
Departamento de Arquitetura
Av.a Universitaria, 1440 Caixa Postal
86/Setor Universitario
74605-010 Goiania **Brazil**

Tel: +55-62/227-1002
Fax: +55-62/224-3617

Universidade de Guarulhos-UNG
Praça Tereza Cristina 1 Caixa Postal
338/Centro
07023-070 Guarulhos **Brazil**

Tel: +55-11/209-9222
Fax: +55-11/940-1133

Universidade Federal da Paraiba-UFPb
Campus Universitario sn/Centro-Cidade
Universitaria
58059-900 Joao Pessoa **Brazil**

Tel: +55-83/224-7315
Fax: +55-83/225-1901

Centro de Estudos Superiores de Londrina
Rua Alagoas, 2050
86020-360 Londrina **Brazil**

Tel: +55-43/327-2150

Universidade estadual de Londrina-UEL
Rod.Celso Garcia CID/PR, 445 Km 379
Campus Universitario Caixa Postal 6001
86055-900 Londrina **Brazil**

Tel: +55-43/321-2000
Fax: +55-43/327-6932

Univerdidade de Mogi das Cruzes
Faculdade de Arquitetura
Av. Dr. Candido Xavier de Almeida Souza, 200
Centro Civico Caixa Postal 411
08780-911 Mogi das Cruzes **Brazil**

Tel: +55-11/469-5233
Fax: +55-11/469-5233

Univerdidade Braz Cubas-UBC
Faculdade de Arquitetura
Av. Francisco Rodrigues Filho, 1233 Caixa
Postal 511/Mogilar
08773-380 Mogi das Cruzes **Brazil**

Tel: +55-11/469-0291
Fax: +55-11/469-6043

Universidade Federal de Alagoas-UFAL
Departamento de Arquitetura
Campus Universitario A.C. Simões-Cidade
Universitaria/ Tabuleiro dos Martins
57072-340 Maceio **Brazil**

Tel: +55-82/322-2438
Fax: +55-82/322-2345

Universidade de Marilia-UNIMAR
Av. Higyno Muzzy Filho, 1001 Campus
Universitario
17525-902 Marilia **Brazil**

Tel: +55-144/338-088
Fax: +55-144/338-691

Universidade Federal do Rio Grande do Norte-UFRN
Curso de Arquitetura e Urbanismo
Campus Universitario KM1 DA BR/101
Caixa Postal 0143/ Lagoa Nova
59072-970 Natal **Brazil**

Tel: +55-84/231-1315
Fax: +55-84/215-3131

Universidade Federal Fluminense-UFF
Curso de Arquitetura e Urbanismo
Rua Miguel de Frias, 09/Icarai
24220-00 Niteroi **Brazil**

Tel: +55-21/717-8080 ext.221
Fax: +55-21/717-4553

Universidade Federal do Rio Grande do Sul-UFRGS
Faculdade de Arquitetura
Av. Paulo da Gama, 110 Farroupilha
90040-060 Porto Alegre **Brazil**

Tel: +55-51/228-1633
Fax: +55-51/227-2295

Faculdades Integradas Instituto Ritter reis-FIIRR
Rua Orfanatrofio, 555/Teresopolis
90840-440 Porto Alegre **Brazil**

Tel: +55-51/233-7166

Universidade Federal de Pelotas-UFPEL
Curso de Arquitetura e Urbanismo
Pr.Sete de Julho, 180 Caixa Postal 354
Campus Universitario
96020-010 Pelotas **Brazil**

Tel: +55-532/215-103
Fax: +55-532/215-023

Universidade Catolica de Pelotas-UCPEL
Curso de Arquitetura
Rua Felix da Cunha, 412 Caixa Postal
402/Centro
96010-900 Pelotas **Brazil**

Tel: +55-532/253-455
Fax: +55-532/253-105
Universidade Federal de Pernambuco-UFPE
Av.Prof.Moraes Rego, 1235 Campus
Universitario/Engenho do Meio
50670-901 Recife **Brazil**

Tel: +55-81/271-8001
Fax: +55-81/271-8029

Universidade Federal do Rio de Janeiro
Faculdade de Arquitetura e Urbanismo
Av. Brigadeiro Trompowsky s/n Cidade
Universitaria/Ilha do Fundão
21945-970 Rio de Janeiro **Brazil**

Tel: +55-21/260-7385
Fax: +55-21/260-7903

Instituto Metodista Bennett
Faculdade de Arquitetura
Rua Marquês de Abrantes, 55 Flamengo
22230-060 Rio de Janeiro **Brazil**

Tel: +55-21/281-1001
Fax: +55-21/205-9159

Faculdade s Integradas Silva e Souza
Rua Uranos 733/Olaria
21060-070 Rio de Janeiro **Brazil**

Tel: +55-21/260-8891

Universidade Santa Ursula
Rua Fernando Ferrari 75 Caixa Postal
16086/Botafogo
22231-040 Rio de Janeiro **Brazil**

Tel: +55-21/551-1949
Fax: +55-21/551-6446

Universidade Gama Filho
Depart. de Arquitetura e Urbanismo
Rua Manuel Vitorino 625-ZC 13 Piedade
20748-900 Rio de Janeiro **Brazil**

Tel: +55-21/594-1303
Fax: +55-21/289-8394

Faculdade de Arquitetura e Urbanismo
de Ribeirão Preto
Rua João Ramalho, 508
14085-420 Ribeirao Preto **Brazil**

Tel: +55-16/636-1010

Unidades Escolares da Instituição Moura
Lacerda-IML
Rua Padre Euclides, 995 Caixa Postal
757/Campos Elisios
14010-420 Ribeirao Preto **Brazil**

Tel: +55-16/636-1010

Univezrsidade do vale de Paraiba-UNIVAP
Pr. Candido Dias Castejon, 75 Centro
12245-720 Sao Jose dos Campos **Brazil**

Tel: +55-12/322-2355

Universidade do Vale do Rio dos Sinos-
UNISINOS
Curso de Arquitetura da
Av. Unisinos, 950 - Novo Campus Caixa
Postal 275/Cristo Rei
93020-000 Sao Leopoldo **Brazil**

Tel: +55-51/592-6333
Fax: +55-51/592-1035

Universidade S. Judas Tadeu-USJT
Rua Taquari, 546
03166-000 Sao Paulo **Brazil**

Tel: +55-11/948-1677

Universidade de Sao Paulo
Faculdade de Arquitetura e Urbanismo
Rua da Reitoria, 109 Caixa Postal
8191/Cidade Universitaria
05508-900 Sao Paulo **Brazil**

Tel: +55-11/212-6200
Fax: +55-11/815-5665

Universidade Mackenzie
Faculdade de Arquitetura
Rua Itambe, 45 Vila Clementino
01239-902 Sao Paulo **Brazil**

Tel: +55-11/256-6611
Fax: +55-11/255-2588

Faculdade de Engenharia da Fundação A.
Penteado-FAAP
Rua Alagoas 903 Cidade Universitaria
01242-001 Sao Paulo **Brazil**

Tel: +55-11/824-0233

Faculdade de Belas Artes de São Paulo
Rua Dr. Alvaro Alvim, 766 Vila Mariana
04018-010 Sao Paulo **Brazil**

Tel: +55-11/549-7122

Universidade Estadual Julio de Mesquita
Filho-UNESP
Praça da Sé, 108, 5 Andar Caixa Postal
30919/Centro
01001-900 Sao Paulo **Brazil**

Tel: +55-11/327-171
Fax: +55-11/361-870

Universidade Federal da Bahia-UFBA
Faculdade de Arquitetura
Rua Augusto Viana s/n Canela
40110-060 Salvador **Brazil**

Tel: +55-71/245-9002
Fax: +55-71/245-2460

Universidade Catolica de Santos
Rua Euclides da Cunha, 241 José Menino
11065-101 Santos **Brazil**

Tel: +55-13/237-9396
Fax: +55-13/237-2149

Universidade de Taubate-UNITAU
Rua 4 de Março, 432 Centro
12020-270 Taubate **Brazil**

Tel: +55-122/322-929
Fax: +55-122/327-660

Universidade de Uberaba-UNIUBE
Av. Guilherme Ferreira, 217 Cidade
Universitária
38010-200 Uberaba **Brazil**

Tel: +55-34/332-3322

Universidade Federal de Viçosa-UFV
Avenida Peter Henry Rolfs s/n Caixa Postal
384 Campus Universitario
36570-000 Vicosa **Brazil**

Tel: +55-31/899-2100
Fax: +55-31/891-1903

Universidade Federal do Espirito Santo-UFES
Av. fernando Ferrari s/nCampus Universitario
de Goiabeiras
29060-900 Vitoria **Brazil**

Tel: +55-27/335-2200
Fax: +55-27/335-2244

Universidad los Lagos
Av. Hollstein 03
Osorno **Chile**

Tel: +56-64/233-236
Fax: +56-64/233-236

Universidad Catolica del Norte
Av. Angamos 0610
Antofagasta **Chile**

Tel: +56-55/241-148
Fax: +56-55/241-724

Universidad del Bio-bio
Avenida Collao no.1202
Concepcion **Chile**

Tel: +56-41/314-364
Fax: +56-41/313-897

Universidad Concepción
Victor Lamas, 1290
Concepcion **Chile**

Tel: +56-41/234-985
Fax: +56-41/240-280

Universidad Desarollo
Arvillo 456
Concepcion **Chile**

Tel: +56-41/242-549

Universidad La Serena
Benavente 980
La Serena **Chile**

Tel: +56-51/226-080

Universidad Central
Casilla 6-D
Santiago **Chile**

Tel: +56-2/527-0323
Fax: +56-2/527-3078

Universidad de Chile
Marcoleta 250
Santiago **Chile**

Tel: +56-2/678-3080
Fax: +56-2/222-9522

Pontificia Universidad Catolica
El Comendador 1916
Santiago **Chile**

Tel: +56-2/232-5057
Fax: +56-2/232-2571

Universidad Finia Terrae
Av. Pedro de Valdivia, 1543
Santiago **Chile**

Tel: +56-2/341-5351
Fax: +56-2/441-5358

Universidad Nacional Andres Bello
Fernandez Concha, 700
Santiago **Chile**

Tel: +56-2/215-1790

Universidad de Santiago
Alameda 3363
Santiago **Chile**

Tel: +56-2/776-1457
Fax: +56-2/779-2732

Universidad Mayor
Portugal 351
Santiago **Chile**

Tel: +56-2/222-2645
Fax: +56-2/222-3836

Universidad UNIACC
Avda. Salvador
Santiago **Chile**

Tel: +56-2/204-3116
Fax: +56-2/204-3116

Universidad de la République
Santo Domingo 1431
Santiago **Chile**

Tel: +56-2/697-2272
Fax: +56-2/697-2445

Universidad Arcis
Huérfanos 1710
Santiago **Chile**

Tel: +56-2/695-5238
Fax: +56-2/697-4023

Universidad Autonoma
Porvenir 580
Temuco **Chile**

Tel: +56-45/245-897
Fax: +56-45/245-897

Universidad de Temuco
Av. Alemania esq. Dr. Carrilho
Temuco **Chile**

Tel: +56-45/235-673
Fax: +56-45/215-252

Universidad del Valparaíso
Parque Alejo Barrios
Valparaiso **Chile**

Tel: +56-32/281-166
Fax: +56-32/234-050

Universidad Tecnica Santa Maria
Avda. Espana 1680
Valparaiso **Chile**

Tel: +56-32/797-499

Universidad Catolica de Valparaíso
Av. Matta, 12 - Recreo
Vina del Mar **Chile**

Tel: +56-32/660-443
Fax: +56-32/212-7446

Universidad de Vina del Mar
Diego Portales, 90
Vina del Mar **Chile**

Tel: +56-32/663-319

Universidad Marítima de Chile
Alvarez, 2138
Vina del Mar **Chile**

Tel: +56-32/670-264
Fax: +56-32/670-148

Universidad de Los Andes
Facultad de Arquitectura
Cra. 1a. E. # 18 A/10
D.E. Bogota **Colombia**

Tel: +57-91/234-5913
Fax: +57-91/284-1890

Universidad Antonio Narino
Facultad de Arquitectura
Calle 58A # 37-18
Bogota **Colombia**

Tel: +57-91/221-3913
Fax: +57-91/221-1204

Universidad Jorge Tadeo Lozano-Bogota
Facultad de Arquitectura Diseno de Interiores
Calle 23 # 4-47 Of.427, Bloque 1
Bogota **Colombia**

Tel: +57-91/334-1777
Fax: +57-91/282-6197
Universidad de América
Facultad de Arquitectura
Avda Circunvalar #20-53
D.E. Bogota **Colombia**

Tel: +57-91/281-9603
Fax: +57-91/243-6672

Universidad Catolica de Colombia
Facultad de Arquitectura
Diag. 47 no.15-68
D.E. Bogota **Colombia**

Tel: +57-91/285-3770
Fax: +57-91/285-8895

Universidad de la Gran Colombia
Facultad de Arquitectura
Carrera 5 #13-39 - Piso 2
D.E. Bogota **Colombia**

Tel: +57-91/286-8200
Fax: +57-91/282-8386

Universidad Javeriana
Facultad de Arquitectura
Carrera 7#40-62
Bogota **Colombia**

Tel: +57-91/338-4547
Fax: +57-91/287-2167

Universidad Nacional de Colombia
Facultad de Arquitectura
Calle 45, Cra. 30
D.E. Bogota **Colombia**

Tel: +57-91/368-1557
Fax: +57-91/368-1551

Universidad Piloto de Colombia
Facultad de Arquitectura
Calle 9 # 45A44
D.E. Bogota **Colombia**

Tel: +57-91/285-5753
Fax: +57-91/285-8471
Universidad de la Salle
Facultad de Arquitectura
Calle 11, no.1-47
D.E. Bogota **Colombia**

Tel: +57-91/282-9641
Fax: +57-91/286-8391

Universidad del Atlantico
Facultad de Arquitectura
Carrera 43 # 50/53
Barranquilla **Colombia**

Universidad Autonoma del Caribe
Facultad de Arquitectura
Calle 90 #46-112
Barranquilla **Colombia**

Corporacion Universitaira de la Costa
Facultad de Arquitectura
Calle 58 #55-66
Barranquilla **Colombia**

Universidad Santo Tomas
Facultad de Arquitectura
Kil 6 Autopista Florida Blanca Ed. Fray
Angelico
Bucaramanga **Colombia**

Tel: +57-976/380-844
Fax: +57-976/352-569

Universidad del Valle Facultad de Artes
Integradas
Ecole d'Architecture
Ciudad Universitaria, Ed.380, Piso 4
Cali **Colombia**

Tel: +57-92/339-1181

Universidad San Buenaventura
Facultad de Arquitectura
La Umbria
Cali **Colombia**

Tel: +57-92/555-2007
Fax: +57-92/555-2006
Email: usb@mafalda.univalle.edu.co

Universidad Jorge Tadeo Lozano
Facultad de Arquitectura
Cra. 4a no. 38-40
Cartagena **Colombia**

Tel: +57-956/647-400
Fax: +57-956/644-714

Corporacíon Universitaria del Sinu
Facultad de Arquitectura
Cra. 3a #29-26
Monteria **Colombia**

Tel: +57-947/840-164
Fax: +57-947/840-677

Universidad Nacional de Colombia
Facultad de Arquitectura e Ingenieria
El Cable
Manizales **Colombia**

Universidad Nacional de Colombia
Facultad de Arquitectura
Autopista Norte Blq. 24
Medellin **Colombia**

Tel: +57-94/2301-0100
Fax: +57-94/230-9630

Universidad Pontificia Bolivariana
Facultad de Arquitectura
Avenida Nutibara #70-20
Medellin **Colombia**

Tel: +57-94/415-9070
Fax: +57-94/411-2372

Fundacion Universitaria de Popayan
Facultad de Arquitectura
Calle 5a # 7-78
Popayan **Colombia**

Tel: +57-928/241-835
Fax: +57-928/221-920

Universidad del Diseno
Facultad de Arquitectura
Apartado 1775-2050 Montes de Oca
San Jose **Costa Rica**

Tel: +506/234-7290
Fax: +506/234-9308
Email: unidis@sol.racsa.co.cr

Universidad Veritas
Escuela de Arquitectura
Rotonda de Zapote Ruta Periférica Apartado
Postal 1380-1000
San Jose **Costa Rica**

Tel: +506/234-0482
Fax: +506/253-1345
Email: veritas@sol.racsa.co.cr

Universidad de Costa Rica
Escuela de Arquitectura
San Pedro de Montes de Oca
San Jose **Costa Rica**

Tel: +506/207-4371
Fax: +506/224-3784

Universidad de las Ciencias y el Arte de
Costa Rica
Barrio Lujan, 50 Norte, 50 Este del Depósito
de Materiales Barrio Lujan
San Jose **Costa Rica**

Tel: +506/257-8814
Fax: +506/221-3475
Email: unicacsa@sol.racsa.co.cr

Universidad Autonoma de Centro America
Stvdivm Genrale Costarricense
Calle 22, Ave.11-13, Apartado 7651-1000
San Jose **Costa Rica**

Tel: +506/223-6766
Fax: +506/222-6528

Universidad de Camaguey
Facultad de Construcciones
Carretera de Circunvalacion, KM 5 1/2
Camaguey **Cuba**

Tel: +53-3/226-1019
Fax: +53-3/226-1126

Instituto Superior Politecnico
"José Antonio Echevarría"
Facultad de Arquitectura
Marianao 19390
La Habana **Cuba**

Tel: +53-7/206-997
Fax: +53-7/277-129
Email: arquitectura@cujae.ispjae.edu.cu

Universidad Central de las Villas
Facultad de Construcciones
Carretera de Camajuani, KM 5 1/2
Santa Clara-Villaclara **Cuba**

Tel: +53-4/228-1561
Fax: +53-4/222-2113

Instituto Superior Politecnico
"Julio Antonio Mella"
Facultad de Construcciones
Santiago de Cuba **Cuba**

Tel: +53-2/263-2689

Universidad Aut. de Santo Domingo
Facultad de Arquitectura
Santo Domingo **Dominican Republic**

Universidad de Cuenca
Facultad de Arquitectura
Av. 12 de AbrilApartado 158
Cuenca **Ecuador**

Tel: +593-7/811-325
Fax: +593-7/880-625

Universidad Catolica Santiago de Guayaquil
Facultad de Arquitectura
KM 1 1/2 Avenida Carlos Julio
ArosemaApartado 09-01-4671
Guayaquil **Ecuador**

Tel: +593-4/200-801
Fax: +593-4/200-071

Universidad Laica Vicente Rocafuerte
de Guayaquil
Facultad de Arquitectura
Av. de las Americas s/n Fente a la Polícia
Guayaquil **Ecuador**

Tel: +593-4/371-563

Universidad Estatal de Guayaquil
Facultad de Arquitectura
Ciudadela Universitaria
Guayaquil **Ecuador**

Tel: +593-7/293-086
Fax: +593-7/397-071

Universidad Particular de Loja
Facultad de Arquitectura
San Cayetano, Apartado 508
Loja **Ecuador**

Tel: +593-7/570-275
Fax: +593-7/563-159

Universidad Eloy Alfaro de Manabi
Facultad de Arquitectura
Via San Mateo
Manta **Ecuador**

Tel: +593-6/622-919
Fax: +593-6/623-214

Universidad Central del Ecuador
Facultad de Arquitectura y Urbanismo
Ciudadela Universitaria
Quito **Ecuador**

Tel: +593-2/229-537
Fax: +593-2/524-320

Universidad Catolica del Ecuador
Facultad de Arquitectura y Diseno
Av. 12 de Octubre y Carrión, Apartado 2184
Quito **Ecuador**

Tel: +593-2/509-885
Fax: +593-2/509-587
Universidad San Francisco de Quito
Facultad de Arquitectura y Arte
Campus.CumbayáApartado 17-120841
Quito **Ecuador**

Tel: +593-2/895-723
Fax: +593-2/890-070

Universidad Internacional Sek
Facultad de Arquitectura
Campus Juan Montalvo, Guapulo
Quito **Ecuador**

Tel: +593-2/223-688
Fax: +593-2/225-972

Universidad Escuela Politecnica Javeriana
del Ecuador
Facultad de diseno e Ingenieria
Quito **Ecuador**

Tel: +593-2/565-504
Fax: +593-2/500-563

Universidad de El Salvador
Escuela de Arquitectura
San Salvador **El Salvador**

Univ. Francisco Marroquin
Facultad de Arquitectura
6ta. Calle Final, Zona 10
Ciudad de Guatemala **Guatemala**

Universidad Mariano Galvez
Facultad de Arquitectura
3a Av. 9-00, Zona 2
01002 **Guatemala**

Universidad Rafael Landivar
Facultad de Arquitectura
Campus Vista Hermosa 111, Zona 16
01016 **Guatemala**

Univ. de San Carlos de Guatemala
Facultad de Ingeniera
Ciudad Universitaria
00012 **Guatemala**

Universite de Haiti
Ecole Polytechnique d'Haiti
Port au Prince **Haiti**

College of Arts, Science, & Technology (CAST)
Caribbean School of Architecture
237 Old Hope Road
Kingston 6 **Jamaica**

University of the West Indies
Faculty of Engineering
Kingston 7 Mona **Jamaica**

Universidad Autonoma de Aguascalientes
Centro Tecnologico
Av. Universidad 902 Edif. 10 C.P.
2100/Ciudad Universitaria
Aguascalientes **Mexico**

Tel: +52-49/123-284
Fax: +52-49/123-284

Universidad Autonoma Metropolitana Azcapotzalco
Division de Ciencias y Artes para el Diseno
Escuela Mexicana de Arquitectura
Av. San Pedro no. 180 - col. Reynosa
Tamaulipas
Mexique D.F. 02200 Azcapotzalco **Mexico**

Tel: +52- 5/382-4332 / 724 4345

Instituto Tecnologico de Campeche
Departamento de Ciencias de la Tierra
Carretera Campeche - Escarcega KM. 9
Campeche C.P. 24500 Campeche **Mexico**

Tel: +52- 981/20033
Fax: +52- 981/20224

Instituto Celayense
Escuela Superior de Diseno y Arquitectura
Paseo del Bajeo y Magnolia - col. Jardines
de Celaya
Guanajuato C.P. 38080 Celaya **Mexico**

Instituto Tecnologico de Chetumal
Carrera de Arquitectura
Quintana Roo Chetumal **Mexico**

Universidad Autonoma de Chihuahua
Escuela de Arquitectura de Chihuahua
Av. Instituto Politecnico Nacional no. 2710 -
Fracc. Quintas del Sol
Chic. C.P. 31250 Chihuahua **Mexico**

Tel: +52-14/110-919

Universidad Autonoma de Guerrero
Escuela Superior de Arquitectura
y Urbanismo
Av. Juarez s/n - col. Santa Cruz
Guerrero C.P. 39000 Chilpancingo **Mexico**

Tel: +52-74/726-143 or 720 584

Universidad de las Americas, Puebla
Departamento de Arquitectura e Interiores
Exhacienda Santa Catarina Martir - a.p. 100
C.P. 72820 Cholula Puebla **Mexico**

Instituto de Ingenieria y Arquitectura
Universidad Autonoma de Ciudad Juarez
Escuela de Arquitectura
Av. del charro No. 610 Norte
Chihuahua Ciudad Juarez Chihuahua **Mexico**

Tel: +52-16/171-312 or 178 374
Fax: +52-16/175-759

Universidad Autonoma de Colima
Facultad de Arquitectura
Campus Universitario - KM 9 Carretera
Colima
Colima C.P. 28400 Coquimatlan **Mexico**

Tel: +52-33/230-330

Universidad Veracruzana-unidad Cordova
Facultad de Arquitectura
Exhacienda San Francisco Tuxpan
Veracruz A.P. 2358 Cordoba **Mexico**

Tel: +52-27/142-313
Universidad la Salle Cuernavaca
Escuela de Arquitectura y Diseno Grafico
Nicolas Bravo Esq. Nueva Inglaterra - Col.
San Cristobal
Morelos Cuernavaca **Mexico**

Tel: +52-73/115-525
Fax: +52-73/113-528

Universidad Autonoma del Estado de Morelos
Facultad de Arquitectura
Av. Universidad no. 1001 - colo. Chamilpa
Morelos C.P. 62000 Cuernavaca **Mexico**

Tel: +52-73/112-288 ext.4546

Universidad Juarez Autonoma de Tabasco
Division Academica de Ingenierea y Tecnologea
KM 1 Carretera Cunduacan - Xalpa /col.
Unidad Chontal
Tabasco Cunduacan **Mexico**

Instituto Superior de Ciencias y Tecnologia
de la Laguna A.C.
Escuela de Arquitectura
Canatlan No. 150 - Parque Industrial Lagunero
Durango C.P. 35078 Gimez Palacio **Mexico**

Tel: +52-17/502-113
Fax: +52-17/502-049 ext.110

Universidad Autonoma de Guadalajara
Artes y Humanidades
Extremo Norte Calzada Independencia -
Fracc. Huentitlan a.p. 1-1429 Central
Jalisco C.P. 44100 Guadalajara **Mexico**

Tel: +52-3/674-6166 or 638 1497
Fax: +52-3/674 4755

Instituto Superior de Estudios Superiores de
Occidente Iteso
Escuela de Arquitectura
Fuego no. 1031 - col. Jardines del Bosque
Jalisco Guadalajara **Mexico**

Tel: +52-3/684-1079

Universidad del Valle de Atemajac
Escuela de Ingenierea y Arquitectura
Av. Tepeyac no. 4800
Jalisco Guadalajara **Mexico**

Tel: +52-3/622-1283 or 622 1287
Fax: +52-3/550-8772

Universidad de Guanajuato
Facultad de Arquitectura
Mendizabal 19-b
Guanajuato C.P. 36000 Guanajuato **Mexico**

Tel: +52-47/321-185 or 321-990 ext.109
Fax: +52-47/323-241

ITESM Campus Sonora Norte
Departamento de Arquitectura
Carretera internacional Hermosillo,
Nogales/KM 9 a.p. 216
Sonora C.P. 83000 Hermosillo **Mexico**

Universidad Anahuac
Escuela de Arquitectura
Av. Lomas Anahuac
Estado de Mexique Huixquilucan **Mexico**

Universidad Iberoamericana Plantel Lein
Carrera de Arquitectura
Libramiento Norte s/n a.p. 26
C.P. 37000 Leon Guanajuato **Mexico**

Tel: +52-47/169-898 or 113-860 or
115-477 ext.107
Fax: +52-47/323-241

Universidad del Bajeo, A.C.
Facultad de Arquitectura
Av. Universidad s/n y Cerro Gordo -a.p. 444,
col. Lomas del Campestre
C.P. 37150 Leon Guanajuato **Mexico**

Tel: +52-47/171-707 or 171-740 ext.27
Fax: +52-47/185-511

Instituto Tecnologico de los Mochis
Ciencias de la Tierra, Escuela de Arquitectura
Blvd. Batiz y 20 de Noviembre col. Centro
Sinaloa C.P. 81200 Los Mochis **Mexico**

Tel: +52-681/25858 orr 25959
Fax: +52-681/50326

Universidad Autonoma de Yucatan
Facultad de Arquitectura
Exconvento de la Mejorada Calle 50 entre 57
y 59 s/n
Yucatan C.P. 97000 Merida **Mexico**

Tel: +52-99/285-215 or 249 012
Fax: +52-99/241-300

Universidad Autonoma de Baja California
Facultad de Arquitectura
Blvd. Benito Juarez s/n - Unidad
Universitaria
Baja California c.p. 21900 Mexicali **Mexico**

Tel: +52-65/664-250

Universidad Anahuac del Sur
Escuela de Arquitectura
Torre No. 131 - Colonia Olivar de los Padres
D.F. 01780 Mexique **Mexico**

Tel: +52-5/683-1100 ext.177 or 199

Universidad Intercontinental
Escuela de Arquitectura
Av. Insurgentes Sur No. 4135 - Colonia
Santa Ursula Xitle
D.F. 14000 Mexique **Mexico**

Tel: +52-5/573-8544 ext.1400

Universidad Nacional Autonoma de Mexique
Facultad de Arquitectura
Ciudad Universitaria, Circuito Interior -fracc.
Coyoacan
D.F. 04510 Mexique **Mexico**

Tel: +52-5/622-1283 or 622 1287
Fax: +52-5/550-8772

Universidad Del Tepeyac
Escuela de Arquitectura
Av. Callao no. 842 - col. Lindavista
D.F. 07300 Mexique **Mexico**

Tel: +52-5/781-4033 or 750-0744 ext.248

Universidad la Salle
Escuela Mexicana de Arquitectura
Benjamin Franklin no. 47 - col. Escandin
D.F. 11800 Mexique **Mexico**

Tel: +52-5/515-5225
Fax: +52-5/271-8585

Universidad Iberoamericana
Departamento de Diseno
Prolongacion Paseo de la Reforma n. 880 -
col. Lomas de Santa Fe
D.F. 01210 Mexique **Mexico**

Tel: +52-5/292-3516
Fax: +52-5/271-8585

Universidad Autonoma Metropolitana Azcapotzalco
Division de Ciencias y Artes del Diseno u.
Xochimilco
Carrera de Arquitectura
Calzada del Hueso no. 110 edif. I, 2o. Piso
D.F. 07300 Mexique **Mexico**

Tel: +52-5/724-5128 or 724-5129
Fax: +52-5/723-5516

ITESM - Universidad Automa de Nuevo Lein
Departamento de Arquitectura
Sucursal de Correos
Nuevo Lein C.P. 64849 Monterrey **Mexico**

Tel: +52-5/724-5128 or 724-5129
Fax: +52-5/723-5516

Universidad Regiomontana
Division de Ingenieria y Arquitectura
15 de Mayo Poniente no. 567
Nuevo Lein C.P. 64000 Monterrey **Mexico**

Tel: +52-8/340-2729
Universidad Michoacana de San Nicolas de
Hidalgo
Escuela de Arquitectura
Edificio PI Ciudad Universitaria - A.P. 17 G
Michoacan C.P. 58120 Morelia **Mexico**

Tel: +52-43/167-148
Fax: +52-43/167-148

Escuela Nacional de Estudios
Profesionales Acatlan
Division de Diseno y Edificacion
Av. Alcanfores y San Juan Totol Tepec -col.
Santa Cruz Acatlan
Estado de Mexique Naucalpan **Mexico**

Tel: +52-5/623-1727

Instituto Politecnico Nacional -
Unidad Tecamachalco
Escuela Superior de Ingenierea y Arquitectura
Fuente de los Leones No. 28 - Fracc.
Tecamachalco
Estado de Mexique C.P. 56500 Naucalpan
Mexico

Escuela Nacional de Estudios Profesionales, Aragin
Carrera de Arquitectura
Unam Rancho Seco s/n Fracc. Bosques de
Aragin
Estado de Mexique C.P. 57170 Nezahualcoyotl
Mexico

Universidad Autonoma Benito Juarez de Oaxaca
Escuela de Arquitectura
Ejido ex-hacienda 5 Seniores
Oaxaca C.P. 68000 Oaxaca **Mexico**

Tel: +52-951/47718 or 65344 ext.123

Instituto Tecnologico de Pachuca
Escuela de Arquitectura
Carretera Mexique - Pachica KM 87.5
Hidalgo Pachuca **Mexico**

Tel: +52-771/13596
Fax: +52-771/13399

Universidad Veracruzana, Unidad Poza Rica
Facultad de Arquitectura
Carretera Poza Riza - Papantla/col.
Haliburton
Veracruz A.P. 1102 Poza Rica **Mexico**

Tel: +52-782/31515
Fax: +52-782/31515

Universidad Iberoamericana Golfo - Centro
Facultad de Arquitectura
KM 3.5 Carretera Federal - col. Puebla,
Atlixco
Puebla **Mexico**

Tel: +52-22/304-448
Fax: +52-22/310-838

Universidad Popular Autonoma del Estado
de Puebla
Facultad de Arquitectura
Av. 21 sur no. 1103
Puebla C.P. 72000 Puebla **Mexico**

Tel: +52-22/320-266
Fax: +52-22/325-251

Instituto Tecnologico de Queretaro
Ciencias de la Tierra de la Carrera
de Arquitectura
Jose Martenez Juarez 1-6 /Apartado Postal
no. 493 /col. Hercules
Queretaro C.P. 76209 Queretaro **Mexico**

Tel: +52-42/163-099 or 163-728

Universidad del Valle de Mexique,
Campus Queretaro
Carrera de Arquitectura
Blvd. Villas de Mesin s/n - fracc. Provincia
Juriquilla
Queretaro C.P. 76000 Queretaro **Mexico**

Itesm Campus Queretaro
Carrera del Departamento de Arquitectura
Henry Ford no. 10/col. Parques Industriales
Queretaro C.P. 76100 Queretaro **Mexico**

Tel: +52-42/110-013 ext.147
Fax: +52-42/173-763

Universidad Autonoma de Coahuila -
Unidad Saltillo
Facultad de Arquitectura
Unidad Campo Redondo Edif. "F"
Coahuila C.P. 25020 Saltillo **Mexico**

Tel: +52-841/28538
Fax: +52-841/285-38

Universidad Autonoma de San Luis Potose
Escuela del Habitat - Carrera de Arquitectura
Av. Salvador Nava y Nino Artillero/Fracc.
Zona Universitaria
San Luis Potose C.P. 78240 San Luis Potose
Mexico

Universidad Autonoma de Nuevo Lein
Facultad de Arquitectura
Pedro de Alba s/n Ciudad Universitaria -
A.P. 4 Sucursal Fi
Nuevo Lein C.P. 66451 San Nicolas de las
Garzas **Mexico**

Tel: +52-8/376-2600 or 376-6237
Fax: +52-8/376-4635

Universidad de Monterrey
Division de Arte Diseno y Ciencias del Medio
Morones Prieto 4500 pte.
Nuevo Lein San Pedro Garza Garcea **Mexico**

Tel: +52-8/338-5050
Fax: +52-8/338-5619

Universidad Autonoma de Tamaulipas
Facultad de Arquitectura
Centro Universitario Tampico Madero/Fracc.
Tamaulipas, Madero
Tamaulipas C.P. 89600 Tampico **Mexico**

Tel: +52-12/270-000 ext.3350 or 3351

Instituto Tecnologico de Tijuana
Carrera de Arquitectura
Calz. Tecnoligico s/n - Frac. Tomas Aquino
Baja California C.P. 22000 Tijuana **Mexico**

Tel: +52-66/234-045

Universidad Iberoamericana
Escuela de Arquitectura
Blvd. C. Universitario No. 2000/Frac. Playas
de Tijuana
Baja California C.P. 22200 Tijuana **Mexico**

Tel: +52-66/301-577
Fax: +52-66/301-591

Universidad Autonoma del Estado de Mexique
Facultad de Arquitectura y Arte
Av. Arteaga Ote. no.704/Col. Americas
Estado de Mexique C.P. 50170 Toluca **Mexico**

Tel: +52-721/54852
Fax: +52-721/40523

Universidad Autonoma de Torrein -
Unidad Torrein
Centro de Estudios Arquitectonico y Urbanismo
Colon y Escobedo
Coahuila Torrein **Mexico**

Tel: +52-17/168-458

Universidad Autonoma de Coahuila
Escuela de Arquitectura
Nucleo Universitario Coahuila
Unidad Torrein Valladolid y Paseo del Ciclin
Col. Ampliaciin Rosita
Coahuila C.P. 27250 Torrein **Mexico**

Tel: +52-17/144-690
Fax: +52-17/202-083

Universidad Autonoma de la Laguna A.C.
Escuela de Arquitectura
Coahuila C.P. 27000 Torrein **Mexico**

Tel: +52-17/185-495 or 185-533 ext.119
Fax: +52-17/176-713

Instituto de Estudios Superiores de Chiapas
Escuela de Arquitectura
Paseo Liman No. 244 - Col. Patria Nueva
Chiapas Tuxtla Gutierrez **Mexico**

Tel: +52-961/41626 ext.26
Fax: +52-961/41621

Universidad Autonoma de Chiapas
Facultad de Arquitectura
Fracc. Colina Universitaria
Chiapas C.P. 29000 Tuxtla Gutierrez **Mexico**

Tel: +52-961/54043 or 50935

Universidad Veracruzana
Facultad de Arquitectura-Zona Xalapa
Zona universitaria/Fracc. Lomas del Estadio
Veracruz C.P. 91090 Xalapa **Mexico**

Tel: +52-28/172-354
Fax: +52-28/172-354

Instituto Tecnologico de Zacatecas
Escuela de Arquitectura
La Escondida
Zacatecas C.P. 98000 Zacatecas **Mexico**

Tel: +52-49/245-366
Fax: +52-49/245-266

Recinto Universitario Ruben Dario
Facultad CC/FF/MM UNAN,
Escuela de Arquitectura
P.O. Box 663
Managua **Nicaragua**

Universidad Nacional de Nicaragua
Facultad de Arquitectura
Managua **Nicaragua**

Universidad Nacional de Ingenieria
Facultad de Arquitectura
Apartado Postal 5595
Managua **Nicaragua**

Universidad de Panama
Facultad de Arquitectura
Apartado Postal 3277
3 Panama **Panama**

Universidad Nacional San Agustin de Arequipa
Facultad de Arquitectura y Urbanismo
Santa Catalina 117
Arequipa **Peru**

Tel: +51-54/234-220
Fax: +51-54/220-604

Universidad Particular de Chiclayo
Av. Juan Manuel Iturregui 133
Chiclayo **Peru**

Tel: +51-44/225-046
Fax: +51-74/240-638

Universidad Nacional de San Antonio Abad del Cusco
Facultad de Arquitectura
Calle Tigre 127
Cusco **Peru**

Tel: +51-84/222-271
Fax: +51-84/238-156

Universidad Nacional del Centro de Huancayo
Facultad de Arquitectura
Calle Real 160, Apt. 77 - Ciudad Universitaria
Cusco **Peru**

Tel: +51-84/235-912

Universidad Nacional Pedro Ruiz Gallo
Facultad de Ingenieria Civil, Sistemas y Arquitectura
Ciudad Universitaria
Lambayeque **Peru**

Tel: +51-74/283-402
Fax: +51-74/283-148

Universidad Nacional de Ingenieria
Facultad de Arquitectura
Av. Tupac Amaru KM 4.5 - Apartado
1301/San Martin de Porres
Lima **Peru**

Tel: +51-1/481-2336

Universidad Ricardo Palma
Facultad de Arquitectura
Av. Benavides cdra. 54/ Urb. las
Gardenias/Santiago de Surco
Lima **Peru**

Tel: +51-1/449-2510

Universidad Feminina del Sagrado Corazon
Av. los Frutales s/n, Urb. Santa Magdalena
Sofia/La Molina
Lima **Peru**

Tel: +51-1/436-3641

Universidad Peruana de Ciencias Aplicadas
Facultad de Arquitectura
Alonso de Molina sn/Monterrico
Lima **Peru**

Tel: +51-1/437-0908
Fax: +51-1/434-2929

Universidad Nacional Federico Villarreal
Facultad de Arquitectura
Pasaje Paez, no.140/Jesus Maria
00011 Lima **Peru**

Tel: +51-1/463-2020

Universidad Nacional de Piura
Campus Universitario, Urb. Miraflores Castilla
Piura **Peru**

Tel: +51-74/343-1 81
Fax: +51-74/342-598

Universidad Antenor Orrego Trujillo
América Sur 3145/Montserrate
Trujillo **Peru**

Tel: +51-44/284-128

Universidad Cesar Vallejo
San Martin 650
Trujillo **Peru**

Tel: +51-44/252-121

Universidad de la Republica del Uruguay
Facultad de Arquitectura
Bulevar Artigas 1031
11200 Montevideo **Uruguay**

Tel: +598-2/400-6366
Fax: +598-2/400-6366
Email: ceda@farq.edu.uy

Colegio de Ingenieros, Arquitectos y Afines
Urbanizacion El Cafetal C
Rio Caribe Qtal/Libe
01061 Caracas **Venezuela**

Tel: +58-2/256-848
Fax: +58-2/987-8859

Universidad Central de Venezuela
Facultad de Arquitectura y Urbanismo
Ciudad Universitaria de Caracas Los
Chaguaralos
Caracas **Venezuela**

Tel: +58-2/605-2034
Fax: +58-2/605-2005

Universidad Jose Maria Vargas
Facultad de Arquitectura
Avenida Sucre, Urbanizacion los dos Caminos
Torre Sucre
Caracas **Venezuela**

Tel: +58-2/285-3831
Fax: +58-2/283-2076

Universidad Simon Bolivar
Coordinacion de Arquitectura
Apartado Postal 89069
Caracas **Venezuela**

Tel: +58-2/906-3081
Fax: +58-2/906-3080

Universidad Rafael Urdaneta
Facultad de Arquitectura
Avenida Milagro frente a la Salida de
Pequiven
Maracaibo **Venezuela**

Tel: +58-61/915-631
Fax: +58-61/916-330

Universidad de Zulia
Facultad de Arquitectura
Ave Zuroma, Nucleo Tecnico. Luz
Apartado Postal 528
Maracaibo **Venezuela**

Tel: +58-61/598-502
Fax: +58-61/912-598

Universidad de los Andes
Facultad de Arquitectura
Apartado Postal 565
Merida **Venezuela**

Tel: +58-74/401-993
Fax: +58-74/401-903

Universidad Nacional Experimental del
Tachira-UNET
Av. Universidad Paramillo
Estado del Tachira San Cristobal **Venezuela**

Tel: +58-76/445-093
Fax: +58-76/565-896

MAP OF FULL AND CANDIDATE MEMBER SCHOOLS

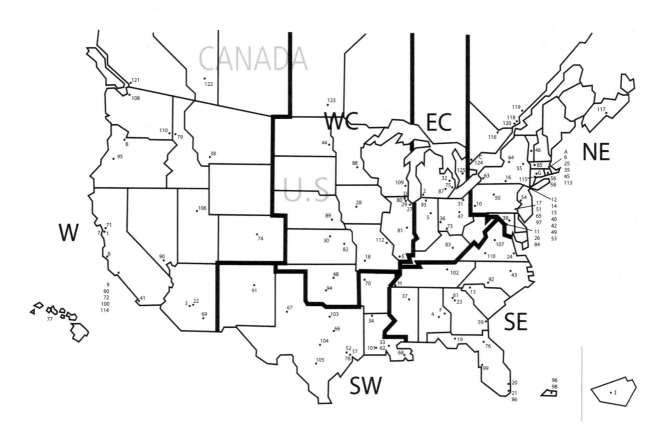

The 134 full ACSA member schools are divided into six constituent regions, as denoted on the map: East Central (EC), Northeast (NE), Southeast (SE), Southwest (SW), West (W), and West Central (WC).

U.S. FULL MEMBER SCHOOLS

1   Academy of Art University
2   Andrews University
3   Arizona State University
4   Auburn University
5   Ball State University
6   Boston Architectural College
7   California College of the Arts
8   California Polytechnic State University, San Luis Obispo
9   California State Polytechnic University, Pomona
10 Carnegie Mellon University
11 Catholic University of America
12 City College of New York
13 Clemson University
14 Columbia University
15 The Cooper Union
16 Cornell University
17 Drexel University
18 Drury University
19 Florida Agricultural and Mechanical University
20 Florida Atlantic University
21 Florida International University
22 Frank Lloyd Wright School of Architecture
23 Georgia Institute of Technology
24 Hampton University
25 Harvard University
26 Howard University
27 Illinois Institute of Technology

28 Iowa State University
29 Judson University
30 Kansas State University
31 Kent State University
32 Lawrence Technological University
33 Louisiana State University
34 Louisiana Tech University
35 Massachusetts Institute of Technology
36 Miami University
37 Mississippi State University
38 Montana State University
39 Morgan State University
40 New Jersey Institute of Technology
41 NewSchool of Architecture and Design
42 New York Institute of Technology
43 North Carolina State University
44 North Dakota State University
45 Northeastern University
46 Norwich University
47 Ohio State University
48 Oklahoma State University
49 Parsons The New School for Design
50 Pennsylvania State University
51 Philadelphia University
52 Prairie View A&M University
53 Pratt Institute
54 Princeton University
55 Rensselaer Polytechnic Institute
56 Rhode Island School of Design
57 Rice University
58 Roger Williams University

59 Savannah College of Art and Design
60 Southern California Institute of Architecture
61 Southern Polytechnic State University
62 Southern University and A&M College
63 University at Buffalo, SUNY
64 Syracuse University
65 Temple University
66 Texas A&M University
67 Texas Tech University
68 Tulane University
69 University of Arizona
70 University of Arkansas
71 University of California, Berkeley
72 University of California, Los Angeles
73 University of Cincinnati
74 University of Colorado
75 University of Detroit Mercy
76 University of Florida
77 University of Hawai'i at Manoa
78 University of Houston
79 University of Idaho
80 University of Illinois at Chicago
81 University of Illinois, Urbana–Champaign
82 University of Kansas
83 University of Kentucky
84 University of Maryland
85 University of Massachusetts, Amherst
86 University of Miami
87 University of Michigan
88 University of Minnesota
89 University of Nebraska–Lincoln
90 University of Nevada, Las Vegas
91 University of New Mexico
92 University of North Carolina at Charlotte
93 University of Notre Dame
94 University of Oklahoma

95 University of Oregon
96 Polytechnic University of Puerto Rico
97 University of Pennsylvania
98 Universidad de Puerto Rico
99 University of South Florida
100 University of Southern California
101 University of Louisiana–Lafayette
102 University of Tennessee-Knoxville
103 University of Texas at Arlington
104 University of Texas at Austin
105 University of Texas At San Antonio
106 University of Utah
107 University of Virginia
108 University of Washington
109 University of Wisconsin–Milwaukee
110 Virginia Polytechnic Institute & State University
111 Washington State University
112 Washington University in St. Louis
113 Wentworth Institute of Technology
114 Woodbury University
115 Yale University

CANADIAN SCHOOLS

116 Carleton University
117 Dalhousie University
118 McGill University
119 Université Laval
120 Université de Montreal
121 University of British Columbia
122 University of Calgary
123 University of Manitoba
124 University of Toronto
125 University of Waterloo

CANDIDATE SCHOOLS

A Massachusetts College of Art and Design
B Portland State University
C Ryerson University
D School of the Art Institute of Chicago
E Southern Illinois University
F Tuskegee University
G University of Hartford
H University of Memphis
I American University of Sharjah

INDEX OF ARCHITECTURE DEGREE TYPES

UNDERGRADUATE PRE-PROFESSIONAL ARCHITECTURE PROGRAM: part of NAAB- or CACB-accredited program

Andrews University
Arizona State University
Ball State University
Carleton University
The Catholic University of America
The City College of New York
Clemson University
Dalhousie University
Florida A&M University
Florida International University
Frank Lloyd Wright School of Architecture
Georgia Institute of Technology
Judson University
Kent State University
Lawrence Technological University
Louisiana Tech University
Massachusetts College of Art
Massachusetts Institute of Technology
McGill University
Miami University
New Jersey Institute of Technology
New York Institute of Technology
NewSchool of Architecture & Design
North Carolina State University
Norwich University
Northeastern University
Ohio State University
Parsons The New School for Design
Philadelphia University
Portland State University
Prairie View A&M University
The Pennsylvania State University
Princeton University
Rice University
Roger Williams University
Savannah College of Art and Design
Southern Illinois University
Syracuse University
Temple University
Texas A&M University
Texas Tech University
Universidad de Puerto Rico
Université de Montréal
Université Laval
University of Puerto Rico
University at Buffalo, SUNY
University of Arkansas
University of Calgary
University of California, Berkeley
University of California, Los Angeles
University of Cincinnati
University of Colorado
University of Detroit Mercy
University of Florida
University of Hartford
University of Houston
University of Idaho
University of Illinois at Chicago
University of Illinois, Urbana-Champaign
University of Kansas
University of Kentucky
University of Louisiana at Lafayette
University of Manitoba
University of Maryland
University of Massachusetts, Amherst
University of Memphis

University of Michigan
University of Minnesota
University of Nebraska–Lincoln
University of Nevada, Las Vegas
University of New Mexico
University of North Carolina at Charlotte
University of Oklahoma
University of Pennsylvania
University of Southern California
University of South Florida
University of Tennessee
University of Texas at Arlington
University of Texas at Austin
University of Texas at San Antonio
University of Toronto
University of Utah
University of Virginia
University of Washington
University of Waterloo
University of Wisconsin–Milwaukee
Washington University in St. Louis
Wentworth Institute of Technology

UNDERGRADUATE PROFESSIONAL ACCREDITED ARCHITECTURE PROGRAM: B. Arch

American University of Sharjah
Auburn University
Boston Architectural College
California College of the Arts
California Polytechnic State University, San Luis Obispo
California State Polytechnic University, Pomona
Carnegie Mellon University
City College of New York
Cooper Union
Cornell University
Drexel University
Drury University
Florida A&M University
Florida Atlantic University
Howard University
Illinois Institute of Technology
Iowa State University
Louisiana State University
Mississippi State University
New Jersey Institute of Technology
New York Institute of Technology
NewSchool of Architecture and Design
North Carolina State University
Oklahoma State University
Pennsylvania State University
Philadelphia University
Polytechnic University of Puerto Rico
Pratt Institute
Rensselaer Polytechnic Institute
Rhode Island School of Design
Rice University
Southern California Institute of Architecture
Southern University and A&M College
Syracuse University
Temple University
Tuskegee University
University of Arizona
University of Arkansas
University of Houston
University of Kentucky
University of Memphis
University of Miami

University of North Carolina at Charlotte
University of Notre Dame
University of Oklahoma
University of Oregon
University of Southern California
University of Tennessee–Knoxville
University of Texas at Austin
Virginia Polytechnic Institute
Woodbury University

GRADUATE PROFESSIONAL ACCREDITED ARCHITECTURAL PROGRAM: M. Arch, with undergraduate architecture degree as prerequisite

Ball State University
Catholic University of America
Clemson University
Cornell University
Dalhousie University
Florida A&M University
Florida International University
Georgia Institute of Technology
Harvard University
Illinois Institute of Technology
Iowa State University
Judson University
Kent State University
Lawrence Technological University
Louisiana State University
Louisiana Tech University
Massachusetts College of Art and Design
McGill University
Miami University
Morgan State University
NewSchool of Architecture and Design
North Carolina State University
Northeastern University
Norwich University
Ohio State University
Portland State University
Prairie View A&M University
Rice University
Ryerson University
Savannah College of Art and Design
School of the Art Institute of Chicago
Southern California Institute of Architecture
Southern Illinois University
Texas A&M University
Texas Tech University
Tulane University
Universidad de Puerto Rico
Université de Montréal
University at Buffalo, SUNY
University of British Columbia
University of Cincinnati
University of Florida
University of Hartford
University of Houston
University of Idaho
University of Illinois at Chicago
University of Illinois, Urbana–Champaign
University of Kansas
University of Louisiana at Lafayette
University of Manitoba
University of Maryland
University of Massachusetts, Amherst
University of Miami
University of Michigan

University of Nebraska–Lincoln
University of Nevada, Las Vegas
University of New Mexico
University of North Carolina at Charlotte
University of Notre Dame
University of Oklahoma
University of Oregon
University of Pennsylvania
University of Southern California
University of Tennessee–Knoxville
University of Texas at Arlington
University of Texas at San Antonio
University of Utah
University of Washington
University of Wisconsin–Milwaukee
Virginia Polytechnic Institute
Washington State University
Washington University in St. Louis
Woodbury University
Yale University

GRADUATE PROFESSIONAL ACCREDITED ARCHITECTURE PROGRAM: M. Arch, available to non-architectural undergraduate degree holders

Academy of Art University
Andrews University
Arizona State University
Boston Architectural College
California College of the Arts
California State Polytechnic University, Pomona
Catholic University of America
City College of New York
Clemson University
Columbia University
Florida A&M University
Florida International University
Frank Lloyd Wright School of Architecture
Georgia Institute of Technology
Harvard University
Illinois Institute of Technology
Iowa State University
Judson University
Massachusetts Institute of Technology
Miami University
Morgan State University
New Jersey Institute of Technology
NewSchool of Architecture and Design
North Carolina State University
Norwich University
Ohio State University
Parsons The New School for Design
Prairie View A&M University
Pratt Institute
Princeton University
Rensselaer Polytechnic Institute
Rhode Island School of Design
Rice University
School of the Art Institute of Chicago
Southern California Institute of Architecture
Syracuse University
Texas A&M University
Tulane University
Université Laval
University of British Columbia
University at Buffalo, SUNY
University of Calgary
University of California, Berkeley

University of California, Los Angeles
University of Cincinnati
University of Colorado
University of Florida
University of Houston
University of Illinois at Chicago
University of Illinois, Urbana-Champaign
University of Kansas
University of Maryland
University of Massachusetts, Amherst
University of Miami
University of Michigan
University of Minnesota
University of Nebraska–Lincoln
University of New Mexico
University of North Carolina at Charlotte
University of Notre Dame
University of Oregon
University of Pennsylvania
University of South Florida
University of Tennessee–Knoxville
University of Texas at Arlington
University of Texas at Austin
University of Toronto
University of Utah
University of Virginia
University of Washington
University of Wisconsin–Milwaukee
Virginia Polytechnic Institute
Washington University in St. Louis
Yale University

GRADUATE PROFESSIONAL ACCREDITED ARCHITECTURE PROGRAM: M. Arch, five or five+ year programs, normally beginning with undergraduate enrollment

Andrews University
Hampton University
Kansas State University
Louisiana Tech University
Montana State University
Morgan State University
North Dakota State University
Norwich University
Prairie View A&M University
Roger Williams University
Southern Illinois University
Southern Polytechnic Institute
Tulane University
University of Detroit Mercy
University of Idaho
University of Kansas
University of South Florida
Washington State University
Wentworth Institute of Technology
Woodbury University

GRADUATE PROFESSIONAL ARCHITECTURE PROGRAM: D. Arch

University of Hawaii at Manoa

GRADUATE POST-PROFESSIONAL ARCHITECTURE PROGRAM: M. Arch, MS, or MA with professional architecture degree (or international equivalent) as prerequisite

Ball State University – M. Arch. II
California Polytechnic State University, San Luis Obispo – MS Arch
Carnegie Mellon University – MS Arch
Columbia University – MS Advanced Arch Design
Cooper Union – M. Arch
Cornell University – M. Arch
Florida A&M University – MS
Florida Atlantic University – MS
Florida International University – MA
Georgia Institute of Technology – MS Arch
Harvard University – M. Arch
Illinois Institute of Technology – M. Arch I
Iowa State University – M. Arch
Kansas State University – MS Arch
Louisiana State University – M. Arch
Massachusetts Institute of Technology – SMArchS
McGill University – M. Arch
Miami University – M. Arch
Mississippi State University – MS Arch
New Jersey Institute of Technology – MS Arch
New York Institute of Technology – M. Arch, MAUD
NewSchool of Architecture and Design – MS Arch
North Carolina State University – M. Arch
Northeastern University – M. Arch
Ohio State University – M. Arch Studies
Parsons The Neew School for Design – M. Arch
Pennsylvania State University – M. Arch
Pratt Institute – MS Arch
Princeton University – M. Arch
Rice University – M. Arch
Syracuse University – M. Arch
Texas A&M University – MS Arch
University at Buffalo, SUNY – M. Arch
University of Arizona – M. Arch
University of British Columbia – MASA
University of California, Berkeley – M. Arch
University of California, Los Angeles – M. Arch
University of Cincinnati – MS Arch
University of Florida – MS Arch
University of Houston – M. Arch
University of Illinois at Chicago – MS Arch
University of Illinois, Urbana-Champaign – MS Arch
University of Kansas – M. Arch
University of Louisiana at Lafayette – M. Arch
University of Maryland – MS Arch
University of Michigan – MS Arch
University of Nebraska–Lincoln – MS Arch
University of New Mexico – M Arch
University of Notre Dame – M. ADU
University of Oklahoma – M Arch
University of Oregon – M. Arch
University of Pennsylvania – M. Arch
University of South Florida – M. Arch
University of California, Los Angeles – M. Arch; MA
University of Colorado – M. Arch
University of Southern California – M Arch
University of Tennessee – M Arch
University of Texas at Arlington – M. Arch
University of Texas at Austin – M. Arch, MS, MA
University of Utah – MS Arch
University of Virginia – M. Arch
University of Washington – M. Arch
Virginia Polytechnic Institute – M. Arch
Washington State University – MS Arch

INDEX OF ARCHITECTURE DEGREE TYPES

Washington University — M. Arch
Woodbury University — M Arch
Yale University — M Arch

GRADUATE NON-PROFESSIONAL ARCHITECTURE PROGRAM: M. Arch, MS, or MA

Carnegie Mellon University — MS Arch
Catholic University of America — MS Arch. Studies
Clemson University — MS Arch
Cornell University — MA
Florida Atlantic University — MS
Georgia Institute of Technology — MS Arch
Harvard University — MDesS
Iowa State University — MS Arch
Massachusetts Institute of Technology — SMArchS
New Jersey Institute of Technology — MS Arch
New York Institute of Technology — M. Arch
NewSchool of Architecture and Design — MS Arch
Ohio State University — M. Arch Studies
Rensselaer Polytechnic Institute — MS Arch Sciences
Syracuse University — M. Arch
Texas A&M University — MS Arch
Texas Tech — MS
Université Laval — M Sc Arch
University of British Columbia — MASA
University of California, Berkeley — MS
University of California, Los Angeles — MA
University of Cincinnati — MS
University of Florida — MS
University of Houston — M. Arch
University of Idaho — MS Arch
University of Minnesota — MS Arch
University of Oklahoma — MS Arch
University of Pennsylvania — MS Arch
University of Southern California, Los Angeles — M. Arch; MA
University of Colorado — M. Arch
University of Texas at Arlington — M. Arch
University of Washington — MS Arch
Virginia Polytechnic Institute — MS Arch
Washington State University — MS Arch

GRADUATE NON-PROFESSIONAL OR POST-PROFESSIONAL ARCHITECTURE PROGRAM: D.Arch program

Rice University

GRADUATE NON-PROFESSIONAL OR POST-PROFESSIONAL ARCHITECTURE OR ENVIRONMENTAL DESIGN PROGRAM: PhD program

Arizona State University
Carnegie Mellon University
Clemson University
Columbia University
Cornell University
Georgia Institute of Technology
Harvard University
Illinois Institute of Technology
Kansas State University
Massachusetts Institute of Technology
McGill University
North Carolina State University
Princeton University
Rensselaer Polytechnic Institute
Texas A&M University
Texas Tech University
Université Laval
University of California, Berkeley
University of California, Los Angeles
University of Florida
University of Illinois, Urbana-Champaign
University of Kansas
University of Maryland
University of Michigan
University of Nebraska–Lincoln
University of Pennsylvania
University of Southern California
University of Texas at Austin
University of Washington
University of Wisconsin–Milwaukee
Yale University

ARCHITECTURAL DESIGN

Academy of Art University
Andrews University
Arizona State University
Auburn University
Ball State University
Boston Architectural College
California College of the Arts
California Polytechnic State University
California State Polytechnic University, Pomona
Carleton University
Carnegie Mellon University
Catholic University of America
City College of New York
Cornell University
Dalhousie University
Drexel University
Drury University
Florida Atlantic University
Florida International University
Frank Lloyd Wright School of Architecture
Hampton University
Illinois Institute of Technology
Judson University
Kent State University
Lawrence Technological University
Louisiana Tech University
Massachusetts College of Art and Design
Massachusetts Institute of Technology
McGill University
Mississippi State University
Montana State University
Morgan State University
New Jersey Institute of Technology
North Carolina State University
North Dakota State University
Northeastern University
Ohio State University
Pennsylvania State University
Philadelphia University
Portland State University
Rensselaer Polytechnic Institute
Rhode Island School of Design
Rice University
Ryerson University
Savannah College of Art and Design
School of the Art Institute of Chicago
Southern Illinois University
Temple University
Texas A&M University
Tulane University
Université de Montréal
University at Buffalo, SUNY
University of British Columbia
University of Calgary
University of California, Berkeley
University of Detroit Mercy
University of Florida
University of Hartford
University of Hawaii at Manoa
University of Houston
University of Idaho
University of Illinois at Chicago
University of Illinois, Urbana–Champaign
University of Kansas
University of Louisiana–Lafayette
University of Manitoba
University of Maryland
University of Massachusetts, Amherst

University of Memphis
University of Michigan
University of Minnesota
University of North Carolina at Charlotte
University of Notre Dame
University of Oklahoma
University of Oregon
University of South Florida
University of Southern California
University of Tennessee–Knoxville
University of Texas at San Antonio
University of Toronto
University of Utah
University of Washington
University of Wisconsin–Milwaukee
Virginia Polytechnic Institute
Washington State University
Washington University in St. Louis
Wentworth Institute of Technology
Yale University

ART AND DESIGN

Academy of Art University
Auburn University
California College of the Arts
Drury University
Florida International University
Frank Lloyd Wright School of Architecture
Lawrence Technological University
Louisiana Tech University
Massachusetts College of Art and Design
New Jersey Institute of Technology
NewSchool of Architecture and Design
North Dakota State University
Pennsylvania State University
Portland State University
Rhode Island School of Design
Savannah College of Art and Design
School of the Art Institute of Chicago
Texas A&M University
University at Buffalo, SUNY
University of Idaho
University of Louisiana–Lafayette
University of Manitoba
University of Massachusetts, Amherst
University of Michigan
University of Toronto
University of Washington
Virginia Polytechnic Institute
Washington State University
Washington University in St. Louis

BUILDING INFORMATION MODELING

Academy of Art University
Arizona State University
Auburn University
Ball State University
Boston Architectural College
California College of the Arts
California State Polytechnic University, Pomona
Carnegie Mellon University
City College of New York
Drury University
Georgia Institute of Technology
Montana State University
Morgan State University

New Jersey Institute of Technology
Northeastern University
Philadelphia University
Rensselaer Polytechnic Institute
Rice University
Savannah College of Art and Design
School of the Art Institute of Chicago
Texas A&M University
Tulane University
University of Hawaii at Manoa
University of Kansas
University of Massachusetts, Amherst
University of Minnesota
University of North Carolina at Charlotte
University of Oklahoma
University of Southern California
University of Utah
University of Washington
University of Wisconsin–Milwaukee
Virginia Polytechnic Institute

BUILDING TECHNOLOGY/ ENVIRONMENTAL SYSTEMS

Arizona State University
Auburn University
Ball State University
Boston Architectural College
California College of the Arts
California Polytechnic State University
California State Polytechnic University, Pomona
Carnegie Mellon University
City College of New York
Cornell University
Dalhousie University
Georgia Institute of Technology
Kent State University
Louisiana Tech University
Massachusetts College of Art and Design
Massachusetts Institute of Technology
Mississippi State University
Montana State University
New Jersey Institute of Technology
North Carolina State University
North Dakota State University
Northeastern University
Pennsylvania State University
Rensselaer Polytechnic Institute
Rhode Island School of Design
Rice University
Ryerson University
Savannah College of Art and Design
School of the Art Institute of Chicago
Southern Illinois University
Temple University
Texas A&M University
University of British Columbia
University of Calgary
University of California, Berkeley
University of Hawaii at Manoa
University of Illinois, Urbana–Champaign
University of Manitoba
University of Massachusetts, Amherst
University of Michigan
University of North Carolina at Charlotte
University of Notre Dame
University of Oklahoma
University of Oregon
University of Southern California

SPECIALIZATIONS WITHIN ARCHITECTURE DEGREE

University of Tennessee–Knoxville
University of Toronto
University of Utah
University of Washington
University of Wisconsin–Milwaukee
Virginia Polytechnic Institute
Washington State University
Washington University in St. Louis
Wentworth Institute of Technology

COMMUNITY DESIGN

Academy of Art University
Andrews University
Arizona State University
Auburn University
Ball State University
California College of the Arts
California Polytechnic State University
California State Polytechnic University, Pomona
Carnegie Mellon University
Catholic University of America
Dalhousie University
Drury University
Florida Atlantic University
Frank Lloyd Wright School of Architecture
Howard University
Judson University
Lawrence Technological University
Louisiana State University
Louisiana Tech University
Massachusetts College of Art and Design
Massachusetts Institute of Technology
McGill University
Montana State University
Morgan State University
New Jersey Institute of Technology
North Carolina State University
North Dakota State University
Northeastern University
Parsons The New School for Design
Pennsylvania State University
Portland State University
Rice University
School of the Art Institute of Chicago
Southern Illinois University
Temple University
Texas A&M University
Texas Tech University
Tulane University
University of Colorado
University of Florida
University of Hartford
University of Hawaii at Manoa
University of Houston
University of Idaho
University of Illinois, Urbana–Champaign
University of Kansas
University of Louisiana–Lafayette
University of Manitoba
University of Maryland
University of Massachusetts, Amherst
University of Memphis
University of Miami
University of Michigan
University of New Mexico
University of North Carolina at Charlotte
University of Notre Dame
University of Oklahoma

University of South Florida
University of Southern California
University of Tennessee–Knoxville
University of Toronto
University of Virginia
University of Washington
University of Wisconsin–Milwaukee
Virginia Polytechnic Institute
Washington State University
Washington University in St. Louis
Wentworth Institute of Technology

COMPUTER-AIDED DESIGN

Academy of Art University
Arizona State University
Auburn University
Ball State University
Boston Architectural College
California College of the Arts
California State Polytechnic University, Pomona
Carleton University
Carnegie Mellon University
Catholic University of America
Cornell University
Drexel University
Florida International University
Frank Lloyd Wright School of Architecture
Georgia Institute of Technology
Hampton University
Illinois Institute of Technology
Louisiana State University
Louisiana Tech University
Massachusetts College of Art and Design
Massachusetts Institute of Technology
McGill University
Montana State University
New Jersey Institute of Technology
New York Institute of Technology
North Carolina State University
North Dakota State University
Northeastern University
Ohio State University
Parsons The New School for Design
Pennsylvania State University
Philadelphia University
Rensselaer Polytechnic Institute
Rice University
Roger Williams University
Ryerson University
Savannah College of Art and Design
School of the Art Institute of Chicago
Southern Illinois University
Temple University
Texas A&M University
Université de Montréal
University at Buffalo, SUNY
University of British Columbia
University of Calgary
University of California, Berkeley
University of Florida
University of Hawaii at Manoa
University of Houston
University of Idaho
University of Manitoba
University of Miami
University of Michigan
University of North Carolina at Charlotte
University of Notre Dame

University of Oklahoma
University of Oregon
University of Southern California
University of Toronto
University of Utah
University of Virginia
University of Washington
University of Wisconsin–Milwaukee
Virginia Polytechnic Institute
Washington State University

ENERGY

Arizona State University
Auburn University
Ball State University
California College of the Arts
California State Polytechnic University, Pomona
Drexel University
Frank Lloyd Wright School of Architecture
Georgia Institute of Technology
Massachusetts College of Art and Design
Massachusetts Institute of Technology
McGill University
Montana State University
New York Institute of Technology
North Carolina State University
Northeastern University
Parsons The New School for Design
Rensselaer Polytechnic Institute
Rice University
Southern Illinois University
University of Arizona
University of British Columbia
University of Calgary
University of California, Berkeley
University of Hawaii at Manoa
University of Houston
University of Idaho
University of Illinois, Urbana–Champaign
University of North Carolina at Charlotte
University of Oregon
University of Southern California
University of Toronto
University of Utah
University of Washington
University of Wisconsin–Milwaukee
Virginia Polytechnic Institute
Washington State University

ENGINEERING

Massachusetts Institute of Technology
McGill University
Université de Montréal
University of Hartford
University of Illinois, Urbana–Champaign
University of Kansas
University of Massachusetts, Amherst
University of Oklahoma
University of Toronto
University of Washington

ENVIRONMENT/SUSTAINABILITY

Academy of Art University
Arizona State University
Auburn University
Ball State University
Boston Architectural College
California College of the Arts
California Polytechnic State University
California State Polytechnic University, Pomona
Carleton University
Carnegie Mellon University
Catholic University of America
City College of New York
Cornell University
Dalhousie University
Drexel University
Drury University
Florida Atlantic University
Florida International University
Frank Lloyd Wright School of Architecture
Georgia Institute of Technology
Hampton University
Illinois Institute of Technology
Judson University
Kent State University
Louisiana State University
Louisiana Tech University
Massachusetts College of Art and Design
Massachusetts Institute of Technology
McGill University
Mississippi State University
Montana State University
Morgan State University
New Jersey Institute of Technology
New York Institute of Technology
North Carolina State University
North Dakota State University
Northeastern University
Parsons The New School for Design
Philadelphia University
Portland State University
Rensselaer Polytechnic Institute
Rhode Island School of Design
Rice University
Ryerson University
Savannah College of Art and Design
School of the Art Institute of Chicago
Texas A&M University
Tulane University
Université de Montréal
University at Buffalo, SUNY
University of Arizona
University of British Columbia
University of Calgary
University of California, Berkeley
University of Colorado
University of Florida
University of Hawaii at Manoa
University of Houston
University of Idaho
University of Illinois, Urbana–Champaign
University of Louisiana–Lafayette
University of Manitoba
University of Maryland
University of Massachusetts, Amherst
University of Memphis
University of Michigan
University of Minnesota
University of New Mexico

University of North Carolina at Charlotte
University of Notre Dame
University of Oklahoma
University of Oregon
University of South Florida
University of Southern California
University of Tennessee–Knoxville
University of Toronto
University of Utah
University of Virginia
University of Washington
University of Wisconsin–Milwaukee
Virginia Polytechnic Institute
Washington State University
Washington University in St. Louis

GRAPHIC DESIGN

Auburn University
California College of the Arts
California State Polytechnic University, Pomona
Massachusetts Institute of Technology
Montana State University
Rhode Island School of Design
School of the Art Institute of Chicago
Texas A&M University
University of British Columbia
University of Toronto
Virginia Polytechnic Institute

HISTORY

Arizona State University
Auburn University
Ball State University
California College of the Arts
California State Polytechnic University, Pomona
Carleton University
Cornell University
Frank Lloyd Wright School of Architecture
Georgia Institute of Technology
Illinois Institute of Technology
Judson University
Kent State University
Louisiana State University
Massachusetts College of Art and Design
Massachusetts Institute of Technology
McGill University
New Jersey Institute of Technology
New York Institute of Technology
NewSchool of Architecture and Design
North Carolina State University
North Dakota State University
Northeastern University
Ohio State University
Parson, The New School for Design
Rice University
School of the Art Institute of Chicago
Southern Illinois University
Texas A&M University
Université de Montréal
University of Arkansas
University of British Columbia
University of Calgary
University of California, Berkeley
University of Florida
University of Hawaii at Manoa
University of Idaho

University of Illinois, Urbana–Champaign
University of Manitoba
University of Maryland
University of Massachusetts, Amherst
University of Miami
University of Michigan
University of Minnesota
University of North Carolina at Charlotte
University of Notre Dame
University of Oklahoma
University of Southern California
University of Tennessee–Knoxville
University of Toronto
University of Utah
University of Virginia
University of Washington
University of Wisconsin–Milwaukee
Virginia Polytechnic Institute
Washington State University
Washington University in St. Louis

HOUSING

Academy of Art University
Arizona State University
Auburn University
Ball State University
California College of the Arts
California State Polytechnic University, Pomona
Carleton University
Dalhousie University
Georgia Institute of Technology
Massachusetts College of Art and Design
McGill University
New Jersey Institute of Technology
Northeastern University
Rice University
Texas A&M University
Université de Montréal
University of British Columbia
University of California, Berkeley
University of Kansas
University of Maryland
University of Massachusetts, Amherst
University of Memphis
University of Oregon
University of Southern California
University of Tennessee–Knoxville
University of Toronto
University of Washington
University of Wisconsin–Milwaukee
Virginia Polytechnic Institute
Washington State University

INTERIOR DESIGN/ARCHITECTURE

Academy of Art University
Auburn University
Boston Architectural College
California College of the Arts
Drexel University
Florida International University
Frank Lloyd Wright School of Architecture
Lawrence Technological University
Louisiana Tech University
Massachusetts College of Art and Design
New Jersey Institute of Technology
Parsons The New School for Design

SPECIALIZATIONS WITHIN ARCHITECTURE DEGREE

Philadelphia University
Savannah College of Art and Design
School of the Art Institute of Chicago
Southern Illinois University
University of Hawaii at Manoa
University of Idaho
University of Louisiana–Lafayette
University of Manitoba
University of Massachusetts, Amherst
University of Memphis
University of Oklahoma
University of Oregon
University of Toronto
University of Washington
Virginia Polytechnic Institute

INTERNATIONAL AND REGIONAL ARCHITECTURE

Arizona State University
Ball State University
California College of the Arts
Catholic University of America
Dalhousie University
Florida Atlantic University
Florida International University
Georgia Institute of Technology
Massachusetts College of Art and Design
Massachusetts Institute of Technology
McGill University
North Carolina State University
North Dakota State University
Pennsylvania State University
Portland State University
Rensselaer Polytechnic Institute
Rice University
Roger Williams University
Savannah College of Art and Design
Texas A&M University
Université de Montréal
University of British Columbia
University of California, Berkeley
University of Hartford
University of Hawaii at Manoa
University of Kansas
University of Louisiana–Lafayette
University of Maryland
University of Massachusetts, Amherst
University of Michigan
University of North Carolina at Charlotte
University of Notre Dame
University of Oklahoma
University of Southern California
University of Texas at San Antonio
University of Toronto
University of Utah
University of Washington
University of Wisconsin–Milwaukee
Virginia Polytechnic Institute
Washington University in St. Louis

INTERNATIONAL DEVELOPMENT

Dalhousie University
Georgia Institute of Technology
McGill University
Northeastern University
Rhode Island School of Design

Rice University
Temple University
Texas A&M University
Université de Montréal
University of Hawaii at Manoa
University of Manitoba
University of Southern California
University of Wisconsin–Milwaukee
Washington State University

LANDSCAPE DESIGN

Academy of Art University
Arizona State University
Auburn University
Ball State University
Boston Architectural College
California State Polytechnic University, Pomona
City College of New York
Florida International University
Frank Lloyd Wright School of Architecture
Miami University
North Dakota State University
Northeastern University
Philadelphia University
Portland State University
Ryerson University
Texas A&M University
University of British Columbia
University of Idaho
University of Manitoba
University of Massachusetts, Amherst
University of Oklahoma
University of Oregon
University of Southern California
University of Tennessee–Knoxville
University of Toronto
University of Washington
Virginia Polytechnic Institute
Washington State University

PHOTOGRAPHY

California College of the Arts
Georgia Institute of Technology
Massachusetts Institute of Technology
School of the Art Institute of Chicago
Université de Montréal
University of Manitoba
University of North Carolina at Charlotte
University of Washington
Virginia Polytechnic Institute

PRESERVATION

Ball State University
Boston Architectural College
California State Polytechnic University, Pomona
Frank Lloyd Wright School of Architecture
Howard University
Kent State University
Lawrence Technological University
Louisiana State University
Montana State University
North Carolina State University
North Dakota State University
Philadelphia University

Pratt Institute
Roger Williams University
Savannah College of Art and Design
School of the Art Institute of Chicago
Southern Illinois University
Texas A&M University
Texas Tech University
Tulane University
Université de Montréal
University of Arizona
University of Colorado
University of Florida
University of Hawaii at Manoa
University of Houston
University of Illinois, Urbana–Champaign
University of Louisiana–Lafayette
University of Manitoba
University of Maryland
University of Miami
University of New Mexico
University of Notre Dame
University of Oregon
University of Southern California
University of Texas at San Antonio
University of Toronto
University of Utah
University of Virginia
University of Washington
University of Wisconsin–Milwaukee

PROFESSIONAL PRACTICE

Arizona State University
Auburn University
Ball State University
Boston Architectural College
California College of the Arts
California State Polytechnic University, Pomona
Carleton University
Cornell University
Dalhousie University
Florida International University
Frank Lloyd Wright School of Architecture
Judson University
Kent State University
Lawrence Technological University
Louisiana Tech University
Massachusetts College of Art and Design
Massachusetts Institute of Technology
McGill University
Montana State University
NewSchool of Architecture and Design
North Carolina State University
North Dakota State University
Northeastern University
Rensselaer Polytechnic Institute
Rice University
Savannah College of Art and Design
Southern Illinois University
Texas A&M University
Université de Montréal
University at Buffalo, SUNY
University of British Columbia
University of Calgary
University of Florida
University of Hawaii at Manoa
University of Kansas
University of Manitoba
University of New Mexico

University of North Carolina at Charlotte
University of Notre Dame
University of Oklahoma
University of Southern California
University of Toronto
University of Washington
University of Wisconsin—Milwaukee
Virginia Polytechnic Institute

SACRED SPACES

Catholic University of America
Judson University
North Carolina State University
Portland State University
Texas A&M University
University of Notre Dame

SUSTAINABILITY

Academy of Art University
Andrews University
Arizona State University
Auburn University
Ball State University
Boston Architectural College
California College of the Arts
California State Polytechnic University, Pomona
Carleton University
Carnegie Mellon University
Catholic University of America
City College of New York
Cornell University
Dalhousie University
Drexel University
Florida International University
Frank Lloyd Wright School of Architecture
Georgia Institute of Technology
Hampton University
Illinois Institute of Technology
Judson University
Kansas State University
Lawrence Technological University
Louisiana Tech University
Massachusetts College of Art and Design
Massachusetts Institute of Technology
McGill University
Mississippi State University
Montana State University
Morgan State University
New Jersey Institute of Technology
North Carolina State University
North Dakota State University
Northeastern University
Pennsylvania State University
Philadelphia University
Portland State University
Rensselaer Polytechnic Institute
Rhode Island School of Design
Rice University
Roger Williams University
Savannah College of Art and Design
School of the Art Institute of Chicago
Texas A&M University
Tulane University
Université de Montréal
University of British Columbia
University of Florida

University of Hawaii]at Manoa
University of Houston
University of Idaho
University of Illinois, Urbana—Champaign
University of Kansas
University of Louisiana—Lafayette
University of Manitoba
University of Massachusetts, Amherst
University of Memphis
University of Minnesota
University of North Carolina at Charlotte
University of Notre Dame
University of Oklahoma
University of Oregon
University of Southern California
University of Tennessee—Knoxville
University of Toronto
University of Utah
University of Washington
University of Wisconsin—Milwaukee
Virginia Polytechnic Institute
Washington State University
Washington University in St. Louis

TECTONICS

Arizona State University
Auburn University
Ball State University
California College of the Arts
Carleton University
Florida International University
Georgia Institute of Technology
Louisiana Tech University
Massachusetts College of Art and Design
Montana State University
New Jersey Institute of Technology
NewSchool of Architecture and Design
North Carolina State University
Northeastern University
Portland State University
Rensselaer Polytechnic Institute
Rhode Island School of Design
Rice University
Savannah College of Art and Design
Université de Montréal
University at Buffalo, SUNY
University of British Columbia
University of Hawaii at Manoa
University of Kansas
University of Louisiana—Lafayette
University of Manitoba
University of North Carolina at Charlotte
University of Notre Dame
University of Southern California
University of Toronto
University of Utah
University of Washington
University of Wisconsin—Milwaukee
Virginia Polytechnic Institute
Washington State University
Wentworth Institute of Technology

THEORY/ CRITICISM

Arizona State University
Ball State University
Boston Architectural College
California College of the Arts
Carleton University
Cornell University
Dalhousie University
Drury University
Florida International University
Frank Lloyd Wright School of Architecture
Georgia Institute of Technology
Illinois Institute of Technology
Kansas State University
Kent State University
Lawrence Technological University
Massachusetts College of Art and Design
Massachusetts Institute of Technology
McGill University
Montana State University
New York Institute of Technology
NewSchool of Architecture and Design
North Carolina State University
North Dakota State University
Northeastern University
Ohio State University
Parsons The New School for Design
Pennsylvania State University
Portland State University
Rice University
School of the Art Institute of Chicago
Temple University
Texas A&M University
Tulane University
Université de Montréal
University at Buffalo, SUNY
University of British Columbia
University of Calgary
University of California, Berkeley
University of Florida
University of Hawaii At Manoa
University of Houston
University of Idaho
University of Illinois at Chicago
University of Illinois, Urbana—Champaign
University of Louisiana—Lafayette
University of Manitoba
University of Maryland
University of Massachusetts, Amherst
University of Michigan
University of Minnesota
University of New Mexico
University of North Carolina at Charlotte
University of Notre Dame
University of Oklahoma
University of Southern California
University of Tennessee—Knoxville
University of Toronto
University of Utah
University of Washington
University of Wisconsin—Milwaukee
Virginia Polytechnic Institute
Washington State University
Washington University in St. Louis

SPECIALIZATIONS WITHIN ARCHITECTURE DEGREE

URBAN PLANNING AND DESIGN

Academy of Art University
Andrews University
Arizona State University
Auburn University
Ball State University
California College of the Arts
California Polytechnic State University
California State Polytechnic University, Pomona
Carleton University
Carnegie Mellon University
Catholic University of America
City College of New York
Cornell University
Drexel University
Florida Atlantic University
Frank Lloyd Wright School of Architecture
Georgia Institute of Technology
Howard University
Illinois Institute of Technology
Judson University
Kent State University
Lawrence Technological University
Louisiana State University
Massachusetts College of Art and Design
Massachusetts Institute of Technology
McGill University
Miami University
Montana State University
Morgan State University
New Jersey Institute of Technology
New York Institute of Technology
NewSchool of Architecture and Design
North Carolina State University
North Dakota State University
Northeastern University
Ohio State University
Parsons The New School for Design
Pennsylvania State University
Portland State University
Rensselaer Polytechnic Institute

Rice University
Roger Williams University
Savannah College of Art and Design
School of the Art Institute of Chicago
Southern Illinois University
Texas A&M University
Université de Montréal
University at Buffalo, SUNY
University of Arizona
University of British Columbia
University of Calgary
University of California, Berkeley
University of Florida
University of Hartford
University of Hawaii at Manoa
University of Houston
University of Idaho
University of Illinois at Chicago
University of Illinois, Urbana—Champaign
University of Louisiana—Lafayette
University of Manitoba
University of Maryland
University of Massachusetts, Amherst
University of Memphis
University of Miami
University of Michigan
University of New Mexico
University of North Carolina at Charlotte
University of Notre Dame
University of Oklahoma
University of Oregon
University of South Florida
University of Southern California
University of Tennessee—Knoxville
University of Toronto
University of Utah
University of Washington
University of Wisconsin—Milwaukee
Virginia Polytechnic Institute
Washington State University
Washington University in St. Louis

A = Associate's; B = Bachelor's; M = Master's; D = Doctoral; C = Certificate

CONSTRUCTION MANAGEMENT/TECHNOLOGY

Auburn University – B, M
Ball State University – B
Carnegie Mellon University – D
Clemson University – B, M
Kansas State University – D
New York Institute of Technology – B
Prairie View A&M University – B
Pratt Institute – B, M
Texas A&M University – B, M
Ryerson University – M
University of British Columbia – B
University of Oklahoma – B
Washington State University – B

ENVIRONMENTAL DESIGN

Arizona State University – M, D
Ball State University – B
Clemson University – D
Kansas State University – D
Morgan State University – B
North Dakota State University – B
University at Buffalo – B
University of British Columbia – B
University of Calgary – M
University of Colorado – B
University of Houston – B

GRAPHIC DESIGN/DIGITAL DESIGN/ COMMUNICATION DESIGN/VISUAL STUDIES

Auburn University – B
Carnegie Mellon University – M
Cornell University – M
Judson University – B
Lawrence Technological University – B
Massachusetts Institute of Technology – M
New Jersey Institute of Technology – B
Roger Williams University – B
Texas A&M University – M

HISTORIC PRESERVATION

Clemson University – M
Columbia University – M
Cornell University – M
Pratt Institute – M
Roger Williams University – B
Savannah College of Art and Design – B
School of the Art Institute of Chicago – M
Tulane University – M
University of Florida – M
University of Maryland – M
University of Southern California – M
University of Texas at Austin – M
University of Utah – C

INDUSTRIAL DESIGN

Auburn University – B
New Jersey Institute of Technology – B
School of the Art Institute of Chicago – M
University of Houston – B
University of Louisiana at Lafayette – B

INTERIOR DESIGN/INTERIOR ARCHITECTURE

Academy of Art University – M
Auburn University – B
Boston Architectural College – B; M
Drexel University – B
Florida International University – B
Florida International University – M
Judson University – B
Kansas State University – M
Kent State University – B
Lawrence Technological University – B, M
Louisiana State University – B
Louisiana Tech University – B
Massachusetts College of Art and Design – B
Miami University – B
Mississippi State University – B
New Jersey Institute of Technology – B
New York Institute of Technology – B
Philadelphia University – B
Savannah College of Art and Design – B
School of the Art Institute of Chicago – B; M
University of Cincinnati – B
University of Idaho – B
University of Louisiana–Lafayette – B
University of Memphis – B
University of Nebraska–Lincoln – B
University of Nevada, Las Vegas – B
University of Oklahoma – B
University of Oregon – B
University of Tennessee–Knoxville – B
University of Texas at Austin – B
University of Texas at San Antonio – B
University of Oregon – M

LANDSCAPE ARCHITECTURE

Arizona State University – B; M
Auburn University – M
Ball State University – B, M
Boston Architectural College – B
California State Polytechnic University, Pomona – B; M
City College of New York – M
Clemson University – B, M
Cornell University – B, M
Florida Agricultural and Mechanical University – M
Florida International University – B; M
Harvard University – M
Illinois Institute of Technology – M
Kansas State University – M
Louisiana State University – B, M
Morgan State University – M
North Dakota State University – B
Oklahoma State University – M
Philadelphia University – B
Texas A&M University – B, M
University of Arizona – M
University of Arkansas – B
University of Colorado – M
University of Nevada, Las Vegas – B
University of Southern California – B; M
University of Tennessee–Knoxville – M
University of Texas at Austin – M

OTHER

Auburn University – M, Design-Build
Boston Architectural College – B, Design Studies
Carnegie Mellon University – M, D, Building Performance; M, D, Computational Design
Columbia University – M, Real Estate Development
Judson University – B, Art

Kent State University – M. Arch + M.B.A.
Lawrence Technological University – B, Transporation Design
Massachusetts Institute of Technology – M, Building Technology; M, Real Estate Development
McGill University – Grad Dipl., Housing
New Jersey Institute of Technology – B, Digital Design, D, Urban Systems
New York Institute of Technology – A, B Arch. Technology; M, Energy Management
Oklahoma State University – B, Arch Engineering
Parsons The New School for Design – M, Lighting Design
Prairie View A&M University – M, Community Development
Rensselaer Polytechnic Institute – M, Lighting
Roger Williams University – B, Art and Arch History
Souther California Institute of Architecture – M, Design Research
Texas A&M University – B, D, Urban and Regional Sciences
University at Buffalo – M. Arch + M.B.A.
University of Houston – M, Space Arch
University of Illinois at Chicago – M, Health Design
University of Louisiana at Lafayette – B, Fashion Design
University of Maryland – M, Real Estate Development
University of Southern California – M, Building Sciences
University of Texas at Austin – M, Sustainable Design

PLANNING

Auburn University – M
California State Polytechnic University, Pomona – B, M
Catholic University – M
Clemson University – M
Columbia University – M, D
Harvard University – M
Kansas State University – M
Morgan State University – M
New Jersey Institute of Technology – M
Pratt Institute – M
Texas A&M University – M
University at Buffalo, SUNY – M
University of Arizona – M
University of Colorado – M
University of Maryland – M
University of Nebraska–Lincoln – M
University of Oklahoma – M
University of Texas at Austin – M; D
University of Wisconsin–Milwaukee – M

SUSTAINABLE DESIGN

Carnegie Mellon University – M
Catholic University – M
Philadelphia University – M
University of Texas at Austin – M

URBAN DESIGN

Arizona State University – M
Columbia University – M
Harvard University – M
Kent State University – M
New York Institute of Technology – M
Pratt Institute – M
Savannah College of Art and Design – M
Université Laval – M
University of Houston – M
University of Maryland
University of Texas at Austin – M

ORGANIZATIONS IN ARCHITECTURE AND RELATED FIELDS

UNITED STATES

There are five major architectural organizations in the United States. All are located in Washington, DC.

The **American Institute of Architects** (AIA) has as its principal membership approximately 70,000 registered architects in the United States. While the thrust of the AIA is directed toward the practitioner, it also maintains career information and scholarship programs. Many cities and all states have AIA chapter organizations.

AIA National Headquarters
1735 New York Ave., NW
Washington, DC 20006
Tel: 800/AIA-3837
Fax: 202/626-7547
Email: infocentral@aia.org
Web: www.aia.org

The **American Institute of Architecture Students** (AIAS) is comprised of over 6,056 student members at its 133 chapters, which are established in U.S. and Canadian schools with architectural programs. AIAS coordinates a variety of student activities, including publication of a semi-annual newsletter and journal, CRIT.

AIAS National Office
Third Floor, 1735 New York Avenue Ave., NW
Washington, DC 20006
Tel: 202/626-7472
fax: 202/626-7414
Email: mail@aias.org
Web: www.aias.org

The **Association of Collegiate Schools of Architecture** (ACSA) has as its principal membership the 125 professional schools of architecture in both the United States and Canada, and, in turn, their faculty. It exists for the purpose of improving the quality of architecture education.

ACSA
Third Floor, 1735 New York Avenue Ave., NW
Washington, DC 20006
Tel: 202/785-2324
Fax: 202/628-0448
Email: info@acsa-arch.org
Web: www.acsa-arch.org

The **National Architectural Accrediting Board** (NAAB) was co-founded by ACSA, the AIA, and NCARB as an independent agency for the accrediting of professional architectural education programs. NAAB periodically reviews and accredits the programs at 110 schools of architecture.

NAAB
Third Floor, 1735 New York Avenue Ave., NW
Washington, DC 20006
Tel: 202.783.2007
Fax: 202.783.2822
Email: info@naab.org
Web: www.naab.org

The **National Council of Architectural Registration Boards** (NCARB) is comprised of the 50 individual state and 4 jurisdictional registration boards of the United States. NCARB recommends model law and regulations to govern the practice of architecture, and sets standards for education, internship, and examination for licensure. NCARB certification facilitates reciprocal registration among states and jurisdictions.

NCARB
1801 K Street, NW, Suite 700
Washington, DC 20006
Tel: 202/783-6500
Fax: 202/783-0290
Email: customerservice@ncarb.org
Web: www.ncarb.org

CANADA

There are four major architecture organizations in Canada. The **Canadian Architectural Certification Board** (CACB) was established to review and certify educational credentials of individuals seeking to enter the licensing process in one of the provinces. In 1991, its mission and structure changed to include the accrediting of professional programs in architecture. In its new form it is a partnership between the schools of architecture, represented by the CCUSA, and the licensing bodies, represented by CCAC. The Board continues to review and certify individual educational credentials of applicants who are not graduates of accredited programs.

CACB
1508-1 Nicholas Street
Ottawa, Canada K1N 7B7
Tel.: 613/241-8399
Fax: 613/241-7991
Email: info@cacb.ca
Web: www.cacb.ca

The **Council of Canadian University Schools of Architecture** (CCUSA) is comprised of the heads of architecture schools in Canada. Its purpose is to promote quality and collaboration in education and practice and to carry on liaison activities with professional and academic organizations.

The **Royal Architectural Institute of Canada** (RAIC) is the national organization to which many practicing architects belong on a voluntary basis. Although the concerns of the RAIC are chiefly those of the architect in practice, its programs include research and scholarship. Information on the profession may be obtained from each provincial association of architecture or from the RAIC.
Tel: 613/241-3600
Fax: 613/421-5750
Email: info@raic.org
Web: www.raic.org

INTERNATIONAL ORGANIZATIONS

Architectural Institute of Japan (AIJ)
26-20, Shiba 5-chome, Minato-ku
Tokyo 108-8414, Japan
Tel: +81-3/3456-2051
Fax: +81-3/3456-2058
Email: info@aij.or.jp
Web: www.aij.or.jp

Architectural Institute of Korea (AIK)
1044-34 Sadang-Dong, Tongjak-Gu
Seoul 156-827, Korea
Tel: +82-2/525-1841
Fax: +82-2/525-1845
Email: webmaster@aik.or.kr
Web: www.aik.or.kr

Asociación de Instituciones de Enseñazna de la Arquitectura de la Republica Mexicana, A.C. (ASINEA)
c/o Manual Aquirre Osete
ASINEA Intl. Relations Coordinator
Escuela de Arquitectura
Universidad Anahuac
Avenida Lomas Anahuac
Apartado Postal 10-844
Mexico DF-11000, Mexico
Tel: +52-5/328-8038
Fax: +52-5/596-1938

Committee of Heads of Architecture Schools of Australia (CHASA)
P.O. Box 3373 Manuka
Canberra ACT 2603, Australia
Tel: +61-6/273-1548
Fax: +61-6/273-1953

Commonwealth Association of Architects (CCA)
54 Old Street, London EC1V 9AL
United Kingdom
Tel: +44-207/490-3024
Web: www.comarchitect.org

European Association for Architectural Education (EAAE/AEEA)
Kasteelpark Arenberg 1
B-3001 Leuven, Belgium
Tel: +32-16/321-694
Fax: +32-16/321-962
Email: eaae@eaae.be
Web: www.eaae.be

Pan American Federation of Architects' Associations (FPAA)
Secretaria General
Gonzalo Ramirez 2030
CP 11-200 Montevideo, Uruguay
Tel: +598-2/493-463
Fax: +598-2/419-556

Royal Australian Institute of Architects (RAIA)
2a Mugga Way, Red Hill ACT 2603
PO Box 3373, Manuka
ACT 2603, Australia
Tel: +61-2/6273-1548
Fax: +61-2/6273-1953
Email: national@raia.com.au
Web: www.raia.com.au

Royal Institute of British Architects (RIBA)
66 Portland Place, London W1B 1AD
United Kingdom
Tel: +44-207/580-5533
Fax: +44-207-255-1541
Email: info@inst.riba.org
Web: www.riba.org

Union Internationale des Architectes (UIA)
51, rue Raynouard
75016 Paris, France
Tel: +33-1/4524-3688
Fax: +33-1/4524-0278
Email: uia@uia-architectes.org
Web: www.uia-architectes.org

ORGANIZATIONS IN ARCHITECTURE AND RELATED FIELDS

The Aga Kahn Program for Islamic Architecture
Attilio Petruccioli
MIT 10-390
77 Massachusetts Ave.
Cambridge, MA 02139-4307
Tel: 617/253-1400
Fax: 617/253-8172
Email: www.akdn.org

AIGA, the professional association for design
164 Fifth Avenue
New York, NY 10010
Tel: 212/807 1990
Web: www.aiga.org

Alpha Rho Chi Fraternity
(National Professional Fraternity for Architecture and
the Allied Arts)
Web: www.alpharhochi.org

American Association of Community Colleges
1 Dupont Circle, NW, Suite 410
Washington, DC 20036-1176
Tel: 202/728-0200
Fax: 202/833-2467
Web: www.aacc.nche.edu

American Design Drafting Association
105 E. Main Street
Newbern, TN 38059
Tel: 731/627-0802
Fax: 731/627-9321
Email: national@adda.org
Web: www.adda.org

American Planning Association (APA)
122 S. Michigan Ave., Suite 1600
Chicago, IL 60603-6107
Tel: 312/431-9100
Fax: 312/431-9985
Web: www.planning.org
Email: APAInfo@planning.org

1776 Massachusetts Ave., NW
Washington, DC 20036-1904
Tel: 202/872-0611
Fax: 202/872-0643

American Society of Civil Engineers
(ASCE)
1801 Alexander Bell Drive
Reston, VA 20191
Tel: 800/548-2723
Web: www.asce.org

American Society of Heating, Refrigeration and Air-Conditioning Engineers, Inc. (ASHRAE)
1791 Tullie Circle, NE
Atlanta, GA 30329
Tel: 404/636-8400
Fax: 404/321-5478
Web: www.ashrae.org

American Society of Interior Designers (ASID)
608 Massachusetts Ave., NE
Washington, DC 20002-6006
Tel: 202/546-3480
Fax: 202/546-3240
Email: asid@asid.org
Web: www.asid.org

American Society of Landscape Architects (ASLA)
636 Eye Street, NW
Washington, DC 20001-3736
Tel: 202/898-2444
Fax: 202/898-1185
Web: www.asla.org

Architectural Research Centers Consortium, Inc.
(ARCC)
Michel Mounayar (President)
College of Architecture & Planning
Ball State University
Muncie, IN 47306
Tel: 765/285-5859
Fax: 765/285-3726
Email: mmounaya@bsu.edu
Web: www.arccweb.org

Association of Collegiate Schools of Planning (ACSP)
Web: www.acsp.org

**Association for Computer-Aided Design
in Architecture** (ACADIA)
Web: www.acadia.org

Council for Educators in Landscape Architecture
(CELA)
P O Box 7506
Edmond OK 73083-7506
Tel: 405/330-4150
Fax: 405/330-4150
Email: cela@telepath.com
Web: www.thecela.org

Council for Interior Design Accreditation (CIDA,
formerly Foundation for Interior Design Education
Research)
146 Monroe Center, NW, Suite 1318
Grand Rapids, MI 49503-2822
Tel: 616/458-0400
Fax: 616/458-0460
Email: fider@fider.org
Web: www.accredit-id.org

Environmental Design Research Association (EDRA)
PO Box 7146
Edmond, OK 73083-7146
Tel: 405/330.4863
Email: edra@edra.org
Web: www.edra.org

Industrial Designers Society of America (IDSA)
45195 Business Ct., Suite 250
Dulles, VA 20166
Tel: 703/707-6000
Fax: 703/787-8501
Email: idsa@idsa.org
Web: www.idsa.org

Interior Design Educators Council (IDEC)
7150 Winton Drive, Suite 300
Indianapolis, IN 46268
Tel: 317/328-4437
Fax: 317/280-8527
Email: info@idec.org
Web: www.idec.org

National Association of Schools of Art and Design
(NASAD)
11250 Roger Bacon Drive, Suite 21
Reston, VA 20190
Tel: 703/437-0700
Fax: 703/437-6312
Email: info@arts-accredit.org
Web: www.arts-accredit.org/nasad

National Building Museum
401 F St., NW
Washington, DC 20001
Tel: 202/272-2448
Fax: 202/272-2564
Web: www.nbm.org

National Endowment for the Arts
1100 Pennsylvania Ave., NW
Washington, DC 20506
Tel: 202/682-5400
Fax: 202/682-5611
Web: arts.endow.gov

National Institute of Building Sciences
1090 Vermont Ave. NW, Suite 700
Washington, DC 20005-4905
Tel: 202/289-7800
Fax: 202/289-1092
Email: nibs@nibs.org
Web: www.nibs.org

National Organization of Minority Architects (NOMA)
5530 Wisconsin Ave., Suite 1210
Chevy Chase, MD 20815-4301
Tel: 301/941-1065
Web: www.noma.net

National Science Foundation
4201 Wilson Boulevard
Arlington, VA 22230
Tel: 703/292-5111
Email: info@nsf.gov
Web: www.nsf.gov

ORGANIZATIONS IN ARCHITECTURE AND RELATED FIELDS

National Society of Professional Engineers
1420 King Street
Alexandria, VA 22314-2794
Tel: 703/684-2800
Fax: 703/836-4875
Web: www.nspe.org

National Trust for Historic Preservation
1785 Massachusetts Ave., NW
Washington, DC 20036
Tel: 202/588-6000
Fax: 202/588-6038
Web: www.nthp.org

Society of Architectural Historians
1365 North Astor Street
Chicago, IL 60610
Tel: 312/573-1365
Fax: 312/573-1141
Email: info@sah.org
Web: www.sah.org

Society of Building Science Educators (SBSE)
Terri Meyer Boake, President
University of Waterloo
School of Architecture
7 Melville Street South
Cambridge, Ontrio N1S 2H4
Canada
Email: tboake@uwaterloo.ca
Web: www.sbse.org

Tau Sigma Delta
(National Honor Society for Architecture and the Allied Arts)
Elizabeth I. Louden, PhD (President)
College of Architecture
Box 42091
Texas Tech University
Lubbock, Texas 79409-2091
Tel: 806-742-3136 x 241
Fax: 806-742-2855
Email : elizabeth.louden@ttu.edu
Web: www.tausigmadelta.org

Van Alen Institute
30 W. 22nd St.
New York, NY 10010
Tel: 212/924-7000
Fax: 212/366-5836
Email: vai@vanalen.org
Web: www.vanalen.org

PROFESSIONAL ORGANIZATIONS

ABET: Accrediting Board for Engineering and Technology
ACSA: Association of Collegiate Schools of Architecture
AIA: The American Institute of Architects
AIAS: American Institute of Architecture Students
APA: American Planning Association
ASID: American Society of Interior Designers
ASLA: American Society of Landscape Architects
CAA: Commonwealth Association of Architects
CACB: Canadian Architectural Certification Board
CCAC: Committee of Canadian Architectural Councils
CCUSA: Council of Canadian University Schools of Architecture
CIDA: Council for Interior Design Accreditation
CIP: Canadian Institute of Planning
FIDER: Foundation for Interior Design Education Research
LAAB: Landscape Architectural Accreditation Board
NAAB: National Architectural Accrediting Board
NCARB: National Council of Architectural Registration Boards
OAQ: Order of Architects of Quebec
PAB: Planning Accreditation Board
RAIC: Royal Architectural Institute of Canada
RIBA: Royal Institute of British Architects

DEGREES

AA: Associate of Arts
AAS: Associate of Applied Science
AB/BA: Bachelor of Arts
BA Arch: BA in Architecture
BA/BS Arch Stud: BA or BS in Architectural Studies
BA Env Des: BA in Environmental Design
BA Arch Sci: BA in Architectural Science
BA Int Des: BA in Interior Design
B. Arch: Bachelor of Architecture (normally used for accredited degrees)
B Arch Des: Bachelor of Architectural Design
B Arch Eng: Bachelor of Architectural Engineering
B Des: Bachelor of Design
BED: Bachelor of Environmental Design
BED Arch: Bachelor of Environmental Design in Architecture
B Env Stud: Bachelor of Environmental Studies
BFA: Bachelor of Fine Arts
B Int Des: Bachelor of Interior Design
B Int Arch: Bachelor of Interior Architecture
B Ind Des: Bachelor of Industrial Design
BLA: Bachelor of Landscape Architecture
BPS: Bachelor of Professional Studies
BS/BSc: Bachelor of Science
BS Arch: BS in Architecture
BS Arch Des: BS in Architectural Design
BS Arch Eng: BS in Architectural Engineering
BS Arch Stud: BS in Architectural Studies
BS Bldg Cons: BS in Building Construction
BS Bldg Des: BS in Building Design
BS Bldg Sci: BS in Building Science

BS Cons Eng: BS in Construction Engineering
BS Cons Tech: BS in Construction Technology
BSCRP: BS in City and Regional Planning
BS Env Des: BS in Environmental Design
BS Int Arch: BS in Interior Architecture
BS L Arch: BS in Landscape Architecture
BS Plan: BS in Planning
BS Urb Plan: BS in Urban Planning
D. Arch: Doctor of Architecture
DED: Doctor of Environmental Design
MA: Master of Arts
MAURP: MA in Urban and Regional Planning
MA Arch: MA in Architecture
MA Int Des: MA in Interior Design
MA Urb Des: MA in Urban Design
M. Arch: Master of Architecture (primarily used for accredited degrees, though also used for post-professional or non-professional degrees)
M. Arch UD: Master of Architecture and Urban Design
M Bldg Cons: Master of Building Construction
M Bldg Sc: Master of Building Science
MCP: Master of City Planning
MCPUD: Master of City Planning and Urban Design
MCRP: Master of City and Regional Planning
MED: Master of Environmental Design
MFA: Master of Fine Arts
MFA Int Des: MFA in Interior Design
M Ind Des: Master of Industrial Design
MLA: Master of Landscape Architecture
MLA Urb Des: MLA in Urban Design
MPCD: Master in Planning and Community Development
MPD: Master of Planning and Design
MRCP: Master of Regional and City Planning
MRP: Master of Regional Planning
MS: Master of Science
MS Urb Des: MS in Urban Design
MS Arch: MS in Architecture
MS Arch Tech: MS in Architectural Technology
MSCRP: MS in City and Regional Planning
MS Hist Pres: MS in Historic Preservation
MS Urb Plan: MS in Urban Planning
MUD: Master of Urban Design
MUP: Master of Urban Planning
MUP Urb Des: MUP in Urban Design
MURP: Master of Urban and Regional Planning
PhD: Doctor of Philosophy

TERMS AND ABBREVIATIONS

ACT: American College Testing Exam
adm: admission
admin: administration
adv: advanced
app: applicant
arch: architecture or architectural
assoc: associate
bacc: baccalaureate
bkgd: background
bldg: building
CAD: computer-aided design
coll: college

com: community
cr: credit(s)
des: design
dipl: diploma
educ: education
engr: engineer(ing)
Eng: English (except in Engineer(ing) in degrees)
env: environment(al)
equiv: equivalent
ex: example(s)
exp: experience
FTE: full-time equivalent
grad: graduate
GRE: Graduate Record Examination
GPA: grade point average
hr(s) : hour(s)
hs: high school
IDP: Intern Development Program
inc: including
ind: industrial
int: interior
lang: language(s)
mgt: management
na: not applicable/not available
prof: professional
prog: program
pt: point
qtr: quarter
rec: recommendation
reg: regional
req: required
SAT: Scholastic Assessment Test
schl: school
sem: semester
soc sci: social science
tech: technology
TOEFI: Test of English as a Foreign Language
undergrad: undergraduate
univ: university
yr: year

INDEX OF MEMBER SCHOOLS